CONTENTS

Alcohol & Drug Problems

A Practical Guide for Counsellors

Second Edition

EDITORS
Susan Harrison
Virginia Carver

FOREWORD
James O. Prochaska

EDITORS OF THE FIRST EDITION
Betty-Anne M. Howard
Susan Harrison
Virginia Carver
Lynn Lightfoot

Centre for Addiction and Mental Health
Centre de toxicomanie et de santé mentale

Addiction Research Foundation
Clarke Institute of Psychiatry
Donwood Institute
Queen Street Mental Health Centre

A World Health Organization Centre of Excellence

Canadian Cataloguing in Publication Data

Main entry under title:

Alcohol & drug problems : a practical guide for counsellors

2nd ed.
ISBN 0-88868-295-6

1. Alcoholism counseling – Canada. 2. Drug abuse
counseling – Canada. 3. Alcoholism counseling. 4. Drug
abuse counseling. I. Harrison, Susan, 1950– .
II. Carver, Virginia, 1940– . III. Ontario. Addiction
Research Foundation. IV. Title: Alcohol and drug problems.

RC564.15.A42 1997   362.29'186'0971   C97-931557-3

For information on other Centre for Addiction and Mental Health resource materials or
to place an order, please contact:
Marketing and Sales Services
Centre for Addiction and Mental Health
33 Russell Street
Toronto, ON M5S 2S1
Canada

Tel.: 1-800-661-1111 or 416-595-6059 in Toronto

E-mail: marketing@camh.net

Web site: www.camh.net

2749 / 08-02   P5630

PREFACE

Susan Harrison
Virginia Carver

This guide is designed for counsellors who are in a position to help their clients deal with the often devastating effects of substance abuse. We cover core considerations for the counsellor — from theories of addiction to specific treatments such as Structured Relapse Prevention — and address the needs of unique client populations such as women, older adults and people with HIV.

Feedback from the first edition *of Alcohol & Drug Problems: A Practical Guide for Counsellors* revealed another important readership — college and university students in disciplines such as social work and medicine who now use this book as a course text.

We have fully revised and updated the text for this second edition, keeping in mind both the needs of our readers and the many emerging issues in the addictions field. New chapters outline topics such as problem gambling, street-involved youth, cocaine and heroin addiction, mutual aid groups, the effects of parental substance abuse, and theories of addiction. As well, new research findings, clinical experiences and case studies have enhanced the practical application of this guide.

We wish, first of all, to thank our authors, who have contributed their expertise and many hours of their time to this guide with one goal in mind — to reduce the harm related to alcohol and drug problems.

Most importantly, we wish to acknowledge Betty Anne Howard, who provided the inspiration and initial concept for the first edition. With the assistance of Lynn Lightfoot, her ARF colleague at the time, she planned the original structure and content of the book and recruited many of the authors for the first edition.

We are also immensely grateful to Ian Kinross, who co-ordinated the editorial work for this second edition, Julia Drake for her editing skills and careful attention to the text and Nancy Leung for her design work. ARF's Library staff, in particular Sheila Strachan-Lacroix, Diane Van Abbe and Sandra Gold, helped many of the authors find the information needed to revise their chapters. Graham Vardy, co-ordinator of ARF's HIV Clinic, generously reviewed the chapter on AIDS. Christine McDermid, of the East Regional office of ARF, contributed her computer expertise in downloading, decoding and copying chapters.

To these contributors and many others behind the scenes, thank you for your help in bringing this second edition to completion.

To our many readers in addictions and related fields, we hope that this guide continues to be valuable in your professional development and in your day-to-day work with clients.

FOREWORD

Creating the Future of Addictions Treatment

James O. Prochaska

This is a time of great opportunity for the field of behavioral health care generally and for the treatment of substance abuse problems specifically. Increasingly, society is recognizing that unhealthy behaviors such as substance abuse generate high costs — not only to the individuals who are affected, but to their families, employers, communities and health care systems.

Consider a few simple statistics. In the United States, health care costs are one trillion dollars per year and growing. Of that total, seven per cent are accounted for by medications, and 50 to 60 per cent are accounted for by behavior — in other words, people's unhealthy lifestyles.

Typically, less than five per cent of these unhealthy behaviors are treated appropriately and professionally. This means there are large unmet needs and great opportunities — but only if we change the way we do science and the ways in which we apply that science.

Leaders in the National Health Service in Great Britain, for example, have examined these simple statistics and declared that they have an "illness system" and not a health system. It is clear that behavior change must become their number one business.

When such leaders look to science for evidence on how to treat high-risk and high-cost behaviors on a population basis, they can become discouraged. The biggest and best-controlled health behavior trials ever completed on a population basis have been reporting in, and the results have been uniformly dismal. These studies have varied in their populations, including prevention and treatment in worksites, schools and communities (Glasgow, 1996; Working Well, 1996; Dare, 1996; COMMIT, 1996; Luepker et al., 1994). They have also varied in their target behaviors, including smoking, alcohol and drug abuse, unhealthy diets, lack of exercise and the other major killers of our time. But they have not varied in their inability to produce significant effects in the intervention populations.

Their inabilities were not due to a lack of time, talent or treasures. Their treatment times ranged from two to five years; their talent included some of the best that our multidisciplinary sciences and professions had to offer; and their budgets ranged from $20 million to $700 million. The problem was probably more basic. The problem was probably with their scientific and professional paradigms. Applying an action-oriented paradigm to entire populations led to serious limitations.

In the Minnesota Heart Health Project, for example, action-oriented programs were offered repeatedly for five years. But in the field's most powerful change programs, individualized and interactive clinics and classes, only four per cent of smokers in the treatment communities participated. We simply cannot impact on the health of our communities if we reach only a small percentage of people with high-risk and high-cost behaviors.

Here is this scientist/professional's vision of how we can create a better future for treating these high-cost behaviors, followed by some thoughts on how this book can help.

First, we would shift paradigms — from an action paradigm to a "stage paradigm" of studying and understanding behavior change. Then we would shift from a *reactive* paradigm of practice, in which we primarily wait for people with substance use problems to come to us, to a *proactive* paradigm in which health professionals reach out to entire populations of high-risk people. In this way, we can interact with people at whatever stage of change they are in to help them progress toward healthier lifestyles.

In England again, over 4,000 physicians, nurses, health educators and counsellors have been trained in the stage paradigm to reach out to all of their patients who abuse alcohol and other drugs, including tobacco, as well as those who eat unhealthy foods and have sedentary lifestyles. The first feedback from this intensive training initiative is a dramatic increase in the morale of the professionals. They now have skills to assist all of their patients, not just the 20 per cent or less who are prepared to take action. And they can assess progress with the 40 per cent starting in the precontemplation stage after brief but tailored interactions.

In the U.S., the main reason physicians do not practise behavioral medicine with substance abuse and other high-risk behaviors is that two-thirds of physicians believe their patients either cannot or will not change their behavior. They have become demoralized by the action paradigm in which they tell patients to quit abusing alcohol or other drugs and the vast majority fail to take immediate and effective action. But we now know that across high-risk behaviors only a minority of people are in the preparation stage and are ready for action-oriented interventions.

If health professionals start to proactively intervene with the entire population of people with substance abuse problems, what might be the consequences for counsellors and therapists who specialize in treating the problems? And how can this book help prepare them for such a future?

First, they need to be prepared to treat many more people, particularly those in the early stages of precontemplation and contemplation. They need to match the needs of people in each stage of change rather than expect their clients to match their favorite treatment modality. A series of studies have demonstrated that the approximately 50 per cent of clients who drop out of treatment quickly and prematurely are disproportionately in the precontemplation stage. Those who finish quickly but appropriately are more likely to be in the preparation or action stages.

One matching method would be to apply relapse prevention approaches with clients who are ready to take action (see Chapter 8). With clients who are not prepared or motivated to take action now, motivational interviewing techniques would be a much better match (see Chapter 2).

With proactive outreach practices, clinicians will need to be prepared to match the needs of the important parts of our populations that have traditionally been underserved by our health care systems. Women, ethnic, social and lifestyle minorities, and groups with limited resources will need to be appreciated for the special needs they have. The second section of this book addresses the needs of many understudied and underserved populations.

Finally, if we are to do justice to entire populations with problems related to alcohol and other drugs, we will need to enhance our knowledge of treating multiple problem behaviors, not just singular problems. How do we respond to people with multiple-diagnoses or with multiple high-risk behaviors, like alcohol abuse, sedentary lifestyles, unhealthy diets, high-risk sexual behaviors, anxiety and depression? From an action paradigm, such individuals, who are quite common, would threaten to be overwhelmed by too many demands to take multiple actions and risk multiple failures. From a stage paradigm, we have found that, in populations with four high-risk behaviors, less than 10 per cent are in the preparation stage for two or more behaviors. So we can begin to take action on the behavior that is most prepared, while enhancing motivation or preparation for behaviors in earlier stages. This book includes state-of-the-science information on the multiple behaviors and disorders that most often accompany addictive behavior.

If we are going to help create a better future for the treatment of addictions, we must be prepared to change our paradigms and our practices. As experts and specialists, there will be demands on us to continue to know more than we ever did before. This book can help move us forward into a more demanding but also more rewarding future that we can create together.

CORE
CONSIDERATIONS

Chapter 1

Theories of 'Addiction' and Implications for Counselling

ALAN C. OGBORNE

Many theories have been advanced to account for alcohol and drug use and especially for "addictive" use characterized by persistence and relapse despite negative consequences. Some theories suggest a primary role for genetic and other biological factors, while others emphasize personality factors or social and environmental factors. Studies have shown that all these factors can contribute to persistent substance use and relapse following periods of abstinence. However, no one set of factors is sufficient to account for all types of alcohol and drug use by humans. Rather, human alcohol and drug use results from complex interactions of biological, psychological and social-environmental structures and processes (Arif and Westermeyer, 1988).

This chapter provides a brief overview of biological, psychological and social-environmental factors relevant to problematic alcohol and drug use and indicates how these factors may interact. Some implications for counselling will also be considered. The focus will be on factors that account for the continuance of drug use once it has started and for relapse following periods of abstinence. Some of these factors can also account for the initiation of substance use, but this is not the concern of this chapter.

FOCUS AND TERMINOLOGY

This book is about ways to help people with alcohol and drug problems. It is not especially about helping "alcoholics" or "drug addicts," although many people may be given these labels by those who know them and by some clinicians and researchers who specialize in the issues of substance use. However, this book has a broader focus and concerns people whose problems with alcohol or drugs vary in kind and severity. This chapter also has a broad focus in that it seeks to give an overview of perspectives and theories of problematic substance use, including use that is frequently labelled "addictive." However, the terms "addictive" and "addiction," and the related term "alcoholism," will generally be avoided, because there are no agreed-upon definitions and they have limited value in many counselling settings. The term "drug abuse" is also troublesome to many experts because it has moralistic implications and will be avoided in what follows. The term "dependence" will be used with respect to alcohol and other drugs on the understanding that this concerns a cluster of cognitive, behavioral and physiological symptoms of varying severity. This is consistent with the use of the term by the World Health Organization (WHO) and the American Psychiatric Association (APA) (WHO, 1992; APA, 1994).

The APA criteria for a diagnosis of *substance dependence* is met when any three of the following types of impairment or distress occur at the same time during a given 12-month period:
(1) tolerance as indicated by the need to increase dosage to obtain the desired effect or reduced effects with continued use of the same dose
(2) withdrawal symptoms characteristic of a particular substance
(3) use in larger amounts or over a longer period than intended by the user
(4) persistent desire for the substance, or unsuccessful efforts to cut down
(5) a great deal of time is spent in efforts to secure access to a substance
(6) social and other activities are given up or reduced due to substance use
(7) use despite persistent or recurrent problems (health, social, etc.).

The phrase "alcohol/drug problem" will be used in relation to the use of alcohol and drugs on the understanding that "problems" are social constructions. In some cases, alcohol or drug use may be a "problem" because it contravenes social norms but is otherwise benign (e.g., occasional use of alcohol by people whose religion forbids it, or the occasional use of cannabis). More serious "problems" may also be defined differently by those variously involved. Thus weekend drunkenness may be intolerable to a spouse but just fine by the drinker's companions. Two important tasks for a counsellor are to assess the nature and extent of their client's alcohol and drug problems and to negotiate a common understanding of problems to be addressed. Relevant issues are discussed in the chapters in this book on assessment and motivational interviewing.

This chapter does not have a section on the so-called "disease" concept of alcoholism because this is not really a testable theory but an analogy with important implications for the ways in which "alcoholism" is regarded and treated. When viewed as a disease, alcoholism becomes a legitimate condition for treatment by medical and allied professionals and not simply a bad habit or a sign of moral weakness. The disease analogy is appropriate if the term disease is understood to include complex conditions such as high blood pressure that are influenced by genetic and lifestyle factors. However, the analogy breaks down when alcoholism is compared with diseases such as tuberculosis or syphilis — diseases with clear causes that can be diagnosed with X-rays or blood tests.

BIOLOGICAL FACTORS

Genetic Inheritance

There is a growing body of evidence that human alcohol use is influenced by genetic factors (Alcohol Health and Research World, 1995). The strongest evidence comes from studies of family histories, studies of twins and adopted children, studies of "racial" groups and animal studies. Genetic factors seem to influence the ways in which humans respond to and metabolize alcohol and contribute to neurological dysfunctions common to early onset problem drinkers (discussed under psychological factors). Human and animal studies have also provided some evidence that genetic factors play a role in preferences for other drugs (Crabbe, McSwigan and Belknap, 1985; Uhl, Persico and Smith, 1992).

The consensus among experts is that many genes influence alcohol-related responses and behaviors and that these responses and behaviors lie on a continuum of vulnerability to alcohol problems. This is consistent with behavioral studies that have failed to find evidence for a clear distinction between problem drinkers and others.

The influence of genetic factors is sometimes interpreted as signifying that alcoholism is an inevitable, progressive and irreversible condition in people who are so disposed. This reflects a limited understanding of the role of genetics in determining complex behaviors and is inconsistent with a great deal of clinical, experimental and survey research. A detailed and very readable summary of this research will be found in the book by Heather and Robertson (1989). We will summarize the main challenges to the notion that the drinking behaviors of "alcoholics" are genetically determined and therefore uncontrollable:

(1) There is overwhelming evidence that those labelled "alcoholics" have periods of normal drinking. Although this may not be advisable, it happens in both clinical and general populations.
(2) It has been shown that "alcoholics" will limit their drinking in laboratory settings when the benefits of reduced drinking are right. These experiments demonstrate the role of environmental contingencies in moderating alcohol consumption even among "alcoholics" (Mello and Mendelson, 1965; Mello, McNamee and Mendelson, 1968).
(3) Experimental studies have shown that alcohol consumption does not precipitate craving among "alcoholics." Studies have also demonstrated the role of expectancies in shaping reactions to alcohol, even among "alcoholics" (Marlatt, Deming and Reid, 1973).
(4) There are large differences between otherwise similar societies in consumption levels and rates of alcohol-related problems. For example, in Norway the per capita consumption of alcohol is only 4.1 litres of alcohol per year, and Norway has a low

5

rate of liver cirrhosis. In comparison, the per capita consumption of alcohol in France is 12.6 litres per year, and France has traditionally had one of the highest rates of cirrhosis in the world. There were also dramatic increases in alcohol consumption from 1945 to 1982 in many industrialized countries and parallel increases in a range of alcohol-related problems (Smart and Ogborne, 1996).

If genetics played a determining role in drinking, we would have to conclude that Norwegians have different genes than the French and that the gene pool of the industrialized world has changed dramatically since the end of the Second World War. Neither conclusion could be supported on other grounds, and neither conclusion is necessary because population levels of drinking and drinking problems are clearly influenced by social customs and economic forces. These same forces also influence the drinking behaviors of individuals.

Of course none of the above evidence rules out the influence of genetic factors on drinking behaviors and drinking problems. There are certainly wide individual differences in preferences for alcohol and capacity to drink large amounts, and genetic factors contribute to these differences. However, other factors are clearly of great importance and need to be accommodated into theoretical models.

When counselling people with alcohol problems, the potential influence of genetic factors should be considered. This can contribute to clients' understanding of their problems and to their recovery. However, care should be taken to ensure that clients also learn to recognize other factors that influence drinking and especially those factors that are within their own control.

Neurotransmitters and Enzymes

There has been a great deal of research on neuro-biological aspects of drug use and many relevant structures and processes have been identified (e.g., drug-specific receptor sites in the brain and the effects of specific drugs and their metabolites on neurotransmitters). The possibility that all addictive behaviors are the result of common physiological or biochemical actions in the brain has also been suggested, and there is currently a good deal of interest in the neuro-transmitter *dopamine*. Some theorists have suggested that all pleasurable activities, including drug use for some people, result from the release of dopamine in specific areas of the brain. Some animal research supports this view, but it is likely that other mechanisms are also involved. Recent non-technical reviews of relevant issues are provided by Ray and Ksir (1996; Chapter 6) and Ellinwood and King (1995).

Research on agents that "block" drug receptors (e.g., the opiate blocking agent Naltrexone) has contributed to our understanding of the biological process underlying drug use and may lead to new pharmacological treatments. Naltrexone has, in fact, been shown to be helpful in the treatment of alcoholism (Volpicelli et al., 1994).

Some addiction treatment services include education on the biological effects of drugs in the belief that this will motivate clients to change their behaviors. However, there is little evidence that this type of drug education influences client outcomes (Holder et al., 1991).

PSYCHOLOGICAL FACTORS

Three types of factors will be discussed: (1) personality traits; (2) so-called psycho-dynamic processes; and (3) conditioned or otherwise learned cognitions and behaviors.

Personality Traits

Hundreds of studies have been conducted in the search for differences between people who have alcohol or drug problems and other people (Cox, 1985). In general, these studies do not support the notion that people with alcohol or drug problems have different personalities than others and, in the early 1970s, one expert called for an end to this type of research, at least in the alcohol field (Keller, 1972). He also proposed that "Keller's Law" would ensure that, whatever traits were considered, the results would show that alcoholics have either more or less of them!

Personality research has, however, continued, and several studies have sought to identify personality characteristics associated with the onset of heavy drinking and drug use in adolescence. The results suggest that such use is more common among adolescents who show pre-drug use signs of rebelliousness, depression and the seeking of sensations, but less clearly among those with low self-esteem (Kandel and Yamaguchi, 1985; Zuckerman, 1983; Stein, Newcomb and Bentler, 1987). However, no specific pre-drug use characteristics or clusters of characteristics have been shown to be either necessary or sufficient to account for the onset or maintenance of drug use in adolescent or other populations.

There is evidence for common pre-drinking personality characteristics in one type of problem drinker (Allen, 1996). The type is characterized by having drinking problems from an early age (late teens or early 20s) and by strong antisocial tendencies. There is also suggestive evidence that such people have a genetically determined brain disorder involving the prefrontal lobes (Tarter, Alterman and Edwards, 1988). The relevant neurological disturbances may be genetically linked and involve the brain's "executive" functions of planning and goal formulation, persistence, self-monitoring and self-evaluation. These disturbances are manifested by childhood hyperactivity, pre-alcoholic essential tremor, left-handedness, low levels of academic achievement, attention deficit disorders, impulsiveness, lack of inhibition, emotional instability, aggressiveness, and antisocial and psychopathic tendencies. These traits can find expression through heavy drinking and a preference for companions who drink heavily. Although there is less relevant research involving users of drugs other than alcohol, there are suggestions that similar neurological disturbances occur in some types of heroin and cocaine users. Alcohol and drug users who exhibit this type of personality trait may benefit from training in coping skills, self-control and relapse prevention (Ball, 1996).

The relationship between alcohol and drug problems and various types of mental illness has been considered in a number of studies (Miller, 1994). The results indicate that drinking and drug use problems are quite common among people with mental health problems and that mental health problems are common among people with alcohol and drug problems. However, the relationships between mental health and substance abuse are complex and difficult to disentangle. Some people with serious mental disturbances (e.g., phobias, rage, anxiety, depression, mania, paranoid delusions) appear to use alcohol and other drugs to self-medicate for mental distress. For others, mental health problems are consequential to or exacerbated by substance use, and these problems tend to decrease with abstinence. While clients who qualify for a dual diagnosis of substance abuse and a mental disorder are generally considered more difficult to treat than "pure" substance abusers, integrated mental health and addictions treatment services seem to be quite successful (Drake et al., 1996).

Psychodynamic Processes

A psychodynamic approach to understanding human behavior emphasizes psychological forces, structures and functions as they develop and change over time. There is a special interest in childhood experiences and conflicts and their influences in later life. Psychodynamic perspectives on alcohol and drug problems focus on unconscious motivation, emotions, self-esteem, self-regulation and interpersonal relationships. The notion that alcohol and drug problems can stem from childhood physical and sexual abuse (remembered or "repressed") has been especially emphasized by therapists with a psychodynamic orientation.

Psychodynamic theories can be traced to the writings of Sigmund Freud and his followers and revisionists. There are perhaps as many variants of a psychodynamic approach to substance abuse as there are psychodynamic theorists. Freud originally proposed that alcoholics were "orally fixated" and thus unable to cope with the demands of adult life. Thus they use alcohol to "escape from reality" (a Freudian concept). Later, Freud proposed that alcoholism was an expression of repressed homosexuality. He reasoned that male homosexuals turned to drink because they were disappointed with relationships with women and because drinking gave them an excuse to be with other men. Other psychodynamic theorists have proposed that alcoholism is a reflection of unresolved dependency conflicts, a striving for power or a form of self-destruction. Oral, anal and phallic "fixations" have also been proposed as explanations for alcoholism (Barry, 1988).

Psychodynamic theory does not feature very prominently in the "mainstream" of current substance use research, and it has not been expanded to accommodate recent research on biological factors. The relationship between psychodynamic and learning theories is problematic. Although both theories emphasize the role of experience (including childhood experiences) and the influence of the "self," learning theorists tend to be more parsimonious and typically challenge the utility of the concept of "repressed" impulses. However, some overviews of the psychodynamic approach to the analysis and treatment of substance abuse seem quite compatible with social learning theory (e.g., Khantzian, 1995).

Psychodynamic concepts and analyses have captured the popular imagination for the greater part of the twentieth century, and they continue to influence many professionals in the human service field. Only radical behaviorists continue to avoid things that go on in the "heart and the head," and practising clinicians of all persuasions seem to pay at least some attention to childhood and family experiences and the "inner" lives of their clients. However, psychodynamic formulations of human behavior have not led to testable assumptions and, in general, they have little unequivocal empirical support. Purely psychodynamic treatments designed to increase "insight" have not been proven to be effective (Holder et al., 1991) and have generally been abandoned. However, various forms of non-psychoanalytic "talk" therapy, and especially client-centred psychotherapy, are often used in conjunction with other types of treatment in specialized addiction treatment programs (Ellis and Rush, 1993).

Learned Responses and Cognitions

Use of alcohol and other drugs activates two basic learning mechanisms. The first, called *classical conditioning,* occurs when an initially neutral stimulus produces the same responses as a conditioned stimulus with which it has been paired. The best-known example occurred when Pavlov rang a bell every time he fed his dogs. Initially, the dogs only salivated at the sight of food. However, in time the dogs began to salivate at the sound of the bell. The bell thus became a conditioned stimulus and salivation a conditioned response.

One example of a classically conditioned response in the area of alcohol and drug use is the onset of "craving" and withdrawal symptoms in response to stimuli associated with drinking or drug use. These stimuli may be internal to the substance user (e.g., feelings of depression or anxiety) or in the external environment (e.g., advertisements, social situations or the sight of a syringe). Through classical conditioning, alcohol- or drug-related stimuli may also invoke mild drug effects that whet the user's appetite for more.

The very low rates of heroin use among American veterans who used heroin in Vietnam may be partly due to a relative lack of classically conditioned external cues for heroin use in the veterans' home situations (Robins, 1974). For most returning veterans, the main external cues for heroin use were not associated with the United States but with Vietnam and the war. Policies were also established to reduce the likelihood of internal cues (e.g., coming down) occurring in the U.S. context. Thus, no soldier was allowed to board a plane for home without passing a urine screening test.

Classical conditioning has also been used to account for increased tolerance to the effects of alcohol and drugs. Neutral cues (say, drinking situations) become conditioned stimuli for the onset of "anticipatory" responses to drinking. By being frequently paired with actual drinking/drug use, these (now conditioned) anticipatory responses become stronger and more alcohol is needed to produce the original effects (Sherman, Jorenby and Baker, 1988).

"Cue exposure" treatments have been used to eliminate classically conditioned alcohol and drug-related responses through "extinction." In these treatments, substance users are presented with or asked to imagine situations in which their preferred substance was typically used, and they were asked to imagine themselves resisting urges to drink or use drugs. The assumption is that classically conditioned responses to these situations (withdrawal symptoms or drug effects) become extinguished through lack of reinforcement. Evidence for the effectiveness of such treatments is mixed (Tobena et al., 1993).

The second learning process activated by drug use is called *operant conditioning.* This occurs when behaviors are shaped by their consequences. Put simply, operant conditioning occurs when positive reinforcements (rewards) are used to increase the frequency of the performance of specific behaviors in specific situations, and negative reinforcement (withdrawal or withholding of rewards) or punishments are used to decrease or eliminate the performance of these behaviors. Through operant conditioning, behaviors come to be evoked in response to the various stimuli or cues associated with the conditioning process. Depending on the schedules of reinforcement used (e.g., continuous, intermittent, response or time-dependent), the relevant behaviors may be very persistent given the appropriate cues.

All drugs used for pleasure can act as positive reinforcers. This is clear from studies showing that animals will learn to perform tasks when drugs are used as rewards. Alcohol or drugs are, of course, positive reinforcers for drinking and drug use behaviors and through experience can become associated with a variety of internal and external cues. For many people, these cues may be rather limited (e.g., only at family meal times and never more than once a week). For others, drinking cues can become highly generalized (e.g., when they are happy, sad, alone or with others, and at any time of the day).

One apparent problem with this view of drinking and drug use is the continued use of alcohol and drugs despite negative consequences such as hangovers, ill health, and social and legal problems. This appears to be contrary to an operant conditioning analysis of drinking and drug use. However, this is not the case because these negative consequences do not occur immediately after alcohol or drug consumption. The immediate effects continue to be positive and reinforcing (alcohol or drug effects and the relief of withdrawal symptoms). A problem drinker or drug user may acknowledge and regret the social problems and other problems associated with substance use and vow, quite sincerely, to abstain in the future. However, without some sort of help (e.g., relapse prevention treatment), he or she may continue to be overwhelmed by stimuli that evoke drinking or drug use (the sight of old friends, anxiety, arguments with spouse, etc.).

It is widely believed that alcohol and drug use can relieve stress and that this can motivate and sustain consumption behaviors. Retrospective and prospective studies with humans lend some support to this stress-reduction theory but other relationships between stressful events and alcohol or drug use are not as strong as the theory suggests. A likely explanation is that, in humans, the experience of stress relief from alcohol or drug use is influenced by expectations that this will occur (Cohen and Baum, 1995).

Expectations of the effects of alcohol or drugs are cognitions and like other cognitions they influence and are influenced by classical and operant conditioning. Through conditioning, expectations and other cognitions become associated with stimuli and rewards but they also influence reactions to stimuli, behaviors and consequences. This is a basic premise of social learning theory (Bandura, 1977), which recognizes the behaving and self-aware individual as an active participant in the learning process rather than as a passive victim of circumstances. The theory also emphasizes that learning takes place through modelling, and is shaped by consequences under the control of the behaving individual. Moreover, reactions to stimuli, rewards and punishments are mediated and modified by changes in cognitions. Thus, an "overwhelming desire to drink" can come to be viewed as a transient "crest of a wave" (Marlatt and Gordon, 1985) with proper attention to the cognitions involved in relapse prevention. Also, one slip after treatment can be seen as either a positive learning experience or as a sign that all is lost.

Social learning theory also recognizes the influence of self-monitoring and self-evaluation, attributions and expectancy effects. The theory has also given rise to the notions of "learned helplessness" (belief in loss of control) and "abstinence violation effects" ("I have relapsed and all is lost").

There is a great deal of experimental and clinical support for a social learning analysis of alcohol and drug use (Wilson, 1988). Further, at least for problem drinkers, several treatments based on this theory tend to have more support from experimental studies than do other types of treatment (Holder et al., 1991). Treatment methods based directly or indirectly on social learning theory are aversion therapy (including covert sensitization), cue-exposure training, social skills training, self-control training and relapse prevention. The development of "motivational interviewing" was also influenced by social learning theory and by theories of client-centred counselling (Miller, 1996). Most of the chapters in this book reflect the influence of both types of theories.

The theory can also explain why other forms of treatment can work for some people. For example, 12-step programs can be seen as creating drug-free environments, as providing social reinforcements for abstinence and related verbal statements, as providing an appealing explanation for problems. Social learning theory does not support the concept of alcoholism as a distinctive entity and regards "loss of control" as a modifiable experience, not as an inevitable, objective consequence of alcohol use. However, the theory does not deny that, for some people, acceptance of the label "alcoholic" and the concept of "powerlessness" over alcohol can become the cornerstones of their recovery.

SOCIAL-ENVIRONMENTAL FACTORS

A vast array of social and other environmental factors has been cited as contributing to the onset and maintenance of problematic substance use and to relapse after periods of abstinence. However, no one factor has been shown to be either necessary or sufficient for problem use or relapse to occur. Thus, like other factors that influence alcohol and drug use, social and other environmental factors exert their influence in the context of a complex, dynamic multi-factor system.

The *availability* and costs of alcohol and other drugs clearly influence overall patterns of use (Single, 1988; Godfrey and Maynard, 1988) and can contribute to the maintenance of problematic use and relapse. We have already noted that, at least in the laboratory setting, price manipulations influence drinking behavior by "alcoholics," and there is evidence that price influences heavy drinkers in the community. Some clinicians have contracted with clients to increase the costs of alcohol and drugs to deter relapse. Thus clients have agreed to make a donation to a despised cause every time they drink, or they have agreed to forfeit a returnable deposit if they take drugs.

The drinking or drug use culture of the dominant society, and especially of clients' peers and family, can also support the maintenance of problematic substance use and contribute to relapse. This is especially so when these cultures promote heavy or illegal substance use and use for utilitarian reasons (i.e., to solve problems).

Many other aspects of family life may also contribute to problematic substance use and relapse. Family members can present models of substance use that are emulated by children. Childhood experiences within distressed or dysfunctional families may leave children vulnerable to substance abuse and a variety of other problems as adults. The following are examples of family-related factors that can contribute to the onset and maintenance of some types of problematic substance use, and it is not difficult to see how they may also contribute to relapse: poverty; being from a group devalued by larger society; alcoholism or drug use among family members; parental abuse and neglect; parental separation; low cohesion; and low mutual support (Goplerud, 1990).

Systems theory has drawn special attention to the influence of other family processes (Pearlman, 1988). This theory proposes that the behavior of individuals is determined and sustained by the dynamics and demands of the key people with whom they interact. This is compatible with social learning theory described above. However, systems theory proposes that behaviors have functions within dynamic systems, even when these behaviors and their supporting systems are objectively problematic or "dysfunctional" for those involved. In the case of alcoholism, systems theory draws attention to ways in which an alcoholic's family copes with and possibly reinforces drinking and the implications for the family if the alcoholic changes his or her behavior.

Systems theory proposes that families or other ongoing social networks develop "rules" of interaction and that these rules can sustain pathological behaviors (e.g., the family implicitly agrees never to plan family events on Friday nights because that is when father goes out to get drunk with his friends). Family members also assume roles that maintain the homeostasis within the family ("enabler," "martyr," "sick person").

Although not central to systems theory, the theory can also accommodate the notion that some family members have "co-dependency" needs that contribute to the maintenance of a dysfunctional homeostasis (Cermak, 1995). This is a highly controversial notion with little empirical support and well-deserved criticism (Babcock and McKay, 1995). Nonetheless, efforts have been made to treat "co-dependency" and to have it recognized as a "disease."

Those who subscribe to systems theory find support for the theory in studies of families with alcoholic members, comparisons of alcoholic and non-alcoholic families, and treatment outcome studies. While the results of this research are consistent with systems theory (Holder et al., 1991), almost all studies have only involved male alcoholics and the results may not generalize to females.

AN INTEGRATED BIOPSYCHOSOCIAL PERSPECTIVE

Figure 1 represents one attempt to capture the multitude of factors that influence substance use and to show how they interact. The model was developed for the World Health Organization (WHO, 1981). It identifies biological, personal and social factors and learning experiences and shows how they may have immediate or more distant influences on the disposition to use drugs. It also shows that social and individual factors can be influenced by the consequences of drug use. Other feedback mechanisms that can have positive or negative influences on future use, depending on the individual users and their circumstances, are also identified.

The model shows that drug actions and their effects may lead to biological responses that account for tolerance and drug-specific withdrawal symptoms. These responses may have both adverse or reinforcing properties. While withdrawal symptoms may initially be aversive, they can be relieved by taking more drugs, and this strengthens the drug-taking response. Repeated experiences of withdrawal can activate a classical conditioning process whereby previously neutral stimuli elicit withdrawal symptoms, or drug-like effects, and lead to further drug use. Over time, through a process of generalization, a variety of internal and external cues (anxiety, stress, social events) may come to be associated with withdrawal symptoms and drug effects. For some people, this process can lead to an extreme narrowing of their repertoire of responses to cues and a tendency to use drugs whenever these cues are present.

On the brighter side, the model shows that drug taking can be reduced by making the experience less reinforcing and making abstinence or reduced use more reinforcing. This can be achieved using a variety of biological, psychological and environmental interventions as previously discussed. While the drug user who relapses after a period of abstinence is at risk of quickly resuming previous use levels due to residual biological alterations and previous learning, this risk may be reduced through the acquisition of new cognitions and skills.

CONCLUSION

Substance use, and especially continued use despite negative consequences, are clearly complex phenomena that cannot be explained by any single set of factors. Rather, substance use is determined by several types of factors that interact in complex ways. Those who counsel people who have problems with alcohol and other substances need to be aware of these complexities yet have the skills to provide practical advice and assistance to individual clients. Despite its overall complexity, however, it is clear that substance use and relapse can be prevented or reduced if those involved can acquire the appropriate cognitions and skills. Skilled and sensitive counsellors can contribute a great deal to this acquisition process as will be evident from any of the chapters in this book.

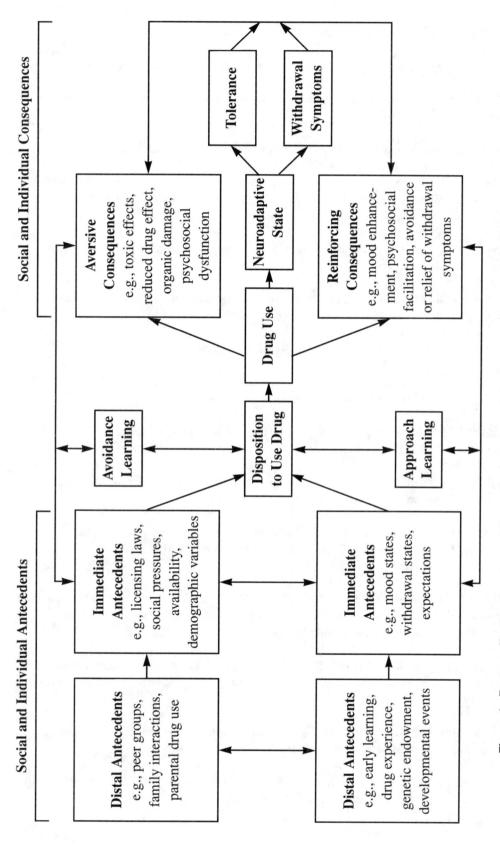

Figure 1. Factors affecting drug use and abuse (From Edwards, Arif and Hodgson (1981), Nomenclature and classification of drug- and alcohol-related problems: A WHO memorandum. Bulletin of the WHO, 59 (2): 225–242. Reprinted with permission.

REFERENCES

Alcohol Health and Research World 19. (1995). The genetics of alcoholism. (Special Edition).

Allen, J.P. (1996). Subtypes of alcoholics based on psychometric measures. *Alcohol Health and Research World* 20 (1): 24–29.

American Psychiatric Association (1994). *Diagnostic and Statistical Manual,* 4th ed. Washington, DC: APA.

Arif, A., and Westermeyer, J. (1988). *Manual of Drug and Alcohol Abuse: Guidelines for Teaching in Medical and Health Institutions.* New York: Plenum Medical Book Company.

Babcock, M., and McKay, C. (eds.). (1995). *Challenging Codependency: Feminist Critiques.* Toronto: University of Toronto Press.

Ball, S.A. (1996). Type A and Type B alcoholism: Applicability across subpopulations and treatment settings. *Alcohol Health and Research World* 20 (1): 30–35.

Bandura, A. (1977). *Social Learning Theory.* New Jersey: Prentice Hall.

Barry, H. (1988). Psychoanalytic theory of alcoholism. In *Theories on Alcoholism*, eds. Chaudron, C.D., and Wilkinson, D.A. Toronto: Addiction Research Foundation.

Cermak, T.L. (1995). Codependency. In *Encyclopaedia of Drugs and Alcohol*, ed. Jaffe, J. New York: MacMillan Library Reference.

Cohen, L., and Baum, A. (1995). Stress. In *Encyclopaedia of Drugs and Alcohol*, ed. Jaffe, J. New York: Macmillan Library Reference.

Cox, W.M. (1985). Personality correlates of substance abuse. In *Determinants of Substance Abuse: Biological, Psychological and Environmental Factors*, eds. Galizio, M., and Maisto, S.A. New York: Plenum Press.

Crabbe, J.C., McSwigan, J.D., and Belknap, J.K. (1985). The role of genetics in substance abuse. In *Determinants of Substance Abuse: Biological, Psychological and Environmental Factors*, eds. Galizio, M., and Maisto, S.A. New York: Plenum Press.

Drake, R.E., Mueser, K.T., Clark, R.E., and Wallach, M.E. (1996). The course, treatment, and outcome of substance disorder in persons with severe mental illness. *American Journal of Orthopsychiatry* 66 (1): 42–51.

Ellinwood, E.H., and King, G.R. (1995). Drug effects and biological responses. In *Encyclopaedia of Drugs and Alcohol*, ed. Jaffe, J. New York: Macmillan Library Reference.

Ellis, K., and Rush, B.R. (1993). *Alcohol and Other Drug Services in Ontario: Results of a Provincial Survey, 1992.* Toronto: Addiction Research Foundation.

Godfrey, C., and Maynard, A. (1988). An economic theory of alcohol consumption and abuse. In *Theories on Alcoholism*, eds. Chaudron, C.D., and Wilkinson, D.A. Toronto: Addiction Research Foundation.

Goplerud, E.N. (1990). *Breaking New Ground for Youth at Risk: Program Summaries.* (DHHS Publication No. [ADM] 89-1658). Washington, DC: Office for Substance Abuse Prevention.

Heather, N., and Robertson, I. (1989). *Problem Drinking,* 2nd ed. New York: Oxford University Press.

Holder, H., Longabaugh, R., Miller, W., and Rubonis, A.V. (1991). The cost effectiveness of treatment for alcoholism: A first approximation. *Journal of Studies on Alcohol* 52: 517–525.

Kandel, D.B., and Yamaguchi, K. (1985). Developmental patterns of the use of legal, illegal, and medically prescribed psychotropic drugs from adolescence to young adulthood. In *Etiology of Drug Abuse: Implications for Prevention* (NIDA Research Monograph Series No. 56, DHHS Publication NO. ADH 85-1335). Washington, DC: U.S. Government Printing Office.

Keller, M. (1972). The oddities of alcoholics. *Quarterly Journal of Studies on Alcohol* 33: 1147–1148.

Khantzian, E.J. (1995). Psychological (psychoanalytic) perspective. In *Encyclopaedia of Drugs and Alcohol, Vol. 1*, ed. Jaffe, J. New York: Macmillan Library Reference.

Marlatt, G.A., Demming, B., and Reid, J.B. (1973). Loss of control drinking in alcoholics: An experimental analogue. *Journal of Abnormal Psychology* 81: 233–241.

Marlatt, G.A., and Gordon, J.R. (eds.). (1985). *Relapse Prevention.* New York: Guilford Press.

Mello, N.K., McNamee, H.B., and Mendelson, J.H. (1968). *Drinking Patterns of Chronic Alcoholics: Gambling and Motivation.* Psychiatric Research Report No. 24. Washington, DC: American Psychiatric Association.

Mello, N.K., and Mendelson, J.H. (1965). Operant analysis of drinking habits of chronic alcoholics. *Nature* 206: 43–46.

Miller, N.S. (1994). Prevalence and treatment models for addiction in psychiatric populations. *Psychiatric Annals* 24 (8): 399–406.

Miller, W.R. (1996). Motivational interviewing: Research, practice and puzzles. *Addictive Behaviors* 21: 838–842.

Pearlman, S. (1988). Systems theory and alcoholism. In *Theories on Alcoholism*, eds. Chaudron, C.D., and Wilkinson, D.A. Toronto: Addiction Research Foundation.

Ray, O., and Ksir, C. (1996). *Drugs, Society, and Human Behavior,* 7th ed. Missouri: Mosby-Year Book Inc.

Robins, L.N. (1974). *The Vietnam Drug User Returns.* Washington, DC: Special Action Office for Drug Abuse Prevention Monograph, Series A, No. 2, May 1974, Contract No., HSM-42-72-75.

Sherman, J.E., Jorenby, D.E., and Baker, T.B. (1988). Classical conditioning with alcohol: Acquired preferences and aversions, tolerance, and urges/craving. In *Theories on Alcoholism*, eds. Chaudron, C.D., and Wilkinson, D.A. Toronto: Addiction Research Foundation.

Single, E.W. (1988): The availability theory of alcohol-related problems. In *Theories on Alcoholism*, eds. Chaudron, C.D., and Wilkinson, D.A. Toronto: Addiction Research Foundation.

Smart, R.G., and Ogborne, A.C. (1996). *Northern Spirits: A Social History of Alcohol in Canada,* 2nd ed. Toronto: Addiction Research Foundation.

Stein, J.A., Newcomb, M.D., and Bentler, P.M. (1987). Personality and drug use: Reciprocal effects across four years. *Personality and Individual Differences* 8: 419–430.

Tarter, R.E., Alterman, A.I., and Edwards, K.L. (1988). Neurobehavioral theory of alcoholism etiology. In *Theories on Alcoholism*, eds. Chaudron, C.D., and Wilkinson, D.A. Toronto: Addiction Research Foundation.

Tobena, A., Fernandez-Teruel, A., Escorihuela, R.M., Nunez, J.F., et al. (1993). Limits of habituation and extinction: Implications for relapse prevention programs in addictions. *Drug and Alcohol Dependence* 32 (3): 209–217.

Uhl, G.R., Persico, A.M., and Smith, S.S. (1992). Current excitement with D-sub-2 dopamine receptor gene alleles in substance abuse. *Archives of General Psychiatry* 49 (2): 157–160.

Volpicelli, J.R., Clay, L.L., Watson, H.T., and Volpicelli, L.A. (1994). Naltrexone and the treatment of alcohol dependence. *Alcohol Health and Research World* 18: 272–278.

Wilson, G.T. (1988). Alcohol use and abuse: A social learning analysis. In *Theories on Alcoholism*, eds. Chaudron, C.D., and Wilkinson, D.A. Toronto: Addiction Research Foundation.

World Health Organization. (1981). Factors affecting drug use and abuse. *Bulletin of the World Health Organization* 59 (2): 225–242.

World Health Organization. (1992). *The ICD-1 — Classification of Mental and Behavioural Disorders, Clinical Descriptions and Diagnostic Guidelines.* Geneva: WHO.

Zuckerman, M. (1983). Sensation seeking: The initial motive for drug abuse. In *Etiological Aspects of Alcohol and Drug Abuse*, eds. Gotheil, E., et al. Springfield, IL: Charles C. Thomas Publishers.

Chapter 2

Motivational Interviewing Techniques

TERRY SODEN AND ROBERT MURRAY

INTRODUCTION

The last 25 years have seen remarkable advances in the assessment and treatment of addictive disorders. These advances have given clinicians far more sophisticated methods of helping clients change their alcohol/drug-taking behavior. The theoretical foundation for these motivational counselling techniques is a more concrete and comprehensive understanding of human behavior as it relates to substance abuse. The importance of the addiction counsellor's underlying beliefs and attitudes (i.e., theoretical orientation) cannot be overstated. As Albert Einstein said, "...the theory determines what we can observe," and what clinicians observe about their clients directly influences their counselling activities.

This chapter discusses the principles, guidelines and strategies emerging from this new theoretical framework of addictions and how people change. It presents a brief historical review of the biopsychosocial model of addictions and a new perspective of motivation. It then examines factors influencing motivation, and the change process, and provides a survey of motivational counselling approaches.

BIOPSYCHOSOCIAL MODEL OF ADDICTION

As we integrate different perspectives and develop more sophisticated conceptual models of substance abuse, the Biopsychosocial Model of Addictions (Donovan and Marlatt, 1988) has emerged as the cornerstone of a new and more comprehensive approach to addictions treatment. Addictions counsellors now see substance abuse disorders as the result of various characteristics within an individual interacting with numerous environmental factors. This process may also lead to a variety of other compulsive behaviors, such as eating disorders, uncontrolled gambling and sexual promiscuity.

From a biopsychosocial perspective, a substance use disorder is conceptualized as "...a complex, progressive pattern having biological, psychological, sociological and behavioral components" (Donovan and Marlatt, 1988, p. 5). Another component, which has been identified by numerous clinicians and 12-step mutual aid programs, is the spiritual aspect of human existence. This notion is not confined to the definitions held by various world religions, but can be considered in its broadest context. For example, spirituality is the "wellspring of creativity" within an individual (Horney, 1942).

Unlike the traditional view of "alcoholism" or "drug addiction," the Biopsychosocial Model maintains that substance abuse is the result of a multitude of factors. It also recognizes that people with problems related to their alcohol and drug use are a varied lot. They differ with respect to:
- patterns of consumption
- family history
- current environmental stressors
- self-esteem and self-efficacy
- coping skills
- employment status and educational achievements
- social supports
- financial resources
- physical and emotional health
- beliefs and attitudes, including those that pertain to their substance use.

In addition, the Biopsychosocial Model recognizes the possibility that problems related to the abuse of substances may develop in anyone (i.e., not confined to a single personality type), and may result in numerous and differing consequences. A variety of treatment options must therefore be considered and available so that treatment planning can match interventions to the needs, strengths and circumstances of each client (Pattison and Kaufman, 1982).

MOTIVATION: AN INTERACTIONAL PROCESS

Understanding motivation as the product of an interactional and/or interpersonal process is significantly different from the traditional attributional model. From the traditional perspective, motivation is a trait that reflects the underlying personality structure of an individual. Clients with problems related to their alcohol and drug use are usually seen as unmotivated because they use defences such as denial, minimization, projection and repression. Research has demonstrated, however, that

...motivation should not be thought of as a personality problem or as a trait that a person carries through the counsellor's doorway. Rather, motivation is a state of readiness or eagerness to change, which may fluctuate from one time or situation to another. This state is one that can be influenced (Miller and Rollnick, 1991, p. 14).

This enlightened view emphasizes the complexity of change, and asserts that factors both external and internal to the person with alcohol or other drug problems influence the change process. Three categories of factors have been identified: environmental/ situational, client, and therapist. The creative use of the forces found within each of these categories can help the clinician and client bring about intentional change.

ENVIRONMENTAL/SITUATIONAL FACTORS

Research has uncovered three primary environmental/situational variables that affect the individual's desire to change or maintain the status quo: time; geographical access; and social support.

Time

Time reflects the inability of clients with substance use problems to tolerate distress (especially that which results from acknowledging a substance use problem and/or its consequences) and the length of time it takes to receive assistance. Typically, these clients contact some component of the treatment system as a result of a crisis but then must wait lengthy periods of time for treatment.

This can decrease the likelihood that a person will follow through on a decision to seek help. The authors of a study on this issue concluded that

> ...the presence of a waiting period between the initial phone call and the client's first appointment is tantamount to dismissing them for a majority of cases. Clinic staff who wish to improve retention rates should eliminate waiting periods and make access to the clinic as immediate and effortless as possible (Stark et al., 1990, p. 74).

Another study found that reducing the waiting period for first face-to-face contact between a client and treatment clinician from 14 to two days increased the number of people entering and staying in treatment (Dennis et al., 1994).

The environmental/situational crises that trigger client contact take a variety of forms, such as loss or threat of loss of significant other(s), employment or health. Many other critical incidents can prompt a person to seek help, including financial difficulties, emotional turmoil and legal problems. The capacity of the "continuum of care" to respond quickly to the person in crisis is a key factor in both initiating and reinforcing the desire to change (Leigh et al., 1984). Given the extensive time it takes for many people with substance use disorders to get support from the treatment system, it is imperative that agencies and workers develop mechanisms that help clients tolerate and manage their anxiety. Clients may be at risk to return to substance use and leave the treatment system if the system cannot respond to their needs while they are struggling with anxiety.

One creative approach to this problem involves matching appropriate clients with healthy, mature members of mutual aid/self-help groups, such as Alcoholics Anonymous (AA) or Narcotics Anonymous. The resulting relationship may give the client more of the daily support and encouragement he or she needs to cope with anxiety. Further, by observing the positive changes made by the recovered person, the client gains hope that change is possible. (See Chapter 9 for more information about mutual aid groups.)

Research also indicates that telephone calls to remind clients of their intake appointments may increase the client's initial attendance rates. A telephone call within one week after the initial session regarding the client's satisfaction with the interview also resulted in increased retention rates through one month of treatment. Calls received more than one week after the initial session had no beneficial effect, suggesting that only prompt responses are perceived by the client as true interest in his or her well-being (Gariti et al., 1995).

Many other strategies and/or resources could also be used to help the client. Where appropriate, the worker may arrange for regular telephone contact, refer to a detoxification centre, or cultivate support of family members. These types of supportive strategies are significantly more likely to cause the client to enter into, comply with and successfully complete treatment (Leigh, Ogborne and Cleland, 1984; Johnson and Pandina, 1991; Huselid, Self and Gutierres, 1991).

Geographical Access

Travelling great distances to attend a treatment service can reduce motivation to enter treatment and engage in aftercare. People in need of help often feel frustrated by inadequate transportation systems, lack of financial resources, and a sense of powerlessness to overcome these barriers to treatment.

Solutions to the above issue may include:
   a) training existing health and social service providers to intervene effectively with substance-abusing clients

    b) developing local outreach treatment and aftercare programs by addiction-specific agencies

    c) co-ordinating local services through strategic planning and community networking activities to better serve these individuals

    d) enhancing the existing continuum of care in local communities.

Social Support

Research shows that social support influences the probability of the person with an alcohol or drug problem entering into, engaging in and successfully completing a process of positive change. It can be provided by family, friends and/or mutual aid/self-help programs, etc.

To assess the potential impact of the client's present social milieu, the counsellor must ascertain the level of support that family or friends can provide, and the probability of their sabotaging the client's efforts. When indicated, the counsellor will need to work with members of the client's social network to ensure they support the person's efforts to change.

There are many issues that the counsellor may need to address with respect to the above. One of the most common is "enabling": when family members or friends unwittingly help the individual avoid the consequences of his or her behavior, thereby encouraging it to continue. An example of enabling involves "Anna," whose partner "Sam" has a drinking problem. Anna tells Sam's employer that Sam is home with the flu when, in fact, he has a hangover.

In such situations, the counsellor's task is: (a) to help the partner understand how "enabling" perpetuates substance abuse and (b) to help the partner find other responses that discourage substance abuse and bolster the development of motivation to change.

Surrogate support systems, such as mutual aid/self-help groups, are most effectively used when the counsellor actively helps the client make contact with the group. Sisson and Mallams (1981) found that when the clinician made the initial telephone call to a suitable AA member on behalf of the client, all of those clients followed through with the contact. When a group of clients were simply encouraged to attend AA and given a schedule of meetings, not one attended any meetings. When counsellors match clients with a compatible 12-Step member, the member can then support the client by explaining the program, informing him or her of meeting times, arranging to take the client to a first meeting, introducing others in the program, and guiding the client in the informal use of this support network.

CLIENT CHARACTERISTICS

The second category of factors that influence motivation are found within the individual and are often referred to as client characteristics. Miller and Hester (1986) found the following five major internal variables that affect motivation: the focus and level of distress experienced by the client; the severity of the substance abuse problem; locus of control; conceptual level; and stage of readiness to change.

Focus and Level of Distress

The clinician must understand the source of the distress and its level of intensity. For example, if it originates from external pressure — a family member or employer threatening either the loss of a significant relationship or financial security — the client may resist any examination of his or her behavior. In such a case, the clinician is well advised to address the resistance through a nonpunitive, motivational therapeutic approach. This can be done by understanding the nature or types of resistance. Munjack and Oziel (1978) suggest that resistance is the result of five different antecedents: (1) the client misunderstanding the counsellor; (2) the client's lack of skills; (3) the client being unable to see himself or herself succeeding; (4) issues arising from previous counselling experiences, such as anxiety or guilt; and (5) the rewards of the client's substance use/abuse.

Motivational interviewing strategies aimed at people with alcohol or drug problems who have been forced into treatment should also include: a) encouraging the client to discuss his or her feelings about being forced to attend the interview; and b) uncovering the functions the substance serves, the level and pattern of consumption, and its social, emotional, physical, psychological and spiritual consequences. This will increase the client's awareness of the impact of substance use on his or her life and therefore provide a new focus for his or her distress.

As the focus shifts in this direction, the client's distress about this behavior often increases dramatically. This distress comes from recognizing that substance abuse interferes with the attainment of one's goals, adherence to one's intrinsic values, and/or progress toward the development of the "ideal self." The distress is further heightened by the threat of the loss of significant relationships, employment and/or health. Such a negative emotional state — coupled with low self-esteem (Perez, 1989), low self-efficacy (the belief that one does not have the skills required to make desired change occur; Annis and Davis, 1989), and the effects of withdrawal[1] — typically leads to an unbearable level of discomfort. This produces a pivotal period during which a client may either stop his or her substance abuse or continue it. It is referred to as the "window of opportunity," when the counsellor helps the client to "hit bottom" without necessarily having to "ride the garbage truck all the way to the dump."

Research shows that clients at this time are especially vulnerable to the influence of motivational strategies, delivered within the context of formal counselling or some other form of helping relationship. Regardless of the clients' point of contact with the treatment system — whatever therapeutic relationship they have — there is a significant increase in the probability that they will begin using adaptive behaviors that lead to positive changes. However, unless clients develop and use adaptive coping skills that increase their sense of self-efficacy and self-esteem, they are left extremely vulnerable to returning to the abuse of alcohol or other drugs. Motivational strategies designed to increase distress, while still maintaining a therapeutic relationship that builds client self-efficacy, will be discussed later in this chapter.

Severity of the Substance Abuse Problem

Level of severity is another client characteristic identified by Miller and Rollnick (1991) that has implications not only for the direction of motivation but also the type and intensity of treatment required. Most current scientific authorities and treatment specialists in the field of addictions "view substance abuse problems on a continuum from nonproblematic to problematic use, rather than as an either/or situation" (Lewis et al., 1988, p. 4). Level of severity is determined by the client's frequency and level of consumption, *combined with* life problems that have been identified through the assessment process.

The above-stated approach to substance abuse problems is relatively new. In the past, many counsellors considered consumption only when attempting to determine the severity of a problem. The Biopsychosocial Model has stimulated the development of a more comprehensive and multidimensional "severity continuum" that also considers the impact of substance abuse on various levels of the client's functioning (Prochaska and DiClemente, 1984; Skinner, 1981).

Regarding motivation, research has found that distress related to an individual perceiving himself or herself as using alcohol or other drugs at a level that puts him or her at risk can *either* increase or decrease motivation to change. Distress experienced by the client, for example, can be so high as to paralyze the individual or be so low as to have little or no impact on willingness to change. The client who does not realistically assess the seriousness of his or her situation must be made aware of the consequences of substance abuse and its impact on affected life areas (Rogers and Mewborn, 1976).

Clients who are overly distressed by the perceived severity of their substance abuse problem must be encouraged to examine their strengths and past successes, thereby raising their self-efficacy and self-esteem. These clients also need help in evaluating what life might be like without substance use. Such motivational interventions reduce distress and create hope and motivation to change (Prochaska and DiClemente, 1984).

Research also indicates that individuals with severe substance abuse problems have often made numerous attempts at treatment without success. This, according to Orford and Edwards (1977), results in lower self-esteem and self-efficacy, leading to negative expectations of their capacity to benefit from treatment. Not surprisingly, this lowers motivation to enter the treatment system again because it seems futile.

A skilfully conducted assessment, done within the context of motivational interviewing, should enable the counsellor to accurately determine the severity of the substance abuse problem. With this information available to both the counsellor and the client, a negotiated decision can be made regarding a treatment plan that *matches* the client's needs and circumstances to the least intrusive but most effective form of treatment (McLellan et al., 1983). When this matching has not been done, clients often receive inappropriate treatment and thus do not invest themselves in it. Because each unsuccessful treatment attempt leaves the client feeling that he or she has failed, it is vital to match the client with the least intrusive treatment that has the highest probability for success.

Locus of Control

The third factor found to influence motivation is locus of control (Rotter, 1966), a concept for understanding the extent of control an individual thinks he or she has over his or her environment.

People with alcohol or drug problems often blame external factors for their consumption, their life situation, and their general sense of helplessness and malaise. This demonstrates a personality-perceptual-behavioral style common to individuals with an external locus of control. This orientation continues into the counselling relationship, with the client making numerous requests for guidance and direction. Even though the ultimate aim is to help them take responsibility for their behavior, during the initial phases of motivational counselling the counsellor should provide consistent feedback that enhances the client's self-esteem while acknowledging that an "...external orientation is associated with higher anxiety and distress, which may in turn influence motivation for treatment" (Donovan and O'Leary, 1979).

Conceptual Level

Conceptual level refers to a client's emotional maturity and interpersonal development. Just as locus of control is viewed as a continuum, so too is conceptual level. A person with an alcohol or drug problem on the low side of the continuum tends to perceive his or her substance abuse problem in simplistic terms. Like a person who believes the external world determines the outcome of his or her behavior, the client on the low side of the conceptual continuum is highly dependent on authority figures for direction, and functions best in a structured environment with simple rules of conduct.

On the other hand, a "high conceptual level" client is cognitively complex, usually thinking in abstract terms. He or she tends to recognize the complexity of his or her problems and finds greatest satisfaction when functioning in an unstructured, flexible counselling situation that allows for independent thought and the freedom to choose alternative treatment approaches, with a counsellor who sees his or her role as a facilitator and not an authoritative teacher.

The counsellor's responsibility is to differentially apply motivational counselling techniques, while being aware of the client's locus of control and conceptual level. In the authors' experience, individuals with moderate to severe substance use problems, when highly distressed, tend to initially present with an external locus of control, combined with a low conceptual level. These clients respond best to a counsellor who makes directive statements and recommends specific structured activities for the client to carry out.

An example of the above is found in many individuals who present at a detoxification centre and remain long enough to experience the distress of withdrawal. They rely on the detoxification attendants for information, direction and nurturing, and assurance that their present unpleasant experience of withdrawal will pass. This need compels such residents to seek out and accept advice without hesitation. However, as they begin to feel better, some of them shift to a higher conceptual level and a more internal locus of control. They become more self-directed and less interested in the advice and direction of others.

In the past, counsellors saw this as evidence of decreasing motivation to change and attempted to alter it by becoming increasingly more confrontive and directive. Although their intention was to be helpful, the outcome was usually resistance to further help — resulting in the client dropping out of treatment. However, we now know that clients who shift from dependence on the counsellor to more self-directed, positive thinking and behavior may be manifesting higher self-efficacy. Research indicates that such individuals are most successful in changing their problematic behavior (Janis, 1982).

During this early phase of recovery, the counsellor should match his or her counselling strategies to the client's shifting dependence, conceptual level and locus of control, and not give in to the temptation to view the client as unmotivated. Instead, a more helpful approach is to support the client's need for independent decision-making and ownership of the therapeutic process.

Stage of Readiness to Change

The client's current readiness to change is the final and perhaps most important factor to consider when engaged in motivational interviewing. This multi-faceted variable is sufficiently complex to have been developed into a theory known as the Trans-theoretical Model of Change, by Prochaska and DiClemente. The theory initially provided an explanation of people with alcohol or other drug problems as they go about the process of changing their behavior. It recognized and acknowledged the difficulties and challenges inherent in altering substance use disorders and clearly describes the nature of recovery. Unlike other conceptual models of addictions and their treatment, which view change as a process of straight line growth, the Transtheoretical Model asserts that a "slip" or relapse is part and parcel of the cyclical nature of changing substance abuse behavior. This model is usually depicted as a "wheel" of change consisting of different stages. The Transtheoretical Model of Change has also been successfully applied to a variety of other problem behaviors, including weight control, high-fat diets, adolescent delinquent behaviors, condom use, sunscreen use and mammography screening (Prochaska et al., 1994).

FIGURE 1

WHEEL OF CHANGE

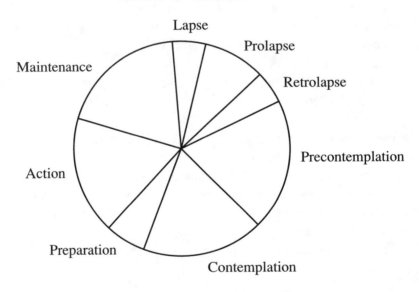

Adaptation of Prochaska and DiClemente's
Transtheoretical Model of Change

The authors' adaptation of Prochaska and DiClemente's model (Fig. 1) includes the stages of "Precontemplation," "Contemplation," "Preparation," "Action" and "Maintenance" (Velicer et al., 1995), and the "Process of Relapse" (Marlatt and Gordon, 1985). The authors' major adaptation to the original model integrates Marlatt's concept of relapse into the Transtheoretical Model of Change. Rather than seeing relapse as a stage, the authors conceptualize relapse as a process that begins in the Maintenance Stage and leads to three distinct stages: Lapse, Prolapse and Retrolapse.

PRECONTEMPLATION STAGE

The first stage is known as Precontemplation — when others see the harm that the substance use is doing to the client, but the client does not. Not surprisingly, individuals in precontemplation who present at a counselling agency do so at the request or insistence of significant others, employers or the judicial system. It is therefore difficult to engage these clients in any meaningful dialogue about their substance use. Their resistance usually takes the form of: a) actual physical withdrawal from counselling, or b) superficial engagement in the assessment process, treatment planning, and the individualized therapeutic activities needed to bring about change.

Process-oriented research (Miller and Sovereign, 1989; Patterson and Forgatch, 1985) shows that the traditional confrontational approach creates a destructive dynamic with the vast majority of clients. For clients in the Precontemplation Stage, this situation is made worse when the counsellor attempts to use strategies more appropriate to clients at other stages of readiness. When clinical strategies and client stage of change are mismatched, clients often react in ways that have historically been interpreted as manifestations of "denial" and "resistance." In reality, however, these are responses to feeling accused, labelled, aggressively confronted, controlled, and not seen as a worthwhile person with strengths and weaknesses, successes and failures, potential and resources. When working with clients in the Precontemplation Stage, the counsellor should try to uncover their reasons for coming to the counselling session, their feelings of being coerced, and how they view their consumption and its consequences (i.e., whether they see it as a problem or as a solution to other problems).

CONTEMPLATION STAGE

The next stage of change, as outlined by Prochaska and DiClemente, is the Contemplation Stage. Clients in contemplation recognize some of the consequences of their alcohol/drug use but are ambivalent about altering their use. The therapeutic task is to help these clients move beyond ambivalence to a feeling of cognitive dissonance (the internal conflict that results from an awareness that their substance use impedes the attainment of their life goals). These clients must also be helped to see how their drug use often clashes with their values and beliefs.

Individuals in the Contemplation Stage are pulled in two directions. On the one hand, they are somewhat aware of the consequences of their substance use. On the other hand, substance use has a positive function in their lives. At the early phase of this stage, clients experience this ambivalence but don't believe they can change their situation. It is important for counsellors to help these clients understand their ambivalent feelings, and how their behavior is problematic, in order to move the change process forward.

PREPARATION STAGE

Prochaska and DiClemente define the Preparation Stage as "a stage that combines intention and behavioral criteria" (Prochaska, DiClemente and Norcross, 1992). This refers to a period of time during which individuals with an alcohol or other drug problem are sufficiently aware of the consequences of their substance use to have experienced the tipping of the decisional balance in favor of intention to take action and change their problematic behavior. Behaviorally, however, they have only made some small changes, but have not yet translated their intentions into full action that would result in a substantive change in their substance use.

Counsellors need to recognize that clients in the Preparation Stage exhibit many of the cognitive and behavioral characteristics typical of the Contemplation and Action Stages. Their role with some clients in this stage is to help them recognize their skills and to come to believe that they are capable of changing their substance use. Individuals in the Preparation Stage may also be "chomping at the bit," wanting to rush into a plan of action. However, a skilfully conducted assessment is needed so that the counsellor and client both understand the nature of the client's problems and his or her strengths and weaknesses. Only in this way can realistic and achievable goals be set and successful treatment outcome ultimately realized.

ACTION STAGE

According to Prochaska and DiClemente, the Action Stage is the shortest, because it's the time when clients are the most enthusiastic and energetic. Such a peak level of effort can only be maintained for a limited period of time. Factors that help maintain the momentum of change throughout this stage include the increasing sense of self-esteem that results from clients "acting on their beliefs in personal self-efficacy," and the positive recognition received from others regarding dramatic changes in problematic behavior (Prochaska and DiClemente, 1984, p. 67). Clients who present in the Action Stage are eager to engage in activities that bring about immediate results — they may feel frustrated by therapists who spend a lot of time trying to understand the origin and complexity of the presenting problem.

The counsellor's primary task with clients in the Action Stage is to acknowledge the difficult work required to make necessary changes. In addition, the counsellor should provide ongoing affirmation of the changes these clients are making. This is particularly important for people with a limited social support network or one that works to sabotage changes that occur.

MAINTENANCE STAGE

The next stage is one in which "...people work to continue the gains attained during action and to prevent relapse to their more troubled level of functioning" (Prochaska and DiClemente, 1984, p. 28). This Maintenance Stage continues the change process, with emphasis on assimilating and integrating the skills and abilities acquired during the Action Stage.

During the Maintenance Stage, clients typically experience life, with all of its natural and unfolding joys, crises and challenges, while still lacking practice at coping with all that life has to offer. Successful maintenance is similar to what Alan F. Klein (1974) describes as a healthy lifestyle containing three fundamental skills:

1. The ability to *learn how to relate oneself to others*. This means making and maintaining rewarding human connections, mutual need-fulfilment, and satisfying communication. This is possible if trust has been established and authoritarian control (or perception of such) has been minimized.

2. The *capacity to choose*. The very essence of adaptation involves the making of successive choices. Decision-making rests upon the ability to make choices and to see the relationship between goals, values, means and end results.

3. The ability to *learn how to learn*. This is the essence of ego functioning. It includes reality-testing, value-testing and coping (pp. 49–50).

The above three basic skills are key elements of a stable sober lifestyle. In the authors' view, the capacity to effectively use these skills is essential to healthy human growth for people in the Maintenance Stage. They are also the primary index of mental health.

Given the time-limited nature of most treatment services, a client's ability to function fully is usually developed following formal treatment. Because the supportive thera-peutic relationship developed during the assessment process and Action Stage is now lost, the Maintenance Stage must include focused endeavors (discussed in detail later in this chapter) to help the client enjoy a balanced lifestyle and prevent relapse. Without the knowledge, skills and abilities to live life as it is, many individuals begin to dread facing reality and recall instead the rewards of using substances to cope with life situa-tions. This places the client in grave danger of entering the relapse process, because it occurs at a time when the client has very little emotional memory of the consequences of abusing substances. This happens at a time when the client is feeling their new lifestyle is filled with too many responsibilities and little or no satisfaction or joy.

Clients respond to this challenging period in a number of ways. First, they may be ambivalent about resuming drug use as a means of coping. This is experienced as an approach-avoidance conflict, in which the client both wants and fears a return to drug use. Second, clients may use the defence mechanism known as "reaction formation." They act overconfident, pretending to believe in their ability to face any emerging life challenge without experiencing any temptation to use drugs. Last, clients may forget to use cognitive strategies, such as "remember when," thus fostering a susceptibility to relapse. If they forget the harmful effects of their previous drug abuse, they also lose the lessons learned from previous struggles. One consequence of such thinking is that the client gradually reduces the daily structure that helped him or her recover, and eventually misplaces the skills and strategies that helped him or her begin, continue and maintain a positive process of change.

Process of Relapse

Discontinuing maintenance strategies signals the onset of relapse, which is a cognitive/affective/behavioral dynamic process and not an event. As was mentioned earlier in this chapter, treatment of substance abuse has traditionally been viewed as a linear process, rather than taking the view of relapse as a stage in the cyclical change/recovery process (Prochaska, DiClemente and Norcross, 1992). Thus, relapse should also be considered, by clinicians and clients alike, not as failure but as part of the cyclical process and as an opportunity

> ...in which clients learn to perceive their addictive behavior [relapse] as something they do rather than as an indication of something they are. By adopting this objective and detached approach, clients may be able to free themselves from the guilt and defensiveness that would otherwise bias their view of their problem (Marlatt and Gordon, 1985, p. 51).

Seen this way, the relapse process becomes a psycho-educational milestone from which the client gains information and feedback vital to the refinement of treatment goals, objectives and strategies. Understanding and using the dynamics and consequences of the relapse process can help them develop more comprehensive interventions that address those issues missed in previous treatment efforts. The scientific literature indicates that the rate of substance re-use among people with alcohol or other drug problems falls somewhere between 50 and 93 per cent (Marlatt and Gordon, 1985).

Within the relapse process, the authors have identified a pre-existing condition followed by three distinct stages. Marlatt and Gordon (1985) refer to the pre-existing condition as an "unbalanced lifestyle." The three stages that the authors have identified are "Lapse," "Prolapse" and "Retrolapse."

LAPSE STAGE

This is defined as the time when the person who had reached the Maintenance Stage and then entered the Process of Relapse first re-uses his or her substance of abuse. Following this event, the individual usually experiences what Marlatt refers to as the "Abstinence Violation Effect," or what the authors refer to as the "Rule Violation Effect." During this time, the person may believe, "What the hell, I've blown it now. I might as well just give up." The person experiences a sense of failure, guilt, remorse and/or greatly diminished self-efficacy. Regardless of this initial reaction, some people immediately re-enter the Action Stage and quickly move on to the Maintenance

Stage. These are people who have experienced the Lapse Stage in the cyclical process of change.

PROLAPSE STAGE

The Prolapse Stage is defined as that period of time when the individual who has begun to re-use his or her substance of abuse *continues* to use despite the recognition that the behavior is problematic and should be stopped. By definition, this person has re-entered the Contemplation Stage and, as such, is once again experiencing ambivalence and the other previously identified characteristics of a person in that stage. People in the Prolapse Stage, according to Prochaska and DiClemente's longitudinal studies, make up 85 per cent of those in the relapse process (1984).

RETROLAPSE STAGE

The Retrolapse Stage is defined as that period of time when the individual who has begun to re-use his or her substance of abuse continues to use with little or no recognition of negative consequences related to the use. This, by definition, indicates that such individuals have re-entered the Precontemplation Stage.

Prochaska and DiClemente maintain that this group constitutes 15 per cent of all who enter the relapse process to the point of ongoing substance abuse. However, the authors have a different perspective. They have worked with thousands of individuals with alcohol or other drug problems, from a variety of cultural, socioeconomic, educational and ethnic backgrounds. In their clinical experience, very few individuals who have truly moved through the various stages of the Wheel of Change to the point of entering the Maintenance Stage can ever forget what they learned about themselves and their negative experiences with substances. Anyone in the Retrolapse Stage may periodically experience an approach-avoidance conflict, low self-efficacy and ambivalence about maintaining their drug use versus changing it. This, by definition, places them in the Contemplation Stage, and not the Precontemplation Stage. Consequently, this makes them amenable to the influence of highly empathic counsellors and the skilful use of motivational interviewing strategies.

THERAPIST CHARACTERISTICS

The last category of factors that influence client motivation are characteristics of the counsellor that become manifest in the "helping relationship" (Prochaska and DiClemente, 1984). They include the therapist's personal needs and resultant behavioral manifestations, and his or her feelings, expectations and quality of empathy.

(A) Needs of Therapist

The personal needs of the counsellor are crucial in determining the quality of interaction with the client. For example, Schorer (1965) found that clinicians with an intense need to see their efforts bring about change in their clients' consumption became overinvolved with their clients, which resulted in increased client dropout. This excessive need to realize "successful results" may reflect the counsellor's irrational belief that he or she is solely responsible for the client's behavior. One reason for this may be the counsellor's own self-esteem. His or her sense of self-confidence and professional competence may depend on the client's success or failure at meeting goals.

Traps that catch counsellors:

1. CONFRONTATIONAL-DENIAL TRAP

The Confrontation-Denial Trap is only one of a number of problematic dynamics identified by Miller and Rollnick (1991) that may ensue when the counsellors' needs to preserve or enhance their own self-esteem get played out in the helping relationship. The Confrontation-Denial Trap occurs when the clinician is so task-oriented that he or she gives little consideration to important process issues, such as the client's need to see himself or herself as owning the therapeutic process. The end result of this trap is that the professional becomes more directive and prescriptive, while the client becomes more entrenched and resistant (Miller and Sovereign, 1989).

Miller and Rollnick (1991) identified other traps that we view as manifestations of this same therapist need. These include the Expert Trap and the Premature-Focus Trap.

2. EXPERT TRAP

In the Expert Trap, the clinician solves the client's problems and imposes "corrective" measures to rectify dysfunctional situations. As with the Confrontation-Denial Trap, the client's self-efficacy and self-esteem are not increased and may even diminish. In a therapeutic relationship, highly directive advice is appropriate with those clients who have a more external locus of control and tend toward the low end of the conceptual-level continuum. However, when the client is contemplating a commitment to alter his or her behavior — or with clients who have an internal locus of control and a high conceptual level — less directive interventions are required. A nondirective but motivational approach tends to elicit self-motivational statements from the client, which generates a greater investment in the change process. Miller and Rollnick (1991) have identified four categories of self-motivational statements:

> (i) *Problem Recognition,* e.g., client says, "It never occurred to me that I was drinking so much."

(ii) *Expression of Concern,* e.g., client says, "I feel that my situation with drugs is really hopeless."

(iii) *Intention to Change,* e.g., client says, "It's about time that I did something about this."

(iv) *Optimism to Change,* e.g., client says, "I'm sure that I've got what it takes to stop drinking."

3. PREMATURE-FOCUS TRAP

As with the Expert Trap, the Premature-Focus Trap tends to inhibit the development of rapport, which is critical to the clarification and formulation of the client's strengths, problem areas, life situation and major concern(s). This trap occurs when the counsellor raises the issue of the client's alcohol/drug problem before the individual is prepared to discuss it. Clients then tend to use such defences as minimization, projection, intellectualization and outright denial to deal with their fear of entrapment and potential loss of control and self-esteem. To prevent this from happening, Miller and Rollnick (1991) say the clinician must "...avoid becoming engaged in a struggle about the proper topic for early discussion. Starting with the client's concerns, rather than those of the counsellor, will ensure that [falling into the Premature-Focus Trap] does not happen" (p. 70).

A clinician's need to be nurturing is another important factor in the development of clients' motivation to change. Research indicates that clinicians who have a high need to nurture retain a significantly greater number of clients throughout the therapeutic process than do those clinicians with a low need to nurture (Schorer, 1965). Based on his study of interpersonal processes between clients and therapists, Coady (1991) found that "...a therapist stance that is nurturing, involving, and mildly influencing may be particularly important for achieving and sustaining a productive therapist-client relationship" (p. 132).

(B) Feelings of Therapist

The focus of the literature, vis-à-vis feelings, has been primarily limited to the therapist's warmth or hostility as they relate to the development and maintenance of the therapeutic relationship. Truax and Carkhuff (1967) comment that:

> It is a rare human being who does not respond to warmth with warmth and to hostility with hostility. It is probably the most important principle for the beginning therapist to understand if he is to be successful in the therapeutic relationship (p. 42).

Many authors (Watzlawick et al., 1974; Anderson and Stewart, 1983; Zimberg et al., 1978; Rogers, 1965; Klein, 1974; Kennedy, 1977) define warmth as a condition that exists in a sound therapeutic relationship. Warmth is the result of the therapist's strategic use of reflective counselling skills (attending, paraphrasing, reflection of feeling and summarizing). The effective use of these skills, combined with the counsellor's acceptance, understanding and positive feedback, encourages clients to disclose in depth their concerns and aspirations. This constitutes the essence of rapport — the most vital aspect of the therapeutic process.

The counsellor's hostility — even when masked — has significant negative impact on motivation. Milmoe et al. (1967) found that clinicians who conveyed hostility in their tone of voice, even if the content of their communication was not overtly hostile, had higher dropout rates among their clients.

(C) Expectations of Therapist

The counsellor's expectations of the client's potential to succeed also affect motivation. Leake and King (1977) discovered that giving clients a "good" or "poor" prognostic label influenced the counsellor's view of the client and subsequent treatment outcome. For example, when clients received a randomly assigned "good" prognosis from an intake worker, the counsellor viewed both the client and the therapeutic relationship with greater optimism, and invested more energy in the treatment process. Thomas et al. (1955) examined the clinician's expectations from the client's perspective. He found that clients' perception of the clinicians' expectations of their potential greatly influenced treatment outcome. In this research, clients who felt their counsellor believed in their capacity to change became more committed to treatment and remained in the therapeutic process.

(D) Empathy of Therapist

The founder of Client-Centred Therapy, Carl Rogers, maintained that the probability of clients changing within a therapeutic relationship increased dramatically when the therapist exhibited "accurate empathy," as well as nonpossessive warmth and genuineness. He stated that empathy is when a counsellor experiences

> ...understanding of his client's private world, and is able to communicate some of the significant fragments of that understanding. To sense the client's inner world of private personal meanings as if it were your own, but without ever losing the "as if" quality, this is empathy, and this seems essential to a growth-promoting relationship. To sense his confusion or his timidity or his anger or his feeling of being treated unfairly as if it were your own, yet without your own uncertainty or fear or anger or suspicion getting bound up in it, this is the condition I am endeavoring to describe (Rogers and Stevens, 1967, pp. 92–93).

The higher and more accurate the level of empathy manifest in a therapist's behavior, the better the treatment outcome. The behavioral manifestations of high empathy include: a) focusing not only on problems and concerns but on clients' strengths and successes; b) clarifying discrepancies; and, c) providing nonjudgmental, objective feedback.

Truax and Mitchell (1971) and Valle (1981) found that, among other variables, the use of accurate empathy was predictive of the rate and number of client relapses at six, 12, 18 and 24 months following conclusion of treatment.

Miller (1980) found that there is a relationship between therapist self-esteem and empathic interventions. This indicates that clinicians need high self-esteem to accurately empathize with their clients. Given that high empathy plays such a vital role in the treatment of drug problems, counsellors who have high self-esteem and exhibit accurate empathy are more likely to engage people in a therapeutic process of change.

The material covered to this point has focused on a variety of critical issues related to motivational interviewing of individuals with substance use disorders. The first issue addressed was the importance of the Biopsychosocial Model of Addictions, which is shifting our perspective from one that is unidimensional to one that is multivariant. Next, we examined how motivation may be influenced by environment/situation, client, and therapist variables and characteristics. The remainder of this chapter will describe specific motivational interviewing strategies designed to increase the probability of clients entering, complying with and successfully completing treatment.

GENERAL MOTIVATIONAL INTERVIEWING PRINCIPLES

Miller and Rollnick (1991) have identified five broad clinical principles that can help counsellors assess and motivate substance-abusing clients: 1) express empathy; 2) develop discrepancies; 3) avoid arguments; 4) roll with resistance; and 5) support self-efficacy.

Express Empathy

This first principle was partially addressed earlier in this chapter, under the heading of Therapist Characteristics. Empathy and its expression were identified in the work of Carl Rogers and others (Murgatroyd, 1986; Kennedy, 1977; Rogers, 1965; Anderson and Stewart, 1983; Priestly and McGuire, 1983; Turner, 1974). They maintained that reflecting an understanding of an individual's situation from his or her perspective, without judging, criticizing or blaming, is predictive of success in treating substance abusers.

> The attitude underlying this principle of empathy might be called "acceptance" ... [which] is a respectful listening to the client with a desire to understand his or her perspectives. Paradoxically, this kind of acceptance of people as they are seems to free them to change, whereas insistent nonacceptance ("You're not O.K.: you have to change") can have the effect of keeping people as they are. This attitude of acceptance and respect also builds a working therapeutic alliance and supports the client's self-esteem — an important condition for change (Miller and Rollnick, 1991, p. 5).

Develop Discrepancies

Developing discrepancies allows the clinician "to create and amplify, in the client's mind, a discrepancy between present behavior and broader goals" (Miller and Rollnick, 1991, p. 56). Throughout the psychological literature, this phenomenon is referred to as creating cognitive dissonance. In layperson's terms, it can be understood as the discrepancy between where you are and where you would like to be. This occurs when one becomes aware that "the cost of the bottle (or drug) exceeds the price on the label" (Soden, 1988) — that his or her substance use conflicts with personal goals, such as good health, vocational or financial success, healthy interpersonal relationships, positive self-image and personal spiritual growth. Such awareness creates a motivating force that tips the balance of ambivalence in the direction of changing the recognized problem. As Miller and Rollnick (1991) state:

> A goal of motivational interviewing is to develop discrepancy — to make use of it, increase it, and amplify it until it overrides attachment to the present behavior. The strategies of motivational interviewing seek to do this in the client, [and] ... involves clarifying important goals for the client, and exploring the consequences or potential consequences of his or her present behavior which conflicts with those goals. When successfully done, motivational interviewing changes the client's perceptions (of discrepancy) without creating a feeling of being pressured or coerced ... [resulting] in the client presenting the reasons for change (p. 57).

Avoid Arguments

Clinicians working with substance-abusing clients have historically manifested their traditional view of motivation by engaging in a variety of interventions that included "labelling" (i.e., giving the client a diagnostic label such as "alcoholic"). Although such confrontational strategies were used with the best intentions, they have always seemed, to some degree, an aggressive attack on clients' self-image and self-esteem. This invariably resulted in feelings of anger and shame, and a defensive reaction that often led traditional clinicians to say "the client is in denial." This is like hitting the client and then blaming him or her for saying "ouch." Research evidence validates the existence of this dynamic and the harm it may cause. Clients often respond to this painful and demeaning process by dropping out of treatment or through other avoidance behaviors, such as superficial compliance with the clinician's power and authority.

Even though motivational interviewing with clients in the "precontemplation" or "contemplation" stages involves helping them acknowledge their substance abuse problem, this process uses interventions that increase the client's awareness and ultimately reflect the client's desire to alter his or her problematic behavior. This is different from the confrontational approach, but similar to the self-labelling process inherent in the philosophy and writings of 12-step self-help programs. As AA founder Bill Wilson stated, "We do not like to pronounce any individual as alcoholic, but you can quickly diagnose yourself" (Alcoholics Anonymous, 1976, p. 31).

Clinicians must distinguish between motivational strategies that engage and enlighten the client, and behaviors that attempt to persuade clients to accept our authoritarian interpretation of their situation. One method of such self-evaluation is to continually monitor the client's response to us. Any indication of resistance or avoidance should prompt us to re-evaluate our behavior to determine whether we are using a destructive confrontational approach and, if so, consider shifting to a more empathic and constructive style that fits the motivational interviewing method.

Roll with Resistance

Mature 12-step self-help members understand and accept others' reluctance to alter behavior that, despite negative consequences, has helped people cope with reality. This philosophy is best embodied in their practice of telling newcomers "what happened to me as a practising substance abuser, my initial resistance to the program and, finally, how it has helped me." Through this process, the mature member conveys an understanding and acceptance of the cautious newcomer's resistance. This leads to a desire to associate with those empathic and inspiring members who have had similar experiences but are now in recovery.

Clinicians who are self-help members should *not* use this process as part of their professional repertoire because:
- It limits their potential to engage clients who find the self-help method unacceptable.
- It limits the client's perspective of the "recovery process" to the pathway taken by the counsellor, even if it conflicts with the client's real needs. This is, in part, due to the client's tendency to view the professional as having the answers to everything. Such a tendency diminishes the client's openness to other members' experience and interpretation of the self-help program.
- It creates role confusion, because the use of counselling communication skills should establish and maintain personal boundaries between the counsellor's membership in a self-help program and his or her role as a counsellor.

"Counsellor self-disclosure" differs from the self-help process of overcoming resistance in three major ways. First, the topic area of the self-disclosure should be limited to specific material being revealed by the client. Second, this strategy should be used only to illuminate the client's own situation, and not for the counsellor's benefit. Third, the counsellor's self-disclosure should be consistently and directly related to the client's experience.

Counsellor self-disclosure and self-help "story-telling" may promote similar outcomes. Done correctly, counsellor self-disclosure reduces the client's sense of uniqueness and isolation, just as the self-help member's story-telling does. It also increases trust and rapport between the counsellor and the client, and promotes the expression of thoughts and feelings previously avoided. Counsellor self-disclosure lets the client see the counsellor as having struggled with similar issues, although not necessarily the problem of substance abuse. The client can then see the similarities between him/herself and the counsellor, as well as positive and negative feelings common to the human experience, thus promoting increased self-esteem and hope.

To overcome resistance, counsellors must also encourage their clients to take responsibility for any new perceptions of themselves and any change in their behavior. This generates a recognition in both counsellor and client that the latter is truly the author of his or her own destiny — even within a therapeutic relationship. As Miller and Rollnick state, the counsellor offers, but does not impose, new perspectives of the client's behavior, and recognizes that "the client is a valuable resource in finding solutions to problems" (1991, p. 60). When this empowering approach is consistently used by the counsellor, the client is encouraged to:

  a) define and prioritize his or her problems (based on thoughtful consideration of the situation)
  b) develop measurable, attainable goals
  c) generate a variety of strategies to achieve these goals
  d) select the most promising strategies and activities
  e) undertake them, in spite of negative reactions from "drinking/drugging buddies" and/or co-dependants.

Support Self-Efficacy

The client's belief in his or her abilities to change is a key element in motivation to change and a good predictor of treatment outcome (Miller and Rollnick, 1991, pp. 60–61). This principle is supported by scientific evidence of the potency of *belief-in-oneself* and *hope for the future* (Maddux et al., 1987), two variables that are critical motivators in changing destructive behavior. Consequently, counsellors who work with people with substance abuse problems must recognize the significance of timely empowerment of clients. Timely empowerment requires sensitivity not only to clients' need for nurturing and support, but also their need to nurture, feel autonomous and feel that they have the skills necessary to fully enjoy and live life without abusing substances.

Counsellors who support self-efficacy help clients accept that only they can change their behavior. "Motivational interviewing does not foster hope that the therapist will change the client" (Miller and Rollnick, 1991, p. 61). Instead, the client must recognize that the therapist's responsibility is to *help the client change him/herself.*

Counsellors may support self-efficacy in a number of ways:
  a) by introducing the client to people who have overcome similar problems
  b) by using strategies that encourage the client to recognize and acknowledge his or her past successes, along with current strengths, skills and abilities
  c) by negotiating therapeutic tasks and objectives that challenge the client's skills and abilities, but also have a high probability for success
  d) by providing, within the therapeutic context, a range of approaches to changing substance abuse behavior, so that the client feels responsible for choosing and carrying out any of the alternatives available.

In effect, the counsellor is following a general philosophy "...that each person possesses a powerful potential for change. Your task as a therapist is to release that potential, to facilitate the natural change processes already inherent in the individual" (Miller and Rollnick, 1991, p. 62).

MOTIVATIONAL STRATEGIES FOR CLIENTS IN THE PRECONTEMPLATION STAGE

The pivotal process of change for clients in the Precontemplation Stage is called "consciousness raising." Consciousness raising makes the client aware of his or her substance use and how it interferes with: a) attaining his or her goals; b) adhering to his or her values and beliefs; and c) how the client wishes to be perceived by others. Consciousness raising is best accomplished through the use of motivational strategies that: i) develop a therapeutic relationship; ii) overcome resistance; and iii) uncover thoughts and feelings about the risks and reinforcers of the substance abuse.

Strategies:

1. USE REFLECTIVE SKILLS TO CONVEY INTEREST, EMPATHY AND A NONJUDGMENTAL ATTITUDE.

The four reflective skills are *Attending, Paraphrasing, Reflection of Feeling* and *Summarizing*. These skills involve responses that reproduce what the client is conveying, without the counsellor adding any information. The major purposes are: a) to allow the counsellor to understand what the client says and means; b) to ensure that the counsellor understands the messages or information that the client provides; c) to encourage the client to express thoughts and feelings that allow the counsellor to respond in a manner that conveys empathy and begins the process of building rapport; d) to reinforce certain aspects of what a client has said, thereby provoking the client to express self-motivational statements; and e) to foster exploration — a nondefensive response to resistance.

2. UNCOVER THE CLIENT'S PERCEPTION OF THE REASON FOR THE INTERVIEW AND HIS OR HER UNDERLYING FEELINGS.

Clients typically come to the initial interview with expectations and apprehension. An individual in precontemplation is usually angry and/or resistant, because he or she has been pressured to attend by a significant other or person in authority. Rather than attempting to convince the individual in precontemplation of the value of the interview and his or her need for "treatment," the counsellor will achieve significantly better results by eliciting the client's perception of the interview, and accepting the accompanying emotional response without judgment. The purpose is not to manipulate the client, but to convey the message that the client and counsellor will collaboratively decide what occurs in the interview.

3. AVOID NEGATIVE LABELLING.

As mentioned earlier, counsellors must avoid negative labelling. Miller and Rollnick (1991) support this perspective: "From the beginning, it is important to avoid labelling, confrontation and giving advice. Ultimately, the clients are the ones who decide what is best. The goal is to encourage them to explore their substance use and possible reasons for concern, taking care to proceed at the client's own pace" (p. 205). Two clinical researchers, van Bilsen and van Emst (1986), also found that labelling caused real damage to the therapeutic relationship: "Our experience was that we were often fighting against our clients instead of motivating them to change" (p. 707). Research has also confirmed that labelling a client does not positively contribute to the outcome of treatment.

4. ORIENT THE CLIENT.

Orienting clients to the therapeutic process is extremely important in preventing the development of avoidable resistance. It's easier to engage clients when the counsellor flexibly employs communication skills that convey creativity, confidence, caring and consideration (Zunin, 1972).

Areas to be covered when orienting clients include:
   (i) defining the general nature and goals of the service being provided;
   (ii) determining and responding to the emotional state of the client;
   (iii) ascertaining the client's expectations of the treatment agency/counsellor and dealing with any misconceptions;
   (iv) explaining the roles and responsibilities of both the client and the counsellor;
   (v) discussing such issues as fees, office hours, availability of the service provider, frequency of appointments and the client's rights.

5. PROVIDE A TIMELY FOCUS ON CONSUMPTIVE BEHAVIORS AND THEIR CONSEQUENCES.

The primary goal of the initial interview is to provide an atmosphere that will motivate the client to explore his or her situation and take appropriate action. Recognizing the need to start "where the client is," at some point the clinician will need to broach the subject of substance use/abuse if the client does not raise the issue. This can be effectively accomplished through a technique known as "funnelling" (Brekke, 1987), which is used to introduce sensitive topics and minimize any potential resistance. Typically, this involves starting with a general definition of the topic area to be explored with a rationale for such enquiry (e.g., the counsellor needs a complete understanding of the client and his or her situation). This enquiry initially focuses on a nonjudgmental exploration of the client's use of substances. The strategies employed include the reflective skills of attending, paraphrasing, reflection of feeling and summarizing, plus open-ended questions. The counsellor then gradually moves to a more specific probing of problems related to substance use, emphasizing the exploration of desired versus actual outcomes of the client's behaviors.

6. EXPLORE THE CLIENT'S RESISTANCE, CONSIDER ITS POSSIBLE CAUSES AND FLOW WITH IT.

Experienced and effective counsellors understand and accept resistance as a natural component of any attempt to change habitual behaviors. Clients in precontemplation tend to exhibit one or more of the following forms of resistance:

(a) Reluctance
A client in precontemplation who exhibits this form of resistance shows a lack of understanding of significant others' concerns and disapproval of his or her substance abuse. The reluctant client's response to such "interference" is an unemotional direct or indirect statement that he or she does not see the need to examine or change behavior that others view as problematic. One way to overcome this form of resistance is to provide personal and meaningful feedback, ensuring that it is done in a sensitive, empathic manner. When this occurs, the client usually does not react immediately, but considers the feedback for some time before accepting or rejecting it. The counsellor's understanding and sensitivity make the client feel free to consider the counsellor's opinion without fear of losing freedom of choice. This approach gives the client an opportunity to carefully weigh the information provided by the counsellor and come to an informed decision regarding his or her substance use.

(b) Rebellion
Clients who employ this form of resistance appear to be heavily invested in the problem behavior. They also want to make their own decisions (internal locus of control). They tend to be hostile and defiant toward individuals who believe they have a substance abuse problem. Examining a variety of interpretations of the "problematic behavior" can be helpful in overcoming rebellion. It is also important to provide the rebellious client with a number of options when negotiating a course of action.

(c) Resignation

Clients in the Precontemplation Stage who use this form of resistance appear to have low self-efficacy and seem to feel overwhelmed by their substance abuse. They feel hopeless, believing that they would have little chance of changing their consumption, even if it was in their best interest to do so. Resignation can be highly contagious, causing the counsellor to join clients in feeling overwhelmed by the complexity of their substance use. However, to be effective, counsellors must resist this tendency and maintain objectivity. They must instil hope and find ways to spark each client's belief that he or she can overcome problems.

(d) Rationalization

Counsellors who are effective in overcoming other forms of resistance may neverthe-less find the client who uses rationalization particularly troublesome. Rationalizing clients continually dispute the perspective or suggestions presented by the counsellor. In response, the counsellor may feel the need to preserve his or her position of authority and may unwittingly engage in a "point-counterpoint" verbal battle — which no one wins. To manage this form of resistance, the counsellor must recognize and work through unresolved issues related to authority figures and self-esteem. Sec-ondly, the counsellor needs to maintain an empathic and reflective stance toward the client. The use of "amplified reflection" can help. This is where the counsellor reflects in an amplified or exaggerated way what the client has said about his or her use of substances (taking care not to be sarcastic or too extreme, as this would proba-bly produce a negative response). By so doing, the counsellor can encourage clients to re-evaluate their perspective without becoming defensive.

7. Clarify discrepancies.

Negative forms of confrontation by the counsellor — such as labels and direct attacks — make clients combative and defensive. A significantly more effective alternative is to use more therapeutic forms of confrontation, which Soden (1987) has described as "discrepancy clarification." Discrepancy clarification allows the counsellor to main-tain a neutral and empathic stance toward clients who are struggling with contradicto-ry beliefs, attitudes, thoughts, feelings and behaviors. It helps clients become more congruent and establishes the counsellor as a role model in using *direct, honest* and *open communication.*

The counsellor deliberately uses a question or compound statement to encourage the client to consider a discrepancy he or she has unknowingly presented. The types of discrepancies or contradictions focused on by the counsellor may include those:

1. Between how the client sees himself or herself and how others see him or her (e.g., sees self as outgoing but is seen by others as quiet and reserved);
2. Between what the client says and how he or she behaves (e.g., the client says he or she is not sad but is talking slowly with head down and tears rolling down his or her cheeks);

3. Between two statements made by the client (e.g., the client says that the really important thing for him or her is to be treated for substance abuse, but later on in the interview states that the priority is reuniting with his or her spouse); and,

4. Between what the client says he or she believes and how he or she acts. (e.g., the client says that he or she believes it is inappropriate to attend a counselling session under the influence of alcohol, but smells of alcohol at the interview).

Discrepancy clarification should never include accusations, evaluations or solutions to the client's problems. This approach should only be used for the benefit of the client and not as a vehicle for the counsellor to vent his or her frustrations. Its major purpose is to aid and strengthen the therapeutic process. The following two examples of counsellor statements demonstrate discrepancy clarification:

Counsellor: "You have stated that you have had nothing to drink today, but I smell something remarkably similar to alcohol, and you seem to be slurring your words. This is very confusing to me. Help me understand how this could be."

Counsellor: "You say that you aren't a reliable person, but you also have told me how you keep your kids' clothes clean, make sure they always have their meals on time, and that you pay all of your bills on their due dates. In addition, you're never late for an appointment. I'm a bit confused. How could an unreliable person act so responsibly and reliably?"

Effective use of discrepancy clarification requires counsellors to adhere to the following guidelines:

a) Use it sparingly and only after a sound therapeutic relationship has been developed in which the client feels safe and secure.

b) Always give positive feedback to the client who is able to clear up a discrepancy.

c) If the client denies the contradiction, do not push it. Instead, reflect the client's feelings about the intervention and suggest that he or she think about it.

d) If the client seems confused or concerned about the counsellor's discrepancy clarification, reflect that feeling, and work with the client on the emotional level until he or she is able to move on.

MOTIVATIONAL STRATEGIES FOR CLIENTS IN THE CONTEMPLATION STAGE

Clients in the Contemplation Stage will either change their problematic behavior or their new awareness of the behavior so that they no longer see it as a problem.

The direction of change clients will take is determined by their level of self-efficacy (Bandura, 1977). Therefore, the counsellor, in addition to exploring the client's ambivalence, also needs to understand and work to increase the client's self-efficacy. To do so, the counsellor will need to use clinical strategies that activate certain processes in the contemplator: processes that have been identified by Prochaska and DiClemente (1983). These processes are:

(A) SELF-RE-EVALUATION

This involves an assessment of one's beliefs and values, and the level of congruency between them and one's thoughts, emotions and behaviors. Additionally, it includes an evaluation of the potential of what one could be without abusing substances.

(B) SELF-LIBERATION

This process involves making choices that will lead to self-efficacy. The choices are the result of accurate information processing, followed by effective problem solving. This process moves clients to actively take steps to change their substance abuse.

Strategies:

Strategies and techniques helpful for clients in the Precontemplation Stage can also help clients in contemplation.

Provide the client with objective feedback using the results of a structured assessment protocol. Although feedback vital to promoting change can be given in an informal manner, conducting a structured and strategic assessment, and providing its results, can help build motivation to change. An assessment in the context of a helping relationship allows the counsellor to gather information essential to the development of an individualized treatment plan. Objective results enable counsellors to provide feedback that is not expressed simply as personal opinion, which the client could easily reject, but as nonjudgmental feedback that allows the counsellor to be seen as the client's ally. This individualized approach also conveys a clear message that the counsellor understands the client's unique situation, which in turn causes the client to carefully consider the assessment results.

COMPLETE A DECISIONAL MATRIX

One strategy that assists in understanding both sides of a client's ambivalence, and which activates the process of "self-re-evaluation," is the "decisional matrix."[2] This involves examining the short- and long-term advantages and disadvantages of both changing and maintaining the status quo.

FIGURE 2   **DECISIONAL MATRIX SHEET**

	+	−	+	−
Substance use/abuse				
Non-use/abuse of substance(s)				
	Short Term		Long Term	

There are many benefits to using the decisional matrix:

1. "It often leads clients to realize that they need to obtain more information about consequences that they had not thought about before" (Janis, 1982, p. 175).
2. It typically increases clients' awareness of the need for detailed plans for any eventuality.
3. It helps clients to consider and evaluate positive alternatives to substance abuse.
4. It promotes rational decision-making as an alternative to impulsive action (Janis, 1982).

Counsellors can use this procedure in three major ways. First, they can give the client a sheet similar to Figure 2, give them instructions on how to complete it, and then ask the client "to re-examine each cell, this time trying to think of additional pros and cons that might be important to consider, including consequences that might not be highly probable but could happen... the counsellor suggests that the client focuses especially on categories that have few or no entries..." (Janis, 1982, p. 172). Another approach is to have a significant other work on the decisional matrix with the client. The counsellor can then help both parties supplement the information in each cell. Finally, the counsellor may ask questions that elicit information for the completion of the decisional matrix. This is especially important for clients who have limited reading or language ability. Regardless of the format used to complete the decisional matrix, the focus of the counsellor should always be on the positive and negative consequences of substance abuse as they pertain to the client's psychological, physical, social and spiritual dimensions.

In summary, the decisional matrix sheet "...can be used with motivational interviewing to penetrate...ambivalence, to clarify the competing motivational factors, and to encourage the person to consider the possibility of change" (Miller and Rollnick, 1991, p. 41).

MOTIVATIONAL STRATEGY FOR CLIENTS IN THE PREPARATION STAGE

Not surprisingly, clients in the Preparation Stage are not willing to make long-term commitments to substance use goals, and typically withdraw from treatment if goals are imposed on them. Motivation for change can be increased, however, if the counsellor negotiates with clients goals that involve relatively small or brief changes with a high probability of success. By putting this in terms of a "personal experiment," it frees the client to take a risk, meet the challenge and, if unsuccessful, return to the counsellor to review the results of the experiment without feeling that he or she has failed.

Strategy:

NEGOTIATE A SHORT-TERM BEHAVIOR CHANGE CONTRACT.

A short-term behavior change contract is a written agreement. It implies that one person or "party" promises to do "something," and that the other person or "party" agrees to do "something" in return. Within such a promise, when it is done between a client and counsellor, both individuals are actually formalizing an agreement to work together to attain or achieve some specific change to the client's behavior or situation. The client's documented intent to change, and the counsellor's formalized support and provision of certain counselling skills, are written so that a record of the commitment is made by both parties.

The following steps are suggested as one manner in which a counsellor can develop a short-term behavior contract:
1) Explore the implications of the client's substance use.
2) Review and summarize the client's statements regarding problems.
3) Review and highlight the client's short-term and long-term goals in relation to the client's needs, strengths, deficits and available external services and resources.
4) Explore and determine activities, actions, behaviors and steps for which the client will be responsible.
5) Explore and explain the activities, actions, behaviors and steps for which the counsellor will be responsible.

Although it is suggested that the ideal form of a behavior contract is a written one, it is not necessarily the most appropriate for all clients. In cases where the goal is simple and can be achieved in one or two sessions, a written contract may not be necessary. Clients probably do not require the extra incentive of a written contract if they are highly skilled, with an internal locus of control, and sufficiently motivated to take action.

MOTIVATIONAL STRATEGIES FOR CLIENTS IN THE ACTION STAGE

The Action Stage begins with a client discontinuing his or her substance abuse. Most clients in this stage usually experience some initial discomfort associated with the "unknown," but also have enough self-efficacy to motivate them to follow through with activities outlined in the treatment plan. They continue or remain in counselling to "...make a public commitment to action; to get some external confirmation of the plan; to seek support; to gain greater self-efficacy; and finally to create artificial, external monitors of their activity" (DiClemente, 1991, p. 199).

Counsellors should affirm positive changes made by these clients and encourage them to take responsibility for any modifications to their behavior and/or lifestyle.

> Offering information about successful models (other successful clients or self-help members) can also help, as long as the models have used a variety of action plans. The purpose of the models is not to offer a rigid prescription for change (which would run counter to motivational interviewing princi- ples), but to engender a sense that success is possible for people like this client (DiClemente, 1991, p. 199).

In the Action Stage, the processes used are not only those activated in the pre- vious stages, i.e., consciousness raising, self-re-evaluation and self-liberation, but also "reinforcement management," "counter-conditioning" and "stimulus control." (For a comprehensive explanation of these processes, see Prochaska and DiClemente, 1984.)

MOTIVATIONAL STRATEGIES FOR CLIENTS IN THE MAINTENANCE STAGE

In the Maintenance Stage,

> ...the individual must work the hardest to maintain the commitment to change over time. It is during this stage that the person will be faced with a plethora of temptations, stressors, and the pull of powerful old habit patterns.... There are two ways of thinking about this stage. One approach is to consider the Maintenance Stage as a period following initial treatment during which the effects of the treatment program gradually wear off over time.... Like a new coat of paint, treatment effects look good at first and only gradually begin to fade as time passes (Marlatt and Gordon, 1985, pp. 22–24).

This stage can also be seen as an opportunity for new learning. "The individual engages in a series of 'learning trials' in which new ways of responding to old temp- tation situations are gradually acquired" (Marlatt and Gordon, 1985, p. 25). From a motivational perspective, this is the most useful way of understanding the Mainte- nance Stage. Seeing it as an opportunity for new learning suggests that — as with any other endeavor to acquire new skills — one will periodically make errors. This trial and error process can increase the client's coping skills, with the greatest number of mistakes occurring in the early phase of the Maintenance Stage.

Analysis of the relapse process over time with various addictive behaviors...
shows that stabilization of the relapse rate begins approximately 90 days after
the initiation of abstinence. Prior to this time, relapse rates are high, particularly within the first month. Beginning in the fourth month, however,
the probability of remaining abstinent throughout the course of the year
stabilizes (Marlatt and Gordon, 1985, pp. 25–26).

Strategies:

1. Provide objectivity at times of despair: help clients see beyond their dark
   moment to the overall progress that they have made and the unlimited potential
   of the future.

2. When the client suffers self-doubt and low self-esteem, remind the client how he or
   she coped with similarly difficult situations in the past.

3. Encourage clients to celebrate anniversaries related to significant turning points.

4. Discuss and normalize the reality of life's challenges and natural crises.

5. Affirm the client's increased self-efficacy whenever he or she is faced with the
   challenge of such events as a career change, family crisis or financial problem.

6. Teach the client a conceptual model for understanding the relapse process and
   techniques for managing it. (For more information on structured relapse prevention, see Chapter 8.)

MOTIVATIONAL STRATEGIES FOR CLIENTS
IN THE LAPSE STAGE

Individuals in the Lapse Stage experience feelings of failure, guilt, remorse and/or
greatly diminished self-efficacy as a result of their re-use of substance(s). They often
think that they have let down those who have shown concern for them. Consequently,
these clients need a counsellor who is highly empathic and who can shift the focus
from these negative feelings and thoughts to a positive exploration of the cognitions
and behaviors that led the client into the relapse process. The client's feelings of failure, etc. can also be reframed as being a clear indication that the individual is committed to changing his or her use of substances and that more work is required to
fine-tune his or her plan for relapse prevention.

Strategies:

1. The counsellor's first responsibility is to assess the client to determine if he or she is in crisis and requires medical attention or needs detoxifying in a nonmedical detoxification centre. A counsellor makes that determination based on the information he or she is able to elicit from the client regarding this recent episode of drinking and/or other drug use. The counsellor needs to know what was used, how much, over how long a period, and the client's mental and physical status. This is required to determine whether the client has taken a combination of drugs that may have a synergistic effect that is possibly life-threatening, or if the person may be at risk when starting to withdraw.

2. The next strategy is to uncover the Rule Violation Effect. How does this person perceive himself or herself, and how does the person feel about this drinking and/or drug-taking episode? The counsellor should also look for any thinking patterns or cognitive content that indicates the client is experiencing suicidal ideation because of the lapse. If such is the case, it may be an emergency that requires immediate medical intervention. In addition, the counsellor needs to help the person shift his or her focus to the positive potential of discovering what precipitated the relapse process and what perpetuated it to the point of initial substance use. Through this exploration, the counsellor can convey the value of this information in planning for the future, and it provides the counsellor with an opportunity to affirm the client's honesty and trust. The client can also be affirmed for his or her apparent readiness to re-enter the Action Stage and move quickly to the Maintenance Stage again — but at a higher, more stable level in the cyclical process of change.

3. Another strategy involves a focus on the client's family and social support system. These "significant others" can also learn from this one episode of re-using. Do they need to examine their own behavior and possible role in the lapse? What circumstances place the client at high risk, and how can these significant others help the client avoid or cope with these situations? Sometimes the client and significant others also need to be reassured that everything isn't lost because of this last episode of substance use. Rather, it is part of this particular person's path to more stable recovery.

MOTIVATIONAL STRATEGIES FOR CLIENTS IN THE PROLAPSE STAGE

Following the Lapse Stage, most clients enter the Prolapse Stage. In this stage they may have all the same feelings and experiences as the person in the Lapse Stage, but almost always with greater intensity. They also experience ambivalence about their continued reuse of alcohol and/or other drugs. They need a counsellor who understands the cyclical nature of change and the clinical issues to be addressed when one is in the Contemplation Stage or the Lapse Stage.

Strategies:

1. Use all of the strategies that apply to the person in the Lapse Stage, as well as the strategies that apply to the Contemplation Stage. The strategies that are vital to the client's movement back into action are those that help the client understand his or her ambivalence and those that help move the individual into the Preparation Stage and a process of refining the recovery plan.

2. Uncover the precipitating action, events, thoughts and feelings that eventually gave rise to the relapse process, and either teach or reinforce how the client can recognize these warning signs that precede the onset of the relapse process and the strategies that can abort the relapse process.

3. With the client, develop a plan for any additional treatment needed that addresses the specific issues or challenges that led the person into the relapse process. The plan should also address the need for the client to have a personally meaningful repertoire of strategies to use when reaching the Maintenance Stage again.

4. Re-emphasize that the client's behavior is evidence that, when recovering from a substance abuse problem, one strives for progress not perfection.

MOTIVATIONAL STRATEGIES FOR CLIENTS IN THE RETROLAPSE STAGE

This stage is a time when an individual returns to substance use and continues to use in a problematic and destructive manner. The counsellor's major task is to raise the client's consciousness regarding the nature of his or her substance(s) use and how it interferes with the client's life goals or values.

Strategies:

1. Use all of the strategies outlined for those in the Lapse Stage.

2. Use the "Looking Back" strategy, which involves an exploration with the client of what it was like when the client was last "clean and sober" or using at a low risk level. Within this exploration, uncover the benefits the client experienced from abstinence or moderation, as well as the things that were unpleasant or difficult for the individual.

3. The previous strategy may lead to the use of Rational Emotive Therapy to alter any irrational beliefs that prevented the Maintenance Stage from continuing. One common irrational notion is that life should always be just and perfect when, in fact, we know that bad things do happen to people who are doing all the "right" things. Most people who have had problems with alcohol and/or other drugs, however, think that once they change their use of substances, life should be a "bed of roses." Consequently, when natural life crises and challenges begin to emerge in the Maintenance Stage, they are ill-prepared to handle them and begin to view life as unpleasant and lacking the contentment they mistakenly believed would be theirs for life. Given such cognitions, the counsellor must help the client develop a more realistic perspective of life, acknowledging that life will hold both pleasant and unpleasant experiences and that both are necessary to our existence. Also, the counsellor must help the client develop strategies for handling unpleasant times without having to revert to re-using substances as a means of coping.

4. Some clients who have reached the Maintenance Stage begin engaging in behaviors that are contrary to their ideal self and, as a result, enter the relapse process and continue to the Retrolapse Stage. These clients need to be assisted in understanding the human condition that we are all in, and in realizing, as Ernest Kurtz states in his book *Not God,* that each of us is a walking paradox, part truth and part fiction.

CONCLUSION

This chapter has focused on the principles, guidelines and strategies emerging from the perspective of motivation as a state of readiness that is influenced by internal and external factors, including the characteristics, attitudes and behaviors of the counsellor. This new understanding of motivation, as it applies to individuals experiencing problems related to substance use/abuse, has as its underpinnings the tenets of the Biopsychosocial Theory of Addictions and the Transtheoretical Model of Change.

The approaches outlined in this chapter, when used with warmth, acceptance, positive regard, immediacy and a sense of being concrete, maximize the counsellor's ability to help his or her clients. However, we also recognize the reality of using motivational interviewing strategies. As clinicians, we can be *responsible to* our clients but *not responsible for* what they do. Because, in the final analysis, it is the clients who ultimately choose to maintain or change their problematic behavior. We must not only accept this reality but, when working with clients who want to change, we must also respect and protect their *right* to freely choose the type and intensity of treatment that they believe will best meet their needs.

Throughout this chapter, our primary consideration has been the knowledge and skills required to influence the intensity and direction of clients' motivation. However, clinical skills alone are not sufficient. We need to be ever mindful of the importance of our beliefs, attitudes, feelings and expectations vis-à-vis our clients. These factors, as they apply to our clients' strengths, resources and problems, are crucial to developing and maintaining a therapeutic relationship that ultimately engages clients in a process with the highest probability of resulting in successful change.

NOTES

[1] Withdrawal is defined as the pain and anxiety an addicted person experiences when he or she stops using alcohol or drugs. It is a biopsychosocial phenomenon. "Part of the pain (of withdrawal) is created by physical damage and the body's need for the addictive substance. Part of the pain is caused by a psychological reaction to losing the primary method of coping with life — the use of addictive drugs. Part of the pain is social, caused by the separation from an addiction-centered lifestyle" (Gorski, 1986). The duration of the pain created by the body's need for the addictive substance depends on the type of substance that one is withdrawing from and the amount of time that the body has become accustomed to having it.

[2] The decisional matrix depicted in Figure 2 is an adaptation of Janis and Mann's (1977) original notion of the decisional balance.

ACKNOWLEDGMENT

The authors wish to thank Linda Giroux for her tireless assistance in the preparation of this chapter.

REFERENCES

Alcoholics Anonymous. (1976). *Alcoholics Anonymous: The Story of How Many Thousands of Men and Women Have Recovered from Alcoholism.* New York: Alcoholics Anonymous.

Annis, H.M., and Davis, C.D. (1989). Relapse prevention. In *Handbook of Alcoholism Treatment Approaches,* eds. Hester, R.K., and Miller, W.R. New York: Pergamon Press.

Bandura, A. (1977). Self-efficacy: Toward a unifying theory of behavioral change. *Psychological Review* 84: 191–215.

Brekke, J.S. (1987). Detecting wife and child abuse in clinical settings. *Social Casework: The Journal of Contemporary Social Work* (June 1987): 332–338.

Coady, N.F. (1991). The association between client and therapist interpersonal processes and outcomes in psychodynamic psychotherapy. *Research on Social Work Practice* 1 (2): 122–138.

Dennis, M.L., Ingram, P.W., Burks, M.E., and Valley Rachal, J. (1994). Effectiveness of streamlined admission to methadone treatment: A simplified time-series analysis. *Journal of Psychoactive Drugs* 26 (2): 207–216.

DiClemente, C.C. (1991). Motivational interviewing and the stages of change. In *Motivational Interviewing: Preparing People to Change Addictive Behavior,* eds. Miller, W.R., and Rollnick, S. New York: The Guilford Press.

Donovan, D.M., and O'Leary, M.R. (1979). Control orientation among alcoholics: A cognitive social learning perspective. *American Journal of Drug and Alcohol Abuse* 6: 487–499.

Donovan, D.M., and Marlatt, G.A. (1988). *Assessment of Addictive Behaviors.* New York: The Guilford Press.

Finney, J.W., and Moos, R.H. (1986). Matching patients with treatments: Conceptual and methodological issues. *Journal of Studies on Alcohol* 47 (2): 122–134.

Gariti, P., Alterman, A.I., Holub-Beyer, E., Volpicelli, J.R., Prentice, N., and O'Brien, C.P. (1995). Effects of an appointment reminder call on patient show rates. *Journal of Substance Abuse Treatment* 12 (3): 207–212.

Gorski, T.T. (1986). *Staying Sober.* Independence Missouri: Independence Press.

Haley, J. (1987). *Problem-solving Therapy.* San Francisco: Jossey-Bass.

Hester, R.K., and Miller, W.R. (1989). *Handbook of Alcoholism Treatment Approaches: Effective Alternatives.* New York: Pergamon Press.

Horney, K. (1942). *Self-Analysis.* New York: W.W. Norton.

Huselid, R.F., Self, E.A., and Gutierres, S.E. (1991). Predictors of successful completion of a halfway-house program for chemically-dependent women. *American Journal of Drug and Alcohol Abuse* 17 (1): 89–101.

Janis, I.L., and Mann, L. (1977). *Decision-Making: A Psychological Analysis of Conflict, Choice, and Commitment*. New York: Free Press.

Janis, I.L. (1982). *Short-term Counseling: Guidelines Based on Recent Research*. New Haven: Yale University Press.

Johnson, V., and Pandina, R.J. (1991). Effects of the family environment on adolescent substance use, delinquency, and coping styles. *American Journal of Drug and Alcohol Abuse* 17 (1): 71–88.

Kennedy, E. (1977). *On Becoming a Counselor: A Basic Guide for Non-Professional Counselors*. New York: The Seabury Press.

Klein, A.F. (1974). *Effective Group Work: An Introduction to Principle and Method*. New York: Association Press.

Leake, G.J., and King, A.S. (1977). Effect of counselor expectations on alcoholic recovery. *Alcohol Health and Research World* 11 (3): 16–22.

Leigh, G., Ogborne, A.C., and Cleland, P. (1984). Factors associated with patient dropout from an outpatient alcoholism treatment service. *Journal of Studies on Alcohol* 45 (4): 359–362.

Lewis, J.A., Dana, R.Q., and Blevins, G.A. (eds.) (1988). *Substance Abuse Counselling: An Individualized Approach*. California: Brooks/Cole Publishing Company.

Maddux, J.E., Stanley, M.A., and Manning, M.M. (1987). Self-efficacy theory and research: Applications in clinical and counseling psychology. In *Social Processes in Clinical and Counseling Psychology,* eds. Maddux, J.E., Stoltenberg, C.D., and Rosenwein, R. New York: Springer-Verlag.

Marlatt, G.A., and Gordon, J.R. (1985). *Relapse Prevention*. New York: The Guilford Press.

McLellan, A.T., Woody, G.E., Luborsky, L., O'Brien, C.P., and Druley, K.A. (1983). Increased effectiveness of substance abuse treatment: A prospective study of patient treatment matching. *The Journal of Nervous and Mental Disease* 171: 597–605.

Miller, W.R. (ed.) (1980). *The Addictive Behaviors: Treatment of Alcoholism, Drug Abuse, Smoking, and Obesity*. New York: Pergamon Press.

Miller, W.R. (1983). Motivational interviewing with problem drinkers. *Behavioral Psychology* 1: 147–172.

Miller, W.R. (1985). *Living As If*. Philadelphia: Westminster Press.

Miller, W.R., and Jackson, K.A. (1985). *Practical Psychology for Pastors*. Englewood Cliffs, NJ: Prentice Hall Inc.

Miller, W.R., and Hester, R.K. (1986). Inpatient alcoholism treatment. *American Psychologist* 41 (7): 794–805.

Miller, W.R., and Sovereign, R.G. (1989). The check-up: A model for early intervention in addictive behaviors. In *Addictive Behaviors: Prevention and Early Intervention,* eds. Loberg, T., Miller, W.R., Nathan, P.E., and Marlatt, G.A. Amsterdam: Swets and Zeitlinger.

Miller, W.R., and Rollnick, S. (1991). *Motivational Interviewing: Preparing People to Change Addictive Behavior.* New York: The Guilford Press.

Milmoe, S., Rosenthal, R., Blane, H.T., Chafetz, M.E., and Wolf, I. (1967). The doctor's voice: Postdictor of successful referral of alcoholic patients. *Journal of Abnormal Psychology* 72: 78–84.

Munjack, D.J., and Oziel, R.J. (1978). Resistance in the behavioral treatment of sexual dysfunction. *Journal of Sex and Marital Therapy* 4: 122–138.

Murgatroyd, S. (1986). *Counselling and Helping.* London: A. Wheaton and Co. Ltd.

Norcross, J., and Prochaska, J. (1983). Clinicians' theoretical orientations: Selection, utilization, and efficacy. *Professional Psychology: Research and Practice* 14: 197–208.

Orford, J., and Edwards, G. (1977). *Alcoholism: A Comparison of Treatment and Advice, with a Study of the Influence of Marriage.* Oxford: Oxford University Press.

Patterson, G.R., and Forgatch, M.S. (1985). Therapist behavior as a determinant for client noncompliance: A paradox for the behavior modifier. *Journal of Consulting and Clinical Psychology* 53: 846–851.

Pattison, E.M., and Kaufman, E. (1982). *Encyclopedic Handbook of Alcoholism.* New York: Gardner Press.

Perez, J.F. (1989). *Counselling the Alcoholic Group.* New York: Gardner Press Inc.

Priestley, P., and McGuire, J. (1983). *Learning to Help.* New York: Tavistock Publications.

Prochaska, J.O., and DiClemente, C.C. (1983). Stages and processes of self-change of smoking: Toward an integrative model of change. *Journal of Consulting and Clinical Psychology* 51: 390–395.

Prochaska, J.O., and DiClemente, C.C. (1984). *The Transtheoretical Approach: Crossing the Traditional Boundaries of Therapy.* Homewood, IL: Dow Jones/Irwin.

Prochaska, J.O., and DiClemente, C.C. (1986). Toward a comprehensive model of change. In *Treating Addictive Behaviors: Processes of Change,* eds. Miller, W.E., and Heather, N. New York: Plenum Press.

Prochaska, J.O., DiClemente, C.C., and Norcross, J.C. (1992). In search of how people change: Applications to addictive behaviors. *American Psychologist* (September 1992): 1102–1114.

Prochaska, J.O., Velicer, W.F., Rossi, J.S., and Goldstein, M.G. (1994). Stages of change and decisional balance for 12 problem behaviors. *Health-Psychology* 13 (1): 39–46.

Rogers, C.R. (1965). *Client-Centered Therapy*. Boston: Houghton Mifflin Co.

Rogers, C.R., and Stevens, B. (1967). *Person to Person: The Problem of Being Human*. Walnut Creek, CA: Real People Press.

Rogers, R.W., and Mewborn, C.R. (1976). Fear appeals and attitude change: Effects of a threat's noxiousness, probability of occurrence, and the efficacy of coping responses. *Journal of Personality and Social Psychology* 34: 54–61.

Rotter, J.B. (1966). Generalized expectancies for internal versus external control of reinforcement. *Psychological Monographs* 80 (609).

Schorer, C.G. (1965). Defiance and healing. *Comprehensive Psychiatry* 6: 184–190.

Sissons, R.W., and Mallams, J.H. (1981). The use of systematic encouragement and community access procedures to increase attendance at Alcoholics Anonymous and Al-Anon meetings. *American Journal of Drug and Alcohol Abuse* 8: 371–376.

Skinner, H.A. (1984). Assessing alcohol use by patients in treatment. In *Research Advances in Alcohol and Drug Problems,* vol. 8, eds. Smart, R. et al., Toronto: Plenum Press.

Soden, T.E. (1987). Counselling communication skills. In *Native Addiction Training*. Toronto: Whitehead Publishing.

Soden, T.E., and Murray, R.D. (1989). Microcounselling skills useful in counselling substance abusers. Unpublished manuscript. Toronto: Addiction Research Foundation.

Soden, T.E., and Murray, R.D. (1990). Motivational strategies useful in counselling substance abusers. Unpublished manuscript. Toronto: Addiction Research Foundation.

Soden, T.E., and Finlay, R. (1990). *Motivation and Change*. Training video package. Toronto: Addiction Research Foundation.

Stark, M.J., Campbell, B.K., and Brinkerhoff, C.V. (1990). Hello, may we help you? A study of attrition prevention at the time of the first phone contact with substance-abusing clients. *American Journal of Drug and Alcohol Abuse* 16 (1/2): 67–76.

Thomas, E., Polansky, N., and Kounin, J. (1955). The expected behavior of a potentially helpful person. *Human Relations* 8: 165–174.

Truax, C.B., and Carkuff, R.R. (1967). *Toward Effective Counselling and Psychotherapy: Training and Practice*. Chicago: Aldine.

Truax, C.B., and Mitchell, K.M. (1971). Research on certain therapist interpersonal skills in relation to process and outcome. In *Handbook of Psychotherapy and Behavior Change: An Empirical Analysis,* eds. Bergin, A.E., and Garfield, S.L. New York: Wiley.

Valle, S.K. (1981). Interpersonal Functioning of Alcoholism Counsellors and Treatment Outcome. *Journal of Studies on Alcoholism* 4: 783–790.

van Bilsen, H.P.J.G., and van Emst, A.J. (1986). Heroin addiction and motivational milieu therapy. *International Journal of the Addictions* 21 (6): 707–714.

Velicer, W.F., Hughes, S.L., Fava, J.L., Prochaska, J.O., and DiClemente, C.C. (1995). An empirical typology of subjects within stage of change. *Addictive Behaviors* (May-June) 20 (3): 299–320.

Watzlawick, P., Weakland, J.H., and Fisch, R. (1974). *Change: Principles of Problem Formation and Problem Resolution*. New York: W.W. Norton.

Walchtel, P.L. (1982). *Resistance: Psychodynamic and Behavioral Approaches*. New York: Plenum Press.

Zunin, L.M. (1972). *Contact: The First Four Minutes*. Toronto: Ballantine Books.

Chapter 3

Case Management

CHRISTINE BOIS AND KATHRYN GRAHAM

The impact of substance abuse on people's lives is complex and pervasive. As a result, many people who seek help for substance abuse are likely to have a complex array of problems requiring assistance in more than one area of their lives. Clients come from all walks of life and all types of social contexts. Ensuring that they are linked with the services needed for long-term recovery requires a careful assessment of each client's strengths and problem areas, as well as treatment planning and referral, and ongoing support. These functions form the main components of case management.

The case manager is responsible for initiating and maintaining a process that can help those with substance use problems to identify and access the appropriate interventions as needed. Case management is based on the assumption that most people with substance abuse problems can best be served by having access to a range of resources, rather than by interacting with a single counsellor/case manager trying to provide direct help for all of the person's problems. It is a flexible, pragmatic approach that is driven by the needs of the client. Because of these characteristics, case management must have a clear program philosophy that is reinforced by supervision.

Case management has been implemented in various ways with different groups of people, especially those with long-term chronic illness and disabilities (Austin, 1983). The importance of case management in the addictions field appears to have been recognized first in Ontario. In 1978, the Task Force Report on Treatment Services for Alcoholics in Ontario identified eight functions describing case-management activities to support people in recovery (Marshman, 1978). Recently, researchers in the United States recognized the need for and value of case management (Willenbring, Ridgely, Stinchfield and Rose, 1991), and the influential report of the U.S. Institute of Medicine (Institute of Medicine, 1990) strongly endorsed the role of case management in addictions treatment.

Since the treatment of other life problems related to drinking can improve outcomes in persons with alcohol problems (Institute of Medicine, 1990), the case manager plays a critical role in identifying problems and linking clients to a range of health, social and legal services. However, for clients with only moderate alcohol problems and relatively few problems in other life areas, case managers can provide motivational counselling and/or brief interventions, thus providing cost-effective access to the least intrusive treatment necessary.

However, the field is still defining case management, and actual applications are likely to differ depending on the program that delivers it (Graham and Birchmore Timney, 1990). For example, a survey of addictions programs in Ontario found that almost all programs provided some form of case management. However, when it is delivered in the context of intensive treatment for addictions, case management tends to be directed more toward individual counselling and less toward systems-level roles such as referral and advocacy (Birchmore Timney and Graham, 1989).

In order for case managers to understand the potential for case management and to maximize its use for clients, its functions need to be described clearly and in clinical terms. This chapter provides brief guidelines for the five functions of clinical case management adopted by the Joint Commission on the Accreditation of Hospitals (1976), which are now commonly used in the general mental health field. These functions are defined as they apply in the context of helping addicted persons:

(1) Assessment: determining an individual's strengths, weaknesses and needs;

(2) Planning: developing a specific service plan for individuals to access resources effectively;

(3) Linking: helping individuals to obtain required services;

(4) Advocacy: interceding on behalf of an individual to ensure access to resources; and

(5) Monitoring: providing ongoing evaluation of progress, support and other interventions as needed.

GENERAL ASPECTS OF CASE MANAGEMENT

The goal of case management is to provide a co-ordinated and effective means of obtaining services for clients. This process is intended to empower clients to act on their own behalf. Four basic principles govern the way in which case management is conducted.

(1) Empowerment: Case management is a client-centred process that is based on the assumption that the client will be actively involved in identifying his or her needs as well as all other aspects of the process. To ensure that the client is actively

involved, the case manager must negotiate effectively — a fundamental process of mutual exploration that empowers the client, helping him or her to develop the power and resources to function independently.

(2) Individualization: Each assessment and treatment plan is different because of the unique strengths and needs of each client. Over time, the supports and services that a client requires will also change in type and intensity.

(3) Dynamic: The case manager and client must constantly re-evaluate the client's treatment plan as more information becomes available and as the client and his or her environment change. The case manager must be flexible to allow this dynamic process to occur. In fact, because services are dictated by the client's needs, the frequency and duration of case management will vary among clients.

(4) Least intrusive: A treatment plan that requires the least structural change in a client's life will be the easiest for the client. Treatment should improve, not disrupt, the client's life.

A number of issues pertain to the overall delivery of case management, such as training and education for case managers, the use of professionals versus para-professionals to deliver case management, and the role of case managers as change agents in the treatment system. These topics will not be addressed in this chapter but have been discussed in detail elsewhere (Graham and Birchmore Timney, 1990; Willenbring et al., 1991). Skills needed by case managers will be discussed, however, since certain skills are critical to the appropriate delivery of clinical case management. First, case managers need fundamental counselling skills that will enable them to listen to clients and build empathic rapport. They also need a good working knowledge of the range of services that could most efficiently address the client's needs. Because case managers spend considerable time and effort linking with other agencies, they need credibility with other agencies, as well as the ability to negotiate and communicate with staff of other agencies in a positive and productive way. Finally, the processes involved in identifying problems and making efficient use of the system require excellent problem-solving skills.

Although the functions of case management will be described separately and in sequence, circumstances rarely allow for these functions to be carried out in a simple, orderly way. In theory, the process begins with assessment, followed by treatment planning and referral. However, the client's needs will affect the order and type of functions provided. For example, a client who wants help for withdrawal after being put out of the house by his or her spouse might be given an immediate referral to a detoxification centre and a legal clinic. In this example, two referrals would have been made before an assessment was completed. Thus, the case-management process must be flexible in addressing functions so that the client is linked to appropriate services at the appropriate time.

ASSESSMENT

Assessment is the foundation of case management. Without an accurate assessment, case-management activities could be misdirected and waste both the client's and the case manager's time. The assessment process includes identifying and defining a person's major strengths and problems. Its primary goal is to obtain information in order to refer clients to appropriate addictions treatment, although it is also needed to link clients to non-addictions services.

Many clients who enter treatment experience ambivalence, anxiety and fear, various life problems, involvement with many agencies and a range of external pressures and supports (Graham, Brett and Bois, 1995). Using a structured but flexible interview format guarantees that the information required will be collected while allowing the case manager to respond to the client's immediate needs. The assessment process allows the client to clarify his or her ambivalence and obtain information to reduce anxiety and fears. The case manager is also continually assessing the client's readiness for change. A key function of the case manager is providing motivational feedback to encourage the client to set and achieve his or her goals.

For many people who abuse alcohol or other drugs, the assessment process provides their first opportunity to gain objective feedback and insight about the chaos of their lives. In some cases, the assessment process may be the only intervention that some clients will want or need. Similarly, although the primary goal of assessment is to refer clients to addictions treatment, some clients will refuse such treatment but will accept referrals to non-addictions agencies to resolve life problems that have led to or resulted from substance abuse. Research has also shown that the assessment process involves more than just matching a client to an appropriate treatment setting (Graham et al., 1995). Therefore, it is important to conduct the assessment in a way that is most useful to the client. To do so, the case manager should not only obtain information about the client's strengths and problem areas, but should also clearly reflect this information back to the client. For example, a client who is feeling devastated because of a drinking and driving offence may be better able to put things into perspective if the case manager points out his or her strengths in other areas such as having a good employment record or positive family relationships.

The assessment process is an opportunity for a client to learn about the association between his or her problems and substance use. For example, sleep disturbances, digestive problems or other physical problems can be linked to alcohol use. Making these links can reassure the client that he or she is not crazy. The client can see his or her problems with some perspective, which gives the client a sense that the problems can be managed. This education process not only provides hope that helps to motivate the client, but it also provides a more objective evaluation of problems and a clear direction for addressing them.

The Assessment Process

The assessment process begins informally when the client and case manager first meet. The formal part of the process begins with the case manager explaining to the client the functions and procedures of assessment. The client can be informed that the assessment is intended to benefit him or her by providing information for later decisions. The client needs to know the kind of information that will be collected, such as alcohol and drug use, and functioning in life areas such as accommodation, marital/family relations, social relations, friends, leisure, education/employment, emotional and physical health, finances, and previous treatment history. The extent to which these life areas are examined will vary with every client. Of course, clients who have more difficulties usually require a more extended assessment. The case manager should provide the client with examples of assessment questions so that he or she can decide whether to participate.

At this point, the case manager's role in the assessment process should be explained to the client. This role includes helping the client to assess his or her strengths and problem areas, providing information about the service system, and helping the client to develop and implement a treatment plan. It is useful to explain how long the assessment process usually takes and that at any time the client may choose not to continue. Before the assessment begins, the case manager must discuss the limits to confidentiality (court subpoenas, medical emergencies, child abuse) and provisions concerning consent forms. Any costs associated with the service should also be discussed.

Many clients will decide to proceed with the assessment; others will require additional support. Some clients might need to explore their fears and expectations about their drug use, particularly their fears about treatment. Others may need referrals to stabilize their lives and to start developing a support network before the assessment begins.

As a support to the client, the case manager may meet with family members to explain the assessment process and to provide them with information on how to support the client. It may be appropriate for troubled family members to become clients themselves. In such instances, they would independently receive case management, including being assessed for problem areas in their lives and their coping methods. When assessing family members, the case manager should fully explore each member's drug use.

Selecting Assessment Instruments

Various assessment instruments are available to the case manager, which are described in a number of publications (Alcohol Health and Research World, 1991;

Annis and Davis, 1991; Donovan and Marlatt, 1988; Graham et al., 1993; Lettieri, 1988; Lettieri, Nelson and Sayers, 1984; NIAAA, 1991; Skinner, 1981; Sobell, Sobell and Nirenberg, 1988; Sobell, Toneatto, Sobell and Shillingford, in press; Sobell and Sobell, 1996). Although we will not discuss these instruments in depth, we will describe some of the considerations relevant to selecting them.

First, the case manager must be familiar with the instruments chosen so that the assessment process can proceed in an orderly but comfortable fashion. In determining which instruments to use and when to use them, the case manager should consider characteristics such as the type of drugs used and the client's age, sex and ethnic background. The case manager must be attuned to sensitive areas for each client and begin the assessment at a point that is comfortable for the client. For example, female clients, particularly older women, may be sensitive to the stigma against female drug users. In these cases, it is advisable to begin with questions on less sensitive life areas; questions related to alcohol/other drug use can be addressed later. Youth, however, may be sensitive to family issues and the case worker should establish rapport before addressing this area.

The case manager must use a flexible approach while also collecting the information required to develop a plan. This process includes choosing instruments that include information required to determine if the client meets program admission criteria.

In conclusion, clients who present for assessment have a range of substance-related problems and a variety of attitudes about disclosing problems in various life areas. The case manager needs to be knowledgeable about the typical concerns of various populations, including the elderly, youth, women, men, family members, natives, and those who have concurrent disorders, in order to be alert to areas of the assessment that are likely to be problematic. This knowledge can help the case manager ensure that the assessment process meets the needs of each client.

PLANNING

The assessment process identifies each client's strengths and problem areas. This information is used to plan appropriate goals and interventions to aid the client's recovery. The treatment planning process also uses information about the client's preference and service availability to determine a recovery plan. Although changes in the plan may occur over time, the plan provides a focus for case management.

Treatment planning comprises two stages: negotiation between client and case manager regarding specific interventions to address identified problem areas, and the development of a manageable plan. The negotiation involves the ability to hear what the client wants, is capable of undertaking and agrees to implement. Consequently, like every client, every treatment plan is unique. It is critical that the client agree to all aspects of the plan. For example, the most appropriate service might be provided in a large urban area, but a client from an isolated rural area might find this option frightening and unacceptable. Treatment planning involves the following four stages: prioritizing problem areas and exploring options with the client; matching services to the client's specific needs; identifying potential barriers to using particular services; and preparing the client for what follows.

Prioritizing Problem Areas

The first step in treatment planning is to prioritize the identified problems. In the assessment process, the case manager assesses the severity of problems as well as the client's strengths in various life areas. These assessments are compared to the client's perceptions. Sometimes both parties have similar perceptions of problems and priorities. At other times, discrepancies emerge and need to be discussed in order to develop an appropriate and acceptable treatment plan. For example, the case manager and client may have different perceptions of the extent to which alcohol is causing problems in the client's life. In this situation, the case manager must determine whether the client is ready to set goals regarding alcohol use. If not, the case manager may need to use motivational counselling techniques. Each problem area needs to be defined in active terms with clear goals. For example, if the client is experiencing marital problems, the goal could be to improve marital communication. Treatment planning would then focus on specific actions to achieve this goal.

Matching Services to the Client's Needs

Once problems and goals have been prioritized through negotiation, the client and case manager begin discussing options for addressing problem areas. The plan must clearly identify the responsibilities of both the client and the counsellor. Each activity must have a clearly defined time frame. For example, if a client decides to seek marital counselling, then a date should be set by which time the client will have made an appointment with a marital therapist.

At the heart of treatment planning is the concept of matching, which involves selecting treatments or alternatives that are most suited to the client's needs and will be most likely to result in a positive outcome. No single treatment is suitable or effective for all persons with alcohol or drug problems. Some need outpatient care, while others need inpatient care. Some benefit from mutual aid groups such as Alcoholics Anonymous, while others do not. In its review, the Institute of Medicine (1990) concluded that treatment outcomes could be improved significantly by matching on the variables of demographic factors, psychiatric diagnoses, personality factors, severity of alcohol problems and antecedents to drinking.

Matching is a complex process because a number of client variables must be considered, including the client's preferences. In fact, client preference is a key factor that determines whether the client will follow through with the plan. However, treatment options also depend on the services available.

The first factor to consider is the severity of the alcohol or drug problem, and to provide the least intrusive assistance. All other things being equal, clients with more severe problems require more intensive treatment. For example, clients with moderate levels of dependence may benefit from outpatient treatment, while those with severe dependence may require day treatment or even a residential program. For some clients, especially those at an early stage of problem use, no addictions-specific treatment may be necessary. In these cases, the process of clarifying problems through assessment and the support of the case manager may be sufficient intervention for the client to resolve an alcohol or drug problem.

Matching is also a consideration when referring clients to non-addictions agencies. These referrals must ensure that the client fits with other clients of the agency and the styles of the service providers. The case manager must have detailed knowledge about the other addictions treatment services and community agencies to which they are making referrals. Case managers should share information about changes in the existing resources, their accessibility, change of staff and any improvement or deterioration in service. These factors help to determine the best treatment plan.

Identifying Potential Barriers

The treatment plan must also identify any barriers to implementing the plan. For example, barriers to attending certain treatment programs might include a lack of transportation, insufficient money or need for adequate child care. But other equally important but less obvious barriers also exist, including the client's beliefs about addictions (e.g., those who drink sherry are not alcoholics) and attitudes toward accepting counselling (e.g., men should be able to deal with their own problems). For non-addictions services, a negative attitude by service providers toward individuals who have alcohol and drug problems may prevent these clients from receiving adequate services. As well, the philosophy and mandate of agencies can be barriers to those with substance abuse problems. For example, some agencies will not provide services unless the client has achieved abstinence.

In directing clients to agencies, the case manager must know more about the agency than just the nature of services offered. The case manager also needs to know how the client will likely experience the agency and its services. Other important factors in the client's life influence decisions to enter treatment and these must be identified in developing the treatment plan. For example, entering treatment may mean giving up a job or an apartment. For a woman, it may mean losing her children. Such risks need to be identified, and both costs and benefits of potential treatment options considered. Treatment planning can be completed in one session or could take several sessions, depending on the client's situation.

Preparing the Client for Treatment

The final stage of negotiating the treatment plan is preparing the client for treatment. The case manager provides information and support to the client in maintaining sobriety before treatment begins. At this stage, the client can express his or her fears about treatment and receive information about what will occur in the various types of therapy. This information is especially helpful for those entering residential treatment. They will need specific information about visiting hours, weekend leaves, contact with family, rules about smoking, and suggestions about the types of things to take (stamps, writing paper, money). Making an appointment to see the client following treatment will provide reassurance about the continuity of care.

LINKING

Linking is the process of referring or transferring clients to services in the formal and informal care-giving systems. The steps involved in each referral will be determined by the client's need for support and his or her capabilities and resources. For example, for a client who has a strong support system and the knowledge and skills to access resources directly, linking may be as simple as providing the client with the name, phone number and address of an agency. However, for a client in distress, who lives in temporary housing and has limited literacy skills, the case manager may need to phone the referral destination directly and arrange transportation there.

The referral process is also affected by the characteristics of the referral agency. For example, the case manager needs to know which route (phone call, letter, referral form) will gain access for the client. It is also useful to know whether referrals should be made only to certain workers.

An important skill in case management is the ability to communicate effectively with the referral agencies to ensure successful access for the client. This means being familiar with the information requirements of each referral agency and providing the appropriate client information, especially regarding any sensitivities (e.g., a woman experiencing the social stigma associated with alcohol problems). This process helps to ensure a good match between the client and the service provider.

ADVOCACY   .

Advocacy involves interceding on behalf of an individual to obtain access to needed resources and support. The counsellor may need to advocate on behalf of a client both with treatment agencies, as well as non-treatment persons such as family members, an employer and so on. For example, in one study of case management, about half of the case manager's contacts were with someone other than the client (Graham et al., 1995). Contacts with other agencies occurred most often during the assessment phase, while client and family contacts occurred throughout the case management process. Co-ordination, a function that is closely associated with advocacy, brings together support and services to enhance the client's treatment plan. Simply put, when advocating for a client, the case manager is obtaining something (a direct service, practical help, information or support) that directly benefits the client. Co-ordination involves activities such as sharing information or negotiating agency roles, which indirectly benefit the client.

The need for these functions varies according to treatment factors and client characteristics. Most advocacy occurs during the assessment stage, whereas co-ordination occurs during all phases of case management. To successfully advocate for clients, the case manager needs to develop a large network of contacts; to successfully intervene in the system, the case manager needs negotiating skills. The case conference is a useful activity that the case manager can use to either advocate or co-ordinate services for the client. When several agencies are involved, a case conference can be used to define each agency's role and to ensure that the client's needs are met.

MONITORING

Monitoring involves ongoing evaluation and then taking action as required. The term "evaluation" is used in two fairly distinct contexts: evaluation at the clinical case level, and evaluation of the program itself. Our discussion will focus on case-level evaluation. Program-level evaluation is a distinct area of study and is addressed in other publications (Commission on Accreditation of Rehabilitation Facilities, 1988; Ellis, Reed and Barnsley, 1990; Graham, 1985; Graham and Birchmore Timney, 1989; Hawkins and Nederhood, 1987; McDermott, Pyett and Hamilton, 1991; Ogborne and Gavin, 1990; Rush and Ogborne, 1991; Rush, Ellis, Allen and Schmidt, 1995). Case evaluation and program evaluation are linked in that the former usually forms the information base for the latter. Our discussion, however, will focus on case evaluation as part of clinical case management.

In case management, case evaluation is the process of collecting and interpreting information in order to monitor three main areas: the client's status/progress, the case manager's actions, and the role of other agencies. Monitoring in each area is done for a specific reason. The client's status is monitored in order to intervene as needed or change the treatment plan as appropriate. The case manager's actions are monitored to ensure that systematic care is provided to the client and for the case manager to identify those strategies that most successfully address particular goals. The role of other agencies is monitored in order to assess the appropriateness of initial referrals made by other agencies to the case manager, and how well referral agencies meet expectations. Since the agency network is constantly changing, monitoring the role of other agencies helps to ensure that services are used appropriately.

Client Monitoring

Client monitoring can be done both informally and formally. Informally, monitoring occurs during every contact with the client. The case manager initially observes the client's condition and notes whether he or she appears healthy, sober, anxious and so on. Every contact with the client would likely include some general monitoring questions (e.g., How are you? How have things been going?) as well as more specific questions relating to general problem areas (e.g., Have things improved with your wife/husband?). There would also be follow-up on areas where particular actions were planned since the last contact (e.g., You were planning on attending this or that program since I last saw you. Were you successful with your strategies for avoiding alcohol?).

Monitoring helps the client to focus on achieving his or her goals, and the treatment plan should be central to this process. That is, the case manager must focus on systematic plans for change rather than on general aspects of the client's life. With the treatment plan as the central core for discussion, the client can remain on track, and there is less risk of discouragement. The monitoring process includes checking whether the client has followed through on referrals and determining whether the services were appropriate. With the client's permission, feedback concerning progress can also be obtained from service providers.

Another important function of monitoring is collecting information to revise the treatment plan. The case manager constantly needs to review the plan with the client and change it as new information becomes available, as different problems arise, and as goals are achieved. This process provides the continuity of care that is particularly important if the treatment plan breaks down. It is also important for the client and case manager to monitor the client's use of substances and identify situations in which he or she is at high risk of relapse. This allows the case manager to intervene and to either provide relapse prevention counselling, if needed, or refer the client as appropriate. Encouraging the client to maintain a realistic perspective is an essential component of monitoring; the client can be reminded of the progress that he or she has made. The case manager, where appropriate, can also enhance the client's support network by providing information (with consent) about the client's plan and need for support to family members, friends or employer.

Crises may occur at any time during this monitoring phase. These may include medical emergencies, suicide attempts, drug overdoses, emotional crises, housing needs or financial crises. Monitoring helps to ensure that the case manager is available to help the client obtain the necessary services as soon as possible and prevent serious disruption of the recovery process.

These examples illustrate the extent to which client evaluation is an integral part of the case-management process. The way the information is documented, however, will determine how useful monitoring can be in identifying and responding to patterns over time within a case. Methods of documentation will be discussed in the next section.

Formal case evaluation involves using more standardized approaches to monitoring. These approaches are used when a more objective or quantitative assessment in a life area is desired. Such measures are often used as part of reassessment where a client's status at discharge or follow-up is compared to his or her status at initial assessment. For example, if a client has not abstained from alcohol during case management, it may be useful to administer standardized measures of recent alcohol consumption and consequences to assess with some accuracy the extent to which the client has improved. Such measures can be useful in revising the treatment plan and in discharge planning. When used as part of follow-up, they can provide information about the success of case management for that client and provide feedback to the case manager on long-term outcomes. Tools for case evaluation are described in a recent document developed by a working group of researchers and clinicians (Graham et al., 1993).

Monitoring Case Management

Case management is flexible in that it is driven by the needs of the client, the characteristics of available services, and, to some extent, the personality of the case manager. The case manager engages in a complex array of activities and it is important to document and evaluate these on an ongoing basis. Monitoring can help the case manager to identify the strategies that he or she finds most successful in a number of areas, such as reducing the rate of "no shows," motivating clients to accept addictions counselling, enlisting family support and so on. Monitoring and documenting the case-management process provide a way of evaluating whether the treatment plan was followed and where revisions were necessary. Appendix A provides a basic template for monitoring case management. This template provides a log of interventions and events for quick review of the case. It can be expanded to include other information relevant to the goals and practices of particular programs. It also organizes information so that data can be easily extracted for program description and evaluation.

Agency Monitoring

It is in the use and co-ordination of other agencies' services that the case-management function differs most from that of an outpatient counsellor. The case manager must not only have good counselling skills but also an up-to-date working knowledge of a wide range of available services (including addictions-specific programs, legal, marital, social services and so on). The case manager must keep abreast of eligibility requirements, cultures and success rates of particular programs. With new programs being developed and existing programs closing or changing their mandates, case evaluation is one of the main ways to continuously update knowledge. As part of the case-management process, the case manager records every interaction with another agency. In addition, part of the follow-up evaluation with clients includes their experiences with the programs to which they were referred. This information can be used to update knowledge about particular programs. It can also be done more systematically by reviewing agency roles as part of closing case files. The case manager should keep files on other relevant agencies. When a case is closed, experiences (both positive and negative) with agencies involved should be added to the agency file. This might include information such as waiting lists, client satisfaction with the agency, the names of the best contact persons at the agency and so on. Effective use of other services is a key component of case management, and monitoring the role of other agencies is the way to ensure that this component is well implemented.

In summary, case management is a complex process that gives clients structured support to address their problems. The process provides the client with the help that he or she wants in a manner and at the time that it is wanted. There are standard functions to guide the case manager, but the process is different for every client since each individual is unique.

Case management will be successful when the case manager has the ability to establish good rapport, has knowledge about substance abuse and the treatment network, and has genuine concern about the client.

REFERENCES

Alcohol Health and Research World. (1991). Vol. 15 (3), entire issue on linking alcoholism treatment research with clinical practice.

Annis, H.M., and Davis, C.C. (1991). *Drug Use by Adolescents: Identification, Assessment and Intervention.* Toronto: Addiction Research Foundation.

Austin, C.D. (1983). Case management in long-term care: Options and opportunities. *Health and Social Work* 8 (1): 16–30.

Birchmore Timney, C., and Graham, K. (1989). A survey of case management practices in addictions programs. *Alcoholism Treatment Quarterly* 6 (3/4): 103–127.

Commission on Accreditation of Rehabilitation Facilities. (1988). *Program Evaluation in Alcoholism and Drug Abuse Treatment Programs.* Tuscon, AZ: Commission on Accreditation of Rehabilitation Facilities.

Ellis, D., Reid, G., and Barnsley, J. (1990). *Keeping on Track. An Evaluation Guide for Community Groups.* Vancouver: Women's Research Centre.

Donovan, D.M., and Marlatt, G.A. (eds.). (1988). *The Assessment of Addictive Behaviors.* New York: Guilford Press.

Graham, K. (1985). *Evaluating Case Management: Asking the Right Questions.* (ARF Internal Document No. 66). Toronto: Addiction Research Foundation.

Graham, K., and Birchmore Timney, C. (1989). The problem of replicability in program evaluation. The component solution using the example of case management. *Education and Program Planning:* 179–187.

Graham, K., and Birchmore Timney, C. (1990). Case management in addictions treatment. *Journal of Substance Abuse Treatment* 7: 181–188.

Graham, K., Price, B., Brett, P., Baker, A., Bois, C., Boyle, B., Chapman, L., Eliany, M., Gaskin, J., Martin, G., Sobell, L., and Thompson, J. (1993). *Directory of Client Outcome Measures for Addictions Treatment Programs.* Toronto: Addiction Research Foundation.

Graham, K., Brett, P., and Bois, C. (1995). Treatment entry and engagement: A study of process at assessment/referral centres. *Contemporary Drug Problems* 22: 61–104.

Graham, K., Birchmore, C., Bois, C., and Wedgerfield, K. (1995). Continuity of care in addictions treatment: The role of advocacy and co-ordination in case management. *American Journal of Drug and Alcohol Abuse* 21: 433–451.

Hawkins, J.D., and Nederhood, B. (1987). *Handbook for Evaluating Drug and Alcohol Prevention Programs.* Rockville, MD: Office for Substance Abuse Prevention.

Institute of Medicine. (1990). *Broadening the Base of Treatment for Alcohol Problems.* Washington, DC: National Academy Press.

Joint Commission on Accreditation of Hospitals. (1976). *Principles for Accreditation of Community Mental Health Service Programs*. Chicago, IL: Joint Commission on Accreditation of Hospitals.

Lettieri, D.J. (ed.). (1988). *Research Strategies in Alcoholism Treatment Assessment*. New York: Haworth Press.

Lettieri, D.J., Nelson, J.E., and Sayers, M.A. (1984). *Alcoholism Treatment Assessment Research Instruments*. NIAAA treatment handbook series. Rockville, MD: NIAAA.

McDermott, F., Pyett, P., and Hamilton, M. (1991). *Evaluate Yourself. A Handbook for Alcohol and Other Drug Treatment Agencies*. Melbourne, Australia.

Marshman, J.A. (1978). *The Treatment of Alcoholics: An Ontario Perspective*. The Report of the Task Force on Treatment Services for Alcoholics. Toronto: Addiction Research Foundation.

National Conference on Social Welfare. 1981. *Case Management: State of the Art*. Final Report, Grant No. 54-P-71542/3-01, submitted to the Administration on Developmental Disabilities, U.S. Department of Health and Human Services, Washington, DC.

NIAAA (National Institute on Alcohol Abuse and Alcoholism). (1991). Assessing alcoholism. *Alcohol Alert* 12: 1–4.

Ogborne, A.C., and Gavin, M.T. (1990). *Quality Assurance in Substance Abuse Treatment: Guidelines for Practitioners*. Toronto: Addiction Research Foundation.

Ontario Ministry of Health. (1985). *Addiction Services Policy*. Toronto: Queen's Park Printer.

Rush, B., and Ogborne, A. (1991). Program logic models: Expanding their role and structure for program planning and evaluation. *The Canadian Journal of Program Evaluation* 6: 93–105.

Rush, B., Ellis, K., Allen, B., and Schmidt, G. (1995). *Assessment and Referral Agencies in Ontario: Results of a Descriptive Study*. Toronto: Addiction Research Foundation.

Skinner, H.A. (1981). Assessment of alcohol problems. Basic principles, critical issues, and future trends. In *Research Advances in Alcohol and Drug Problems*, Vol. 6, eds. Israel, Y., Glaser, F.B., Kalant, H., Popham, R.R., Schmidt, W., and Smart, R.G. New York: Plenum Press.

Sobell, L.C., Sobell, M.B., and Nirenberg, T.D. (1988). Behavioral assessment and treatment planning with alcohol and drug abusers: A review with an emphasis on clinical application. *Clinical Psychology Review* 8: 19–54.

Sobell, L.C., Toneatto, T., Sobell, M.B., and Shillingford, J.A. In press. Alcohol problems: Diagnostic interviewing. In *Diagnostic Interviewing,* 2nd ed., eds. Hersen, M., and Turner, S.M. New York: Plenum Press.

Sobell, L.C., and Sobell, M.B. (1996). *Timeline Followback*. Toronto: Addiction Research Foundation.

Willenbring, M.L., Ridgely, M.S., Stinchfield, R., and Rose, M. (1991). *Application of Case Management in Alcohol and Drug Dependence: Matching Techniques and Populations*. Rockville, MD: U.S. Department of Health and Human Services.

APPENDIX A

BASIC TEMPLATE FOR MONITORING CASE MANAGEMENT

Client I.D. _____

Case Manager _____

Date	Location of contact
	1. office
	2. other
	   (specify)
		Duration of contact	Type of contact
			1. in person
			2. telephone
			3. written
			4. other
			   (specify)
				People involved in contact
				1. client
				2. other
				   (specify)
					Main areas addressed (and other infor-mation about the client's status)	Future plans

Chapter 4

Ethical and Professional Issues

WAYNE SKINNER

This is not a systematic treatment of ethical and professional issues in clinical work in addictions. It is an essay offered from a personal viewpoint. Rather than providing firm answers to key questions, it is intended to encourage reflection and promote (and provoke) discussion and dialogue about the ethics of addictions treatment.

Clinical practice in addictions lacks a unified view of key ethical and professional issues. This is not surprising, given that addictions workers have so many different professional and life-experiential points of origin. Some of us have professional clinical training — in social work, nursing or psychology, for instance; some of us have come to the helping role through the process of our own recoveries. Some of us have little professional training, but are rich in practical experience; some of us are just the opposite, theoretically strong but not well grounded in clinical practice. Some of us have specific training in addictions; some of us rely on general knowledge about human biopsychosocial functioning.

In short, addictions counsellors are a diverse group. Our views about the nature of substance use problems and our practices — our methods of intervention — are varied, and at times conflict with each other. These differences need not be seen as problems to be eliminated, of course; they deserve to be appreciated and celebrated. But when it comes to establishing consensus and setting up clear-cut and broadly supported ways of acting and conducting ourselves, we do not face an easy task.

Conduct is at the heart of ethics and professional roles. How do I behave? How should I behave? Those who belong to a helping profession with a code of ethics already have a framework within which conduct will be evaluated. Agencies also have policies and procedures that guide the actions of their staff. Additionally, legal statutes and regulations govern confidentiality, reporting of abuse and neglect, and the duty to take action regarding imminent client self-harm or threats to others. From one perspective, the field may seem quite bare of unifying standards and guidelines; from another, many regulations and rules guide and shape the conduct of the helper.

Our challenge is to see the diversity of people who work within the field of addictions treatment as one of its fundamental realities, one of its special strengths. Between the two poles of the volunteer and the trained professional is a great array of individuals of varied skills and experience, linked by a shared intention to make a positive difference in the lives of people with problems related to substance use.

The fertile diversity of the addictions treatment field ensures that even the most basic beliefs and attitudes are not uniformly held and are often contested and debated. One may ask, "What is addiction?" only to receive a dizzying barrage of answers, many of which contradict each other. Some will call addiction a disease. Others will say that it is genetically based or a learned behavior. Still others will insist that it is a socially constructed concept. Whatever the answer, each specific response will guide decisively how we understand the nature of substance use problems and what should be done about them. Indeed, our notions of the helping role and of what constitutes proper, ethical conduct will be shaped by the beliefs and attitudes we hold about human beings and human behavior.

So, let that be our first point here: professional conduct and ethical standards are themselves formed (though not totally determined) by what we take to be human nature, by how we see addiction problems, and by what we think needs to be done about them. It is easy to see why having a single set of facts, a single set of procedures, a single set of beliefs, and a single point of view would be appealing. It helps to quiet the voices of doubt that might otherwise rise within us or be heard in the questions of others. It eliminates the otherwise necessary struggle we have to engage in when, in a particular situation, we have to sort out the right thing to do.

Perhaps the most ethical position a helper can hold today is one that is open to critical self-reflection and self-evaluation. Such a helper is prepared to assess the intention and measure the effectiveness of what he or she is doing. Intentions in helping are often the very best, but intentions alone are a poor measure. The history of medical practice shows the harm that can be unwittingly inflicted by the well-intentioned helper. Surgery without respect for the need for aseptic procedures, blood transfusions that contain undetected contaminants, use of medication with side effects that outweigh potential benefits: these are just a few examples. Many methods that were the standards of care and treatment in the past would be flagrantly unethical today. What will the practitioners of the future have to say about the addictions interventions that we practise today?

Members of formal disciplines with their own codes of ethics and professional values may think that they are exempt from the labors of reflection. But the ethical challenge itself consists of this: to be able to locate in a specific situation what is unique to it and what is universal. That determines when general rules should be applied or whether the particular circumstances are paramount. For example, confidentiality is a guiding principle of professional conduct among counsellors, but there are times when other considerations must be given precedence — where the safety of an individual from death or grievous harm is at stake, for example. The counsellor also has a legal obligation to report cases of suspected child abuse to the appropriate child protection agency. When orienting clients to the rules of the counselling relationship, it is important to spell out and define the boundaries and limits to the process.

How can the helper evaluate whether aspects of his or her conduct and duty (which is at least a double duty: to the individual and to the community) are ethically defensible and socially acceptable and, if they are not, what to do about it? Several types of dilemma commonly occur in clinical work. First, the conflict can occur totally within the helper's self. One way this happens is when the worker feels caught between "want to" and "ought to." Extreme, though not uncommon, examples would be feeling strongly attracted to or repulsed by a client. The helper is expected to be especially adept at recognizing the feelings that are evoked by contact with other people. Being able to work with feelings that usually undo or subvert ordinary relationships is the hallmark of the counselling experience. But when the helper feels immobilized by, or pulled towards, behavior that opposes his or her sense of what he or she should be doing, then an ethical problem has emerged and must be addressed responsibly.

"Responsibly" is a good word to use here, because it encourages us to recognize not only that there is conduct that is proper to being a helper and a counsellor, but also that the counsellor is "response-able": that is, able to make the ethically required response. The response can take a variety of forms. Feeling unable to talk to colleagues or a supervisor, or deliberately avoiding doing so, is a likely sign that the counsellor is avoiding a matter of professional responsibility. This does not mean that consultation is always required: careful evaluation often leads the worker to an ethically supportable decision about how to proceed. But consultation should always be an option that the helper is willing to pursue. Not being able to candidly discuss a dilemma with professional colleagues is itself a sign that factors other than professional conduct are guiding the helper's behavior.

One key to the helping relationship is the realization that it involves taking the client into our care — "our" meaning both the agency and the helper. The enduring measure of the helping relationship is that we do not take advantage of the client, especially given the vulnerability and dependence that the helping relationship, to be effective, must sometimes permit. Even when the helper believes there is a mutual interest or consent between helper and client, there can be no suspension of ethical standards regarding relationships.

When attraction or repulsion is so strong as to interfere with the helper's tasks, it would seem to be in the best interests of the client (and the counsellor) to transfer the client to another counsellor. This must, of course, be done in a skilled and sensitive way, with care being taken to avoid projecting the helper's own conflicted dynamics onto the client. Many clients already tend to take on too much responsibility for failed events.

Stereotypically, we think of the helper's attraction to a client and the problems it might bring. It is just as important to think of the subtle ways that the client's behavior may be objectionable, offensive or a threat. Dealing with violence, aggression or other negative behavior may offend the helper's beliefs and sensibilities, so that the helper may even resist finding ways of engaging the client, which can be crucial to therapeutic success. Clients with substance use problems may behave in ways that are socially ridiculed or forbidden. They may be stigmatized because of health problems frequently associated with marginalized lifestyles, such as prostitution. Cultural differences can sometimes alienate the helper from the client to the extent that they interfere with the professional obligation to offer care.

Besides an internal conflict between feelings and duties, between "want" and "ought," the worker may feel caught between two duties or ethical imperatives (two "oughts"). Confidentiality and duty to inform have already been mentioned. The work of exploring painful issues with the client can itself be thought of in ethical terms. The adage "primum non nolire" (Above all, do no harm) is an old motto in medicine. In encouraging clients to address painful experiences, feelings and thoughts — sometimes confronting them — the helper should be very clear about why he or she is doing this. What effect, or result, is being sought? In what state does it leave the client? Working at close quarters with a vulnerable person carries with it the challenge to be purposeful and to know the limits as well as the possibilities of the helping experience. For example, therapists sometimes try to produce a breakthrough by getting a client to give up control over feelings. It is often easy to produce such effects. But again, the helper has to answer why it needed to be done, and how it affected the client.

Another ethical dilemma emerges when there is a conflict between helper and client about what should be done. The therapeutic relationship is, in terms of power, asymmetrical: the helper has more than the client. This is not to say that the client is totally powerless, but the advantages tend to favor the counsellor. The self-reflective helper should consider to what degree his or her behavior is an exercise in power and control, rather than a purposeful attempt to help the client. Ways in which power circulates in the counselling relationship can reinforce rather than release the client from the dynamics of dependence and feelings of inadequacy commonly encountered in the treatment of substance use problems. The issue is not for the helper to deny or to avoid the power of his or her position, but to see how it works and affects the helping process. The helper's goal could be to use the strategic advantages he or she enjoys in the relationship (e.g., the worker knows more about the client than the client knows about the worker; the worker can usually direct what is talked about, when meetings begin and end, etc.) to help empower the client toward his or her healthy possibilities.

Additionally, conflicts that align a client and worker against a community standard or value can be seen as an ethical issue. An important part of the helper's role is to advocate for the needs of the client, needs that sometimes can only be remedied at the societal level and that sometimes conflict with public values. Examples in the world of addictions treatment are easy to find. Consider the need for harm reduction strategies for intravenous drug users. In this case, the formal social rule is that such behavior is illegal and therefore prohibited. Taking that stance alone, the only permissible intervention would be immediate cessation of the drug use behavior, followed by abstinence. Yet while counsellors in addiction programs help clients discontinue drug use, public health concerns have led to advocacy of harm reduction measures such as needle exchanges, free condoms and methadone programs. The goal expands beyond discontinuing unwanted behavior to the reduction or avoidance of harmful consequences. This alliance of client and therapeutic interest opposes public opinion (and established therapeutic philosophies, in some cases).

In the belief that ethical issues are an inherent part of all helping relationships, I have identified and illustrated three forms of dilemma that have ethical implications for the helper: first, between what the helper wants to do and what he or she feels is the correct thing to do (between personal desire and personal duty); second, between what the client feels is right and what the helper believes (between you and me); and third, between what the helper and client agree on and social standards or rules (between us and them). In each of these situations, the helper's beliefs about human beings, substance use problems, the helping role, prospects for treatment, as well as the helper's thoughts, feelings and assumptions about the particular client — all of these, along with other factors, shape and define ethical issues that require responses that go beyond the routine. Not so long ago, corporal punishment might have been tolerated or even valued as a sign of parents' dedicated attention to the proper upbringing of children — that is, as a form of ethical behavior. Now we see in this behavior a dynamic of victimization that has toxic intergenerational aspects. It has become a crime.

Ethics and professional roles are not items to consider tangentially in addictions treatment. Because values and beliefs are so central to the helping project itself, they are at the heart of the very routines and assumptions that we take for granted. Extraordinary situations bring the ethical dimension into particularly sharp relief, but an essential part of the professional role is a commitment to keeping the most commonplace actions and convictions open to scrutiny and challenge.

Consider some very simple questions that any helper could ask in trying to see if his or her conduct meets an ethical standard. First, are there aspects of my work with a particular client that I would be embarrassed to see appear on the clinical record? If the details of my work with clients are accurately presented in the file, then I am being open about my work and prepared to have it evaluated by my peers. If I am holding back information regarding in-session events and my personal conduct, is it something that a detached and objective observer would be able to understand and accept?

Second, are there features of my work that I avoid sharing with my peers and in supervision? The mark of a competent helper is not that he or she knows all the answers but is always open to self-examination and in pursuit of self-improvement. Are there aspects of my work that I withhold because I know or suspect they are wrong, or because they would not pass review by my peers, or because I fear my work is of poor quality? Being able to seek out consultation, sharing information with colleagues, being open to different ways of doing things — these are signs of a helper who seeks most of all to be optimally helpful to clients.

Third, even (or especially) assuming that my intentions are of the highest order, what are the effects of my actions? Ultimately, ethics must be less concerned about why I do what I do than with the effects my actions have on others. What do I intend? And — more importantly — what is the result? For the ethical helper, there can be ultimately only two measures for this question of effects: the one given by the client and the one that is empirically (or factually) based.

Addictions is a field in which an inventory of specific ethical standards is not likely to be found. Instead, the process of helping is one that requires ongoing critical self-appraisal by the helper and openness to the word of the client and the work of the evaluator. Work that is clearly and honestly documented is the product of a responsible helper, as is an attitude of openness that seeks and invites dialogue and consultation about the demanding aspects of working with individuals with problems related to substance use.

Taking a person into our care is a task and a calling that puts the interests of the help-seeker first in ways that do not compromise our duty to enhance the safety and health of the community. The ethics of clinical practice require us to recognize the balance — grounded in both meanings of the phrase "taking care" — that enables the client to heal and grow and the community to be safe and to evolve. The ethical helper is one who continuously and openly struggles with this challenge.

ILLUSTRATIVE EXAMPLES OF ETHICAL/PROFESSIONAL DILEMMAS

Sometimes, an issue has a clear "right and wrong" nature to it, so that it is not hard to know if behavior is proper or improper. Sometimes, there are clear legal parameters, which define a course of action that must be pursued. Where there is a clear sense of proper action or a legal requirement, the client may still define his or her best self-interest in ways that are not congruent with what is right or necessary. This can add to the dilemma that the helper may feel in determining the best course of action for the situation. There are, of course, many situations with no consensually defined moral standard or legal requirement to provide guidance. The helper is left having to come to his or her own resolution of a perplexing situation that requires some sort of response or action.

What follows are examples of situations that can challenge the helper because of the conflicts they may raise within ourselves, between ourselves and others, or between others. The goal here is not to provide the "right" answer, but to draw on real clinical vignettes to raise issues that deserve to be thought about and discussed. A vignette or "situation" will be presented, followed by commentary that is intended to open discussion rather than resolve the matter.

Situation 1

A client approaches you complaining about the conduct of another worker. In the context of follow-up contact, the worker, an experienced and respected professional, called on the client at her home without having scheduled an appointment. After a brief conversation at the doorway of the client's apartment, the worker, in saying goodbye to the client, gave the client a hug and a kiss on the lips. The client appears to be confused and upset in telling you this information, but is not making a formal complaint about the worker, whom the client feels has been helpful to her.

COMMENTARY 1

The first response needs to be to the client. If possible, find a place where you can have an undistracted conversation with the client. There are two main reasons: to allow her to tell her story and to determine what type of response and support she needs. In doing that, you will be able to collect the facts that will help you determine your next steps. Once you have listened to the client and addressed her needs, it is important to document the facts, even in rough note form, at this point. If the information suggests that the helper crossed a boundary of proper conduct with the client, you may find yourself wondering if you should check out the facts by approaching the worker or whether you should involve the worker's supervisor. The argument for talking directly to the worker could include the need to get a full picture of the situation. The problem then becomes you assuming an investigatory role, which might be properly given to someone else with supervisory authority in the agency. You might feel that to report the matter to a supervisor displays a lack of loyalty to a colleague on the basis of a hearsay report. But ultimately the complaint deserves to be drawn to the attention of whoever supervises the helper's work. Whether or not the client's report leads to disciplinary action, the worker's ongoing involvement with the client needs to be resolved, as should a clear communication to the worker that he not have further contact with the client, including any subsequent discussion of the incident. Some twists to consider: If the client wanted to share this with you alone and have it go no further, should that have a limiting effect on your informing the helper's supervisor? Would it make a difference if the gender of either the client or helper was different (i.e., if the helper was a woman, and/or if the client was a man)?

Situation 2

You are counselling an adult client who is sharing information about childhood sexual abuse and current unusual sexual practices. The client is receiving care in a program where many other staff have access to the chart. You wonder about how much of this information you should include in the record, and whether you should record it at all.

COMMENTARY 2

Confidentiality is an important principle of client care, but so is having a full and thorough record of the client's course of treatment. Aside from wanting to thoroughly document the clinical record, one could ask why it would be necessary to chart copious detail about events that are likely to be — in the very least — embarrassing to the client. It might be sufficient to thematically identify the issues that are being explored in counselling rather than detailing them. If there is a need to document details, the counsellor might keep a file in a secure place. If there are questions about how to work with the client, it could be addressed in individual or peer supervision, rather than making a matter for general report in the whole team. In responding to clients — who share many things in the course of addictions treatment — it is important to have a clear sense of what services can be provided by your service versus what can best be provided elsewhere. Sometimes clients open up important issues that cannot be effectively dealt with because of treatment context, lack of expertise or time restraints. In this case, the client appears to be reaching out. It is important to think carefully about what information to put in circulation among staff by detailing in the chart. There is often a need-to-know among members of a treatment team, but that need not involve complete documentation of the therapeutic exchange between worker and client.

Situation 3

You are working with a parent who has custody of a child, but who is, in your view, becoming increasingly neglectful. Your attempts to help change the client's behaviors, so they are more positive, have not been fruitful. You mention your concern to your supervisor, who in turn consulted the agency's director. The official response is that there is no evidence of abuse or of harmful consequences of neglect, and that reporting the woman would send an ambiguous message to parents seeking treatment for addiction problems. You remain increasingly concerned about the mother's neglectful behavior.

COMMENTARY 3

Even though the child isn't being abused or hasn't come to harm because of the parent's neglect, you did well to seek consultation and advice. It had a definite direction to it, but it is at odds with your own view of the fragility of the child's situation. In Ontario, if a helping professional has reason to suspect child abuse or neglect, he or she is required by law to report the case to the Children's Aid Society. The fact that colleagues or supervisors do not agree that there's a need to report does not absolve the helper of the responsibility to decide for himself or herself. Reporting can be done anonymously or openly. If such a course of action is deemed necessary, it is often valuable to include the client. If he or she knows of your intention and the reasons for it, the client might elect to play an active role in the process, particularly if he or she can accept that the best interests of the child are your motivating force.

Situation 4

You are counselling a couple. You are informed by one of them that he has been diagnosed with HIV. You ask if he has informed his partner of the diagnosis. He responds that he has not and has no intention of doing so. You ask if they are practising safer sex, to which he responds that he is here to deal with his addiction problems, not to talk about their sexual habits. He explicitly states that he does not want any of this brought up in couple's counselling sessions. You mention that you are concerned about the risks to the partner. The client repeats that he does not want to discuss it.

COMMENTARY 4

You are bound to respect client confidentiality, except in certain circumstances where law or the duty to protect life require disclosure of information. Could this be one of those exceptional circumstances? In all likelihood, it is probably not. But there is much in this to ensure that the issue is not clear-cut. First of all, the partner does not have an automatic right to know that the client is HIV-positive. It is, most of us would say, the client's duty to inform, but that is not the same as compelling the client to inform. The client is obligated to not knowingly pass on the infection. But, because the worker does not know about the actual risk factors in the couple's relationship, it would not be fair to jump to conclusions. It would be easy here to become alarmed and polarized by the client's position. That could quickly undermine the therapeutic relationship. By respecting the client's desire not to have to talk about it in the couple's sessions, the helper could suggest an alternative approach by meeting individually with the client. The goal would be to acknowledge the client's feelings, to explore his apprehensions about sharing the information with his partner, and to look at a wide range of life issues, including sexuality, within the context of substance use. By trying to maintain a therapeutic frame, by empathizing with the client's predicament, and by offering supportive contact, it might be possible to help both client and partner, without becoming involved in a struggle about what the client should and should not do. For further discussion, I will leave this unanswered question: What should the counsellor do if it is revealed that the couple does have unprotected sex occasionally and that the client has not informed the partner of his HIV status?

Situation 5

Your client is a drug user who reveals that he is engaged in continuing criminal behavior related to drug trafficking. Currently unemployed, the client claims the activity allows him to support his family (he has two children) and to make real headway in paying off his considerable debts, especially now that he is drug-free.

COMMENTARY 5

Congratulations! You have created therapeutic conditions facilitating client self-disclosure. Your reward is to find out something you might have preferred not knowing. Many people with addiction problems engage in illegal acts, before, during and after treatment. There is of course strong evidence that treatment reduces rates of illegal activity. The types of illegal activity can vary, from driving while impaired, to possession of cannabis, to trafficking in heroin or cocaine. For illegal substances, the fact of possession is a criminal offence. Some programs would discharge people for continued criminality while in treatment. If that is an expectation, it should be stated clearly at the beginning of treatment. Such an explicit condition would probably ensure that disclosures of continued criminality would be rare. Where the client has privileged you with problematic information, the key thing is to be able to determine if it can be addressed within the counselling relationship or whether you have to assume another posture. In law, the requirements about reporting are specific rather than general. There is no obligation to act on the basis of the client's self-report of such criminal behavior. If summoned to court, one would be required to give evidence under oath. It would be easy to react with irritation and intolerance if the client makes this kind of disclosure. It could also be an opening for an important therapeutic opportunity. The client might have ambivalent feelings about the behavior, so that discussion could affect his motivation to change and the decisional balance to pursue different options. This would also allow for exploration of risk factors related to the behavior, not just for relapse, but for violence and for arrest and incarceration. By preserving a therapeutic, client-centred frame, the worker can continue to promote positive change with the client.

Situation 6

Your client, an 18-year-old man, recently moved out on his own after years of conflict with his parents and extended family members, who live in the same home. He is using a range of substances, with a number of overdoses and other acts of self-harm in his past. The youngest of four children, none of whom now live at home, he reports that he was the victim of physical abuse by both parents, and of several incidents of sexual abuse by an uncle who lives with them. You inform the client of his rights to make a complaint to the police, who would lay charges against both parents and the uncle. The young man is upset at this proposal, claiming it would be socially embarrassing and would lead to negative consequences in his community. He tells you he would never take action against a family member.

COMMENTARY 6

If a child (under age 16) is being physically or sexually abused, you, as a professional helper, are obligated to report this information. If the child has left the home and there are other children present who are at risk, you also have an obligation to report. In this case, the victim is of adult age, there are no children at risk in the home, and the client does not want to take action. The client's right to decide must be respected. That said, there are services and supports that can assist the client, should he want help. By being respectful and supportive to the client, a helping process can be initiated that may help him improve feelings about himself and eventually become empowered to take the legal action that is available to him. Or he may elect to respond to family and social pressures. The choice is his. By sharing his story with the helper, he is looking for help with his own circumstances and self-management. This appears to be a formidable project in itself.

POSTSCRIPT

These illustrations are meant not so much to give the reader specific answers to particular ethical and professional dilemmas that may be encountered in working with addictions clients, but to open up the area for discussion and dialogue. There are obligations in law that apply to addictions workers (see Chapter 5, Legal Issues). There are also moral and ethical principles to which we, as individuals and as members of helping professions, are committed. Finding the path that helps us adhere to these principles and be optimally helpful to our clients requires more than formulaic thinking. Along with our principles and values, our willingness and commitment to think of each situation in terms of its unique aspects, and to talk about these matters with co-workers and the clients involved, can guide us to respond appropriately to these difficult issues that predictably emerge in counselling.

Chapter 5

Legal Issues

ROBERT M. SOLOMON AND SYDNEY J. USPRICH

INTRODUCTION

Without question, the legal environment has become more challenging for all professionals. Thus, it is not surprising that those involved in health care are increasingly being sued, and called upon in disciplinary hearings and other legal contexts to explain and justify their conduct. There has been a parallel trend toward recognizing and protecting the legal rights of clients, especially those who are young. Legal issues will continue to play a greater role in the working lives of all health care professionals, including those in the substance abuse field. This chapter is designed to help addiction workers understand the basic legal principles governing assessment and treatment.

In addition to the legal issues inherent in any treatment relationship, several complicating factors can arise in the substance abuse field. First, some clients only reluctantly enter treatment in response to a probation order or at the insistence of an employer, spouse, parent, or registrar of motor vehicles. What impact do such pressures have on an addiction worker's legal obligations to the client?

Second, some clients may be under the provincial age of majority, yet still have the legal capacity to give a valid consent to treatment. It may be difficult to determine in a specific case whether a particular underage client is competent to consent to the proposed treatment. Assuming that a client is competent to consent, how should a treatment professional respond to inquiries about the case from parents, school officials, welfare workers or the police?

Third, alcohol and drug use frequently involves conduct that is not only illegal, but which may also endanger the client and others. Does a treatment professional have any legal obligation to inform the police of a client's criminal activities? Moreover, can a treatment professional be held civilly liable for failing to warn third parties of the dangers posed by a client?

Such issues arise because substance abuse treatment often cuts across the criminal justice, health care, child welfare, education and employment systems. Rather than provide an exhaustive legal analysis of these systems and their possible effects on treatment, this chapter focuses on basic legal principles governing treatment relationships and explains their special application to addiction workers.

Even in terms of the general principles, it is not possible to review the relevant statutes and cases in every jurisdiction in Canada. Consequently, the body of this chapter outlines the major principles, and some references to more specific principles are provided in the endnotes. The reader should understand that the exact legal rules vary from jurisdiction to jurisdiction to reflect differences in provincial case law and statutes.

The first section of this chapter examines the law governing consent to treatment, including general principles of consent; informed consent; exceptions to the general principles of consent; consent forms and the burden of proof; competence to consent; substitute consent; and factors that invalidate consent. Section 2 examines confidentiality; privilege; disclosure of client information; reporting obligations; and civil liability for failing to control or warn.

CONSENT TO TREATMENT

Introduction to Consent Issues

One hallmark of our legal system is the importance that it attaches to the protection of a person's physical integrity. Whether couched in terms of physical inviolability, autonomy, self-determination or privacy, the basic interest is the same — namely, an individual's right to control his or her own body. This concept may be viewed as a double-edged sword in that the law protects the individual's right to decide, whether the person's decision is wise or foolish.

The law's concern with protecting the individual is clearly illustrated by the fact that virtually any physical interference with another person may result in both criminal[1] and civil liability.[2] In the absence of consent, the defendant will be held liable unless he or she can establish explicit legal authority to justify the interference. In these situations, however, treatment professionals are rarely charged with a criminal offence. Rather, the issue of consent typically arises in determining whether there is a valid defence to a civil action for the tort (wrongful act) of battery.

Battery is defined as intentionally bringing about harmful or socially offensive physical contact with another person.[3] Merely touching a client may give rise to liability; the victim need not suffer any physical injury. Any surgical procedure, administration of drugs or treatment involving physical contact may constitute battery. Once the client establishes that physical contact occurred, the burden of proof shifts to the treatment professional to establish a valid defence.[4] If the defendant cannot prove that the client consented or there is another defence, then the defendant will be held liable for all the consequences of the battery. In most cases, the key issue is not whether physical contact occurred, but whether the treatment professional can establish the defence of consent.

The legal principles governing the defence of consent have developed almost exclusively from cases involving surgery and other physical interventions. However, the tort of battery is also relevant to alcohol and drug treatment programs that include physical examinations, taking blood samples, the administration of drugs, or other physical contact. Alcohol and drug treatment that involves only the taking of a history, questionnaires, counselling or similar non-physical interactions cannot give rise to a battery claim. Nevertheless, the issue of consent and the principles governing it are still relevant in these situations.

General Principles of Consent

As a general rule, a treatment professional must obtain consent to initiate any test, procedure, surgery, counselling or physical examination. Consent should be obtained in advance and should cover the intervention as well as any related issues regarding record-keeping, confidentiality, reporting obligations and other disclosures of information. The consent must relate to the specific treatment or counselling undertaken.[5] If the client is competent to give a valid consent, then his or her consent alone is required.[6] The consent of the next-of-kin is only relevant if the client is not competent to give consent. Even in these circumstances, the validity of a substitute consent is limited.[7]

To be valid, consent must be given "voluntarily," in the sense that the client's decision is the product of his or her conscious mind,[8] but the legal definition of volition is extremely broad. For example, clients who reluctantly consent to drug treatment because it is a term of probation, or because they have been threatened with being fired from a job or expelled from school, will still be held to have consented "voluntarily."

A client may consent implicitly or explicitly.[9] The fact that a client comes for treatment provides a broad measure of *implicit* consent. Clients may seek alcohol or drug treatment, and yet expressly limit the scope of their consent. An addiction worker may refuse to treat the client if these limitations are unreasonable. However, the worker cannot ignore or override the client's stated prohibitions.[10]

Informed Consent

To be valid, a client's consent must be based on a full and frank disclosure of the nature of the treatment and its risks. In keeping with the rise of client rights, the courts are requiring that clients be given sufficient information to make an informed decision about the proposed treatment and its alternatives. This does not mean that clients must be told of all the possible risks.[11]

The legal principles governing informed consent are summarized below.
- A practitioner's failure to disclose the risks of a procedure or treatment may give rise to a negligence suit.
- Practitioners must disclose to their clients all of the "material risks" associated with the proposed treatment.
    - (a) A low probability of a serious consequence, such as a four per cent chance of death or a 10 per cent change of paralysis, constitutes a material risk. Courts have increasingly held that very small risks of death or serious injury are material (e.g., *Meyer Estate* v. *Rogers* (1991), 6 C.C.L.T. (2d) 102 (Ont. Gen. Div.) — 1/40,000 to 1/100,000 risk of a severe reaction to a diagnostic dye).
    - (b) A high probability of a relatively minor consequence, such as a 35 per cent risk of a minor infection, may also constitute a material risk.
- Practitioners are also obligated to disclose non-material risks that they know, or ought to know, would be of particular concern to the client.
- Practitioners should also discuss with the client the consequences of leaving the problem untreated, as well as alternative treatments and their risks.
- Practitioners must answer all questions openly and honestly, even if the answers would discourage the client from consenting.
- Practitioners do not have to disclose information to clients who have expressly stated that they do not want to be informed of the risks.
- Practitioners who do not meet these disclosure standards are in breach of their duty of care. However, the client must establish that the failure to be informed caused or contributed to his or her injuries. In effect, the failure to inform must have induced the client to consent to treatment that he or she would not otherwise have had, and that treatment must have caused the client's loss.

Exceptions to the General Principles of Consent

The courts have relaxed the strict requirements of consent in three situations. First, in an unforeseen medical emergency where it is impossible to obtain the patient's consent, a health professional is allowed to operate without consent to preserve the patient's health or life.[12] This right is granted to health care professionals in order to save lives. This is the basis upon which emergency room staff are permitted to operate on unconscious accident victims.

The second exception to the consent requirement involves clients who have given a general consent to a course of therapy, treatment program or operation. In such situations, a client will be viewed as implicitly consenting to any subordinate tests, procedures or interventions that are necessarily incidental to the broader course of treatment.[13] However, this implied consent will be negated if the client objects. While it may not be legally necessary, it is wise to obtain a specific consent for any subordinate procedures that pose significant risks or involve sexually, legally or emotionally sensitive issues.

Third, at one time, the courts permitted health care professionals to withhold information from a client, if the disclosure would undermine the client's morale or discourage him or her from having needed treatment.[14] However, recent cases have rejected or narrowed the therapeutic privilege doctrine. For example, the judge in *Meyer Estate* v. *Rogers* (1991), 6 C.C.L.T. (2d) 102 (Ont. Gen. Div.), stated that the doctrine is no longer part of Ontario law. In *Pittman Estate* v. *Bain* (1994), 112 D.L.R. (4th) 257 (Ont. Gen. Div.), the court acknowledged the therapeutic privilege to withhold information, but defined it very narrowly. Health care professionals do have some discretion, but this is best viewed as being limited to how they inform clients, the technical matters they discuss, and the emphasis they place on the relative risks of undergoing versus foregoing treatment.

Consent Forms and the Burden of Proof

Unless a statute provides otherwise, a client may give consent orally or in writing. Since the client's presence provides some measure of consent, it is not necessary to obtain written consent for routine treatment sessions. However, it is wise to obtain written consent for treatment that involves significant risks, is complex or innovative, or entails potentially sensitive legal, sexual or emotional issues. Similarly, written consent is recommended if the client is immature, unstable or lacks good judgment. Based on these criteria, addiction workers are advised to obtain written consent at the outset of treatment.

A signed consent form provides only some evidence of consent, not conclusive proof. The key legal issue is not whether a client signed a consent form, but whether he or she understood the nature of the treatment and its risks, was given sufficient information to make an informed decision, and consented to treatment. A signed consent form is only as good as the information it contains and the circumstances in which it is presented to the client. A signed consent form will be of little value in the following situations:
• it is written in technical language that the client cannot understand;
• it is presented as a mere technicality, or there is no opportunity to read it;
• it is written in very general language that does not specifically identify the treatment and its risks; or
• the client is in severe pain, intoxicated or drugged when signing it.

Competence to Consent

To be valid, consent must be given by a client who is legally competent. The general test of competence is defined in terms of whether the client has the ability to understand the general nature of the proposed treatment and its risks. This is a very low threshold test that is applied on a case-by-case basis. As stated earlier, if the client is competent to consent, then his or her consent alone is relevant. Indeed, it would be inappropriate even to discuss a client's treatment with the next-of-kin without the client's consent, because this would involve a breach of confidence. Consequently, addiction workers should treat the assessment of a client's competence to consent as a preliminary issue of critical importance.

Minors

General Principles: The age of majority varies across Canada. Moreover, this legislation typically does not govern the age of consent to treatment. In the absence of a statute to the contrary, the test of competence is the same whether the client is a minor or an adult. Generally, the court will assess whether the client is capable of understanding the nature of the proposed treatment and its risks. If a minor meets this test, then his or her consent is valid and parental consent is unnecessary. In some cases, the courts have relied on indications of independence as a guide to a minor's competence. As the following case illustrates, Canadian courts are increasingly recognizing the right of young people to make their own treatment decisions.

C. v. *Wren* (1986), D.L.R. (4th) 419 (Alta. C.A.)

The plaintiffs sought an injunction to prohibit a doctor from performing an abortion on their 16-year-old daughter. As was then required by the *Criminal Code,* the daughter had obtained approval from a therapeutic abortion committee. The court sympathized with both the parents and their daughter in this "painful dispute" over the ethics of the proposed abortion. However, the legal issue was clear — could this 16-year-old girl give a valid consent to a therapeutic abortion? The court concluded that the daughter understood the nature of the procedure and its risks, and therefore was competent to give a valid consent. Consequently, the parents' application for an injunction was dismissed.

Statutory Age of Consent Provisions: The general test of competence applies unless a statute provides otherwise. In any one jurisdiction, several statutes may impose age-of-consent requirements for specific types of treatment. (For Ontario examples, refer to the *Human Tissues Gift Act,* R.S.O. 1990, c. H.20, and the *Child and Family Services Act (CFSA),* R.S.O. 1990, c. C.11.) Since this chapter cannot review all relevant legislation in each province, the Ontario *CFSA* is used to illustrate the operation of statutory provisions.

The *CFSA* applies to any "agencies," "societies," "licensees" and "persons" funded by the Ministry of Community and Social Services to provide "child development," "child treatment," "child welfare," "community support," and "Young Offender" services, and other "specified" services.[15] However, the *CFSA* does not apply to treatment provided under the *Public Hospitals Act* and *Mental Health Act* or to the *Regulated Health Professions Act*. Consequently, an addiction worker providing treatment in an outpatient clinic of a public hospital would be governed by the common law's flexible test of competence. In contrast, the same person providing identical treatment in an agency funded by the Ministry of Community and Social Services would be subject to the *CFSA*'s age-of-consent provisions.

The *CFSA* establishes different age requirements for consent, depending on the type of treatment:

- A person age 16 years or older may consent without parental knowledge or approval to any services or care (s. 27(1)).
- A person under age 16 needs parental consent for residential care services (s. 27(2)).
- A child age 12 or older may consent to counselling services without parental approval or consent. However, if the child is younger than 16, the counsellor is required to advise the child of the desirability of involving his or her parents (s. 28).

Summary: Unless a statute provides otherwise, minors can give a valid consent to alcohol and drug treatment. The key issue is whether the minor is capable of understanding the nature of the proposed treatment and its risks. If the minor meets this test of competency, the consent of the parent or guardian is not required. As in Ontario, several provincial statutes may impose age-of-consent requirements for certain types of treatment. The end result is that the age-of-consent to alcohol and drug treatment is governed by a complex tangle of common law and statutory provisions that vary from province to province.

ADULTS

The general test of competence is the same whether the client is a minor or an adult. The principles apply equally to those in custody or under other legal restraints, unless there is express statutory authority to the contrary.[16] If the person is competent, his or her consent to treatment must be obtained. Although a client's refusal to consent to treatment may constitute a breach of probation, another criminal offence or a violation of parole, that does not alter an addiction worker's obligation to abide by the client's decision.

The issue of an adult's competency may also arise in cases involving mentally ill or senile clients. However, the mere fact that a client is, for example, mentally ill does not mean that he or she is incapable of giving a valid consent. Rather, addiction workers must assess the ability of each client to understand the nature of the proposed treatment and its risks. Although this principle is relatively easy to state, it may be extremely difficult to apply in many situations,[17] such as that of an occasionally disoriented alcoholic.

The role of health care professionals in treating those suspected of impaired driving has caused some confusion. Although this issue is more relevant to hospital emergency staff than to addiction workers, a brief summary of the current law follows. Health care professionals must refuse police requests to take blood samples or conduct other tests on unwilling or unconscious suspects for enforcement purposes. These situations must be distinguished from medical emergencies in which it is impossible to obtain the suspect's consent. In such cases, the staff may perform any medical procedures needed to save the life or preserve the health of the suspect. Nevertheless, blood samples or test results should not be given to the police. Rather, the police must obtain a search warrant authorizing seizure of that evidence.[18]

In 1985, Parliament introduced a special warrant that authorizes the taking of blood from unconscious drinking and driving suspects in limited circumstances. A health care professional acting pursuant to this warrant is protected from both civil and criminal liability. Nevertheless, the legislation permits health care professionals to refuse to participate in the procedure.[19]

Substitute Consent

The issue of substitute or next-of-kin consent arises only if the client is not competent to give or withhold consent. In such circumstances, the law permits the client's parents, guardians or next-of-kin to make treatment decisions on the client's behalf. However, problems can arise in locating a substitute decision-maker to exercise this authority in cases involving "skid-row" alcoholics, street youth or transients. Additional difficulties may occur if the parents or next-of-kin disagree on the appropriate course of action.[20]

The power to exercise substitute consent is not absolute. The decision to give or withhold such consent must be made in the client's best interests.[21] Thus, a court could invalidate a parental decision to refuse drug treatment for their incompetent child, if the parents' refusal was not in the child's best interests. The court could order that the child be given treatment or that the child be made a ward of the provincial child welfare agency. In turn, the agency would ensure that the child received the needed treatment.

Factors That Invalidate Consent

Once it is established that a client consented, it must be determined whether any factor negates the consent. If the consent is negated, the addiction worker's legal position is the same as if there had been no consent. Three factors negate consent: mistake; duress (coercion); and deceit (fraud).

If the client consented to treatment under a mistaken belief that the treatment professional was responsible for creating, the client's consent would be negated.[22] This issue would arise if an addiction worker inadvertently overstated the benefits of the treatment, or failed to adequately answer the client's questions. While it is important to encourage clients to have beneficial treatment, care must be taken not to overstate the benefits or understate the risks.

Consent is invalid if it was obtained as a result of duress. However, the courts have defined duress as an immediate threat of physical force.[23] As long as the courts continue to use this restrictive definition, the issue of duress is unlikely to arise in a typical alcohol or drug treatment situation. The fact that a client only reluctantly consented to avoid being thrown out of the house, expelled from school or charged with breach of probation does not constitute duress. Conversely, the issue of duress would arise if a client consented because of a threat of being physically restrained or drugged.

A client's consent is also invalid if it was obtained as a result of deceit. The courts have limited the concept of deceit to situations in which a person lied or acted in total disregard for the truth. Deceit will only negate consent if it relates to the nature of the act, as opposed to some other matter.[24] The issue of deceit would arise if, for example, a counsellor knowingly misled research subjects into believing that they were receiving an active drug, when they were being given a placebo.

Conclusion

Subject to limited exceptions, treatment relationships in our legal system are based on consent. Although consent issues usually arise in relation to medical procedures, they apply equally to psychological assessment, treatment and counselling. Therefore, prior to initiating treatment, addiction workers should ensure that they have obtained a valid consent. The following checklist is intended to help with this task.

CONSENT CHECKLIST

☐ Is this an emergency situation in which the health practitioner is authorized to intervene without consent?

☐ If not, has the client explicitly consented to the proposed treatment?

☐ If not, has the client implicitly consented?

☐ Is there adequate proof of consent? Is this a situation in which the consent should be in writing?

☐ Is the consent valid in that the client consented voluntarily?

☐ Is the consent valid in the sense that it is an informed consent? (Have the risks and benefits of the proposed treatment, as well as treatment alternatives, been explained? Have the material risks been disclosed? Have the client's questions been fully and frankly answered?)

☐ Is the consent valid in that the client is competent? (Does the client have the capacity to understand the nature of the procedure and its risks?)

☐ If the client is incompetent, has a valid substitute consent been given?

☐ Are there any factors that will invalidate the consent (i.e., mistake, duress or deceit)?

CONFIDENTIALITY, PRIVILEGE, DISCLOSURE OF CLIENT INFORMATION, REPORTING OBLIGATIONS, AND CIVIL LIABILITY FOR FAILING TO CONTROL OR WARN

Confidentiality

The term "confidentiality" has several meanings in common usage. However, when used in a legal context, confidentiality refers to the obligation to not *willingly* disclose information that has been received in confidence.[25] Consequently, addiction workers would not be in breach of their confidentiality obligation if they disclosed information without a client's consent, because they were required to do so by a search warrant, subpoena or other court order. Nor would counsellors breach confidentiality if they complied with the province's mandatory child abuse reporting provisions or disclosed information as required by other statutes.

The public tends to view confidentiality as an absolute guarantee of silence. Many people believe that information given in confidence to health care professionals will never be disclosed without explicit consent. As a result, addiction workers may find themselves caught between their legal obligations to comply with court orders or mandatory reporting provisions, and their clients' reasonable, but mistaken, understanding of confidentiality. To avoid being seen as betraying a client's trust, addiction workers should explain to their clients the meaning and limits of confidentiality. This should be done at the outset of the relationship, when the issue of confidentiality is first raised.

An obligation of confidentiality will not usually arise until after a health care professional has entered a counselling or other treatment relationship with a client. The courts will likely hold that a confidentiality obligation begins when it would be reasonable for the client to expect privacy. Although not all telephone requests for appointments or information would give rise to such an obligation, some might. For example, a reminder for an eye appointment left with a client's secretary is likely to be treated differently than a reminder for an appointment with an addictions counsellor. Obviously, the more serious the matter and the more emotionally, sexually or legally sensitive the issue, the greater the expectation of privacy.

An obligation of confidentiality applies to all information that clients provide in confidence, whether that information relates to the clients or other people. However, the obligation of confidentiality is generally limited to statements and observations made *within* the professional relationship. Thus, no confidentiality obligation would be imposed on an addictions counsellor who happens to see an intoxicated client stagger to his car at a shopping mall. Like any other member of the public, the counsellor could choose to call the police. However, the counsellor would have to limit his or her statements to the observations at the mall and would breach confidentiality if he or she disclosed any information from the treatment relationship.

Addiction workers may be under several different sets of confidentiality obligations at any one time. First, a number of provincial statutes impose confidentiality obligations on health care professionals in specific situations. Second, addiction workers may be subject to ethical and professional codes of confidentiality. Third, an individual who promises, either implicitly or explicitly, to maintain confidentiality will be required to honor that obligation. Fourth, the courts are likely to assume that confidentiality is an inherent element of all therapeutic relationships. Thus, even in the absence of a statute or professional code, those who hold themselves out to the public as counsellors may be expected to treat client information as confidential.

Depending on the source of the obligation, a breach of confidentiality can lead to penal, professional and civil liability consequences. A person who breaches a statutory confidentiality obligation may be prosecuted. For example, an addiction worker in Ontario who wrongfully discloses information from a client's psychiatric record may be prosecuted under the *Mental Health Act* and fined up to $25,000.[26] If an addiction worker is a member of a regulated profession, such as psychology, breaching confidentiality may be grounds for a finding of professional misconduct and may lead to a fine, reprimand or licence suspension. A breach of confidentiality may also result in civil liability in negligence or in the emerging tort action for the intentional breach of confidence.

Privilege

The legal term "privilege" means the right to refuse to disclose confidential information when testifying, when faced with a subpoena for client records, or when subject to a mandatory reporting obligation.[27] As a rule, persons called as witnesses in court or before other legal tribunals must answer all relevant questions put to them.[28] Similarly, those served with subpoenas or other court orders are bound to provide the records or files that are sought. Privilege is an exception to these general rules. In the absence of privilege, a person who defies a court order or refuses to answer questions when testifying may be found in contempt of court.

Traditionally, the only professional relationship to which privilege applied was that between solicitors and their clients. Solicitor-client privilege is based on the view that our legal system requires clients to speak freely with their lawyers. This will only occur if such communications remain confidential. However, even solicitor-client privilege is limited. It only applies to statements about past criminal offences and not statements about ongoing or future crimes. Nor does it apply to physical evidence. Although other professionals, such as priests, police, psychologists, journalists and social workers, have claimed a comparable need for privilege, the common law has not granted such automatic protection to these relationships.

The Supreme Court of Canada has recognized that courts have discretion to grant privilege on a case-by-case basis to confidential communications outside of solicitor-client relationships.[29] However, the party seeking privilege must meet the following four requirements: the communication must have originated in confidence; confidentiality must be essential to maintaining the relationship; the relationship must be one that society values and wishes to foster; and the injury to the relationship from disclosure of the information must outweigh the benefit of having the information available to resolve the case.

Communications made in the course of most care relationships would likely satisfy the first three requirements. First, clients expect that the information they give to counsellors or other health care professionals will be kept confidential. Indeed, most professionals explicitly state that all information their clients provide will be kept confidential. Second, successful treatment relationships are largely built on trust. Most clients would not be willing to disclose intimate or personal details of their lives unless they are assured of confidentiality. Without such information, an addiction worker would be unable to accurately assess the client's problems and provide appropriate care. Third, society has an interest in promoting successful treatment relationships.

The fourth requirement has been the most difficult to satisfy. If the confidential information is relevant to the case, the courts have tended to deny privilege and order disclosure. Not surprisingly, judges have what may be viewed as an institutional bias in ruling that the interests of justice in resolving cases outweigh the importance of granting privilege and maintaining confidentiality. This is particularly true in criminal, child abuse and child custody cases.[30] The courts also appear to be more reluctant to grant privilege when it is sought by an accused, as opposed to his or her victim.

Despite frequent recommendations that privilege be extended, legislatures have been reluctant to grant immunity from disclosure. Even where legislation purports to provide privilege, the courts have tended to interpret privilege narrowly, on the basis that the interests of justice require disclosure of all relevant information. Furthermore, a provincial statute that privileges specific communication may be challenged if it conflicts with federal legislation that authorizes disclosure of that same communication.[31]

In summary, while almost all information that addiction workers obtain in the course of providing treatment is confidential, little, if any, is privileged. Perhaps more importantly, privilege is granted on a case-by-case basis and an addiction worker can never know at the time of making a record whether it will be privileged. Consequently, addiction workers should assume that they may be questioned, and their records examined, in court some day. This realization should encourage addiction workers to take their record-keeping obligations seriously and adopt a professional and objective tone.

Disclosure of Client Information

CLIENTS' ACCESS TO THEIR RECORDS

Treatment and care records do not belong to clients. Rather, they are the property of the agency and the people providing the service. Nevertheless, the Supreme Court of Canada has indicated that the client has a right to this information.[32] The professional is not required to produce the records immediately or turn over original documents. He or she may offer to prepare a summary of the record or review the file with the client. However, if the client demands access to the complete treatment record, the court will usually grant that request.

If the treatment professional believes that allowing the client access would harm or endanger the client or a third party, the professional can refuse the request and apply to the court. The Supreme Court has held that the burden of proof is on the treatment professional to justify the denial of a client's request for access. This Supreme Court case has two important implications. First, addiction workers should assume that their clients may read the entire file some day. Second, addiction workers should not promise colleagues or other third parties that their comments about the client will remain confidential, because they may not be able to keep such a promise.

DISCLOSURE WITH A CLIENT'S EXPRESS OR IMPLIED CONSENT

In the absence of a statute to the contrary, an addiction worker ordinarily cannot disclose client information without that client's consent — not even to employers, family members, probation officers or the police. Even simple inquiries, such as whether a person is a client, are best left unanswered with an explanation that all client information is confidential. Even if the client was referred by an employer, probation officer or other third party, the addiction worker must generally obtain the client's consent before disclosing information to another party.

Although the client's express consent is usually required, implied consent may be assumed in some situations. First, treatment professionals are permitted to share confidential client information without express consent for the purposes of providing proper care.[33] For example, a counsellor who suspects that his or her client is suicidal may consult a colleague who is an expert in that area to determine how best to proceed. In such a case, the colleague is subject to the same confidentiality obligations as the addictions counsellor. Second, treatment professionals may be permitted to disclose patient information without consent in compassionate circumstances. For example, hospitals treating unconscious accident victims routinely notify the next-of-kin. Third, there appears to be a right to share confidential information for internal administrative purposes, such as audits and quality assurance reviews.

Depending on the circumstances, there may also be an implicit right to share confidential information with a client's parents, spouse, employer or other referring agency. For example, if the client's parents attended the initial session, the addiction worker may discuss with them, at a later date, information from the first session. Clients often approach treatment professionals to document their claim for an employment, insurance or government benefit. In many such cases, it is obvious that there is implied consent to disclose client information to the party providing the benefit. It has been suggested that client information may also be used without consent for research or teaching purposes, provided the client cannot be identified. Although some statutes authorize such disclosures in limited circumstances, there does not appear to be any common law authority for this proposition. Given the increasing concern about privacy, addiction workers are well advised to obtain express consent in all of these situations.

Reporting Obligations

REPORTING CRIMINAL OFFENCES

In addition to facing court orders and search warrants, treatment professionals may be required by statutes to report certain information to appropriate authorities. However, contrary to what many people believe, there is no general obligation to report federal or provincial offences, to assist the police or to answer police questions.[34] With the exception of treason,[35] the *Criminal Code* does not make it an offence to fail to report to police any crimes that have been or may be committed.

Consequently, addiction workers are not required by federal law to report a client's illicit drug use to the police, nor even acknowledge that a client is in treatment. Addiction workers can refuse to respond to a police officer's or probation officer's requests for client information, but they cannot lie or deliberately mislead officers. Staff who do so may be charged with obstructing justice or similar offences.[36]

PROVINCIAL REPORTING OBLIGATIONS

Provincial statutes impose a number of mandatory reporting obligations on health care professionals and others. These obligations vary from province to province. Moreover, they tend to be defined precisely, applying to named categories of professionals in very specific circumstances. The major reporting obligations are designed to help control communicable diseases, hazardous driving and child abuse. In these situations, the perceived threat to the public is viewed as outweighing the client's right to confidentiality, thus justifying the reporting obligation.

Most provinces have legislation that requires medical professionals to report to public health officials patients who have specified communicable diseases. Physicians providing services to patients who are not hospitalized may be required to report any patient whom they believe has a communicable disease. Hospital administrators have a similar reporting obligation with respect to their patients. Educators may also be required to report any student whom they suspect has a communicable disease. The list of diseases is extensive and typically includes AIDS, hepatitis, tuberculosis, venereal diseases and various types of influenza. Failure to report is an offence in some provinces and can result in fines. Generally, no action or other proceeding may be brought against a person who makes the required report in good faith.[37]

Most provinces have legislation that requires physicians to report the name, address and clinical condition of any patient of driving age who has or may have a condition that may make driving hazardous. Although these provisions were probably intended to deal with medical conditions, such as failing eyesight, heart disease and epilepsy, they are broad enough to encompass substance abuse. However, the legislation is usually limited to medical practitioners and optometrists.[38] Consequently, addiction workers would have no legal obligation to report a client who admits to alcohol- or drug-induced blackouts while driving. Indeed, if they were to report such clients, they might be in breach of their confidentiality obligations. Such dilemmas can occur in various circumstances, and approaches to handling these problems are covered later in this chapter.

The most comprehensive reporting obligations are contained in provincial child protection legislation. Two sets of reporting obligations may apply — one that applies to everyone and a broader set that applies to those who have contact with children in a professional capacity, such as teachers, child care workers and the police. The obligation to report is defined broadly, usually in terms of having a reasonable suspicion that a child has been, or may become, abused. Child abuse is also defined broadly to include physical and sexual mistreatment as well as the failure to provide appropriate medical and psychological treatment. This broad definition would include children who are not receiving treatment for their drug or alcohol problems, and children who are endangered by their parents' substance abuse. Thus, an addiction worker may be required to report to provincial child welfare officials an alcoholic parent who, despite continued blackouts, continues to drive with his or her children.

The failure to report child abuse as required may be a provincial offence that is sub-ject to a substantial fine. The legislation usually provides that no civil action can be brought against a person who has reported as required, even if it turns out that there was no abuse. Child protection legislation takes precedence over any conflicting pro-visions of other provincial statutes — and over professional confidentiality obliga-tions, except for solicitor-client privilege.[39]

The following summary of Ontario's legislation illustrates a number of common features of various child abuse reporting provisions.

Child Abuse Reporting: Child and Family Services Act
R.S.O. 1990, c. C.11.

• Any person who has a reasonable belief that a child is or may be in need of protec-tion must report the belief and the information on which it is based to a Children's Aid Society (CAS). The term "child in need of protection" is defined broadly to include a child who has suffered physical, emotional or sexual harm, or who is at substantial risk of suffering such harm.

• Every person who performs professional or official duties with respect to a child and, in the course of the duties, develops a suspicion that a child is suffering or has suffered abuse must report the suspicion to a CAS. Under s. 85(1)(b), a professional who fails to report is guilty of an offence, punishable by a fine of up to $1,000.

• Under s. 37(2), "a child in need of protection" is defined to include the following situations:
    (a) physical or emotional harm inflicted by the person having charge of the child, or caused by that person's failure to adequately protect and super-vise the child;
    (b) sexual molestation or exploitation by the person having charge of the child, or failure by that person to protect the child when he or she knew or ought to have known about the possibility of sexual molestation or exploitation; and
    (c) failure by the person having charge of a child to provide medical care to alleviate harm or suffering, or treatment to alleviate a mental, emotional or developmental condition that could seriously impair the child's development.

• "Child abuse" is defined by reference to the definition of a "child in need of protec-tion." Although the definition of child abuse is narrower than the definition of a child in need of protection, it does include the circumstances outlined above.

• Scope and limits of the reporting obligation: The obligation usually applies to chil-dren under 16 and takes precedence over conflicting provisions of other provincial statutes. Despite their confidentiality obligations, health care professionals must report any case of suspected child abuse or any child in need of protection.

• Protection from liability: Under s. 72(7), no action may be brought against a person for complying with these reporting obligations, unless he or she acted unreasonably or in bad faith.

Civil Liability for Failing to Control or Warn

Traditionally, the law did not require an individual to control the conduct of another person, whether to protect that person or others who might foreseeably be endangered. Although the courts continue to pay lip service to the concept that "you are not your brother's keeper," they have recognized a growing number of special relationships in which one party will be held civilly liable for the conduct of another. It is now well established that such a relationship exists between parents and children, teachers and students, police and prisoners, and employers and employees. The courts are increasingly prepared to hold that a similar relationship exists between health care professionals and their clients.[40]

Several challenging issues may arise in applying these principles to addiction workers. Consider a situation in which an intoxicated or "high" client attends a counselling session and causes a car accident while driving home. The counsellor may be sued for negligently allowing the client to leave in a condition that posed a foreseeable risk of injury to the client and others. Such a case might succeed if the counsellor had been negligent in failing to recognize the client's intoxication, or had realized that the client was impaired but did not make a reasonable effort to stop him or her. Although the issue has not arisen concerning health care professionals, the Canadian courts have greatly expanded the scope of liability for failing to reasonably manage the intoxicated.[41]

A health care professional who learns of a client's plan to commit a serious crime may be held accountable for failing to warn or otherwise protect the intended victim. Although Canadian courts have not yet addressed this issue, some American courts have imposed liability on health care professionals in these situations. In the leading case of *Tarasoff* v. *Regents of the University of California*,[42] the court held that a psychologist owed a duty of care to warn the intended victim of one of his patients. The patient, who was being treated at the University Hospital, told his psychologist that he would kill his former girlfriend when she returned from her vacation. The psychologist concluded that the patient was dangerous, and contacted campus police. The patient was picked up, briefly detained, then released. Neither the former girlfriend nor her family were warned. When the former girlfriend returned from vacation, the patient killed her. In imposing a "duty to warn" on the psychologist and the university, the court emphasized that the psychologist's confidentiality obligation to his patient ended when public peril began.

An addiction worker may realize during treatment that a young client is endangered by his or her substance abuse, physical condition or home situation. If the client is within the age limit of the provincial child protection legislation, then the matter must be reported. In this case, there is no breach of confidentiality, because the disclosure is mandated by law.

A more difficult situation arises if the client is older and no mandatory reporting obligation exists. If the worker breaches the client's confidence, it is possible that he or she may be sued or prosecuted. However, this is unlikely if the worker breached confidence in a reasonable effort to protect the client from serious harm. If the worker maintains confidentiality and the client is injured, then the worker *may* be sued for failing to protect the client.

As in *Tarasoff,* the situation becomes more complex when the choice is between maintaining the client's confidentiality and protecting an innocent third party. There have been several successful suits against American health care professionals for failing to act in these circumstances, but no comparable Canadian cases. Although there is no clear legal solution, it is best to intervene and err on the side of safety.

Conclusion

Health care professionals should assume that all client information is confidential, but that nothing will be privileged. As a working guideline, information should not be disclosed without the client's consent, unless the professional is compelled by law to do so.

The statutory requirements governing disclosure and reporting are complex and varied. These may be supplemented by the rules that agencies or institutions adopt. Moreover, additional requirements may be imposed by the governing bodies of particular professions. This chapter covered the general principles and specific examples of common situations, but it is up to each addiction worker to determine the requirements that pertain to his or her specific situation.

ENDNOTES

[1] *Criminal Code*, R.S.C. 1985, c. C-46, s. 265(1).

[2] Depending on the facts, a physical interference can give rise to one or more tort actions: battery (physical contact); assault (threat of immediate physical contact); and false imprisonment (imposition of a total restraint of movement).

[3] See for example, *Bettel* v. *Yim* (1978), 20 O.R. (2d) 617 (Co. Ct.).

[4] *Allan* v. *New Mount Sinai Hospital* (1980), 28 O.R. (2d) 356 (H.C.), reversed on other grounds (1981), 33 O.R. (2d) 603 (C.A.); *McBain* v. *Laurentian Hospital* (1982), 35 C.P.C. 292 (Ont. H.C.); and E. Picard, "Onus of Proving Consent to Trespass to the Person: On Whom Does It Rest?" (1979), 17 *Alta. L. Rev.* 322.

[5] *Parmley* v. *Parmley and Yule*, [1945] 4 D.L.R. 81 (S.C.C.); and *Schweizer* v. *Central Hospital* (1974), 6 O.R. (2d) 606 (H.C.).

[6] *Johnston* v. *Wellesley Hospital*, [1971] 2 O.R. 103 (H.C.); *Gillick* v. *West Norfolk and Wisbech Area Health Authority*, [1985] 3 All E.R. 402 (H.L.); and *C.* v. *Wren* (1986), 35 D.L.R. (4th) 419 (Alta. C.A.).

[7] *In Re B (A Minor)*, [1981] 1 W.L.R. 1421 (C.A.); *Re Superintendent of Family & Child Service and Dawson* (1983), 145 D.L.R. (3d) 610 (B.C. S.C.); and *"Eve"* v. *"Mrs. E."* (1986), 2 S.C.R. 388.

[8] *Smith* v. *Stone* (1647), 82 E.R. 533 (K.B.); and *Gilbert* v. *Stone* (1648), 82 E.R. 539 (K.B.).

[9] *O'Brien* v. *Cunard S.S. Co. Ltd.* (1891), 28 N.E. 266 (S.J.C. Mass.); *Reynen* v. *Antonenko* (1975), 30 C.R.N.S. 135 (Alta. S.C.); and *Strachan* v. *Simpson*, [1979] 5 W.W.R. 315 (B.C. S.C.).

[10] *Mulloy* v. *Hop Sang*, [1935] 1 W.W.R. 714 (Alta. S.C.); *Allan* v. *New Mount Sinai Hospital* (1980), 28 O.R. (2d) 356 (H.C.), reversed on other grounds (1981), O.R. (2d) 603 (C.A.).

[11] *Reibl* v. *Hughes* (1981), 114 D.L.R. (3d) 1 (S.C.C.); *Hopp* v. *Lepp* (1980), 112 D.L.R. (3d) 67 (S.C.C.); and *Haughian* v. *Paine* (1987), 40 C.C.L.T. 14 (Sask. C.A.).

[12] *Marshall* v. *Curry*, [1933] 3 D.L.R. 260 (N.S. S.C.) and *Murray* v. *McMurchy*, [1949] 2 D.L.R. 442 (B.C. S.C.).

[13] *Male* v. *Hopmans* (1967), 64 D.L.R. (2d) 105 (Ont. C.A.); and *Villeneuve* v. *Sisters of St. Joseph of Diocese of Sault Ste. Marie* (1971), 18 D.L.R. (3d) 537 (Ont. H.C.).

[14] *Kenny* v. *Lockwood*, [1932] 1 D.L.R. 507 (Ont. C.A.); and *Male* v. *Hopmans* (1967), 64 D.L.R. (2d) 105 (Ont. C.A.).

[15] R.S.O. 1990, c. C.11, ss. 27 and 28.

[16] *Attorney General of British Columbia* v. *Astaforoff*, [1984] 4 W.W.R. 385 (B.C. C.A.); and *Attorney-General of Canada* v. *Notre Dame Hospital* (1984), 8 C.R.R. 382 (Que. S.C.).

[17] *Kelly* v. *Hazlett* (1976), 1 C.C.L.T. 1 (Ont. H.C.); *MacKinnon* v. *Ignacio, Lamond and MacKeough* (1978), 29 N.S.R. (2d) 656 (S.C.); and *Re T,* [1992] 4 All E.R. 649 (C.A.).

[18] *Pohoretsky* v. *The Queen* (1987), 33 C.C.C. (3d) 398 (S.C.C.); *R.* v. *Dyment* (1988), 45 C.C.C. (3d) 244 (S.C.C.); and *R.* v. *Greffe,* [1990] 1 S.C.R. 755.

[19] *Criminal Code*, R.S.C. 1985, c. C-46, ss. 256 and 257.

[20] See for example, *Pentland* v. *Pentland* (1978), 86 D.L.R. (3d) 585 (Ont. H.C.); and *Re T,* [1992] 4 All E.R. 649 (C.A.).

[21] "*Eve*" v. "*Mrs E.*" (1986), 2 S.C.R. 388. But see *Re B,* [1987] 2 All E.R. 206 (H.L.).

[22] *Boase* v. *Paul,* [1931] 4 D.L.R. 435 (Ont. S.C.); *Parmley* v. *Parmley and Yule,* [1945] 4 D.L.R. 81 (S.C.C.); and *Guimond* v. *Laberge* (1956), 4 D.L.R. (2d) 559 (Ont. C.A.).

[23] *Latter* v. *Braddell* (1880), 50 L.J.Q.B. 166 (C.P.); and *Re Riverdale Hospital and C.U.P.E.* (1985), 19 L.A.C. (3d) 396.

[24] *R.* v. *Maurantonio* (1967), 65 D.L.R. (2d) 674 (Ont. C.A.); and *Bolduc* v. *R.* (1967), 63 D.L.R. (2d) 82 (S.C.C.).

[25] *Halls* v. *Mitchell* [1928] 2 D.L.R. 97 (S.C.C.); *Cronkwright* v. *Cronkwright* (1971), 14 D.L.R. (3d) 168 (Ont. H.C.); and *R.* v. *Dersch,* [1993] 3 S.C.R. 768.

[26] R.S.O. 1990, c. M.7, ss. 35 and 80.

[27] P. Sim, "Privilege and Confidentiality: The Impact of *Slavutych* v. *Baker* on the Canadian Law of Evidence" (1984), 5 Advocates' Q. 357; and P. McWilliams, *Canadian Criminal Evidence,* 3rd ed. (1988), Chapter 35.

[28] See for example, *Canada Evidence Act,* R.S.C. 1985, c. E-10, s. 46.

[29] *Slavutych* v. *Baker,* [1976] 1 S.C.R. 254.

[30] *R.* v. *R.S.* (1985), 19 C.C.C. (3d) 115 (Ont. C.A.); *Gibbs* v. *Gibbs* (1985), 48 C.P.C. 163 (Ont. S.C.); and *R.* v. *Gruenke,* [1991] 3 S.C.R. 263.

[31] See for example, *R.* v. *B.* (1979), 2 Fam. L. Rev. 213 (Ont. Prov. Ct.).

[32] *McInerney* v. *MacDonald* (1992), 93 D.L.R. (4th) 415 (S.C.C.).

[33] However, some discretion must be exercised in disclosing confidential information even to colleagues. See *Re: Lavasseur and College of Nurses of Ontario* (1983), 18 A.C.W.S. (2d) 126 (Ont. H.C.).

[34] See for example, *Koechlin* v. *Waugh* (1957), 11 D.L.R. (2d) 447 (Ont. C.A.); *R.* v. *Carroll* (1959), 23 D.L.R. (2d) 271 (Ont. C.A.); *Rice* v. *Connolly,* [1966] 2 Q.B. 414; *Kenlin* v. *Gardiner,* [1967] 2 Q.B. 510; and *Colet* v. *The Queen,* [1981] 1 S.C.R. 2.

[35] *Criminal Code,* s. 50(1)(b).

[36] *Ibid.,* ss. 129(a) and 139(2).

[37] See for example, the *Health Protection and Promotion Act,* R.S.O. 1990, c. H.7, ss. 25–26; *Public Health Act,* C.S.A. c. P.-27.1, ss. 33 (1)–35; and *Health Act,* R.S.B.C. 1979, c. 161, s. 88.

[38] See for example, *The Highway Traffic Act,* S.M. 1985–86, c. 3, s. 28(1); *Motor Vehicle Act,* R.S.B.C. 1979, c. 288, s. 221; *Highway Traffic Act,* R.S.O. 1990, c. H.8, s. 203(1). See also *Motor Vehicle Act,* R.S.N.S. 1989, c. 293, s. 279(7)–(9), which authorizes, but does not require, medical practitioners to report patients who may be unfit to drive.

[39] See for example, *The Child and Family Services Act,* S.M. 1985–86, c. 8, ss. 9(4), 17 and 18; *Child Welfare Act,* C.S.A. c. C.-8.1, ss. 3–5; *Family and Child Services Act,* S.B.C. 1980, c. 11, s. 7; and *Children's Services Act* 1976, c. 8, s. 78(1) and (2).

[40] See generally, J. Fleming, *The Law of Torts,* 8th ed. (1992), pp. 151–55.

[41] *Jordan House Ltd.* v. *Menow,* [1974] S.C.R. 239; *Crocker* v. *Sundance Northwest Resorts Ltd.* (1988), 44 C.C.L.T. 225 (S.C.C.); and *Hall* v. *Hebert* [1993] 2 S.C.R. 159. But see *Stewart* v. *Pettie* (1995), 23 C.C.L.T. (2d) 89 (S.C.C.), which appeared to narrow the scope of alcohol-related liability.

[42] 17 Cal. Rptr. 3d (U.S. 1976).

Chapter 6

Tips for Testifying in Court

SYDNEY J. USPRICH, ROBERT M. SOLOMON AND CATE SUTHERLAND

WHY ME?

Addiction workers who deal with clients involved in the criminal justice system may, at some point, be required to appear in Criminal Court. The most common reasons for an addiction worker being called to testify are (1) to provide evidence about a client's attendance (or nonattendance) or participation in a treatment program; and (2) to explain addiction assessment findings or treatment recommendations relating to a client.

Addiction workers may also be required to appear in Family Court to testify in child welfare matters. Some children in our society are, unfortunately, affected by the substance abuse of adults. When such a situation comes to the attention of an authority, the matter is often referred to court for resolution. Specific situations that may require a counsellor's testimony include court cases in which the Children's Aid Society (CAS) is following a complaint that a child needs protection; and disagreements between parents or others regarding custody of, or access to, children. Family Court also handles criminal matters involving Young Offenders (ages 12 to 17).

Testifying in court does not rank high on anyone's list of enjoyable activities, but if you are subpoenaed as a witness in a trial or other hearing, you are obligated to attend and give evidence. Remember that *you* are not on trial. You are simply doing your duty by telling the court what you know in order to help the court arrive at a fair decision.

For the layperson, the courtroom can be an intimidating place and appearing there can be stressful. But the experience need not be as unpleasant as some people fear. The more you understand about the process of testifying, and the better prepared you are, the less uncomfortable the experience will be.

Providing testimony in an efficient, professional manner is an easily learned skill. This chapter outlines a number of steps you can take to reduce your stress and ensure that the image you present in court reflects the credibility and quality of your program. It offers advice on preparing for court appearances and tips on courtroom deportment.

PREPARATION

Learn about Courts

Preparation should start long before you are required to appear in court. If you have never been to Criminal Court before, sit through some criminal proceedings to familiarize yourself with the procedures. Pay close attention to how things are done so that you will know what to expect. This will help eliminate the fear of the unknown.

If you want to observe the proceedings in Family Court, prior arrangements may be required. Since matters handled by Family Court involve children, the proceedings are closed to the public for the obvious reason of preserving the child's privacy. However, you can usually arrange to observe in Family Court by calling the court office to explain your purpose.

After you have observed some court proceedings, envision yourself on the stand, calmly responding to questions. Before your first court appearance, it may help to have someone rehearse, or role-play, with you.

Talk to the Lawyers

Once you learn that you may be called as a witness, determine whether you will appear for the Crown or the defence counsel (the client's lawyer). You will probably have been contacted by a lawyer for the side planning to call you as a witness. It is wise to advise the lawyer as early as possible concerning any dates on which it would be difficult to attend court. For example, you may have vacation travel plans that would make it extremely disruptive and expensive to attend court on certain dates. The earlier the lawyer knows this, the easier it will be to arrange a more convenient date.

As part of their preparation, most lawyers try to meet their prospective witnesses to review the witnesses' evidence. Accordingly, you may be contacted long before the trial by the lawyer or someone else from his or her law firm to discuss your testimony.

There is no legal requirement for you to participate in this sort of discussion. In a strict legal sense, a subpoena obligates you only to appear in court and give evidence. Although you are not required to co-operate, you might benefit from doing so. In addition to being helpful to the lawyer, the pre-trial discussion can help you as a witness. You will learn in advance the type of questions that you will be asked when you testify.

The lawyer for the other side may also contact you to discuss the case and the evidence that you will be giving. You are not required to participate in any such discussion, but there is nothing improper about doing so. The side calling a witness does not "own" that witness; any witness is free to talk to the other side to the extent that he or she wishes. You may wish to seek guidance from your employer or from the lawyer representing your side as to whether, and to what extent, you should co-operate with the other side.

After reviewing your records and speaking to the lawyer(s), you will have some idea of what you plan to say in court. But remember, sometimes questioning takes unexpected turns. For example, the Crown attorney may tell you that you will be asked to testify on the client's poor attendance in the program, but on cross-examination the defence lawyer may focus on the subject matter of the client's sessions.

Review Your Client's Records

Preparation for testifying also involves reviewing your client's records. Thorough and accurate records are indispensable to witnesses. Records help reconstruct the facts of a case. A trial often takes place several years and hundreds of clients after an event occurred, and the records may be the only way the addiction worker can recall sufficient details about the case.

In addition, the records themselves can be invaluable during the trial or hearing. A record that the witness made or approved close to the time of the event can be used by the witness while testifying.[1] Furthermore, the actual record may be admissible as documentary evidence, even if the witness does not testify.[2] At times this course of action is vital. For example, if the potential witness has died or is otherwise unavailable, the record may become the sole source of information and evidence.

The state of the records can influence a witness's credibility in court. A witness who faces the court armed with a complete record of facts and observations is in a strong position. If the record is accurate, objective and complete, the witness will be perceived as organized, methodical and conscientious.

But be forewarned that a file can be taken from you to be entered as an exhibit if you use it on the stand. When you take a file to court, *always* photocopy the contents beforehand and leave the copies in your office.

Make Notes

Apart from reviewing official records, it is often useful to make additional notes as soon as you are informed that you will be a witness. Litigation is a slow process and considerable time may elapse before the trial takes place. As soon as you know that you may be a witness, make notes of everything that you can remember about relevant matters to help preserve your memory of those events. Since these notes are made some time after the events in question, they cannot be used by the witness when testifying. Nonetheless, the notes can be useful at a later date to refresh your memory and help you recall the events about which you will be testifying.

DAY OF THE TRIAL

When the day comes, arrive at the courthouse a few minutes early, let the lawyer for whom you are appearing know that you are there, ask if there are any last-minute changes, and briefly review your testimony.

If the trial is in progress, you should check with the court usher to see whether there has been an order excluding witnesses. At some trials, the presiding judge may make such an order at a lawyer's request. The effect of this order is that witnesses are not allowed to be in court to hear other witnesses prior to giving their own testimony. In that event, it would be improper for you as a witness to enter the courtroom, so you could simply wait, or ask the usher to take a note to the lawyer.

Bring any relevant records or documents, as instructed by the lawyer who requested your testimony. In addition, bring any personal notes that you have made, which you can review to refresh your memory prior to testifying.

When you are called to the witness stand, you will be "sworn in" before providing evidence. The usual procedure is to be sworn in by taking an oath on the Bible. Since the Christian Bible contains the Old Testament, many members of the Jewish faith are content to swear on the standard Bible. If your religious beliefs require that the oath be taken in a different way, this is permissible, but you should inform the lawyer in advance so that arrangements can be made. For example, a Muslim may wish to take the oath on the Koran, which may not be routinely available. As well as informing the lawyer in advance of any special requirements, it may be simplest for the witness to bring along the appropriate holy book or other objects needed.

Witnesses who object to swearing a religious oath have the option of "affirming" the truth.[3] This is simply a solemn promise, without any religious connotations, to tell the truth. It is best if you advise the lawyer in advance that you intend to affirm, rather than take an oath.

GIVING EVIDENCE

After the oath or affirmation formalities conclude, you are ready to give your evidence. The lawyer calling a witness begins with what is known as "examination-in-chief" or "direct examination." Once the lawyer who called you as a witness finishes asking questions, it then becomes the turn of the lawyer for the other side. This questioning is called "cross-examination." At the conclusion of the cross-examination, the witness's testimony has usually ended, but sometimes the original lawyer may ask further questions in "re-examination."

The judge, who may also ask questions at any stage, usually tells you when you are finished as a witness.

Be Clear and Concise

When giving evidence, as a rule, give brief, direct answers to direct questions. Do not elaborate unless specifically requested to do so and, even then, be concise.

Answer only what is asked of you. Do not offer information that is not requested, even if you think it is important. Remember, you are not in court to tell a story, but merely to provide evidence. In addition, do not allow yourself to get caught up in explaining the rationales of your field. Speak only about the particular client in his or her particular situation.

Provide your testimony in a clear, well-modulated voice, loud enough to be heard by all. Speaking inaudibly implies that you do not have confidence in the information you are providing and makes it difficult for others to understand you.

Take your time. Hurried answers are sometimes incorrect answers. Give your answers in words so that a proper record can be made. For example, answer "yes," rather than nodding your head. If you happen to respond with physical motions or gestures, the lawyer questioning you may describe your response by "talking it onto the record." For example:

LAWYER: How big was the knife?
WITNESS: About this long.
LAWYER: The witness is indicating with her hands a length of about six inches.

In assessing a witness's evidence, the court often considers not only what you say, but how you say it. Your credibility can be affected by both your verbal and nonverbal presentation on the stand. You should answer in a clear, straightforward manner and avoid being either hesitant or arrogant. Nevertheless, if you are unsure about something, it is not fair to anybody to answer with a confidence that you do not feel.

Court Decorum

Stand (or sit, if invited to do so) in the witness box as calmly as you can, without giving the impression that you are a mannequin. There is a fine line here. You do not want to appear so relaxed that you seem indifferent to the proceedings. On the other hand, you do not want a ramrod posture to project an air of nervousness and rigidity. Also, if you are standing, keep your hands out of your pockets.

Wear your "poker face" to court. Do not visibly react to what you hear. You should appear totally objective at all times.

Courts generally have rather specific, though unwritten, rules on what is considered proper attire — conservatism is the name of the game. This usually means suits, or at least a shirt and tie for men, and suits or dresses for women. Generally, hats are not permitted in court.

When sitting in court before or after giving evidence, do not talk during the proceedings. If you find it necessary to communicate with someone, speak in the most discreet whisper. Better yet, pass a note.

Addressing Members of the Court

When giving evidence, speak directly to the person asking the question, and make eye contact. Never address the defendant directly while you are on the stand. Do not refer to an adult client by his or her first name; use "Mr." or "Ms."

Lawyers are also addressed as "Mr." or "Ms.," or simply "Sir" or "Ma'am" (Madam). Although it will rarely arise, you may wish to refer to a trial lawyer other than the one who is currently questioning you. Aside from referring to the lawyer by name ("Mr./Ms. Smith"), you may — especially if you don't know the lawyer's name — refer to him or her as "counsel" (counsel for the plaintiff) or "counsel for Mr. Jones, the hospital, etc."

You should address the judge as "Your Honor" or "My Lord/Lady." The correct terminology will depend on the level of court in which the trial takes place. You can ask the lawyer beforehand, or simply listen to how the lawyers address the judge and copy their terminology. As an easy alternative, simply address the judge as "Sir" or "Ma'am" (Madam). If you need to refer to the judge in the third person, the correct form is "His/Her Honor" or "His Lordship/Her Ladyship."

Do not address the judge directly unless he or she has spoken to you first. The only exception to that rule is when you need to refer to the file or your notes. Generally, you are expected to provide your testimony without looking in the file while you are on the stand. If it is necessary to do so, turn to the judge and ask: "May I refer to my notes, Your Honor?" The judge will probably give permission. But, if the witness must rely on notes rather than his or her recollection, lawyers have the right to determine whether the notes are reliable. This typically consists of questions about when the notes were made.

Direct Examination

Direct examination typically begins with mundane matters such as the witness's name and relevant qualifications. Rather than the witness being asked questions to elicit this routine introductory material, the lawyer will often recite the information and simply expect the witness to agree.

> LAWYER: You are Mary Smith and are employed as a counsellor at the Central Addictions Centre?
> WITNESS: Yes, sir.
> LAWYER: The Central Addictions Centre is located at 123 Main Street in downtown Blankville?
> WITNESS: That's right.
> LAWYER: I understand that in your professional capacity you were providing counselling to John Doe in May of 1996?
> WITNESS: Yes, he had been seeing me professionally from March through June of that year.

Particularly if you are being called as an "expert" witness, the lawyer may wish to bring out extensive details of your professional qualifications such as education, experience and membership in professional bodies. Such issues should be discussed well before the trial, so that the witness can be properly prepared with the appropriate information. Indeed, the lawyer may have requested a curriculum vitae or résumé for this purpose.

Cross-Examination

The lawyer who did not ask a witness to testify may try to achieve several goals through cross-examination. The lawyer may try to get additional information from the witness that will help the other side, or additional facts that may weaken evidence already given. The lawyer may try to get the witness to qualify a previously given answer, concede that there is some doubt on a particular point, or admit that an alternative explanation is possible.

Sometimes, the lawyer may attempt to weaken evidence by discrediting a witness. There may be an effort to suggest that the witness is mistaken, biased, forgetful or not credible for a variety of other reasons.

Some lawyers will ask convoluted or awkward questions, and it can be difficult to understand just what they want to know. Listen carefully to the question being asked and make sure you understand before you reply. Do not hesitate to admit your confusion. Simply say, "I'm sorry, I do not understand the question. Could you please repeat it?" This forces the lawyer to rephrase the question in a clearer form, and has the added advantage of giving you a few extra seconds to form an answer.

Although lawyers should not do so, sometimes they ask "double-barrelled" questions. This is especially likely in cross-examination where the lawyer is permitted to ask leading questions that require only a "yes" or "no" answer. If you simply answer yes or no, it may be unclear whether your single answer is in response to both halves of the question or only the last part. It is best to respond to such double questions by explicitly answering both halves. For example, a witness might be asked, "Was the client intoxicated and did he attempt to attack you?" Rather than answering "yes," it is clearer if the witness were to say, "Yes, he appeared drunk and attempted to attack me."

Another awkward type of question is one framed in the negative. For example: "You didn't see him do it, did you?" A simple reply of "no" could mean either "No, I didn't see" or "No, I disagree with you. I did see." Make sure that your answer is properly understood by responding fully: "No, I did not see."

A common device that lawyers use in cross-examination is to cut a witness off before he or she can give a full answer or a qualification to an answer. The result may be that a particular answer may be misleading because it is incomplete. If that should happen, ask the lawyer, firmly and courteously, to let you complete your answer. Often, however, the judge or the other lawyer will intercede on your behalf, asking that you be allowed to finish.

Keep in mind that, sometimes, cross-examination gets rough. While it may feel like a personal attack, it is not. Remember, a lawyer's first obligation is to his or her client and it is the lawyer's duty to test all evidence vigorously. While the lawyer may be aggressive toward you on the stand, you will probably find that this ends at the courtroom door.

Must I Answer?

Generally, witnesses must answer all relevant questions put to them. Privilege is one of the few exceptions to that general rule.[4] The legal term "privilege" means the right to refuse to disclose confidential information when giving testimony.[5] Traditionally, the only professional relationship to which privilege applied was that between solicitors and their clients — not to addiction workers and their clients. In the absence of privilege, a person who refuses to answer a question when required to do so may be jailed for contempt of court.

Canadian law has no equivalent to the American device of "taking the Fifth." Under the Fifth Amendment to the U.S. *Bill of Rights,* a witness may refuse to answer a question that tends to incriminate him or her. In Canada, a witness would have to answer such a question. However, the *Canadian Charter of Rights and Freedoms* protects a witness from having any incriminating answer used against him or her in any other proceedings (except a prosecution for testifying falsely).[6] This protection automatically applies to all the witness's answers without the witness having to ask for it.

Limits on Testimony

Generally, a witness's testimony is confined to information within his or her personal knowledge. That is, evidence based on his or her own observations rather than on what other people may have told the witness. As a result, a witness is not usually allowed to give what lawyers call "hearsay" evidence.

The rule against hearsay means that you will often not be allowed to repeat what other people have told you. The hearsay rule is complex and not always easy to apply. First, the rule has many exceptions that permit hearsay evidence to be given. Second, hearsay evidence will not always be in the obvious form ("Charlie told me..."). For example, information that the witness obtained from someone else's notes may be considered hearsay.

The important point is that, as a witness, you are not expected to be a lawyer with expert knowledge of the hearsay rule. In discussing your evidence with the lawyer before the trial, he or she can advise you as to what conversations you may or may not be allowed to repeat because of the hearsay rule. If the issue arises while you are giving evidence and you are unsure whether, for example, you can repeat a given conversation, it is always appropriate to ask the trial judge whether you may say what someone has told you.

In situations where you are allowed to testify as to statements that other people have made, these statements may sometimes involve obscene or offensive language. There is no need to be embarrassed by this. The judge and the lawyers have undoubtedly heard such language before. Bear in mind that it is not you who used that language; you are merely quoting what someone else has said. The importance of the evidence might depend on the fact that the speaker used that sort of language. While it is best to quote the speaker's words as accurately as possible, you could paraphrase the words if you are truly uncomfortable in repeating them. In that case, however, you should make clear that you are doing so.

Another area with restrictions on testimony involves the giving of opinions or conclusions by a witness. Only an "expert" witness testifying specifically on a matter within his or her area of expertise may give an opinion. An ordinary witness must testify only as to his or her observations, not the opinions or conclusions that the witness may have drawn from those observations. However, a witness may give opinions concerning common matters on which, in a sense, everybody is an "expert." For example, a witness could testify that someone appeared drunk, was happy or sad, and so forth. Again, you are not expected to be a lawyer and to know all the fine distinctions. The lawyers and the judge will provide guidance as to what you may or may not say.

The lawyers and the judge have a shared responsibility to keep inadmissible evidence out of the trial. If some evidence that you are about to give is inadmissible because of the hearsay rule, the opinion rule, or for some other reason, you may be interrupted and instructed not to give that evidence. Sometimes this interruption will take the form of an objection by the lawyer who is not currently questioning you. He or she will interrupt by saying "objection" or "I object." If that happens, you should stop what you are saying. The trial judge, after listening to both lawyers' arguments, will decide whether the evidence is admissible and will advise you whether you can continue.

Family Court

Many of the procedures related to testifying in Criminal Court also apply to Family Court. However, a few differences between these courts are noted in this section. For example, as a witness in Family Court, you are less likely to be permitted in the courtroom during other testimony in the case. In this situation, you will be instructed to wait in the outer area until called to provide your testimony.

Another minor difference involves the number of lawyers who participate in the proceedings. In provincial criminal matters, there are typically two lawyers — the Crown and the defence. Child welfare cases, however, often have more than two lawyers, as anyone who is a party in the case could be represented. A child could have a separate lawyer, as could the Children's Aid Society, if involved, and other parties, such as the parents (separately or together) or a third party seeking custody or access. This does not necessarily mean that each lawyer will have many questions or that you will be on the stand for a longer period, although both are possible. Typically, one or two lawyers will elicit the main parts of your testimony. The others may ask a few more questions to clarify or obtain slightly different types of information.

This leads to the most important differences between Family and Criminal Court — the nature of testimony and witness status. In child welfare matters, there can be a wider interpretation of the relevance of evidence, giving lawyers more latitude in the questions asked or the avenues that may be explored with witnesses. Decisions are made, based on testimony from proceedings, that profoundly affect the lives of children. Thus, it is understandable that the Court would wish to hear any information that could be pertinent.

So, while you conscientiously prepare by first determining the *expected* direction of your testimony and carefully reviewing your client files, realize that questions may arise that do not seem directly related to the client's treatment or your involvement with the client. In such situations, you must carefully determine whether you know the answer. Remember, witnesses can only testify about what they know.

Consider the following scenario to illustrate the point. Let's suppose that, during treatment, Mr. Smith, a single father, reports that his drinking has been a problem for about 10 years. Among other things, he tells you that he is often hungover and that he often slips some whiskey in his morning coffee, while his 12-year-old son, Junior, is eating breakfast. Mr. Smith says his son is often with a babysitter while he is at a bar, and when he drinks at home, his son stays in his room. He also admits that he has missed a couple of Junior's school functions because he was drinking, which made his son angry. Mr. Smith says he feels bad about all of this and intends to make it up to Junior. Later, in court, you are asked about Mr. Smith.

> LAWYER: How has Mr. Smith's drinking problem interfered with his ability
>   to be a good father to Junior?
> WITNESS: I'm sorry. I can't answer that question. As Mr. Smith's addiction
>   worker, I am not qualified to comment on his abilities as a father.

The point is that you must consider the whole question and its implications, then decide whether you can answer it as asked. Mr. Smith provided plenty of information about his drinking and his son, but the question was about his "ability to be a good father." Carefully heed previous advice in the chapter about answering questions, and do not extrapolate pieces of information. For instance, the information in Mr. Smith's scenario speaks volumes about his alcohol problem, but really says nothing concrete about his ability to care for the child.

Another aspect of the special nature of testimony in Family Court involves the witness's status. The limits on testimony by a witness or "expert" witness are described elsewhere in the chapter. For addiction workers and other professionals, it seems common in Family Court that questions venture into a "grey" area between the two types of witnesses. In this area, somewhere between personal and expert knowledge, it is assumed that the witness has a certain amount of knowledge, based on overall experience and observations, as a result of employment in the profession. Questions and answers in this arena need the assent of the court, which is often prompted by an objection from one lawyer to another lawyer's question, usually on the basis that it calls for an opinion or is not specific to the client.

If allowed, such questions are typically very general in nature and, unless the worker has a head full of statistics, do result in the witness providing a sort of personal "semi-opinion" or conclusion. Examples of these types of questions are: "Based on your experience, is it common for a person's drinking problem to affect other family members?" or "In the five years you have been employed as an addiction worker, what have you observed about...?" Again, think, and try to avoid bias. There are no absolutes in this field, so avoid the use of "never" or "always" in your answers. Start to answer with phrases similar to, "It is my experience that..." or "I have observed that...." Also, if need be, insert qualifiers such as, "It is my experience that it is common for..., but that it does not occur in every case."

Finally, a very mild caution about "expert" status. It is typically reserved for those with significant experience, who have been advised prior to the case that they will testify as an expert. Then, the witness's status is established at the beginning of the witness's testimony. Still, expert status can be sought, without prior warning, during a witness's testimony.

The testimony of addiction workers is often very important to determinations made in Family Court. Be prepared and take the responsibility seriously. Your expertise and confidence can help the court.

CONCLUSION

Although testifying in court will never be a delight, it need not be a dreaded, anxiety-filled experience. Understanding what is expected of you as a witness will make testifying less intimidating. Good preparation is even more important. While this may seem like a lot of work for a few minutes on the stand, the effort will be worthwhile. If you are adequately prepared, you will feel more comfortable and be able to give your evidence in a relaxed, straightforward manner. This will enable you to make a better impression as a witness and to leave court feeling that you made a significant contribution to the administration of justice.

ENDNOTES

[1] See J. Sopinka, S. Lederman and A. Bryant, *The Law of Evidence in Canada* (1992), pp. 849–857.

[2] See *Ares* v. *Venner*, [1970] S.C.R. 608. For an example of a statutory provision, see the *Ontario Evidence Act*, R.S.O. 1990, c. E.23, ss. 35 and 52.

[3] See for example, *Canada Evidence Act*, R.S.C. 1985, c. C-5, s. 14.

[4] For a comprehensive review of privilege, see P. McWilliams, *Canadian Criminal Evidence*, 2nd ed. (1984), pp. 915–924 and 963–976.

[5] For more detailed discussion of privilege in this book, refer to the chapter entitled "Legal Issues in Addictions."

[6] *Canadian Charter of Rights and Freedoms*, s. 13.

REFERENCE

Ministry of the Solicitor General and Correctional Services. (1985). The courtroom experience. In *The Adult Probation Enforcement Guide*, Section 12 (internal training manual). Toronto: Author.

Chapter 7

Guidelines for Advising on Treatment Goals

MARTHA SANCHEZ-CRAIG AND D. ADRIAN WILKINSON

INTRODUCTION

When treating clients for alcohol problems, the therapist has to decide whether to discuss a choice of goals with the client. Allowing clients to choose between abstinence and moderation is still anathema to many in the field of treatment. Others, with equal passion, see the denial of choice as a denial of the dignity and respect that they are ethically bound to accord their clients. This furious controversy has been portrayed as a clash of ideologies, or as a straightforward disagreement about the interpretation of scientific facts. Others have argued that, since this is a controversy only in certain cultural contexts, it must be largely sociocultural in origin. (Readers can review Duckert, Koski-Jannes and Ronnberg, 1989; Fingarette, 1988; Heather, 1989; Heather and Robertson, 1983; Kissin, 1983; MacAndrew and Edgerton, 1969; Peele, 1984, 1987; Sobell and Sobell, 1986/87; Wallace, 1987a, 1987b for varied treatments of these issues.)

We believe that all of the above interpretations of the controversy are valid:
1. There are differing conceptions of alcohol dependence, some consistent with choice of goal, others not (Chaudron and Wilkinson, 1988; Sobell and Sobell, 1986/87). These various conceptions often lead to definitional problems that preclude the possibility of a resolution. These are ideological differences.
2. Interpretations of the scientific data vary. Scientists have failed to reach consensus about valid empirical tests of the advisability of offering choice to clients, so there are varying interpretations of these data (Heather, 1989; Heather and Robertson, 1983; Sobell and Sobell, 1986/87).
3. There is considerable cultural variation in the perceived importance of the issue, so the importance of cultural context is clear (Miller, 1986; Peele, 1984, 1987).

This chapter makes no attempt to resolve any of these issues. It is a practical guide for those who already believe that most clients with alcohol-related problems should be encouraged to choose whether to aim for abstinence or moderation. Those who doubt the wisdom of offering such choice are referred to the extensive literature aimed at resolving such uncertainty. Those convinced of the rashness of encouraging choice must only deplore the inclusion of this chapter in a book such as this.

AIMS OF THE CHAPTER

Our aim is to review empirical and conceptual factors that have a direct bearing on the advice one should give to clients who are in the process of choosing their goal. Then we attempt to identify the information that should be brought to the client's attention, in the hopes of influencing the decision process. We offer guidelines to identify the minority of clients who, in our opinion, should not be offered choice. We also suggest a sequence that permits the most effective provision of advice to clients selecting their goals. Thus, most of the chapter is very practically oriented.

CLIENTS WHO SHOULD NOT BE ENCOURAGED TO CHOOSE THEIR GOAL

Broadly speaking, we identify two groups of clients who should not be offered the choice between abstaining or moderating their use of alcohol:
1. Clients should not be offered this choice if it is illegal for them to use alcohol. The legal prohibition might relate to the age of the client or to a court order, such as conditions of probation.
2. Clients may be judged mentally or developmentally incompetent to exercise responsible choice. Under this circumstance, it is a clear professional responsibility not to offer choice. In some jurisdictions, alcohol use might not be legally proscribed in the young, but their status as minors could nonetheless rule out discussion of alcohol use as an option. In addition, since alcohol use can result in serious cognitive impairment (Parsons, Butters and Nathan, 1987), some alcohol-dependent persons may not be mentally fit to choose their goal responsibly. This state may be transitory for some clients, such as those who come to treatment sessions intoxicated, when the issue of goal choice would not be fruitfully addressed.

With these general exceptions, we believe clients should be encouraged to choose their goals. This does not, of course, mean that the therapist will not attempt to influence the choice. The therapist should have significant input into the decision process, sometimes actively recommending one option, on the basis of the considerations set out in the following sections.

INFORMATION TO BE REVIEWED
AS A PRECURSOR OF CLIENT CHOICE

Client's Medical Status

Certain medical conditions contraindicate any alcohol use by the client. Examples of such medical conditions would be active liver disease or cirrhosis, pancreatitis, bleeding ulcers, or esophageal varices. Identifying these problems is a medical process. As a check against the existence of any such problem, clients should ask their physician whether they have any physical condition that would advise against any use of alcohol. The physician's opinion should be reviewed with the therapist in considering the goal. Therapists should strongly recommend abstinence for clients whose physicians advise them not to drink. If the client insists that he or she will continue to drink, the therapist should urge the most minimal levels of use, such as purely ceremonial use.

Risks of Alcohol Consumption

Clients should know the risks of alcohol consumption, both acute and chronic. We attempt to ensure that the clients know the risks of intoxication, the effects of varying doses of alcohol, and the long-term health risks of different levels of use. The relevance of individual differences (e.g., gender, physique) to the risks of drinking is also stressed. Our program stresses the theme that "All drinking has risks. If you want to avoid the risks, don't drink." This applies to the risks of intoxication and to chronic effects.

Family History and the Choice of Goal

About 40 per cent of the clients in our programs report a history of alcohol dependence among first-degree relatives (a positive family history). We have found that clients with a positive family history have rates of successful outcome very similar to those with a negative family history (Sanchez-Craig, Wilkinson and Walker, 1987). Clients with a positive family history are not more likely in our program to choose abstinence as their goal. However, in achieving moderate drinking they tend to use alcohol much less frequently than their successful counterparts with a negative family history. This research finding is now reviewed with our clients as something to consider when setting their own goal. We also inform them that another investigator has reported a positive family history to be predictive of abstinent outcome among clients in a program offering choice of goals (Miller and Joyce, 1979).

Drinking History and the Choice of Goal

The client's lifetime history of drinking is discussed in the treatment sessions when considering the choice of goal. Our reason for doing so is conceptually, rather than empirically, based. If the client has an extensive history of problem-free drinking, or of problem-free drinking in well-specified circumstances (e.g., when drinking at home with the family), then the choice of moderation as the goal is more likely to be supported by the therapist. When the history involves problems associated with alcohol use from the outset of drinking, and almost all drinking episodes being of heavy consumption, then abstinence is more strongly recommended. The rationale for this position is that clients will probably be more successful in re-acquiring old habits of moderation, or maintaining the habit of situationally specific moderation, than in acquiring a brand-new pattern of alcohol use.

In addition, a history of intoxication on almost all occasions of drinking suggests that intoxication has been the sole purpose of alcohol use. *Clients aiming for moderation should do so to enjoy alcohol use for refreshment, to enhance food experiences, and to participate in ceremonial and social functions, but not explicitly for the purpose of intoxication.* Hence, if the sole attraction of alcohol has been intoxication, moderation, as conservatively recommended by ourselves, is likely to be an unattractive goal and is discouraged by the therapist. The cultural milieu of the client is likely to be particularly relevant to this consideration. In certain cultures, such as Scandinavian, intoxication is a fairly common objective of alcohol use, whereas other cultures, such as Italian and Spanish, strongly disapprove of intoxication. Canada, being multicultural, contains considerable local cultural variations in attitudes to alcohol use and intoxication. These variations should be borne in mind in working with clients.

An important further consideration when reviewing the client's history is how the client has acted in the past when intoxicated. If intoxication has been associated with marked changes in behavior, particularly antisocial behaviors or recklessness, then the risks associated with any drinking are increased. Hence, a history of such behavior changes when intoxicated would influence therapists to increase the strength of recommendations for abstinence as the goal.

History of Treatment and the Choice of Goal

Many clients tell us that they have avoided seeking treatment because they were afraid that a goal of lifelong abstinence would be imposed upon them, and that treatment personnel would not consider them serious about change unless they accepted the imposed goal. With such clients, we stress that flexibility of goal choice is a feature of our approach.

Other clients tell us that they have experience with abstinence-based approaches, and that abstinence is their preferred route. We also see clients who have sampled "12-step" approaches and programs that insist on abstinence as the only appropriate goal, but who felt those concepts didn't apply to themselves. In each of the types of case presented here, the past history of treatment (or avoidance of treatment) quickly focuses the therapist on important aspects of the self-concept and probable goal preference of the client.

In addition to considering the client's attitudes to previous treatment efforts, it is important to review the outcomes. In our experience, clients with a history of lengthy periods of successful abstinence often want to return to that path, though preferring a new treatment approach with a different philosophical or theoretical basis. We have also seen some clients who have become determined to switch from successful abstinence to moderate drinking, and are looking for guidance on how to minimize the risks of the transition. We do not counsel clients to switch from long abstinence to moderation, but will assist those who have decided on their own to make the change and who ask for help. Recent long-term follow-up studies in Sweden show that many ex-patients successfully select this route without any therapeutic assistance (Nordström and Berglund, 1987).

A third type of outcome is reported by clients who have received traditional treatment, but rejected the idea of "loss of control over drinking." After participating in the previous program, these clients unsuccessfully attempted to moderate their drinking. They come to us seeking advice on how they can more effectively attempt moderation of alcohol use.

Alcohol Dependence and the Choice of Goal

One of the principal objectives of many programs incorporating flexibility of goals has been to encourage persons who are not severely dependent on alcohol to enter treatment. The rationale has been that such persons are often deterred from approaching treatment facilities for fear that abstinence will be the only legitimate goal of treatment (see e.g., Sanchez-Craig, Wilkinson and Walker, 1987; Sanchez-Craig and Wilkinson, 1986/87). Interviews with clients about their reasons for avoiding treatment for years (despite recognizing the problems caused by their use of alcohol) confirm the validity of this assumption in many cases. Thus, programs offering moderation are frequently targeted to clients who are not severely dependent on alcohol. Another reason for aiming for clients who are not severely dependent on alcohol has been the controversial nature of the goal of moderation. It is less contentious to offer choice when clients with severe alcohol dependence have been excluded from a study. Clients with severe alcohol dependence have a high incidence of illnesses (e.g., cirrhosis, esophageal varices) that contraindicate any drinking, and hence flexibility of goal choice is seen as less desirable for this group. Furthermore, many severely dependent drinkers have had numerous contacts with treatment agencies and self-help groups, and already believe that choice of goals is not a realistic option. Early studies also suggest that clients with relatively low levels of alcohol dependence were more likely to moderate drinking successfully, whereas abstinence was relatively more often achieved by the severely dependent drinkers (Orford, Oppenheimer and Edwards, 1976; for review see Sobell and Sobell, 1986/87).

Gender and the Choice of Goal

It has been reported in a number of studies that women are more likely than men to achieve an outcome of successful moderate drinking after treatment (Miller and Caddy, 1977; Sanchez-Craig et al., 1989, 1991). This finding applies when the outcome criterion is an arbitrary definition of moderate drinking selected by the investigators. When reports of alcohol-related problems are the outcome measure, the gender difference is less likely to be observed. In addition, there appears to be a gender difference in the type of intervention to which males and females are most responsive (Sanchez-Craig et al., 1989, 1991). Hence, though there is some evidence that women are more likely to attain a consistent outcome of moderate drinking, we do not believe that current data warrant different advice to women and men about abstinence or moderation as their goal.

The Role of Client Preferences and Beliefs

It derives directly from the philosophical grounding of our approach (Sanchez-Craig, 1990) that client preferences and beliefs are among the most crucial data we consider when working with clients on the selection of their goals. However, this is not merely an ideological preference. There are data that are entirely consistent with the pragmatic value of this position, and we review them briefly here.

Among traditionalists, client preference for flexibility in treatment goals tends to be seen as evidence of "denial." This presumed symptom of the disease of alcoholism is considered part of the innate personality of the "alcoholic" (Miller and Sovereign, 1989), which must be challenged and overcome before treatment can succeed. It is certainly true that many alcohol-dependent persons minimize, trivialize and rationalize their dependence, but it does not necessarily follow that this is a symptom of disease. Alternatively, such denial may be viewed as a natural psychological reaction to the judgments of others about one's behavior and abilities. In line with an alternate formulation of denial is the evidence that directive, or confrontational, therapists generally tend to engender resistance in their clients (Patterson and Forgatch, 1984). Thus, the denial by traditionalists of autonomy for their clients can provoke a reactive denial of problems by the clients. This is not to say that excessive drinkers do not falsely deny that their drinking causes problems. The issue is how best to undercut such denial. In many cases, confrontation merely seems to strengthen it.

Miller (1983, 1985, 1987) has reviewed the literature on motivation for treatment and its relation to client goals, and concluded that:

> Personal goals are an important aspect of motivation for change. The provision of negotiable and alternative treatment goals can encourage early intervention, compliance with recovery related programs, and favorable treatment outcome (1987, p. 133).

As a direct test of this conclusion, Miller and Sovereign (1989) varied the directiveness of feedback to clients who received their "Drinker's Check-Up," an assessment aimed at motivating heavy drinkers to change their drinking patterns. Clients who received directive feedback showed significantly greater resistance (arguing, interrupting and changing the subject) and denial (minimizing the problem), than those who were given the same feedback in a nonconfrontational, nondirective manner. The resistant clients had poorer outcomes. Thus, therapist behavior engendered resistance and contributed to poorer outcome.

Orford and Keddie (1986) examined the relative importance of client preferences and beliefs versus level of dependence as predictors of outcome among clients offered a choice of goals. They found that client preferences and beliefs appear to be more strongly related to outcome than level of dependence.

Sanchez-Craig et al. (1984) randomly assigned problem drinkers to the goal of abstinence or to a condition allowing client choice of goal. Clients who were offered choice were more accepting of the assigned goal, were more successful in the initial phases of treatment, and required fewer elective counselling sessions during the aftercare phase of the program. Of particular importance was the subsequent discovery that the benefits of choice were most apparent among those clients who were the heaviest drinkers before treatment (Sanchez-Craig and Lei, 1986), and who had higher levels of alcohol dependence. In short, clients given choice were less resistant and more successful, particularly those with evidence of a more severe problem. Thus it appears that a preference for respecting the judgment of clients is more than just a philosophically based value held by certain therapists. It has beneficial effects on the outcome of treatment.

Many therapists sincerely believe that giving any credence and respect to the opinions of "alcoholics" about their ability to moderate their drinking successfully is either naive or professionally irresponsible. Failure to confront alcoholic denial is considered by such clinicians to be "enabling the alcoholic's addiction." Our problem with this position is precisely that it represents a statement of belief by certain therapists. The assertion has not been scientifically or clinically tested. In our view, the "denial" of greatest concern here is the denial of appropriate services to persons with alcohol-related problems because of the untested beliefs of many treatment personnel. There is nothing wrong with having a diversity of treatment approaches for alcohol dependence, since we do not definitively know of an effective treatment, and there are strong theoretical and empirical reasons for expecting that there is no uniquely good approach (Cox, 1987; Miller and Heather, 1986). If one view of appropriate treatment prevails, and its disciples are able to suppress the offering of alternative approaches without scientific justification, then our clients and the public will be very poorly served. In the absence of evidence to the contrary, we urge that clients be given the dignity of being treated as if they are not self-deluded, which is the basic assertion of the construct of denial.

Environmental Constraints on the Choice of Goal

A number of environmental constraints mitigate against advising moderation as the goal of treatment in some cases. We review those most frequently encountered below.

FAMILY AND SOCIAL NETWORK

If attempting to moderate drinking is likely to cause serious tensions in the client's family, or with other close associates, then we tend to urge consideration of abstaining, at least in the medium term. Sometimes such tensions are based on other family members being successful graduates of programs stressing the disease concept of alcoholism, and the imperative for abstinence. In other cases, family members may have been frequently wounded (emotionally or physically) by the client's intoxicated behavior so that the prospect of any drinking is stressful enough to jeopardize the relationship.

LEGAL STATUS

If a client has been referred because of a legal problem caused by alcohol use, or involving intoxicated behavior, it may be imprudent to counsel a goal of moderation. This is clearly the case when drinking is precluded by the terms of probation. Sometimes abstinence is a strong recommendation of the client's legal counsel, and this again should weigh heavily. In general, if drinking has caused legal problems that are unresolved at the time of treatment, abstinence is likely to be a prudent goal.

OCCUPATIONAL FACTORS

Certain work environments promote drinking. Working in bars and restaurants on the service or the entertainment side frequently involves high availability of alcohol and considerable social pressure to imbibe. Because of these conditions, some of our clients who work in such establishments have opted for abstinence. Members of the armed forces often have access to alcohol at low prices through the various social clubs for military personnel. In such settings, social pressures to drink are quite often strong. Because of the combined pressures of high availability and strong social pressure, this occupational group may also prefer to abstain.

CULTURAL FACTORS

As we have previously discussed, in certain cultures moderate alcohol use in social gatherings is very much the norm, whereas in others occasional heavier use is more common (MacAndrew and Edgerton, 1969). When discussing treatment goals with clients, such variation in cultural background, and the influence it can have on the meaning of alcohol use, are relevant to goal selection.

Another "culture" that can influence the client's preparedness for moderate drinking is the "culture of youth." In Canada, in our experience, many young persons have most of their early drinking experiences outside the family with peers at parties where the objective of drinking is frequently intoxication. Consequently, many become "problem drinkers" with almost no experience of being a moderate user of alcohol. Thus, the history of almost exclusively immoderate use of alcohol suggests a longer period of abstinence before a goal of moderation is attempted, and a thorough examination by therapist and client of the personal meaning of alcohol use to the client.

MODERATE DRINKING: HOW MUCH IS TOO MUCH?

By moderate drinking we mean drinking at a level that does not jeopardize one's health, one's ability to carry out day-to-day responsibilities (at home, at work, or in the community), or one's safety or the safety of others. This definition implies that moderate drinking involves abstaining in a number of circumstances, such as before or during driving, or conducting hazardous tasks (at work or play), and when pregnant.

Note that this is not a prescription for "safe" or risk-free drinking. The only incontrovertibly safe level of drinking is abstinence. Many of our clients acknowledge that fact but still wish to attempt "low-risk" drinking. Then they ask what guidelines we can give them. We inform them of the levels of consumption that our clients have reported when they claim to suffer no adverse consequences of their drinking (Sanchez-Craig, 1986; Sanchez-Craig and Israel, 1985). In a number of studies, we have found that very few clients who stay within these guidelines report adverse consequences of their drinking. Some who drink over the guidelines also report no adverse consequences of drinking, but the risk increases as the levels of drinking increase.

Those who become moderate drinkers after attending our clinic have the following profile to their drinking:

- They have two or more abstinent days each week.
- They do not drink more than four standard drinks (if male) or three standard drinks (if female) on any day.
- They do not drink more than 12 standard drinks (if male) or nine standard drinks (if female) in any week.
- They avoid drinking to cope with problems of daily life (i.e., drinking to blunt emotions or facilitate some action such as asserting oneself).
- They do not use alcohol frequently in association with recreational activities and free-time activities.

EDITORS' NOTE: These authors' guidelines are based on a clinical population (people who have had problems and who are reducing their consumption). Guidelines developed for the general population often differ. For example, the Addiction Research Foundation recommends no more than two drinks on any day for the general population.

We stress that the pattern of drinking that is established should fit with the person's lifestyle, while avoiding adverse consequences of drinking. *We also stress that the limits that clients set should be what they judge to be their upper limit of sensible drinking. The goal is not a target that the client is aiming to achieve on each day drinking or in each week, but is the upper limit of what they consider prudent for themselves.*

Setting the Goal

THE INITIAL GOAL

In discussing with clients their approach to their longer-term goal (whether abstinence or moderation), we present three possible routes:

1) to taper down from the present high level of alcohol use until the level of the longer-term goal is reached (be it abstinence, or a specified level of moderate use). This route is seldom selected; those who select it usually have rather high levels of daily consumption (usually 10 or more drinks) and fear the effects of abrupt withdrawal of alcohol.

2) to abstain or start drinking at a moderate level immediately, and continue with the selected pattern.

3) to start with an initial period of abstinence, before deciding on the longer-term goal. This allows more time to carefully weigh the pros and cons of each option. It is the route we generally recommend to clients.

Our program thus distinguishes between the initial goal of treatment and the longer-term goal. If the client believes that he or she can accomplish it, we recommend an initial goal of a short period of abstinence – usually two or three weeks. (The research that supports this recommendation is presented and reviewed in Sanchez-Craig and Lei, 1987; and Sanchez-Craig, Wilkinson and Walker, 1987.) The client is presented with the following rationale for an initial period of abstinence:

- We have found that clients who manage to abstain for the first three weeks of the program are more successful at achieving long-term moderation outcomes.
- An initial period of abstinence will cause a significant reduction of tolerance for alcohol, so that returning to previous levels of consumption would cause unpleasant effects of intoxication. In addition, marked loss of tolerance is a gratifying objective indication of physical benefits of the change in drinking.
- Cognitive abilities dulled by long-term heavy use of alcohol are likely to improve significantly in two to three weeks of abstinence, but not with mere reduction of use, even if it's quite substantial.
- Clients will discover how they cope spontaneously with temptations to drink and with social pressures to drink. Discovery of such existing coping skills can significantly facilitate the achievement of the longer-term goal, whatever that goal might be.

SPECIFYING THE GOAL

The goal of abstinence need not be specified beyond being identified. Abstinence means not drinking alcoholic beverages under any circumstances. If a client selects a goal of abstinence we usually make an agreement about a date on which that goal's suitability will be reviewed. Moderate use can range from rare ritual or ceremonial use through to specified levels of regular drinking. When clients specify their goal we ask them to specify seven conditions of moderation as follows:

- **Maximum daily quantity:** the maximum number of drinks that will be consumed in any one day.
- **Maximum frequency:** the maximum number of drinking days in any one week.
- **Maximum weekly quantity:** the maximum number of drinks to be consumed in any one week. (Note: This is often less than the product of maximum daily quantity times maximum frequency.)
- **Types of beverage:** the varieties of alcoholic beverage that the client plans to avoid completely. Most frequently mentioned in this category are straight liquor or cocktails. These more concentrated beverages can more readily lead to intoxication.
- **Contexts for abstinence:** situations of high risk for drinking excessively, in which the client resolves not to drink at all.
- **Contexts for drinking:** environmental, social, cognitive or emotional contexts in which the client has identified low risk of excessive drinking and good coping skills, and in which moderate consumption may occur.
- **Assessment period:** the number of weeks or months over which the client will assess the goal's suitability.

Clients are always urged to attempt realistic goals. By this we mean goals that may initially be challenging, but which the client believes he or she can attain. We encourage clients not to set goals that they are unlikely to achieve. It is preferable to approach the ultimate goal gradually than to set oneself up for disappointment by selecting unrealistic goals.

We also review with clients the most constructive way of interpreting failure to achieve one's goal, i.e., as an opportunity for learning how to be more successful in the future, rather than as failure and an indication of personal inadequacy.

Clients are instructed to remember that the goal is not "carved in stone." It can be adjusted from time to time until it suits the client's lifestyle, while causing no alcohol-related problems. From time to time (e.g., holidays), clients may relax the criteria for a brief period. However, we stress that changes to the goal should be very deliberate, and should not be undertaken while the client is under the influence. Changing the goal on such occasions can serve as a rationalization for drinking too much.

As part of the treatment plan we routinely structure a set of follow-up appointments to review the client's success in achieving the goals of the intervention. At these sessions further adjustments can be made to the specified goal. Structuring the follow-up emphasizes that the client should continue to abide by the treatment plan in order to succeed over the long term.

A FINAL WORD

Whether the therapist likes it or not, the client ultimately chooses his or her goal. The approach and considerations laid out in this chapter can serve as the basis for making that choice rational and collaborative. In our experience, dogmatic assertions by therapists about what clients can and cannot do tend to undermine the establishment of a collaborative therapeutic relationship.

REFERENCES

Chaudron, C.D., and Wilkinson, D.A., (eds.). (1988). *Theories on Alcoholism.* Toronto: Addiction Research Foundation.

Cox, W.M. (ed.). (1987). *Treatment and Prevention of Alcohol Problems: A Resource Manual.* Orlando, FL: Academic.

Duckert, F., Koski-Jannes, A., and Ronnberg, S. (eds.). (1989). *Perspectives on Controlled Drinking.* Helsinki: Hakapaino Oy.

Fingarette, H. (1988). *Heavy Drinking: The Myth of Alcoholism as a Disease.* Berkeley: University of California Press.

Heather, N. (1989). Controlled drinking treatment: Where do we stand today? In *Addictive Behaviors: Prevention and Early Intervention,* eds. Loberg, T., Miller, W.R., Nathan, P.E., and Marlatt, G.A. Amsterdam: Swets and Zeitlinger.

Heather, N., and Robertson, I. (1983). *Controlled Drinking* (revised edition). London: Methuen.

Hill, S.Y. (1986). Physiological effects of alcohol in women. In *Women and Alcohol: Health-related Issues.* NIAAA Research Monograph No. 16. Washington, DC: U.S. Government Printing Office.

Kissin, B. (1983). The disease concept of alcoholism. In *Research Advances in Alcohol and Drug Problems,* vol. 7, eds. Smart, R.G., Glaser, F.B. Israel, Y., Kalant, H., Popham, R.E., and Schmidt, W. New York: Plenum.

MacAndrew, C., and Edgerton, R.B. (1969). *Drunken Comportment: A Social Explanation.* Chicago: Aldine.

Miller, W.R. (1983). Motivational interviewing with problem drinkers. *Behavioral Psychotherapy* 11: 147–172.

Miller, W.R. (1985). Motivation for treatment: A review with special emphasis on alcoholism. *Psychological Bulletin* 98: 84–107.

Miller, W.R. (1986). Haunted by the Zeitgeist: Reflections on contrasting treatment goals in Europe and the United States. In *Alcohol and Culture: Comparative Perspectives from Europe and America,* ed. Babor, T. New York: Annals of the New York Academy of Sciences.

Miller, W.R. (1987). Motivation and treatment goals. *Drugs and Society* 1: 133–151.

Miller, W.R., and Caddy, G.R. (1977). Abstinence and controlled drinking in the treatment of problem drinkers. *Journal of Studies on Alcohol* 38: 986–1003.

Miller, W.R., and Heather, N. (eds.). (1986). *Treating Addictive Behaviors: Processes of Change.* New York: Plenum.

Miller, W.R., and Joyce, M.A. (1979). Prediction of abstinence, controlled drinking and heavy drinking outcomes following behavioral self-control training. *Journal of Clinical and Consulting Psychology* 47: 773–775.

Miller, W.R., and Sovereign, R.G. (1989). The check-up: A model for early intervention in addictive behaviors. In *Addictive Behaviors: Prevention and Early Intervention,* eds. Loberg, T., Miller, W.R., Nathan, P.E., and Marlatt, G.A. Amsterdam: Swets and Zeitlinger.

Nordström, G., and Berglund, M. (1987). Aging and recovery from alcoholism. *British Journal of Psychiatry* 151: 389–392.

Orford, J., and Keddie, A. (1986). Abstinence or controlled drinking in clinical practice: A test of the dependence and persuasion hypotheses. *British Journal of Addiction* 81: 495–504.

Orford, J., Oppenheimer, E., and Edwards, G. (1976). Abstinence or control: The outcome of excessive drinking two years after consultation. *Behavior Research and Therapy* 14: 409–418.

Parsons, O.A., Butters, N., and Nathan, P.E. (eds.). (1987). *Neuropsychology of Alcoholism: Implications for Diagnosis and Treatment.* New York: Guilford.

Patterson, G.R., and Forgatch, M.S. (1984). Therapist behavior as a determinant for client non-compliance: A paradox for the behavior modifier. *Journal of Consulting and Clinical Psychology* 53: 846–851.

Peele, S. (1984). The cultural context of psychological approaches to alcoholism. *American Psychologist* 39: 1337–1351.

Peele, S. (1987). Why do controlled drinking outcomes vary by investigator, by country and by era? *Drug and Alcohol Dependence* 20: 173–201.

Sanchez-Craig, M. (1986). How much is too much? Estimates of hazardous drinking based on clients' self-reports. *British Journal of Addiction* 81: 251–256.

Sanchez-Craig, M. (1990). Brief didactic treatment for alcohol and drug-related problems: An approach based on client choice. *British Journal of Addiction* 85: 169–177.

Sanchez-Craig, M., Annis, H.M., Bornet, A.R., and MacDonald, K.R. (1984). Random assignment to abstinence and controlled drinking: Evaluation of a cognitive-behavioral program for problem drinkers. *Journal of Consulting and Clinical Psychology* 52: 390–403.

Sanchez-Craig, M., and Israel, Y. (1985). Pattern of alcohol use associated with self-identified problem drinking. *American Journal of Public Health* 75: 178–180.

Sanchez-Craig, M., and Lei, H. (1987). Disadvantages to imposing the goal of abstinence on problem drinkers: An empirical study. *British Journal of Addiction* 81: 505–512.

Sanchez-Craig, M., Leigh, G., Spivak, K., and Lei, H. (1989). Superior outcome of females over males after brief treatment for the reduction of heavy drinking. *British Journal of Addiction* 84: 395–404.

Sanchez-Craig, M., Spivak, K., and Davila, R. (1991). Superior outcome of females over males after brief treatment for the reduction of heavy drinking: Replication and report of therapist effects. *British Journal of Addiction* 86: 867–876.

Sanchez-Craig, M., and Wilkinson, D.A. (1986/87). Treating problem drinkers who are not severely dependent on alcohol. *Drugs and Society* 1: 39–67.

Sanchez-Craig, M., Wilkinson, D.A., and Walker, K. (1987). Theory and methods for secondary prevention of alcohol problems: A cognitively based approach. In *Treatment and Prevention of Alcohol Problems: A Resource Manual,* ed. Cox, W.M. New York: Academic Press.

Sobell, M.B., and Sobell, L. (1976). Second-year treatment outcome of alcoholics treated by individualized behavior therapy. *Behavior Research and Therapy* 14: 195–215.

Sobell, M.B., and Sobell, L., (eds.). (1986/87). Moderation as a goal or outcome of treatment for alcohol problems: A dialogue. *Drugs and Society* 1: 1–171.

Wallace, J. (1987a). Waging the war for wellness. Part I: The attack of the "antitraditionalist lobby." *Professional Counsellor* (January/February): 21–39.

Wallace, J. (1987b). Waging the war for wellness. Part II: The attack upon the disease model. *Professional Counsellor* (March/April): 21–27.

Chapter 8

Structured Relapse Prevention

HELEN M. ANNIS, MARILYN A. HERIE AND LYN WATKIN-MEREK

The chronic, relapsing nature of alcohol problems has long been recognized. However, only in relatively recent years have researchers begun to focus on the factors that affect the process of relapse (Litman Eiser, Rawson and Oppenheim, 1979, 1984; Wilson, 1980), and on the development of "relapse prevention" treatment strategies (Annis, 1986; Marlatt and Gordon, 1985).

By definition, relapse involves a failure to maintain behavior change, rather than a failure to initiate change. Treatment approaches based on social learning theory, specifically Bandura's theory of self-efficacy, hold that the strategies that are effective in *initiating* a change in drinking or drug use behavior may be ineffective at *maintaining* that change over time and avoiding relapse (Bandura, 1977, 1978, 1986).

Structured relapse prevention (SRP) is a cognitive-behavioral counselling program that has been developed in recent years at the Addiction Research Foundation (Annis, 1986; Annis and Davis, 1989a,b; Annis, Schober and Kelly, 1996). SRP counselling is based on social learning theory, and incorporates treatment strategies found to be effective in both initiating and maintaining change. SRP counselling also considers client readiness for change, since there is now widespread recognition in the addictions field that client motivation must be taken into account in the provision of treatment. Prochaska and DiClemente's (1984) transtheoretical model has had a major impact on how we think about client motivation in the addictions treatment field. SRP comprises five components (see Table 1), each of which is matched to a stage of change. Clients progress through each component, advancing to the next level when they are ready. As indicated by the dotted line arrows in Table 1, some clients may not progress through the stages in a linear fashion due to setbacks in their level of readiness for change.

At intake to SRP counselling, all clients receive a comprehensive assessment (Component 1), followed by feedback of results during one or more motivational interviewing sessions (Component 2). Clients who are willing to change their alcohol or

141

drug use will collaborate with their counsellor to develop an individually tailored treatment plan (Component 3). Only clients in the "action" stage of change — those who decide to try to implement the treatment plan and work toward change — sign a formal treatment contract and enter SRP counselling. The first phase of SRP focuses on powerful techniques designed to initiate and stabilize change (Component 4), while the second phase focuses on reducing clients' reliance on initiation strategies and substituting strategies that have greater potential for long-term "maintenance" of change in substance use behavior (Component 5).

Components of the Outpatient Counselling Program in Relation to Five Stages of Change					
PROGRAM COMPONENT	STAGE OF CHANGE				
	Precontemplation	Contemplation	Preparation	Action	Maintenance
1. Assessment	↓				
2. Motivational Interviewing					
3. Individual Treatment Plan					
4. SRP "Initiation" Counselling					
5. SRP "Maintenance" Counselling					

TABLE 1

Each component of the treatment process is described in greater detail below, beginning with a discussion of the type of client for whom this treatment approach is likely to be most effective.

SCREENING FOR CLIENT SUITABILITY

SRP is based on a behavioral model that assumes that clients perceive some benefit to working with a therapist to change their substance use. Even clients who are only contemplating change at the time of intake to treatment, but who have much to lose in terms of family and work stability, may be motivated by the early stages of this treatment approach. SRP is an outpatient approach, and it requires some social stability on the part of the client. In terms of Prochaska and DiClemente's model of change (1984; 1992), some relapse prevention procedures can be viewed as ways of narrowing the gap between contemplation and action, of demonstrating to the client that change can be gradual and relatively nonthreatening, thus motivating him or her to attempt to control the drinking or drug use.

It is also important to consider the client's belief system. Some clients feel strongly that their drinking problem reflects deep-seated psychological conflicts, and consequently they may insist on an exclusively psychodynamic approach to therapy. In such cases, it would be unproductive to recommend SRP treatment. More commonly, a client will initially expect the therapist to take control of and solve his or her substance use problem; such clients must learn that they must take an active role in designing and completing homework assignments so that they, in effect, become their own therapist. Clients who believe in the disease model of alcoholism or strongly adhere to the philosophy of Alcoholics Anonymous (AA) are still likely to be suitable candidates for SRP; they must simply accept the value of learning to prevent relapse by dealing more effectively with high-risk substance use situations. The client's initial belief in abstinence as a treatment goal should be assessed to ensure that there is no discrepancy between therapist and client expectations. The question of a treatment goal should be resolved at the outset of treatment.

Finally, empirical findings on the SRP approach to date suggest that clients with clearly defined areas of substance use risk benefit more from SRP than do clients whose substance use is more generalized across situations (Annis and Davis, 1991). Whether clients with generalized (i.e., undifferentiated) profiles on the Inventory of Drug-Taking Situations (IDTS-50, see below) might show greater gains from prolonged treatment is not yet known.

OVERVIEW OF SRP TREATMENT

SRP Component 1: Assessment

The counsellor's manner in conducting the assessment is of critical importance. The client collaborates with the counsellor in the assessment process, in determining what problems, if any, must be addressed. Regardless of the client's readiness to change, a comprehensive pre-treatment evaluation provides important information to share objectively and nonjudgmentally with the client.

At the Addiction Research Foundation, our assessment process includes a comprehensive psychosocial and legal history, including previous addiction treatment experiences (Addiction Research Foundation, 1993); instruments designed to measure the amount and frequency of alcohol use (Sobell and Sobell, 1992) and drug use (Wilkinson and LeBreton, 1986); as well as brief measures of the severity of alcohol and drug dependence (Skinner, 1982; Skinner and Horn, 1984).

In addition, two treatment planning tools are administered to assess the client's stage of change (Commitment to Change Algorithm) and to identify any antecedents to alcohol and drug use (Inventory of Drug-Taking Situations). These treatment planning tools are described in more detail below.

STAGES OF CHANGE

The Commitment to Change Algorithm for Alcohol (CCA-A) and Drugs (CCA-D) is a brief and easy-to-use tool that has been developed to assess clients' readiness to change (Schober and Annis, 1996a). The CCA is based on the transtheoretical model (Prochaska and DiClemente, 1984), and classifies clients into one of five stages of change based on recent drinking or drug use, reported intention to change, and recent quit/change attempts. Clients are placed in the highest stage for which they qualify.

Examples of the CCA-A and CCA-D are shown in Table 2, along with the definitions used for reduced drinking limits and quit attempts. Because the criteria for different stages are clear, a client's advancement to a higher stage, or regression to an earlier stage, can be readily tracked throughout treatment.

High test-retest reliability for the CCA has been reported (Schober and Annis, 1996a), and analyses are under way examining the convergent validity of CCA and SOCRATES (Miller et al., 1990), the predictive validity of CCA in relation to treatment retention and outcome, and the relationship of health beliefs to CCA stages of change (Schober and Annis, 1996b).

ANTECEDENTS TO ALCOHOL AND DRUG USE

The Inventory of Drug-Taking Situations (IDTS-50; Annis and Martin, 1985) is a 50-item assessment and treatment planning tool designed to provide a situational analysis of a client's alcohol or drug use. This information is critical in understanding a client's motivation for substance use and in designing an individually tailored treatment program. The frequency of the client's past drinking or drug use across eight risk areas is assessed, following the classification system developed by Marlatt and Gordon (1980). These risk areas comprise unpleasant emotions, physical discomfort, pleasant emotions, testing personal control, urges and temptations, conflict with others, social pressure to use and pleasant times with others.

The IDTS generates a personalized profile that provides a situational analysis of the client's alcohol or drug use; Figure 1 shows a sample IDTS profile of a cocaine user. This client is at high risk when experiencing unpleasant emotions and urges and temptations; thus, treatment planning would emphasize strategies targeted to these risk areas. The IDTS may be administered either in writing or by using computer interactive software.

COMMITMENT TO CHANGE ALGORITHM (CCA): INTERVIEW USED TO CLASSIFY A CLIENT INTO ONE OF FIVE STAGES OF CHANGE

Alcohol

Did you drink during the last 30 days? (YES or NO)

Are you considering quitting or reducing drinking[1] within the next 30 days?

    YES   or   NO → code **PRECONTEMPLATION**

- Were you continuously abstinent during the last 30 days or did you reduce drinking[1] during the last 30 days?

    YES   or   NO →

- Did you follow through on at least one quit attempt[2] or one attempt to reduce drinking[1] during the last 30 days?

    YES → code **PREPARATION**   or   NO → code **CONTEMPLATION**

- Were you continuously abstinent for more than the last 60 days or did you reduce drinking[1] for more than the last 60 days?

    YES → code **MAINTENANCE**   or   NO → code **ACTION**

Other Drug

- Did you use (name of drug) during the last 30 days?
- Are you considering quitting (name of drug) within the next 30 days?

    YES   or   NO → code **PRECONTEMPLATION**

- Were you continuously abstinent from (name of drug) during the last 30 days?

    YES   or   NO →

- Did you follow through on at least one quit attempt[3] from (name of drug) during the last 30 days?

    YES → code **PREPARATION**   or   NO → code **CONTEMPLATION**

- Were you continuously abstinent from (name of drug) for more than the last 60 days?

    YES → code **MAINTENANCE**   or   NO → code **ACTION**

1 Reduced drinking refers to drinking within the following limits: does not drink daily; drinks no more than 4 drinks (if male) and 3 (if female) on any day; drinks no more than 9 drinks in a week (if female) and 14 (if male).
2 Quit attempt (alcohol) refers to successful abstinence as perceived by client
3 Quit attempt (drug) refers to successful abstinence for a minimum of 11 consecutive days.

TABLE 2

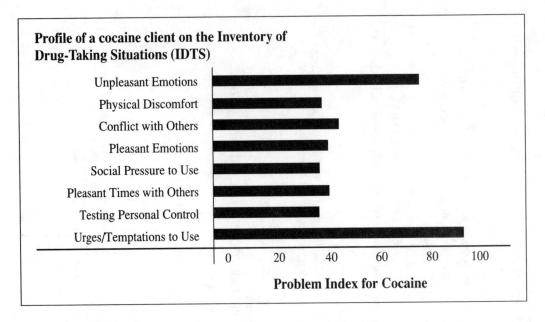

FIGURE 1

SRP Component 2: Motivational Interviewing

A motivational interviewing approach is designed to help clients build commitment and decide to change (Miller and Rollnick, 1991). Thus, motivation is not viewed as a static character trait, but rather as an expression of an individual's natural ambivalence toward change. In other words, motivation is a changeable state over which the counsellor can have considerable influence by actively engaging clients in changing their drinking or drug use. In SRP, the assessment process is conducted using techniques to build client motivation; for example, the personalized objective feedback of assessment results is excellent in building a client's commitment to change (Allsop, 1990; Saunders, Wilkinson and Allsop, 1991).

Motivational interviewing is particularly important for clients who are beginning to contemplate change. In the contemplation stage, skilful open-ended questioning about assessment findings and client concerns can frequently "tip the balance" toward a resolution to change. During these sessions, asking the client to weigh the costs and benefits of continuing substance use against the costs and benefits of change is especially helpful (Appel, 1986). The decisional balancing approach allows contemplators to explore issues relating to expected gains versus losses, concerns about change, and their strengths, weaknesses and overall confidence. The process of clients taking responsibility for decision making is, in itself, important in laying the groundwork for change. In fact, until the contemplator moves further along the motivational continuum, counselling strategies aimed at treatment planning ("preparation") or initiating change ("action") will likely result in client resistance.

Although motivational interviewing sessions are particularly appropriate for clients in the contemplation stage of change, clients at the precontemplation stage may be nudged into contemplation through nonconfrontational feedback of assessment findings (Miller and Rollnick, 1991). Exploring the risk implications of assessment data through the use of open-ended questions, reflection and summarizing can encourage precontemplators to focus on the costs of continued use and the benefits of change. Research supports the notion that clients progress from precontemplation to action when the client's perceived benefits of changing outweigh the perceived drawbacks (Prochaska, 1994; Prochaska et al., 1994).

If clients are already at the "preparation," "action" or "maintenance" stages, adopting a motivational interviewing style in providing assessment feedback can reinforce commitment to change, as well as validate the steps that have already been taken toward change.

SRP Component 3: Individualized Treatment Plan

One of the most important components of SRP counselling is treatment planning. The client must at least be in the "preparation" stage of change, so that he or she is ready to actively collaborate with the therapist in designing an individually tailored treatment plan. We have found the following tools and techniques to be helpful in encouraging client collaboration in the development of a treatment plan for SRP counselling: goal setting and self-monitoring; identifying problem drinking/drug use situations; identifying coping strengths and weaknesses; and contracting for treatment. Each step is described in more detail below.

GOAL SETTING AND SELF-MONITORING

Goal setting and self-monitoring can be useful ways of facilitating client participation in the treatment planning process. Clients use self-monitoring forms to record their alcohol or drug use goal each week — including their level of confidence in achieving this goal — as well as a daily record of any substance use that took place, the circumstances surrounding that use, risky situations encountered and coping strategies used. Clients then discuss the self-monitoring with their counsellor during subsequent treatment sessions.

IDENTIFYING PROBLEM DRINKING/DRUG USE SITUATIONS

A fundamental part of planning for SRP treatment involves agreeing on the client's most problematic drinking/drug use situations. The IDTS, which is given at assessment, provides this information in a systematic way, based on the types of situations that triggered alcohol/drug use over the past year. After discussing the IDTS results and the daily monitoring, clients are asked to rank the three most problematic triggers to alcohol/drug use that they want to work on in treatment, and to give specific examples of past drinking/drug use experiences for each situation. This exercise allows clients to analyse past situations in detail in order to identify what they might do differently in similar situations in the future. In addition, because the maintenance phase of SRP counselling focuses on planned exposure to high-risk situations for alcohol/drug use (see below), it is important that both client and counsellor have a detailed overview of past drinking or drug use scenarios.

IDENTIFYING COPING STRENGTHS AND WEAKNESSES

The strengths, supports and coping responses already available to a client are invaluable in preventing relapse, and they form the groundwork for developing successful homework assignments. The client must become more aware of his or her strengths and learn to use them effectively. Coping responses that the client may have used successfully in other areas may be quite effective, with only minor alterations, in addressing problem drinking or drug use situations. At this point in treatment planning, the therapist's task is to establish the client's existing repertoire of general coping behaviors, personal strengths and environmental resources. The process of reviewing the client's repertoire should provide a better appreciation of the possibilities open to the client, and should allow the client to focus on his or her strengths and successes rather than failures. Each of the following resource areas should be explored.

Environmental Supports. Would friends or family members who have provided support in the past be willing to do so now? Could people at work be called upon when difficulties arise? Does the client feel comfortable going to groups (Alcoholics Anonymous; Narcotics Anonymous) or individuals (a local minister)?

Behavioral Coping. Has the client ever attempted to solve problems that might have led to substance use, resolved to do something constructive and followed through? Has the client developed alternative activities or rewards that could replace substance use, even if they have not been actively pursued for some time? Has the client ever sought information or advice from family or friends? Has the client successfully avoided or left a high-risk situation without drinking or using drugs?

Cognitive Coping. Can the client reason things out, connect actions and consequences, and plan alternative ways of dealing with a situation? Can the client appreciate the positive benefits of not using and believe that he or she would benefit personally from change? When confronted by urges or temptations to drink or use drugs, can the client distract himself or herself by thinking of other things or imagining a positive outcome?

Affective Coping. Can the client face negative thoughts or emotional turmoil and value feelings of control and self-discipline? Does the client have strong spiritual beliefs that provide comfort? Can he or she passively accept things that cannot be changed? Does the client have emotional outlets for releasing tension or anger?

The client's current strengths in each area should be noted, along with any other ideas that the client would like to try for successful coping. Both the therapist and the client can refer to this list when discussing homework assignments. The client should be encouraged to use his or her strengths when faced with unanticipated drinking situations. Because current empirical evidence suggests that reliance on a wide range of coping responses, rather than a more restricted repertoire, is related to avoidance of relapse (Litman et al., 1979, 1984), the client should be encouraged to draw on a wide variety of coping alternatives.

SRP treatment also provides clients with a wide range of coping skills assignments, which are designed to help enhance and expand their coping repertoire. Clients select from a list of topics, which are then addressed during treatment sessions or provided as homework assignments. For example, during the early weeks of treatment clients often choose to work on coping with cravings or increasing social support. Later treatment sessions might address anger management, relaxation or healthy relationships.

CONTRACTING FOR TREATMENT

Finally, the client is informed of the program's orientation, attendance requirements, expectations for participation in planning and executing homework, and the limits of client confidentiality. Other possible treatment options are also presented. The client is then asked to decide whether he or she wishes to work toward change in alcohol/drug use by entering SRP counselling. This decision is formalized with the signing of a treatment contract.

SRP Component 4: "Initiation" Counselling

SRP counselling is divided into two phases: initiation (Component 4) and maintenance (Component 5) (Annis, 1990). The "initiation" phase focuses on counselling strategies suitable for clients in the "action" stage of change. That is, only clients who have decided to change and have signed a treatment contract enter this first phase of SRP counselling. This is because there is reason to believe that it can be detrimental to use action-oriented counselling procedures with clients who have not yet decided to change (Rollnick, 1985).

This phase of SRP incorporates the substance use triggers identified by the client in the treatment plan. The focus is on assisting clients to anticipate substance use triggers for the coming week, and to identify and commit to alternative coping strategies that don't involve drinking or drug use. Clients must begin to identify and plan for high-risk situations in advance, so that they can prepare alternative coping strategies.

Clients are encouraged to use coping plans that are known to be powerful strategies in initiating behavior change. These strategies include avoiding risky situations (e.g., drug use settings and drug-using friends) and seeking out social support (e.g., from reliable friends or family members). Table 3 shows the Weekly Plan (Initiation Phase) Form that clients complete to guide them in anticipating substance use triggers, and using relatively "safe" initiation strategies such as avoidance and social support to cope.

NAME: _____ SUBSTANCE: _____ DATE: _____

SRP WEEKLY PLAN — INITIATION PHASE

The early weeks of changing your alcohol or drug use can be a challenging time. We call this early period of behavior change the "Initiation Phase," which can last for anywhere from one month to much longer. Research has shown that "initiating" a change in your behavior is easier and more effective when you use some of the following powerful strategies.

- Think about what you have to lose if you don't change. What are the factors "pushing" you to change your drinking or drug use at this time?
- Think about situations that could arise and present a risk for you. Plan ahead of time what you will do so that you aren't caught off-guard.
- Avoid risky places and alcohol- or drug-using friends.
- Involve your spouse, another family member, a trusted friend or sponsor.
- During the first couple of weeks of changing your drinking or drug use, living in a supportive environment can be especially helpful.
- If you want to stop drinking, consider discussing the use of alcohol-sensitizing or anti-craving medication (e.g., Antabuse®, Temposil® or Naltrexone®) with your doctor. These drugs can be a big help in getting you over those difficult first few weeks.
- Set a goal for your drinking or drug use — make a commitment to yourself.

Below is some space for you to think about what you would like to accomplish in the coming week and how you will do so.

GOAL: _____

Confidence in achieving this goal: ❑ 0% ❑ 20% ❑ 40% ❑ 60% ❑ 80% ❑ 100%

Describe **two substance use triggers** that are likely to arise over the coming week: Indicate the following: Where will you be? What time of day? Who, if anyone, will be present? What will you be doing, thinking, feeling?	For each of the two triggers, describe **several coping strategies** that you will be prepared to use: You may want to use some of the strategies listed above, or plan other ways of coping that will work for you.

TABLE 3

For clients who have difficulty stabilizing abstinence while attending SRP outpatient sessions, the use of a protective drug or an anti-craving medication may be considered as part of the initiation phase of SRP counselling. An example of the integration of a pharmacological agent (calcium carbimide) with SRP homework assignments is given in Annis (1991), with the results of a randomized controlled trial presented in Annis and Peachey (1992).

SRP Component 5: "Maintenance" Counselling

Component 5 is the second phase of SRP counselling, and focuses on strategies suitable for clients in the "maintenance" stage of change. These clients have successfully implemented a change in their use of alcohol and/or other drugs for a period of at least 60 days (Commitment to Change Algorithm discussed above).

Although it can be argued that the term "relapse prevention" should be restricted to clients in the "maintenance" stage of change, in practice, clients do not progress from an exclusive use of "initiation" strategies (Component 4) to "maintenance" strategies (Component 5). Instead, clients tend to combine both action and maintenance strategies throughout treatment, coming to increasingly rely on maintenance phase strategies towards the end of treatment. The distinction between initiation and maintenance strategies is emphasized, so that clients are aware of which strategies they are using. The objective is to encourage clients to rely less on initiation strategies and to gain confidence in the use of maintenance strategies before treatment ends.

The fifth component of SRP counselling is based on research exploring the difference between powerful initiation versus maintenance of change coping strategies (Bandura, 1986; Marlatt and Gordon, 1985). This last phase of treatment involves four stages: graduated real-life exposure to a client's high-risk situations for substance use; homework tasks within each type of risk situation; slowly reducing clients' reliance on initiation strategies (including reliance on pharmacological agents); and the design of homework tasks to promote self-attribution of control. These maintenance of change counselling strategies are discussed in greater detail in Annis (1990) and Annis and Davis (1989a; 1989b).

The Weekly Planning Form that is used to help clients to incorporate these maintenance strategies is shown in Table 4. Several differences from the Weekly Plan (Table 3) for initiation-phase sessions should be noted. While clients in the initiation phase are asked to focus on *anticipating* drug-use triggers that are likely to arise naturally over the coming week, "maintenance stage" clients are also asked to actually plan on *entering* self-identified high-risk situations.

Homework assignments must be designed so that clients experience success and begin to build confidence (self-efficacy) in their ability to cope in high-risk situations. Multiple homework assignments (i.e., three or more) should be agreed upon at each treatment session, so that the client quickly learns that a high-risk situation does not automatically imply a relapse. These homework assignments should draw on a wide variety of the client's coping strengths and resources. As the client's confidence grows, he or she moves up the hierarchy to more difficult situations. At this later stage, a slip or "lapse" is unlikely to be the major setback it might have been early in treatment because the client has already begun a "snowball effect" in the growth of self-efficacy. By the end of treatment, the client should take most of the responsibility for designing his or her own homework assignments.

NAME: _____   SUBSTANCE:_____   DATE:_____

SRP WEEKLY PLAN — MAINTENANCE PHASE

Congratulations! You've successfully made some changes in your drinking or drug use. The next step is to maintain those changes and prevent relapse. Research has shown that two of the most powerful strategies for maintaining behavior change are to:

1. take stock of all of the high-risk situations that you are likely to encounter as a natural part of your lifestyle, and
2. gradually enter these situations, starting with a lower risk and working your way up.

The idea behind planning to enter situations in which you might be tempted to drink or use drugs is that, if these situations are likely to arise at some point, it's better for you to be in control of where and when they do. The following are more tips for maintaining behavior change.

• Experience each risk situation a few times before moving on to the next one.

• Make sure that you take the credit for success! For example, in the initiation phase of change, we encouraged you to seek the support of others. Now that you are learning to maintain change, it's important for you to know that you can "do it on your own" if you have to.

• Make sure that the situation you plan to enter is challenging, but not too challenging.

• If you are having difficulty with entering high-risk situations, you may be moving too quickly. Take your time! You can always go back to using some of the initiation strategies (like avoiding people, places and things, or relying on the support of others) until you feel more confident.

Two powerful strategies to help maintain changes in your drinking or drug use are setting a goal and planning to enter risk situations. Below is space for you to plan what you would like to accomplish in the coming week.

GOAL: _____

Confidence in achieving this goal: ❏ 0% ❏ 20% ❏ 40% ❏ 60% ❏ 80% ❏ 100%

HOMEWORK ASSIGNMENT Planned Exposure to a Substance Use Trigger	**OUTCOME REPORT**
Describe triggering situation: _____ _____ _____ Planned experience: When? _____ Where? _____ Who present? _____ Coping plan (be specific, describe exactly what you will say and do, what you will be thinking, etc.): _____ _____ _____	Did you attempt this assignment? ❏ No ❏ Yes Were you successful? ❏ No ❏ Yes Comment: _____ _____ _____ Did you use? ❏ No ❏ Yes If Yes, how much? _____ What, if anything, might you try doing differently next time? _____ _____

TABLE 4

In summary, clients who are in the "action stage" or initiation phase are encouraged to use avoidance (e.g., avoidance of drug use settings, drug-using friends), social support (e.g., a reliable friend or family member) and perhaps a protective or anti-craving medication. Clients who are in the "maintenance stage," however, are expected to use a greater variety of coping alternatives that will make them more self-reliant. Consistent with research on the relationship of coping repertoire to outcome (Bliss, Garvey, Heinhold and Hitchcock, 1989; Curry and Marlatt, 1985; Moser, 1993) and the superiority of many active coping strategies compared with simple avoidance (Moser and Annis, 1996; 1993; Shiffman, 1985), clients in the "maintenance stage" are encouraged to develop a broad repertoire of coping alternatives that include active as well as avoidant cognitive and behavioral coping responses.

CLIENT PROGRESSION IN SRP COUNSELLING

Although SRP counselling has been presented as a highly structured, ordered sequence of five counselling components, in practice a dynamic interplay occurs between counselling components and a client's readiness to change. Counselling components are designed to enhance client readiness to change, and client stage of change affects the choice of counselling components. While some clients may proceed in a linear fashion through the stages of change and counselling components, others may not. For example, an action-stage client who experiences a lapse to substance use while receiving initiation-stage counselling procedures, may need earlier counselling components such as continued assessment and motivational interviewing. Similarly, a preparation-stage client, when faced with signing an individual treatment contract, may experience uncertainty regarding the decision to change requiring further exploration of the costs and benefits of change through motivational interviewing. Thus, the SRP treatment model takes into account clients' readiness to change — the SRP components can be individually tailored to fit clients' ongoing needs.

MONITORING OUTCOME
AND CHANGES IN SELF-EFFICACY

At the first treatment session and toward treatment discharge, the client should complete the Drug-Taking Confidence Questionnaire (DTCQ-50; Annis and Martin, 1985b), which is a 50-item self-report questionnaire designed to assess Bandura's concept of self-efficacy for alcohol- and drug-related situations. Clients are asked to imagine themselves in a variety of situations, derived from the work of Marlatt and Gordon (1980), and for each situation to indicate on a six-point scale (ranging from 0 = not at all confident; 20 = 20 per cent confident, 40 = 40 per cent confident; 60 = 60 per cent confident; 80 = 80 per cent confident; to 100 = very confident) how confident they are that they will be able to resist the urge to drink heavily or use drugs in that situation. A client's response on the DTCQ-50 will allow the therapist to monitor the development of the client's self-efficacy in relation to coping with specific substance use situations over the course of treatment.

The purpose of treatment is to effect a rise in self-efficacy across all areas of perceived risk. If the client fails to show growth of confidence in coping with a particular risk situation, further work in this area should be considered before the client is discharged from treatment. The therapist must consider possible reasons for the lack of development of confidence in the identified area. For example, has the client successfully performed homework assignments involving entry into situations of this type? If so, what self-inferences is the client drawing from those experiences? Such an inquiry by the therapist should suggest the reason for the client's lack of confidence in relation to the particular risk area and suggest what further work needs to be done before treatment completion.

EMPIRICAL SUPPORT FOR SRP COUNSELLING

The SRP counselling process focuses heavily on the conduct of homework assignments, particularly in the "initiation" (or action) and "maintenance" phases. A study by Annis and Davis (1988), evaluating the homework component of SRP counselling, found that clients successfully completed the vast majority of homework assignments. Assignments generated by the client were more likely to be completed successfully (90 per cent) than those generated by the therapist (73 per cent), emphasizing the importance of active client participation. Although homework assignments, particularly during the maintenance phase, involve entry into risk situations for substance use, most clients were successful in adhering to their treatment goal. Typically, any slips ("lapses") occurred outside of homework assignments. Interestingly, negative mood states and interpersonal conflict increased the likelihood that a lapse would become a serious relapse.

Clinical trials evaluating the effectiveness of SRP counselling have supported the following conclusions:
   1) In the year following SRP treatment, most clients dramatically reduce their substance use (Annis and Davis, 1988; Graham, Annis, Brett and Venesoen, 1996).
   2) Group-delivered SRP counselling can be equally effective as individual SRP counselling for clients with both alcohol and drug problems (Graham, Annis, Brett and Venesoen, 1996).
   3) Clients with well-differentiated profiles on the Inventory of Drug-Taking Situations do better in SRP counselling than clients with undifferentiated profiles, while the reverse is true under more traditional counselling (Annis and Davis, 1991).

4) Clients with good outcomes show high confidence (self-efficacy) and make good use of coping strategies when faced with high-risk situations (Moser and Annis, 1996).

5) The greater the number and variety of coping strategies used by the client, the lower the likelihood of relapse (Moser and Annis, 1996).

Further research is needed to establish the relative effectiveness of SRP counselling for clients with different substance use disorders, and to evaluate the SRP counselling components in relation to client readiness for change.

In conclusion, it is widely recognized that change in addictive behavior is associated with client motivation for change (Cox, 1990; Marlatt and Gordon, 1985, Sobell and Sobell, 1993). Some attention has been focused on the possibility of matching counselling strategies (Miller and Rollnick, 1991; Rollnick, 1985), as well as population health policy interventions (Prochaska, 1994), to client readiness for change as a means of enhancing addictive behavior change. This chapter describes an SRP outpatient treatment program in which the use of five counselling components is discussed in relation to five client stages of change (i.e., precontemplation, contemplation, preparation, action and maintenance).

ADDITIONAL INFORMATION

The following materials are available from the Marketing Department, Addiction Research Foundation, 33 Russell Street, Toronto, ON M5S 2S1 (Telephone: 1-800-661-1111):

Annis, H.M., Herie, M.A., and Watkin-Merek, L. (1996). *Structured Relapse Prevention: An Outpatient Counselling Approach.* Includes all assessment instruments, homework assignments, and session-by-session checklists.

Annis, H.M., and Martin, G. (1985). *Inventory of Drug-Taking Situations* (IDTS-50). Computer interactive software is also available.

Annis, H.M., and Martin, G. (1985). *Drug-Taking Confidence Questionnaire (DTCQ-50).* Computer interactive software is also available.

Annis, H.M., Turner, N.E., and Sklar, S.M. (1997). *Inventory of Drug-Taking Situations (IDTS-50) User's Guide.*

Annis, H.M., Sklar, S.M., and Turner, N.E. (1997). *Drug-Taking Confidence Questionnaire (DTCQ-50) User's Guide.*

REFERENCES

Addiction Research Foundation. (1993). *Core Client Interview: Behaviour Change and Relapse Prevention Unit.* Toronto: Addiction Research Foundation.

Allsop, S. (1990). Relapse prevention and management. *Drug and Alcohol Review* 9: 143–153.

Annis, H.M. (1986). A relapse prevention model for treatment of alcoholics. In *Treating Addictive Behaviors: Processes of Change*, eds. Miller, W.R., and Heather, N. New York: Plenum.

Annis, H.M. (1990). Relapse to substance abuse: Empirical findings within a cognitive-social learning approach. *Journal of Psychoactive Drugs* 22 (2): 117–124.

Annis, H.M. (1991). A cognitive-social learning approach to relapse: Pharmacotherapy and relapse prevention counselling. *Alcohol and Alcoholism*, Suppl. 1: 527–530.

Annis, H.M., and Davis, C.S. (1988). Self-efficacy and the prevention of alcoholic relapse: Initial findings from a treatment trial. In *Assessment and Treatment of Addictive Disorders*, eds. Baker, T.B., and Cannon, D.S. New York: Praeger.

Annis, H.M., and Davis, C.S. (1989a). Relapse prevention. In *Handbook of Alcoholism Treatment Approaches,* eds. Hester, R.K., and Miller, W.R. New York: Pergamon Press.

Annis, H.M., and Davis, C.S. (1989b). Relapse prevention training: A cognitive-behavioral approach based on self-efficacy theory. *Journal of Chemical Dependency Treatment* 2 (2): 81–103.

Annis, H.M., and Davis, C.S. (1991). Relapse prevention. *Alcohol Health and Research World* 15 (3): 204–212.

Annis, H.M., and Martin, G. (1985a). *Inventory of Drug-Taking Situations* (IDTS-50). Toronto: Addiction Research Foundation.

Annis, H.M., and Martin, G. (1985b). *Drug-Taking Confidence Questionnaire* (DTCQ-50). Toronto: Addiction Research Foundation.

Annis, H.M., and Peachey, J.E. (1992). The use of calcium carbimide in relapse prevention counselling: Results of a randomized controlled trial. *British Journal of Addiction* 87: 63–72.

Annis, H.M., Schober, R., and Kelly, E. (1996). Matching addiction outpatient counselling to client readiness for change: The role of structured relapse prevention counselling. *Experimental and Clinical Psychopharmacology* 4.

Appel, C.P. (1986). From contemplation to determination: Contributions from cognitive psychology. In *Treating Addictive Behaviors: Processes of Change*, eds. Miller, W.R., and Heather, N. New York: Plenum Press.

Bandura, A. (1977). Self-efficacy: Toward a unifying theory of behavioral change. *Psychological Review* 84 (2): 191–215.

Bandura, A. (1978). Reflections on self-efficacy. *Advances in Behaviour Research and Therapy* 1: 237–269.

Bandura, A. (1986). *Social Foundations of Thought and Action*. Englewood Cliffs, NJ: Prentice Hall.

Bliss, R.E., Garvey, A.J., Heinhold, J., and Hitchcock, J.L. (1989). The influence of situation and coping on relapse crisis outcomes after smoking cessation. *Journal of Consulting and Clinical Psychology* 57: 443–449.

Cox, W.M. (ed.). (1990). *Why People Drink: Parameters of Alcohol as a Reinforcer*. New York: Gardner.

Curry, S.G., and Marlatt, G.A. (1985). Unaided quitters' strategies for coping with temptations to smoke. In *Coping and Substance Use,* eds. Shiffman, S., and Wills, T.A. New York: Academic Press.

DiClemente, C.C., Prochaska, J.O., Fairhurst, S.K., Velicer, W.F., Velasquez, M.M., and Rossi, J.S. (1991). The process of smoking cessation: An analysis of precontemplation, contemplation and preparation stages of change. *Journal of Consulting and Clinical Psychology* 59: 295–304.

Graham, K., Annis, H.M., Brett, P.J., and Venesoen, P. (1996). A controlled field trial of group versus individual cognitive-behavioral training for relapse prevention. *Addiction* 91 (8): 1127-1139.

Litman, G.K., Eiser, J.R., Rawson, N.S.B., and Oppenheim, A.N. (1979). Differences in relapse precipitants and coping behaviors between alcohol relapsers and survivors. *Behaviour Research and Therapy* 17: 89–94.

Litman, G.K., Stapleton, J., Oppenheim, A.N., Peleg, M., and Jackson, P. (1984). The relationship between coping behaviors, their effectiveness and alcoholism relapse and survival. *British Journal of Addiction* 79 (3): 283–291.

Marlatt, G.A., and Gordon, J.R. (1980). Determinants of relapse: Implications for the maintenance of behavior change. In *Behavioral Medicine: Changing Health Lifestyles,* eds. Davidson, P., and Davidson, S. New York: Brunner/Mazel.

Marlatt, G.A., and Gordon, J.R. (1985). *Relapse Prevention: Maintenance Strategies in the Treatment of Addictive Behaviors.* New York: Guilford.

Miller, W.R., and Rollnick, S. (1991). *Motivational Interviewing.* New York: Guilford.

Miller, W.R., Tonigan, J.S., Montgomery, H.A., Abbott, P.J., Meyers, R.J., Hester, R.K., and Delaney, H.D. (1990). *Assessment of Client Motivation for Change: Preliminary Validation of the Socrates (Rev) Instrument.* University of New Mexico, Albuquerque, NM: Center for Research on Addictive Behaviors.

Moser, A.E. (1993). *Situational Antecedents, Self-efficacy and Coping in Relapse Crisis Outcome: A Prospective Study of Treated Alcoholics.* Toronto: York University.

Moser, A.E., and Annis, H.M. (1996). The role of coping in relapse crisis outcome: A prospective study of treated alcoholics. *Addiction* 91 (8): 1101–1113.

Prochaska, J.O. (1994). Strong and weak principles for progressing from precontemplation to action on the basis of twelve problem behaviors. *Health Psychology* 13 (1): 47–51.

Prochaska, J.O., and DiClemente, C.C. (1984). *The Transtheoretical Approach: Crossing Traditional Boundaries of Therapy.* Homewood, IL: Dow Jones/Irwin.

Prochaska, J.O., and DiClemente, C.C. (1992). Stages of change in the modification of problem behaviors. In *Progress in Behavior Modification* 28, eds. Hersen, M., Eisler, R., and Miller, P.M. Sycamore, IL: Sycamore Publishing Company.

Prochaska, J.O., Velicer, W.F., Rossi, J.S., Goldstein, M.G., Marcus, B.H., Rakowski, W., Fiore, C., Harlow, L.L., Redding, C.A., Rosenbloom, D., and Rossi, S.R. (1994). Stages of change and decisional balance for twelve problem behaviors. *Health Psychology* 13 (1): 39–46.

Rollnick, S. (1985). The value of a cognitive-behavioral approach in the treatment of problem drinkers. In *The Misuse of Alcohol: Clinical Issues in Dependence Treatment and Prevention*, eds. Heather, N., Robertson, I., and Davies, P. New York: New York University Press.

Saunders, B., Wilkinson C., and Allsop, S. (1991). Motivational interviewing with heroin users attending a methadone clinic. In *Motivational Interviewing,* eds. Miller, W.R., and Rollnick, S. New York: Guilford Press.

Schober, R., and Annis, H.M. (1996a). Commitment to change in individuals seeking treatment for excessive drinking. Manuscript submitted for publication.

Schober, R., and Annis, H.M. (1996b). Stages and processes of change in individuals seeking treatment for excessive drinking. Manuscript in preparation.

Shiffman, S. (1985). Preventing relapse in ex-smokers: A self-management approach. In *Relapse Prevention,* eds. Marlatt, G.A., and Gordon, J.R. New York: Guilford Press.

Skinner, H.A. (1982). *Drug Abuse Screening Test.* Toronto: Addiction Research Foundation.

Skinner, H.A., and Horn, J.L. (1984). *Alcohol Dependence Scale: User's Guide.* Toronto: Addiction Research Foundation.

Sobell, L.C., and Sobell, M.B. (1992). Timeline Followback: A technique for assessing self-reported ethanol consumption. In *Measuring Alcohol Consumption: Psychosocial and Biological Methods*, eds. Allen, J., and Litten, R.Z. Totowa, NJ: Humana Press.

Sobell, M.B., and Sobell, L.C. (1993). *Problem Drinkers: Guided Self-Change Treatment.* New York: Guilford.

Wilkinson, D.A., and LeBreton, S. (1986). Early indicators of treatment outcome in multiple drug users. In *Treating Addictive Behaviors: Processes of Change*, eds. Miller, W.R., and Heather, N. New York: Plenum Press.

Wilson, G.T. (1980). Cognitive factors in lifestyle changes: A social learning perspective. In *Behavioral Medicine: Changing Health Lifestyles*, eds. Davidson, P.O., and Davidson, S.M. New York: Brunner/Mazel.

Chapter 9

Mutual Aid Groups

HELEN YOUNGSON

"Mutual aid," "self-help," and "support groups" are terms that are used interchangeably in the literature, but they often signify slightly different entities. In this chapter, the term mutual aid designates those group experiences that are "owned by the consumer" (Lavoie, Borkman and Gidron, 1994) and that bring people together with the common purpose of helping each other in their recovery. The term self-help, over the last few years, has come to mean using books, tapes, exercises, the Internet and other resources for self-directed recovery from a wide variety of problems, including alcohol and drug abuse. However, the term self-help is used in this chapter to signify the more collective experience.

OVERVIEW

As we work with clients, it is important to acknowledge the significant place of mutual aid groups in recovery from alcohol and drug abuse. To recover successfully from substance abuse, clients must make major lifestyle, internal and interpersonal changes. It takes time for these changes to occur and become comfortably part of a person. It often takes longer than counsellors' schedules or clients' budgets can allow.

Mutual aid groups offer support and guidance for these changes at minimal cost, and they can be available for years. Also, aid from those who have longer recovery can help on those evenings and weekends when professional help is not usually available. There are, as well, clients who need frequent and/or long-term reassurance and support that is beyond the mandate of most agencies.

Mutual aid groups allow opportunities for clients to make social contacts, practise life skills, learn to take responsibility, form healthy relationships and solve problems. As McCrady and Irvine (1989) note: "Most studies consistently find an association between AA attendance and positive treatment outcome, suggesting that AA involvement is one factor associated with positive treatment outcome." In addition, Humphreys, Mavis and Stoffelmayr (1994) note that 12-step programs both appeal to and benefit disenfranchised groups, namely "women, racial minorities, and persons of low social class."

As Miller (1989) advocates, our role as professionals is to help our clients, where appropriate, to link with the mutual aid groups of their choice, making sure that they have been properly informed about their options. This client self-matching, he maintains, reduces resistance and improves the chances of recovery. If necessary, the counsellor may negotiate with the client regarding a more appropriate option.

What Is a Mutual Aid Group?

Ideally, mutual aid groups are formed by people who share a common health or social problem, situation or concern. Sometimes concerned professionals will help establish a group until indigenous leadership emerges. In other situations, the professional may remain to give leadership on an ongoing basis. However, this latter situation seems to be less mutual aid, and more a therapy process and support group, because it is highly dependent on the goodwill and staying power of the counsellor and/or the sponsoring agency. As Reissman and Carroll (1995) point out, the mutual aid model is diluted. Also, some recently developed mutual aid programs have costs associated with participation.

Members of a mutual aid group come together to share their knowledge and experiences, offer support to each other, pool their resources, and discuss and create their own solutions. There is an underlying belief that: "Helping you helps me" (Hill, 1984).

Mutual Aid Complements the Treatment Continuum

The problems caused by alcohol have been of concern for centuries, but in many parts of the world there was little hope of recovery from alcohol once it had established its hold. In the 1930s and 1940s, those coming to the attention of the medical community and the courts were the "down-and-outers" whose families had given up hope. The earliest of contemporary mutual aid groups, Alcoholics Anonymous (AA), was founded in 1935 in Ohio. The hope and success achieved by AA members came to the public's attention in 1940.

In the United States, individuals who had recovered themselves began to establish alcohol recovery homes. In Ontario, resources were found to study and treat alcohol abuse and, in 1949, the Alcoholism Research Foundation was established (now known as the Addiction Research Foundation). And so, the treatment continuum began to develop from detoxification, assessment and referral, outpatient and residential centres to the process of aftercare, which includes halfway, three-quarter way houses and mutual aid groups. Research has shown the efficacy of mutual aid as part of aftercare (U.S. Department of Health and Human Services, 1993).

With more education, prevention programs and self-help manuals, clients are appearing for treatment much earlier in their drinking or drug-taking experience. The need for a variety of mutual aid groups to address the needs of different populations is now indicated by research and practice (Kirkpatrick, 1978; Zweben, 1995; Bishop, 1995; Humphreys and Woods, 1993; Delgado and Humm-Delgado, 1993; Reissman and Carroll, 1995).

Many agencies find it helpful to ask their clients to attend a mutual aid group as part of their treatment plan. Counsellors often educate their substance-abusing clients on the merits of joining a mutual aid group, and they use the client's subsequent experience as part of their therapy (exploring the client's feelings and reactions to the group experience). A few agencies offer mutual aid experiences out of their own facilities. These groups are then available to their graduates for as long as they are needed. Other counsellors start mutual aid groups for particular client populations to meet those clients' specific requirements.

MUTUAL AID GROUPS AVAILABLE TO HELP SUBSTANCE ABUSERS

Eight alcohol- and drug-specific mutual aid groups are described in this chapter: the three 12-step programs, Alcoholics Anonymous (AA), Cocaine Anonymous (CA) and Narcotics Anonymous (NA); Moderation Management (MM); Rational Recovery (RR); Self Management and Recovery Training (SMART); Secular Organizations for Sobriety (SOS); and Women for Sobriety (WFS).

Other 12-step programs, including Overeaters Anonymous, Nicotine Anonymous, Gamblers Anonymous, Adult Children of Alcoholics, Al-Anon (for family members), Alateen (for children of alcoholics), are also available in many communities. These groups, which have similar formats to AA's, will not be covered here. The local AA office can usually redirect you to the local source of information on Al-Anon, etc.

Room and Greenfield (1993) found "that 12-step programs emerge as the most widely diffused form of group seeking/group therapy in the U.S. population," and the same may be true in Canada.

Two of the mutual aid groups, Rational Recovery and SMART Recovery, have more professional involvement than do the others.

While all mutual aid groups described below exist internationally, none are as accessible as AA, which is available in most communities in North America. The headquarters of the groups described are included at the end of this chapter. Metropolitan areas hold the most promise for the existence of a variety of mutual aid groups that include special groups for special populations (i.e., women, gays, the ethno-cultural community, cocaine addicts, mothers). Of course, at any time, professionals can take the initiative, with the assistance of persons in recovery, to establish a group that more closely meets their clients' needs.

As you will notice, more space is devoted to AA, which is the most accessible, has the most information available (books, pamphlets, videos, etc.), and has been the subject of many studies and reviews.

Alcoholics Anonymous

Alcoholics Anonymous (AA) has stood the test of time in its over 60 years of existence. In 1995, its estimated worldwide membership was over two million, with about 90,000 groups in 141 countries (Alcoholics Anonymous World Service, 1995).

MEETINGS

Depending on the size of the community, the number of meetings available ranges from one to 200. Locations include church basements, recreation centres and, in some cases (for greater anonymity for high-profile members) in homes. Some sites are accessible to people in wheelchairs. Some communities have AA groups for aboriginals, women only, men only, police, pilots, gays, hearing-impaired persons, nonsmokers, etc. Some offer meetings in languages other than English or French.

Closed meetings
The format may be a small, closed (to all but AA members) discussion group based on the "Big Book" (an account of how the first 100 AA members achieved continuous sobriety [AA, 1976]), the Twelve Steps, the *Grapevine* (a monthly magazine), or on topics chosen by the group. No "cross-talk" is allowed (i.e., one person shares what he or she has to say without interruption from other participants). Someone who is in distress may have to wait to talk about his or her problem until after the discussion. Someone in the group usually responds to newcomers by offering to speak to them after the meeting. Those with reservations about joining the AA program may share these thoughts in the group or in fellowship afterwards. Often members will share how they resolved these issues and suggest that the person read the *Twelve Step* book and/or attend 12-step discussion groups.

Open meetings
The other common type of meeting, and the one recommended for newcomers is the "open speaker meeting," where members, observers, guests, friends and people checking to see if they have a drinking problem are welcome. It may be a large group

of 50 or so, or a small one of 15. Usually someone is on hand to greet everyone, and visitors are not expected to introduce themselves unless they desire to do so. At these meetings, a standard format is followed. Meetings open with a moment of silence, followed by the Serenity Prayer. Then various persons (chosen by the chairperson before the meeting starts) come forward to read the Preamble, How It Works from Chapter 5 of AA's "Big Book" (AA, 1976), the Twelve Steps and the Twelve Traditions. Speakers also share their messages of courage, strength and hope, and they describe their use of AA slogans. At these meetings, colored chips are distributed to people who have reached intervals towards their first year of continuous sobriety. A collection is taken (usually a dollar), while announcements of coming events are made. Then the Lord's Prayer is said by those who want to recite it. In some meetings, members join hands if they wish to do so. Everyone is encouraged to stay after meetings for coffee and fellowship, and some meetings serve food. If someone is celebrating an AA "birthday" (the number of years that person has remained sober), there may be a "birthday cake." Free pamphlets are also available for members and visitors. The local office (listed in the phone book and usually answered by volunteers) can direct a caller to the nearest and the most appropriate meeting for her/him.

GUIDING PRINCIPLES

AA adheres to the principles that are outlined in its Twelve Traditions (AA, 1985) developed by the founders to foster unity among groups. The group's welfare is paramount. No one is excluded from membership. All that is required is "a simple desire to stop drinking." Leadership exists to serve the members (i.e., no one governs and opportunities to chair meetings, sit on committees and convene at events are shared among members who volunteer). All groups are autonomous and self-supporting. The collections taken at meetings pay for the rent, coffee, celebrations of sobriety and to maintain the office and phones locally, regionally and internationally.

It is believed that alcoholics respond most favorably when attracted rather than coerced (AA, 1994). While some treatment centres, judges and criminal lawyers may insist on clients attending AA meetings, AA lets its friends (counsellors, nurses, doctors, ministers, police, etc.) promote AA. Through its local Public Information and Co-operation with the Professional Community Committees, AA makes information available via the phone book, meeting lists, its offices, pamphlets and educational packages for professionals.

AA insists that all members be anonymous and what is said at meetings is not repeated at the public level. Privacy, confidentiality and anonymity are expected for *all* involved in the program.

AA also refuses to ally itself with outside organizations or causes to prevent problems that may arise around "money, property and prestige." Further, no one member can speak on behalf of AA. The decisions made at business, district and international meetings are consensual and dependent on the ultimate authority, God (as expressed in the group conscience that exists at the small group level). This makes change a slow, thorough and democratic process.

AA's primary purpose is to carry its message to anyone who suffers from the disease of alcoholism. The AA disease concept removes the stigma of self-blame. At the same time, people are provided with a model of recovery based on responsible collective action (Reissman and Carroll, 1995).

CONCEPT OF HIGHER POWER

Each member, whether agnostic, atheist, Christian, Jew, Buddhist or other, is encouraged to develop the concept of a "Higher Power" (which some may call God, the Master of the Universe, the Creator, etc.). A Higher Power is "that intuitive sense of a vital principle or animating force" (Reissman and Carroll, 1995). Basically, what is being asked is that each person find something beyond himself or herself to rely on. It is believed that this allows the ego to find its proper place. As McCrady and Irvine (1989) mention, substance abusers are very self-absorbed and "that recognizing and accepting change is impossible in a personal vacuum which allows no one else to be involved." This notion of surrender bothers some potential AA members who feel that they have already surrendered to alcohol with disastrous results. But herein lies one of the many paradoxes found in AA. Members find that it is in the process of complying, surrendering and obeying, that they gain control over alcohol and their lives, and they experience freedom. Just as one complies with a doctor's prescription or the laws of the land, the prospective AA member is asked to work Step Three (turning one's will and one's life over to a Higher Power) when she or he is ready.

Initially for some AA members, their group becomes their Higher Power. Others rely on "good orderly direction" in their life. Yet others develop a new concept of God that differs from the one they remember from childhood. They often note that this "new God" is a loving, nurturing and benign (if not benevolent) force, who is ever present and available. As one speaker shared at an AA Regional Conference, she "empowered herself with her Higher Power" (Heather, 1996).

PROCESS

The program's 12 steps are seen as necessary for members to implement to achieve sobriety.

Twelve Steps
1. We admitted we were powerless over alcohol — that our lives had become unmanageable.
2. Came to believe that a Power greater than ourselves could restore us to sanity.
3. Made a decision to turn our will and our lives over to the care of God *as we understood Him.*

4. Made a searching and fearless moral inventory of ourselves.

5. Admitted to God, to ourselves and to another human being the exact nature of our wrongs.

6. Were entirely ready to have God remove all these defects of character.

7. Humbly asked Him to remove our shortcomings.

8. Made a list of all persons we had harmed, and became willing to make amends to them all.

9. Made direct amends to such people wherever possible, except when to do so would injure them or others.

10. Continued to take personal inventory and when we were wrong promptly admitted it.

11. Sought through prayer and meditation to improve our conscious contact with God *as we understood Him,* praying only for the knowledge of His will for us and the power to carry that out.

12. Having had a spiritual awakening as the result of these steps, we tried to carry this message to alcoholics and to practise these principles in all our affairs.

Members are encouraged to attend meetings regularly, especially early in their sobriety, to learn from others. Regular participation offers a routine, which may be lacking in other areas of their lives. New members learn to identify with speakers, which can decrease their sense of isolation. Since it is believed that a problem shared is a problem halved, new members are also encouraged to discuss any perplexing, practical, emotional or relationship problems with someone before they leave the meetings.

Most learning is self-discovered and often has an "aha!" quality. People are free to "take whatever they see or hear, and leave the rest." The power of the language in the literature is demonstrated as members use the phrases as prescriptions for action (e.g., a person is encouraged to "go to any lengths" to "get" the program). As AA's old-timers say, the richness of the program takes years to understand and to use.

Members are asked to join a group that feels comfortable to them, to attend every week and to take responsibility for group life (i.e., make coffee, go to business meetings, etc.) — in other words, to "get active." By investing oneself in the program, a person develops a sense of belonging and community, and these new behaviors contribute to an improved quality of life and thinking. According to Reissman and Carroll (1995), this may replicate the unconditional love and acceptance of family, which some members may not have experienced before.

Newcomers are told: "Keep It Simple, don't drink, go to meetings and, one day at a time, things will get better ... a fine life beyond description awaits you." They can learn through AA in several ways: on their own, with others in discussion groups, at AA retreats and seminars, and with sponsors.

A study of AA's "Big Book," *Alcoholics Anonymous: The Story of How Many Thousands of Men and Women Have Recovered from Alcoholism,* and the book,

The Twelve Steps and Twelve Traditions, is encouraged. The Big Book's main purpose is to show other people with drinking problems "precisely how thousands of members of AA have recovered" (AA, 1976).

Part of the process that happens to all recovering persons in AA is internal. AA's steps, slogans, suggestions, readings, speakers and, in fact, all interactions encourage people to look inward, to reflect and to use all aspects of their day as opportunities to learn and grow and to address issues that were obscured by substance use.

SPONSORSHIP

Newcomers are encouraged to look around at meetings and get to know other members until they find someone with whom they feel comfortable and whose sobriety/serenity they admire. Newcomers then ask their chosen member to be their sponsor. AA recommends that the sponsor and sponsored person be of the same sex. "This custom usually promotes quick understanding and reduces the likelihood of emotional distractions that might take the newcomer's mind off the purpose of AA" (AA, 1994A).

Sponsors are mentors who, by virtue of more sobriety and serenity, provide a model and assist those they sponsor by listening and sharing their experiences in similar situations or relationships. They also share how they use the tools of the program to help them feel better without drinking. They often give feedback on the problem at hand and encourage the person being sponsored to see the situation in a more realistic/positive/less self-centred light. The sponsor refers elsewhere when the issue raised is beyond the mentor's experience or the scope of the AA program. The sponsored person is free to accept all or part of what is said. The relationship is one of trust and acceptance, which develops over time.

When a sponsored person has sufficient sobriety and has worked the 12 steps, he or she is often encouraged by his or her sponsor to also become a sponsor — to give back what he or she has received. It is believed that, in giving, one receives. Most sponsors acknowledge how much *they* learn from the people they sponsor and the task of sponsorship. Most members have a sponsor whom they can turn to in times of trouble and of joy (which can be high-risk times for drinkers) throughout their life in the fellowship of AA.

SERVICE

Part of the expectation of a member in AA is that he or she will give service. In the beginning, this may mean preparing for meetings or cleaning up after them — greeting people at the door, making coffee, moving chairs and packing up books. After some months, one may be asked to speak at a meeting and attend business meetings. Later on, a person may be elected, or may volunteer, to attend district meetings on the group's behalf and report back at the next business meeting. If one wishes, responsibilities may increase with continued sobriety. AA life encourages taking responsibility, being accountable and learning leadership skills. It also allows people to give back what they receive, to share hope and experience, and to feel useful and increase their self-respect.

RESISTANCE TO AA

Counsellors or clients may object to some aspects of the AA program. They may find the spiritual approach unfamiliar or too heavy. They may find attendance at meetings with "alcoholics" repugnant. They may feel that they are not as bad, as crazy or down-and-out as others they see at meetings. Some people may be frightened by the number of men, older adults or straight persons. They may not want to be in church basements, in groups, asking for help or receiving help. They may find the sameness of meetings boring or ritualistic. They may fear that they may become dependent on AA and their Higher Power. They may still want to drink or use drugs. Many meetings are now nonsmoking, and people may not like that aspect of AA. Some people may find it too much for their egos to concede to being powerless over alcohol. Some may also find the slogans (e.g., "Easy Does It," etc.) too childish to be helpful.

It is for this reason that AA members suggest that newcomers who want to do something about their drinking should give the program a chance by attending many different types of meetings over a three-month period (90 meetings in 90 days); talking to the "winners"; helping with the chairs; reading AA literature; and trying to keep sober *one day at a time*.

Some of the obstacles to attending AA are issues for anyone in recovery. Most people do not like to feel powerless or out of control, let alone admit that, especially to strangers. However, recovery from substance abuse requires many changes, and members report that overcoming this first challenge of AA attendance paves the way for other attitude and behavioral changes.

FROM THE MEMBERS

AA's goal is to provide tools for people who want to stop drinking and to help them find a new way of life that will bring peace and serenity. The program of recovery, the traditions and slogans, the opportunity for service, the fellowship and the encouragement of continual growth and discovery are the means to the goal. These means are also vehicles to banish alcohol, restlessness, irritability, discontent, old angers and old fears (AA, 1976).

Those who find that AA works for them declare that they indeed find sobriety, that the compulsion to drink leaves, and that they find a new freedom, a way to cope with reality, an extended family, and acceptance of life and peace of mind never experienced before. They also find that these gifts can be enjoyed and retained by giving service when asked, attending the meetings found to be helpful, and by being grateful. Many continue in AA for many years, because they encounter friends who understand, help to readjust their distorted focus on some days, and support them through difficult life changes. They also like the calm that meetings provide and report a sense of responsibility to ensure that AA is always there when anyone reaches out for help (AA, 1976).

Cocaine and Narcotics Anonymous

Two other mutual aid 12-step programs, available specifically to drug users, are Narcotics Anonymous (NA) and Cocaine Anonymous (CA). They formed more recently than AA, and they serve the different needs and subcultures of their members.

These nonprofit fellowships/societies of men and women have a simple message: "We have found a way to live without using drugs and we are happy to share it with anyone for whom drugs are a problem" (NA, 1996a). The NA way offers a drug-free way of life and "recovery in NA focuses on the problem of addiction, not on any particular drug" (NA, 1996c). NA and CA literature and books are available at the respective meetings. Much of what has been covered about the steps, traditions, process, meetings, groups for special needs, learning, etc. in AA applies to CA and NA.

Research findings suggest that participation by drug users in mutual aid groups may improve outcomes independent of other factors (American Psychiatric Association, 1995; U.S. Department of Health and Human Services, 1993) by providing peer support for continued participation in treatment, avoiding drug-using peers and high-risk environments, and intervening early in patterns of thinking and behavior that may lead to relapse.

Many CA and NA members attend AA, where they may find other members who have more months or years of being straight and sober and thus provide the hope and example that newcomers seek. Because CA and NA may not exist in smaller communities, those seeking to stop their drug taking may go to AA meetings. Many are aware that, in the absence of the preferred substance, they will use alcohol to excess in search of relief.

For many years, AA members were reluctant to identify with or entertain the stories of drug users at open meetings. However, the diminishing number of newcomers who are dependent solely on alcohol has meant that AA welcomes all who want to do something about their drinking — whether or not they have also used licit or illicit drugs — as long as they have, as AA founder Bill W. stated, "a genuine alcoholic history" (AA, 1996).

Information on local CA and NA meetings is available from the organizations' World Service Offices (listed at the end of this chapter) or the white pages of the telephone directory.

Moderation Management

"MM is a recovery program and new national self-help network for people who have made a healthy decision to reduce their drinking" (Moderation Management, 1996). Its main aim is to help people reduce their drinking to a level that no longer causes them problems. It provides support to those who choose moderation. Those who choose abstinence are referred to abstinence-based programs (AA, SMART Recovery, RR and WFS). It is not intended for alcoholics, chronic drinkers or former dependent drinkers who have stopped drinking. It is intended for problem drinkers who have experienced mild to moderate levels of alcohol-related problems (Moderation Management, 1996).

It is a layperson-led network of support groups that follows a nine-step program to help members reduce their drinking. It is a nonprofit registered charity, with no dues or fees, which started in 1994 in the United States. It now numbers 60 groups, and interest has been shown in Canada.

MM offers the following (Moderation Management, 1996):

1. A supportive mutual-help environment that encourages people who are concerned about their drinking to take action to change as soon as possible, before drinking problems become severe.
2. A nine-step professionally reviewed program, which provides information about alcohol, moderate drinking guidelines and limits, drink-monitoring exercises, goal-setting techniques, and self-management strategies. Members also work on taking "small steps" toward finding balance and moderation in other areas of their lives.
3. Some free literature is available at meetings. Self-help and professional books, audiotapes, videos and interactive computer programs that describe moderation programs are available through the network. Individual groups are building small "libraries" for loaning to members.
4. An electronic mailing list is the one of the best ways to keep up on recent MM happenings, ask questions, make comments and suggestions, philosophize, and find out where groups are forming. Until there is more staff, it may be the only way to distribute information on a timely manner (a printed newsletter is a long way off).
5. Presentations and workshops are available for professionals and organizations.

MM guidelines and limits for moderate drinking are available free at meetings and in the organization's handbook, *Moderate Drinking,* which is available at some public libraries. The program claims consistency with U.S. Department of Health and Human Services standards.

Rational Recovery

Rational Recovery (RR) is an international network of mutual aid groups founded in 1985 by Jack Trimpey. Initially the system used trained mental health professionals as advisers, while layleaders set up and ran the meetings. Attracted to its cognitive-behavioral approach (Rational-Emotive Behavior Therapy [REBT]), many psychologists became involved and helped establish groups in their communities.

Bishop (1995) reports that these psychologists became uncomfortable when Trimpey set up a privately owned corporation (Rational Recovery Systems Inc.) to train and license professionals for basically lay-led self-help groups. In 1993-94, Trimpey developed his Addictive Voice Recognition Training (AVRT), discussed below, along with a "structural" approach to addictions.

By 1993, more than 10,000 people, in more than 500 groups, mainly in the United States, had gone through RR. In 1996, RR had six groups operating in Canada. Many groups have maintained RR's original form (i.e., not using AVRT), while others operate with a combination of REBT and other models of cognitive-behavioral therapy (CBT) and AVRT (Bishop, 1995). Trimpey now advocates that a person can use the self-help materials he has produced and achieve lifelong abstinence in four months without a group (Rational Recovery Systems, 1996). The head office suggests that anyone accessing RR on the Internet has all that he or she needs to recover, which makes RR useful to those who are not "joiners."

The approaches in RR are helpful to those who want to develop greater self-control, rather than look to an external source of help (i.e., a group or a Higher Power). The RR office claims people have what it takes within themselves to recover.

Abstinence is required. Functioning RR groups may use all or some of the ideas detailed below, since all groups are autonomous and loosely knit. Some choose to continue using Rational-Emotive Behavior Therapy as well as incorporating the new approach of Trimpey as described by Bishop (1995) below.

Basic tenets of Rational Recovery
1. People are largely responsible for their behaviors, including addictive behaviors.
2. A person can recover; many people can gain control over their addictive behaviors.
3. Lifetime membership is not required; many people can recover in a year or two.
4. Labelling of all kinds is discouraged; a person does not have to call him/herself an alcoholic to begin to recover.

5. Alcoholism may or not be a disease; however, a person has to find a way to cope and take responsibility for his/her life in any case.

6. The value of a person is not linked to his/her behavior, addictive or otherwise. A person will not be a better person if he/she gives up alcohol or some other addictive behavior; he/she may be a happier person, a person who has better relationships and can keep a job, but behavioral change does not affect the "goodness" of the self.

7. A person is not, *ipso facto,* "in denial" if he/she does not accept the basic AA tenets.

8. A person is not doomed to a life of alcoholism if he/she does not accept help from AA, a rehabilitation clinic, a hospital and so on. People can recover on their own, with or without the help of professionals and/or self-help groups." (Bishop, 1995)

"The Beast"

This is both a metaphor and an acronym that many find useful as a reminder that the urge to drink or use drugs is dangerous and must be resisted. It is explained by Bishop (1995) as follows:

B = Boozing opportunity when you think of drinking.

E = Enemy recognition, when you hear the mental voice.

A = Accuse the thought of drinking of being the real enemy.

S = Self-control and self-worth are now yours for the taking.

T = Treasure your sobriety; a lot is at stake.

It is believed that by listening for "The Beast" in others, one becomes aware of one's own addictive thinking (Trimpey, 1992).

Trimpey argues that addictions are the result of urges emanating from the mid-brain. "In AVRT there are no steps, sponsors, Higher Powers, psychological theories, enablers, triggers, warning signs of relapse, or religious teachings." The "sole cause of addiction is the 'Addictive Voice' that enlists all neocortical resources in its quest for endless intoxication" (Bishop, 1995). Trimpey now maintains that only someone who has recovered can treat an addicted person.

Brief, inexpensive educational programs teaching the AVRT skill of abstinence are available through locally owned and operated Rational Recovery Centres, including a centre on Vancouver Island.

PROCESS

Their literature suggests that persons wanting to recover should first read Trimpey's book *The Final Fix: AVRT.* Then one should listen to the audiotapes, watch the video, enrol in AVRT at a Rational Recovery Centre, attend local RR Self-Help Network discussion groups and subscribe to *The Journal of Rational Recovery* (Rational Recovery Systems, 1996). It is believed that abstinence is a skill that can be learned. "If you've tried quitting many times, AVRT shows you exactly how it is done ... once started, AVRT becomes almost effortless"(Rational Recovery Systems, 1996).

SMART Recovery

Self Management and Recovery Training (SMART Recovery) is an outgrowth of Rational Recovery. In 1993–94, many of the psychologists involved as advisers in RR withdrew and formed the SMART Recovery Network. It numbers 200 groups and is based on cognitive-behavior training and rational thinking (Bishop, 1995). It is a program of "sensible self-help" with trained co-ordinators (Alcohol and Drug Abuse Self-help Network, 1996). In 1996, the only Canadian group operated in Morin Heights, Quebec.

SMART Recovery is a free self-help program for recovery from chemical dependency. The emphasis is on learning how to increase one's motivation to quit. Handling urges and developing new ways of coping are stressed. The goal is to create a healthy, positive lifestyle. Permanent abstinence is regarded as the most rational, easy solution. When success is achieved, graduates may choose to leave or to stay with their group to help others (SMART Recovery, 1996).

MEETINGS

Ten or 12 people usually attend the meetings, which are frequently led by a trained co-ordinator who may be a professional. Each group has an adviser, a professional therapist who may or may not attend every meeting. This adviser is available to the co-ordinator for guidance in group functioning, to teach a new Rational Emotive Behavior Therapy (REBT) strategy, or if a member is in trouble. Members are encouraged to read core books.

Groups meet once or twice weekly and the aim is to help participants overcome their addictive behaviors by gaining more control over their thinking, emotions and behaviors and by developing effective relapse prevention skills. There is no standard format for meetings. Participants may talk (in some groups for up to 10 minutes each) about their problems in recovery and their fears about relapse. They are often taught, by the co-ordinator or adviser, strategies to avoid relapse and how to analyse their thinking, using Ellis's ABCDE formula (Bishop, 1995). Social skills training and practice (such as role-playing) may be part of the program. These strategies give direction to the discussion and questioning. Cross-talk is encouraged, and confrontation between members occurs as members try to help each other recognize the irrationality of their thinking and behavior. Participants exchange phone numbers and keep in touch between meetings. A collection is taken to defray costs.

TRAINING AND EDUCATION

Co-ordinators and advisers receive training to assist members to train themselves in this different approach to thinking, behaving and feeling. Subscriptions to a quarterly newsletter cost $10 (U.S.) per year.

RESISTANCE TO RR AND SMART

Bishop reports that, because of the emphasis on rationality and the absence of a spiritual focus, many find RR and Smart Recovery helpful, but some find the confrontation upsetting. Some people may want to gain more self-control to continue drinking, and still others return to AA. Some consider RR and SMART "as unsatisfactory as AA"(Bishop, 1995).

SOS Secular Organizations for Sobriety (Save Our Selves)

Secular Organizations for Sobriety, "a self-empowerment approach to sobriety" (Secular Organizations for Sobriety, 1996) was launched in 1986 in co-operation with the Council for Democratic and Secular Humanism. It is a nonprofit network of lay-led community groups with the sole aim of helping people maintain their sobriety/ recovery. It numbered 100,000 members in 1996 (Secular Organizations for Sobriety, 1996a).

SOS is an alternative recovery method for substance abusers who are uncomfortable with the spiritual content of 12-step programs. It credits the individual for achieving and maintaining his or her own sobriety and encourages the use of the scientific method to understand alcoholism. It has no opinion on outside matters and does not wish to become embroiled in controversy (Secular Organizations for Sobriety, 1996b).

All who sincerely desire sobriety are welcome. The main priority in the substance abuser's life must be sobriety — "the Sobriety Priority." Abstinence is required and anonymity is respected. Honest, clear and direct communication of feelings and thoughts is encouraged. Members are expected to choose nondestructive, nondelusional, rational and sober approaches to living the "good life" (Secular Organizations for Sobriety, 1996c).

SOS groups have a maximum of 20 people. Leadership is shared. People with similar problems get together in a safe, nonjudgmental environment. The structure and format of the meeting are established by the group. Sobriety anniversaries are acknowledged. New members are encouraged to attend meetings at least once a week for the first six months, followed by "booster meetings" as needed. Pamphlets and books are available at meetings. The SOS National Clearinghouse publishes a quarterly newsletter; subscriptions are $18 per year.

SOS founder James Christopher describes the methods advocated by SOS in his most recent book, *SOS Sobriety: The Proven Alternative to 12-Step Programs.*

Women for Sobriety

Women for Sobriety (WFS) was established in 1975 by Jean Kirkpatrick, a woman in recovery, who discovered that AA didn't meet all her needs as a woman. She believed that women needed their own groups, free from men and role expectations, in which to share their experiences and to grow stronger. There are currently 23 groups in southwestern Ontario and four on Canada's west coast.

The WFS program "is an affirmation of the value and worth of each woman," as is shown by its Thirteen Statements of Acceptance, which follow:
1. I have a drinking problem that once had me.
2. Negative emotions destroy only myself.
3. Happiness is a habit I will develop.
4. Problems bother me only to the degree I permit them to.
5. I am what I think.
6. Life can be ordinary or it can be great.
7. Love can change the course of my world.
8. The fundamental object of life is emotional and spiritual growth.
9. The past is gone forever.
10. All love given returns twofold.
11. Enthusiasm is my daily exercise.
12. I am a competent woman and have much to give to others.
13. I am responsible for myself and my sisters.

Kirkpatrick (1978) maintains that these statements lead a woman to see herself positively and increase her self-confidence. She learns to see herself as able to overcome her drinking and other problems as well. The changes she experiences are reinforced by the group. The groups provide acceptance, nurturing and a sense of belonging. They provide a place to release anxiety, share fears, and to learn to trust.

MEETINGS

Eight to 12 women usually attend meetings, which are held in places such as homes, women's treatment centres and shopping mall facilities. The discussion or "conversation" (Kirkpatrick, 1978) is led by one of the members. After opening with a reading of the Statement of Purpose, the group discusses one of the Thirteen Statements of Acceptance, personal problems in recovery, or a topic as suggested in the monthly bulletin. For the closing, women join hands and state: "We are capable and confident, caring and compassionate, always willing to help another, bonded together in overcoming our addictions." Following this, a donation is taken to pay for the group's expenses and to support its headquarters. Women for Sobriety wishes to be independent and self-supporting, and united in a common cause.

Most groups meet once a week but may meet more often as required. Meetings never last longer than 90 minutes.

MEMBERSHIP

Membership is open to any woman who has a problem with alcohol and who wants to stop drinking and find a new way of life. It is believed that the dependence on alcohol, acquired to overcome stress, loneliness, emotional deprivation, etc., has to be resolved through abstinence and personal change. A woman has to make the decision to take responsibility for herself and her actions. Unlike AA, a recital of a woman's entire drinking history is not required, since there are no open speaker meetings.

USING THE WOMEN FOR SOBRIETY PROGRAM

Woman are advised to first make the "decision to accept responsibility for your life and for your actions"(Kirkpatrick, 1978). Then each woman is expected to attend meetings and volunteer to lead a group, call a member and help others. It is believed that, by helping others, a woman helps herself.

Each member subscribes to the monthly newsletter, *Sobering Thoughts*. Most importantly, she is expected to spend 20 minutes early each morning in meditation. At this time, she is to read and think about the Thirteen Statements of Acceptance, selecting one statement as her thought for the day, which she is expected to use, live and practise. WFS is a "program of mind development through which we create new habits and a new life, a new way of living" (Kirkpatrick, 1978). Behavioral change is promoted by positive reinforcement, cognitive strategies, letting the body help, and dynamic group involvement. The object of WFS is "to lead all of us to a new philosophy of life." (Kirkpatrick, 1978). "Members of WFS live by the WFS philosophy: forget the past, plan for tomorrow and live for today" (Women for Sobriety, 1996).

PEN PAL PROGRAM

In the absence of a local WFS group, women can become part of the Pen Pal Program and correspond with recovered women. Abundant literature, workbooks, videos and audiotapes are available at a nominal cost from WFS headquarters. After a year of sobriety, some women might consider starting a group in their own communities. The office will notify members of the Pen Pal Program when a new group is starting near them (Women for Sobriety, 1996A).

177

WHAT A COUNSELLOR CAN DO

1. RECOGNIZE THE VALIDITY AND IMPORTANCE OF MUTUAL AID GROUPS.

As mentioned, most professionals in the field recognize that support and encouragement are necessary to substance abusers if they are to maintain the changes in behavior, thoughts and coping found in therapy and in a sober way of life. This has been reinforced by research (Lavoie, Borkman and Gidron, 1994; McCrady and Irvine, 1989; Reissman and Carroll, 1995; U.S. Department of Health and Human Services, 1993). Thus it is appropriate for the counsellor to introduce the idea that research and practice indicate that substance abusers must have ongoing support for as long as is needed. Such support can be found at minimal cost in a mutual aid group. The counsellor can offer a description of the available choices in mutual aid groups. If choices don't exist, the counsellor will: a) work with the client to overcome any resistance to the existing mutual aid group; b) help to establish a mutual aid group more to the client's liking; or c) work with the client to find other support for a sober life, through family, friends or other groups.

2. VISIT AND BECOME FAMILIAR WITH LOCAL MUTUAL AID GROUPS.

The descriptions here are but vague reflections of the vitality and scope of actual meetings and membership. You will feel more comfortable referring clients to groups if you have visited them. Former clients may be willing to take you and introduce you to the program of recovery in person. Your own reactions to the meeting, the people, the speaker and the program may provide you with some food for thought and the desire to talk with others who have attended or are members.

It is a good idea to become familiar with the various types and sizes of meetings, so that you can help clients make good choices. Some research indicates (McCrady and Irvine, 1989) that clients are good candidates for AA if they have severe drinking problems, an affective rather than a cognitive focus, concerns about the purpose and meaning of life, good interpersonal skills, and a high need to belong. Clients are also most likely to benefit from mutual aid if they join a group whose members are similar to them in age, culture and occupational status (American Psychiatric Association, 1995; Zweben, 1995).

3. MAKE CONTACTS.

Keep in touch with clients who have settled into membership in mutual aid groups and develop a list of people who will keep you informed and who are willing to take a client to her or his first meeting.

4. ASK CLIENTS TO BECOME INVOLVED IN MUTUAL AID EARLY IN THEIR THERAPY.

This is a helpful manoeuvre for several reasons. It allows the client to become used to group life, the members and the process before they leave therapy. It allows you, as their counsellor, time to explore their issues about the mutual aid group and to deal with any resistance to ongoing mutual aid they may have. As McCrady and Irvine

(1989) say: "It is important that counsellors show knowledgeable and *unambivalent* interest in client's progress in their mutual aid group."

5. TRY OTHER RESOURCES AVAILABLE TO COMPLEMENT YOUR SKILLS.

a) Using Prochaska, DiClemente and Norcross's "stages of self-change" model in therapy, you could help clients discover where they are in their mutual aid participation and begin to work with them to move to the next stage. The chapter by Soden and Murray in this book will assist.

b) Bishop (1989) describes the way in which you can integrate REBT and AVRT into your practice.

c) McCrady and Irvine (1989) and Zweben (1995) also offer an in-depth approach to integrating AA with professional practice.

6. KEEP AN OPEN MIND.

Research continues and new findings may suggest different approaches. As Miller (1989) asserts: "No one approach stands out from all the rest but neither are all treatments equally effective (or ineffective)." There is no one answer to the complex phenomena of substance abuse. Professional energy spent on preserving turf, defending one approach/one particular mutual aid group/one "pet" theory, puts the client at risk for relapse.

It is wise to be sensitive to a client's reaction to and preferences for a particular group.

CONCLUSION

A mutual aid group member, sober for 15 years, said her experience with mutual aid was similar to a group of geese flying south. Her story, as described by Kort and Smith (1993), noted that science has learned the following:

> As each bird flaps its wing, it creates uplift for the bird immediately following it. By flying in a V formation, the whole flock can fly at least seventy per cent farther in a day than if each bird flew on its own....Whenever a goose falls out of formation, it feels how hard it is to try to fly against the wind on its own, and it quickly gets back into formation to fly with the flock....When the lead goose gets tired, it rotates back in the wing and another goose flies in the front of the point....The geese in the back honk to encourage those at the front to keep up their speed. When a goose weakens or is hurt and falls out of formation, two geese follow it down to help and protect it. They stay with the goose until it is able to fly or until it dies. Then they set out again, either on their own or with another formation, until they catch up with the group.

Similarly, from her mutual aid group she receives: a common direction, a lighter load, help to be and do things beyond her individual capacity, support, encouragement through thick and thin, and a sense of kinship with the world and her fellow members. What a contrast to life as a practising alcoholic!

RESOURCES

Alcoholics Anonymous World Services, Inc.
Box 459, Grand Central Station
New York, NY 10163 USA
Phone: (212) 870-3400
Fax: (212) 870-3137
Web site: http//www.alcoholics-
   anonymous.org/index.html

Cocaine Anonymous World Service Office
3740 Overland Avenue, Suite G
Los Angeles, CA 90034 USA
Phone: (310) 559-5833
Fax: (310) 559-2554
E-mail: CAWSO@CA.org
Web site: http://www.ca.org/

Moderation Management
PO Box 6005,
Ann Arbor, MI 48106 USA
Phone: (313) 677-6007
Web site: http://comnet.org/mm/

Narcotics Anonymous Canada
World Service Office
150 Britannia Rd. East, Unit 21
Mississauga, ON L4Z 2A4
Phone: (905) 507-0100
Fax: (905) 507-0101

Narcotics Anonymous
P.O. Box 9999
Van Nuys, CA 91409 USA
Phone: (818) 773-9999
Fax: (818) 700-0700
E-mail: lynnl@sprynet.com
Web site: http//www.wsoinc.com/

Rational Recovery Self-Help Network
Box 800
Lotus, CA 95651 USA
Phone: (916) 621-2667
E-mail: rr@rational.org.
Web page: http://www.rational.org/recovery

SMART Recovery Network
24000 Mercantile Blvd. Suite 11,
Beachwood, OH 44122 USA
Phone: (216) 292-0220
Fax: (216) 831-3776
E-mail: SRMail1@aol.com

SOS
P.O. Box 5
Buffalo, NY 14215 USA
Phone: (716) 636-7571

SOS National Clearinghouse
The Centre for Inquiry, West
5521 Grosvenor Blvd.
Los Angeles, CA 90066 USA
Phone: (310) 821-8430 Fax: (310) 821-2610
E-mail: sosa@loop.com
Web site: http//:www.codesh.org/sos/
   CFIFlynn@aol.com

Women for Sobriety
P.O. Box 618
Quakertown, PA 18951 USA
Phone and Fax: (215) 536-8026
E-mail: WFSobriety@aol.com
Web site: http//www.mediapulse.com/wfs/

Don't Forget the Internet

A wealth of self-help information
sites and electronic discussion groups
are accessible through the Internet.
For starters, check out:
**The Guide to Addictions Information
on the Internet**
(www.arf.org/isd/links/mainpage.html)
at the Addiction Research Foundation's
web site. See under Self-Help in the
subject index.

Suggested Books, Tapes and Pamphlets

REFERENCES

Alcoholics Anonymous. (1976). *Alcoholics Anonymous: The Story of How Many Thousands of Men and Women Have Recovered from Alcoholism,* 3rd ed. New York: Alcoholics Anonymous World Services.

Alcoholics Anonymous. (1984). *Pass It On: The Story of Bill Wilson and How the AA Message Reached the World.* New York: Alcoholics Anonymous World Services.

Alcoholics Anonymous. (1985). *The Twelve Steps and Twelve Traditions.* New York: Alcoholics Anonymous World Services.

Alcoholics Anonymous. (1994). *About AA: A Newsletter for Professionals* (Fall/Winter). New York: Alcoholics Anonymous World Services.

Alcoholics Anonymous. (1994a). *Questions and Answers on Sponsorship.* New York: Alcoholics Anonymous World Services.

Alcoholics Anonymous. (1995). *AA Everywhere-Anywhere: 60th Anniversary Celebration.* New York: Alcoholics Anonymous World Services.

Alcoholics Anonymous. (1996). *Problems Other Than Alcohol.* New York: Alcoholics Anonymous World Service.

American Psychiatric Association. (1995). Practice guidelines for the treatment of patients with substance use disorders: Alcohol, cocaine, opiates. *American Journal of Psychiatry* 152 (11): supplement.

Bishop, F.M. (1995). Rational-Emotive Behavior Therapy and two self-help alternatives to the 12-step model. In *Psychotherapy and Substance Abuse*, ed. Washton, A.M. New York: Guilford.

Canadian Centre on Substance Abuse. (1992). *Self-Help and Substance Abuse.* Ottawa: Author.

Christopher, J. (1992). *SOS Sobriety: The Proven Alternative to 12-Step Programs.* Amherst, NY: Prometheus Books.

Delgado, M., and Humm-Delgado, D. (1993). Chemical dependence, self-help, and the Hispanic community. In *Hispanic Substance Abuse*, eds. Mayer, R.S., Kail, A.L., and Watts, T.D. Springfield, IL: Charles C. Thomas.

Hill, K. (1984). *Helping You Helps Me: A Guide Book for Self-Help Groups.* Ottawa: Canadian Council on Social Development.

Humphreys, K., and Woods, M.D. (1993). Researching mutual help group participation in a segregated society. *Journal of Applied Behavioral Science* 29 (2): 181–201.

Humphreys, K., Mavis, B., and Stoffelmayr, B. (1994). Are twelve step programs appropriate for disenfranchised groups? In *Self-Help and Mutual Aid Groups: International and Multicultural Perspectives*, eds. Lavoie, F., Borkman, T., and Gidron, B. New York: Haworth Press.

Kennedy, M., and Humphreys, K. (1994). Understanding world view transformation in members of mutual help groups. In *Self-Help and Mutual Aid Groups: International and Multicultural Perspectives*, eds. Lavoie, F., Borkman, T., and Gidron, B. New York: Haworth Press.

Kirkpatrick, J. (1978). *Turnabout: Help for a New Life*. New York: Doubleday and Company.

Kort, M., and Smith, S. (1993). *Stop Smoking Program: Facilitators Guide*. Toronto, Ontario: Addiction Research Foundation.

Lavoie, F., Borkman, T., and Gidron, B. (eds.). (1994). *Self-help and Mutual Aid Groups: International and Multicultural Perspectives*. Part 1, Vol. 11 (1). New York: Haworth Press.

"M.", H. (1996). Address to the 45th Eastern Ontario Fall Conference, Ottawa on tape. Val Belair, PQ: TLS.

McCrady, B.S., and Irvine, S. (1989). Self-help groups. In *Handbook of Alcoholism Treatment Approaches*, eds. Hester, R.K., and Miller, W.R. New York: Pergammon Press.

Miller, W.R. (1989). Treating alcohol problems. In *Handbook of Alcoholism Treatment Approaches*, eds. Hester, R.K., and Miller, W.R. New York: Pergammon Press.

Miller, W.R. (1989b). Matching individuals with interventions. In *Handbook of Alcoholism Treatment Approaches*, eds. Hester, R.K., and Miller, W.R. New York: Pergammon Press.

Moderation Management 1996. Web page. Ann Arbor, MI: Moderation Management.

Moderation Management. (1996). *Moderate Drinking*. Ann Arbor, MI: Author.

Narcotics Anonymous. (1990). *Youth and Recovery*. Van Nuys, CA: Narcotics Anonymous World Service Office.

Narcotics Anonymous. (1995). *For the Newcomer*. Van Nuys, CA: Narcotics Anonymous World Service Office.

Narcotics Anonymous. (1996). *An Introductory Guide*. Van Nuys, CA: Narcotics Anonymous World Service Office.

Narcotics Anonymous. (1996a). *Welcome to Narcotics Anonymous*. Van Nuys, CA: Narcotics Anonymous World Service Office.

Narcotics Anonymous. (1996b). *Am I an Addict?* Van Nuys, CA: Narcotics Anonymous World Service Office.

Narcotics Anonymous. (1996c). *Drug Problems? We've Been There.* Ottawa: Narcotics Anonymous Ottawa Area Office.

Rational Recovery Systems. (1996). *AVRT and It Comes with a Guarantee!* Lotus, CA: Rational Recovery Systems.

Reissman, F., and Carroll, D. (1995). *Redefining Self-Help. Policy and Practice.* San Francisco: Jossey-Bass.

Room, R., and Greenfield, T. (1993). Alcoholics Anonymous, other 12-step movements and psychotherapy in the U.S. population 1990. *Addiction* 88: 555–562.

Secular Organizations for Sobriety. (1996). *A Self-Empowerment Approach to Recovery.* Buffalo, NY: Secular Organizations for Sobriety.

Secular Organizations for Sobriety. (1996a). *SOS International Newsletter* 9 (2). Buffalo, NY: Secular Organizations for Sobriety.

Secular Organizations for Sobriety. (1996b). Home Page. Los Angeles: SOS National Clearing House.

Secular Organizations for Sobriety. (1996c).*The Sobriety Priority.* Buffalo, NY: Secular Organizations for Sobriety.

SMART Recovery. (1996). *Alcohol or Drug Problem?: Now There Is a Scientific Alternative!* Beachwood, OH: Alcohol and Drug Abuse Self-help Network.

Trimpey, J. (1992). *The Small Book: A Revolutionary Alternative for Overcoming Alcohol and Drug Dependency.* New York: Delacorte.

U.S. Department of Health and Human Services (1993). *Recovery Training and Self-Help: Relapse Prevention and Aftercare for Drug Addicts.* Rockville, MD: National Institute on Drug Abuse.

Women for Sobriety. (1996). *Women and Addictions: A Way to Recovery.* Quakertown, PA: Women for Sobriety.

Women for Sobriety. (1996a). *"New Life" Literature.* Quakertown, PA: Women for Sobriety.

Zweben, J.E. (1995). Integrating psychotherapy and 12-step approaches. In *Psychotherapy and Substance Abuse*, ed. Washton, A.M. New York: Guildford.

Chapter 10

Physical Effects of Alcohol and Other Drugs

MELDON KAHAN

Alcohol and drug counsellors can play an important role in maintaining their clients' physical health. They are frequently called upon to explain the health risks of alcohol and drugs, and to inform clients of ways to minimize these risks. They often communicate with the client's family physician and other health care providers. They may be the first professionals to become aware of signs and symptoms of impending illness in a client. For these reasons, therapists need to be familiar with the physical effects of alcohol and drugs. This chapter presents a brief summary of the health effects of the main drugs of abuse.

ALCOHOL

Most adults in our society drink alcohol moderately and without problems. However, excess alcohol use creates a huge burden of sickness, death and health care costs, outweighing the combined effects of all other drugs of abuse except tobacco. Following is a discussion of some common alcohol-related problems.

GASTRITIS

Gastritis is a common complication of heavy alcohol consumption. Alcohol causes irritation and erosion of the lining of the stomach, producing discomfort and pain in the upper abdominal area. Gastritis is potentially serious, because it can result in internal bleeding, the symptoms of which are bloody or dark-brown vomit, and bloody or black, tarry stools. Gastritis often heals quickly with abstinence. A wide variety of medications promote healing by reducing the production of acid in the stomach.

Alcohol also causes inflammation in the esophagus (esophagitis) and pancreas (pancreatitis). Symptoms of esophagitis include heartburn and vomiting. Pancreatitis causes severe abdominal pain and vomiting, often requiring hospitalization.

ALCOHOLIC LIVER DISEASE

Alcoholic liver disease occurs in three stages. The first is called "fatty liver," in which the liver accumulates fat and becomes enlarged. This stage is usually asymptomatic. The second stage is alcoholic hepatitis, or inflammation of the liver. This stage may be asymptomatic, but sometimes patients become seriously ill. They may develop jaundice, the signs of which are yellow skin, dark urine and whitish stools. They may also develop vomiting, fever and pain in the liver area (right upper abdomen below the ribs).

Repeated episodes of alcoholic hepatitis lead to the third stage, cirrhosis, which is a major cause of death in Canada. In cirrhosis, large portions of the liver have died and been replaced by scar tissue. This may render the liver incapable of fully metabolizing dietary proteins, creating the buildup of intermediate chemicals that are toxic to the brain. This can lead to a condition called hepatic encephalopathy, in which patients become drowsy and forgetful, and eventually sink into a coma and die. Encephalopathy can be treated with a low-protein diet and laxatives such as lactulose.

Cirrhosis also causes death through internal bleeding. Blood normally flows from the intestines into the portal vein, and from there into the liver. The scar tissue in the cirrhotic liver impedes the flow of blood in the portal vein, causing it to back up into veins in the esophagus. These veins then become swollen and engorged, a condition called "esophageal varices." Varices sometimes burst, causing profuse and often fatal bleeding. Ascites, a condition in which the abdomen fills with fluid and protrudes, is also due in part to obstructed blood flow.

While mortality from cirrhosis can be reduced through liver transplantation and medication such as Propylthiouracil, the mainstay of treatment is reduced alcohol consumption. Clients with alcoholic liver disease should be told that fatty liver and alcoholic hepatitis are reversible with abstinence or reduced drinking; the liver has a tremendous capacity to heal itself. While cirrhosis is not reversible, clients often lead normal lives as long as they abstain completely from alcohol. Reduced drinking strategies are not recommended for patients with cirrhosis, since even moderate alcohol consumption may promote liver damage.

TRAUMA

While moderate consumption of alcohol has a mild disinhibiting and relaxing effect, acute alcohol intoxication causes sedation, impaired judgment, poor motor co-ordination and slow response time. It also affects mood and behavior, causing impulsivity, anger and depression. For this reason, alcohol consumption is a major cause of trauma-related death and injury, including motor vehicle crashes, work-related injuries and violence (assaults and suicide). Even moderate alcohol consumption can impair driving ability.

DEMENTIA

Heavy drinking is associated with a number of neurological disorders. (For more details on the cognitive effects of alcohol, see Chapter 23.) One common and serious disorder is dementia, defined as a global decrease in cognitive functioning. Alcoholic dementia differs from the most common form of dementia, Alzheimer's Disease, in that it is potentially reversible with abstinence (although only some recover, and recovery may only be partial). The cognitive changes of alcoholic dementia may be subtle, such as decreased ability to think abstractly. Counsellors who suspect dementia should refer the patient to a neurologist or psychologist for neuropsychological testing and possibly a brain (CT) scan. Patients should be advised of the diagnosis, and of the potential for recovery with abstinence.

CEREBELLAR DISEASE

Alcohol can damage the cerebellum, a part of the brain that controls balance and equilibrium. Patients with cerebellar disease have tremors of the hands and walk with a wide-based gait, as if they were on a moving ship; sometimes they are unable to maintain their balance without a cane or walker.

PERIPHERAL NEUROPATHY

Alcohol may damage the nerves in the feet and legs, causing a condition known as peripheral neuropathy. Patients with this syndrome have decreased sensation in their feet, and may experience painful burning sensations.

WERNICKE-KORSAKOFF SYNDROME

Heavy drinkers often eat poorly, and the metabolism of alcohol depletes the body's stores of the B vitamins. This can lead to a severe deficiency of vitamin B1 (thiamine), causing Wernicke-Korsakoff Syndrome. In the Wernicke's phase of this syndrome, patients become drowsy and unresponsive, and their walking and eye movements become unco-ordinated. Wernicke's is a medical emergency, requiring prompt administration of intravenous thiamine. If not treated in time, patients develop Korsakoff's, exhibiting marked impairment of short-term memory. Patients with Korsakoff's may not remember an event that occurred 10 minutes earlier; to mask their confusion and make sense of their lives, they sometimes fabricate events ("confabulation"). Patients with Korsakoff's rarely recover and frequently require institutionalization.

BLACKOUTS

A blackout is a type of amnesia in which patients are unable to remember events that took place during the previous evening's drinking binge. Patients may on occasion behave in a bizarre or dangerous manner during a blackout.

ALCOHOL WITHDRAWAL

Alcohol withdrawal can follow extended periods of heavy daily drinking. It begins six to 24 hours after the patient's last drink, and may persist for up to seven days. Symptoms include tremors, sweating, fast pulse, high blood pressure, vomiting and anxiety. Grand mal seizures are not uncommon. Other complications include irregular heartbeat, hallucinations and delirium tremens (the DTs). Patients with delirium tremens become confused and disoriented, and may die of cardiovascular collapse.

Alcohol withdrawal is effectively treated by providing a calm, supportive environment and, if necessary, judicious use of benzodiazepines. Twenty milligrams of diazepam, administered orally every hour until symptoms subside, is the preferred drug treatment because it provides quick relief of symptoms and circumvents the need for take-home prescriptions of benzodiazepines.

REPRODUCTIVE EFFECTS

Cirrhosis of the liver causes a relative excess of estrogen in men, resulting in impotence, small testicles and breast enlargement (testicular feminization syndrome). Alcohol can cause irregular menstrual cycles in women, and infertility in both men and women.

Heavy drinking during pregnancy may result in fetal alcohol syndrome (FAS), the features of which are delayed growth, cognitive impairment, and facial abnormalities such as short eye openings. FAS children have cognitive-behavioral problems such as hyperactivity, speech disorders and deficits in learning and memory. These problems persist into adolescence and adulthood. FAS is thought to be the leading preventable cause of mental retardation.

Not all children exhibit the full syndrome; some have only subtle cognitive deficits with no facial abnormalities, a condition known as fetal alcohol effects (FAE).

A safe level of alcohol consumption during pregnancy has not been established, and abstinence is the most prudent recommendation.

CARDIOVASCULAR EFFECTS

Heavy drinkers are at risk of high blood pressure, stroke and irregular heart rhythms. Moderate drinkers may have a lower risk for heart attacks than nondrinkers, perhaps because alcohol has beneficial effects on cholesterol.

PSYCHIATRIC EFFECTS

Heavy alcohol consumption can induce severe depression. Alcohol-induced depression usually resolves within two to four weeks of abstinence, distinguishing it from a primary affective disorder. Heavy drinkers are at substantially greater risk for suicide than the general population, partly because of alcohol-induced depression, and partly because of the impulsivity and emotional volatility associated with acute intoxication.

SAFE LIMITS

A safe upper limit of alcohol consumption has not yet been firmly established, partly because of the widely varying effects of alcohol on the body; what may be safe for the heart may not be safe for the liver. Most recommendations set an upper limit of two to three standard drinks per day, and 12 to 14 drinks per week. Some recommendations suggest lower limits for women, because they are more prone than men to develop alcoholic liver disease. Other recommendations advise at least two days of abstinence per week, to give the liver a chance to recuperate and to diminish the strength of the drinking habit.

EFFECTS OF ALCOHOL ON BLOOD TESTS

Therapists are sometimes asked by their clients to interpret the results of blood tests taken by an alcohol treatment facility. One common abnormality in test results is an elevated level of gamma-glutamyl transferase (GGT), a liver enzyme. The liver increases production of this enzyme in response to heavy drinking. Also, liver cells damaged through alcoholic hepatitis become "leaky," allowing greater quantities of the enzyme to escape into the bloodstream. With abstinence or reduced drinking, GGT usually returns to normal within four to eight weeks.

Alcohol causes red blood cells to increase in size, as measured by a test called mean cell volume (MCV). MCV returns to normal within one to two months of abstinence or reduced drinking.

Blood tests such as GGT and MCV are not as sensitive as a clinical interview in detecting alcohol problems. However, periodic tests can be used to confirm clients' self-reports of reduced alcohol intake.

PHARMACOLOGICAL TREATMENT OF ALCOHOL DEPENDENCE

Naltrexone (ReVia) has been shown in several controlled trials to reduce the intensity and frequency of alcohol binges and cravings. Alcohol causes release of opioids in the brain, giving drinkers a sense of euphoria. Naltrexone blocks the action of opioids, thus diminishing the pleasurable and reinforcing effects of alcohol. Naltrexone cannot be used in patients who take opiates regularly. Antidepressants such as fluoxetine (Prozac) also reduce alcohol consumption by increasing the concentration of serotonin in the brain.

Disulfiram (Antabuse) and calcium carbamide (Temposil) act by inhibiting a liver enzyme that metabolizes alcohol, causing the buildup of a toxic metabolite called acetaldehyde. Patients who drink while on these drugs experience chest pain, headache, flushed face, vomiting and an irregular heartbeat. The reaction is potentially fatal, because blood pressure can drop precipitously and the heart can go into a dangerous rhythm. The patient should be instructed not to drink for at least seven days after taking Antabuse and two days after taking Temposil. These medications may be a useful treatment adjunct in highly motivated patients who do not feel confident in their ability to resist spontaneous impulses to drink. Temposil, which has a quicker onset of action than does Antabuse, can be used for short periods (a few days) when patients expect to encounter high-risk drinking situations.

OPIATES ("NARCOTICS")

Opiates act on receptors in brain cells to create a sense of euphoria and tranquillity. Tolerance builds up quickly; chronic heroin users often report that the drug no longer gets them "high" but merely staves off withdrawal symptoms. Commonly abused oral opiates include oxycodone (contained in Percocet and Percodan), codeine (Tylenol 3), hydrocodone (cough syrups such as Tussionex and Hycodan), hydromorphone (Dilaudid) and morphine. Injectable opiates include morphine, meperidine (Demerol) and heroin.

OVERDOSE

Opiates suppress the centres in the brain that control respiration and heartbeat, with potentially fatal results. Heroin users are at particular risk, because the purity of street heroin can vary widely.

WITHDRAWAL

Opiate withdrawal is somewhat similar to a bad case of the flu. Patients experience sweating, muscle aches, runny nose and runny eyes, goose bumps, chills and nausea. Patients in opiate withdrawal are restless and uncomfortable, and they have strong cravings for opiates. Withdrawal peaks at two to three days after the last drug use, and resolves by five to seven days.

Opiate withdrawal is generally safe, and complications such as seizures do not occur. A major exception is withdrawal during pregnancy (see below). Opiate withdrawal can be treated over one to two weeks with tapering doses of methadone or with clonidine, a nonnarcotic drug that blocks the nervous impulses in the brain that cause withdrawal symptoms. Treating withdrawal with opiates other than methadone should only be done if the risk of double-doctoring is remote, or if the patient is in a carefully supervised inpatient setting.

METHADONE MAINTENANCE

Methadone is a long-acting oral narcotic closely regulated by the College of Physicians and Surgeons. In the appropriate dose, methadone relieves withdrawal symptoms and drug cravings, without causing sedation or euphoria. Patients in methadone maintenance programs drink a methadone solution daily in the presence of a nurse or pharmacist. They are required to provide regular supervised urine samples for drug testing, and to attend regular outpatient counselling sessions. Methadone maintenance programs have been convincingly shown to be the most effective treatment modality for chronic heroin addicts.

REPRODUCTIVE EFFECTS

Pregnant women addicted to heroin have a high infant mortality rate, due to delayed growth of the fetus and to premature labor. Opiate withdrawal during pregnancy can induce uterine contractions, causing miscarriage in the first trimester or premature labor during the third trimester.

To avoid these risks, pregnant women addicted to opiates should, as a rule, be offered methadone maintenance. Heroin-dependent women on methadone have better prenatal care, improved nutrition and substantially lower infant mortality rates than those not on methadone. However, they have higher infant mortality rates than women not using any drugs. Methadone crosses the placenta, and may inhibit the growth of the fetus.

Infants born to mothers using heroin or methadone may develop prolonged and severe withdrawal, often requiring several weeks of hospitalization. Seizures can occur during infant withdrawal.

COCAINE

Cocaine causes a rapid buildup of neurotransmitters in the brain to produce an intense euphoria and stimulation of the heart and nervous system. The euphoria usually lasts no more than 20 minutes, but the effects on the heart and nervous system last for hours. With time, the neurotransmitters become imbalanced, so that a chronic cocaine user may experience agitation and paranoia rather than euphoria following use.

Cocaine can be injected into the vein, smoked (in the form of "crack," a rock made by mixing cocaine with baking soda), or inhaled through the nose ("snorting"). The latter method irritates the lining of the nose and creates a milder euphoria than injecting or smoking, so heavy users tend to inject or smoke the drug.

WITHDRAWAL

Cocaine withdrawal occurs in three phases. The first phase is the "crash," in which patients who have completed a binge of cocaine sleep deeply for one to two days. This is followed by one or more weeks of intense cravings for cocaine, depression, insomnia with nightmares, and feelings of emptiness and irritability. Following this is the "extinction" phase, in which patients experience episodic cravings for cocaine that gradually diminish in intensity and frequency over a period of months. Whether these phases represent a true physiological withdrawal remains controversial.

OVERDOSE

Cocaine overdose produces seizures, severe hypertension and rapid heartbeat, fever and delirium, and eventually coma and death.

CARDIOVASCULAR EFFECTS

Cocaine can trigger a marked rise in blood pressure, a rapid and irregular heartbeat, and spasms of the blood vessels in the body. This can result in strokes, brain hemorrhages, heart attacks, and ruptured aneurysms. While patients with underlying hypertension or heart disease are at greatest risk for these dangerous complications, they have been reported to occur even in young healthy adults taking small doses of cocaine.

REPRODUCTIVE EFFECTS

Cocaine taken during pregnancy can cause separation of the placenta from the uterus, resulting in severe maternal hemorrhage and fetal death. Cocaine can also trigger premature labor. Regular use of cocaine during pregnancy may cause delayed growth of the fetus, due to poor blood supply through the placenta. Some studies also suggest that cocaine use during pregnancy causes birth defects of the kidneys, irritability at birth, and delays in language development.

OTHER PHYSICAL EFFECTS

Grand mal seizures are very common among cocaine users. Typically they occur within minutes of use, and last no more than one to two minutes. Like other stimulants, cocaine suppresses the appetite, leading to marked weight loss.

PSYCHIATRIC EFFECTS

Cocaine can have profound psychiatric effects. Patients acutely intoxicated on cocaine display a wide variety of psychiatric symptoms, including delusions, paranoia, hallucinations (especially tactile), delirium and severe anxiety. Paranoid delusional disorders and other types of psychoses have been linked with chronic cocaine use; they may persist for months after the cocaine use has ceased, and antipsychotic medication is often required. Cocaine can induce a severe depression, and heavy users are at high risk of suicide.

Stimulants other than cocaine, such as amphetamines, may result in similar problems. They differ mainly in the duration of intoxication: while a cocaine "high" typically lasts less than half an hour, amphetamine intoxication may persist for hours.

BENZODIAZEPINES

Benzodiazepines are among the most commonly prescribed of all drugs. Their main action is to diminish anxiety and induce sleep, but they are also used to treat alcohol withdrawal and prevent certain types of seizures. Patients do not necessarily develop tolerance to the anxiety-reducing or sleep-inducing effects of benzodiazepines.

A number of benzodiazepines are available on the market. They differ in their duration of action; for example, diazepam (Valium) and chlordiazepoxide (Librium) are long-acting, and triazolam (Halcion) and alprazolam (Xanax) are short-acting. They also differ in their dependence liability, that is, their ability to induce a pleasant euphoria that could tempt some patients to abuse them. Diazepam, triazolam, alprazolam and lorazepam (Ativan), for example, have higher dependence liabilities than oxazepam (Serax) or chlordiazepoxide.

OVERDOSE

Benzodiazepines are relatively safe drugs, with little risk of lethal overdose, unless used in combination with other psychoactive drugs such as alcohol.

WITHDRAWAL

Patients who abruptly stop their use of benzodiazepines are at risk for serious withdrawal if they have been using large amounts daily for prolonged periods (50 mg or more of diazepam, or the equivalent dose of another benzodiazepine, for more than one month). Seizures, confusion and hallucinations can occur.

Patients who suddenly stop taking therapeutic doses of benzodiazepines (30 mg or less of diazepam, or the equivalent dose of another benzodiazepine) tend to experience two groups of symptoms: anxiety-related symptoms (emotional volatility, insomnia, irritability, poor concentration, panic attacks); and subtle neurological symptoms (mild visual distortions, or distortion of visual and auditory stimuli; blurry vision, unsteadiness of gait, déjà vu sensations). Serious complications of withdrawal, such as seizures, generally do not occur in patients stopping therapeutic doses. Nonetheless, withdrawal can be intensely uncomfortable, and may last weeks or months. Therapists should watch for signs of depression and suicidal ideation during tapering.

Because of its long duration of action, diazepam is the drug of choice in treating withdrawal. Patients who are taking very high doses require daily tapering, usually in an inpatient setting. Patients on therapeutic doses may be tapered slowly as outpatients over a period of several weeks or months (a maximum tapering rate of 5 mg of diazepam per week is suggested).

Because therapeutic doses of benzodiazepines do not generally result in severe social disruption or physical harm, and because withdrawal can be prolonged and difficult, the decision to withdraw a patient should be made only after a careful assessment of the risks and benefits (including psychiatric assessment if necessary). A program of therapeutic support must be in place before tapering is attempted.

REBOUND INSOMNIA

Benzodiazepines suppress the deep and the rapid eye movement stages of the sleep cycle. When withdrawn suddenly, patients experience a fitful sleep interrupted by vivid dreams. This may take several weeks to resolve.

OTHER EFFECTS

Benzodiazepine use increases the risk of motor vehicle accidents, and can cause falls and confusion in the elderly.

PSYCHIATRIC EFFECTS

Benzodiazepines can contribute to depression, particularly in patients taking large doses and in patients with a pre-existing major affective disorder. Benzodiazepines can have a disinhibiting effect on patients with psychosis and with certain underlying personality disorders.

Patients who taper off benzodiazepines sometimes report feeling more alive, energetic and clear-thinking. They may be more able to make important life decisions, and may benefit more from psychotherapy.

SEDATIVE-HYPNOTICS

Sedative-hypnotics such as Placidyl, Noludar and Seconal have been largely replaced by benzodiazepines, although Fiorinal, a drug used to treat headaches, remains a common drug of abuse. Fiorinal is a combination of ASA, codeine and a barbiturate known as butalbital.

Patients who abruptly stop high doses of sedative hypnotics occasionally develop a dangerous and potentially fatal withdrawal, with seizures, delirium, psychosis and cardiovascular collapse. Chronic abusers of sedative-hypnotics should be advised not to discontinue them abruptly until they have been assessed by a physician knowledgeable in the management of withdrawal.

Sedative-hypnotics can also induce depression, and overdoses with these drugs are frequently fatal.

CANNABIS

Chronic daily users of cannabis often use the drug not for its mild hallucinogenic effects but for relief of anxiety, anger or boredom. Patients who suddenly stop cannabis use after taking high doses for long periods of time may experience a mild withdrawal consisting of one to two days of nausea, tremor, anxiety and sleep disorders. Chronic users may miss its mood-stabilizing effect and experience anxiety and emotional volatility after stopping use.

Cannabis intoxication can trigger severe anxiety and rapid heartbeat. As with cocaine and hallucinogens, cannabis can induce psychosis.

HALLUCINOGENS

Hallucinogenic drugs such as LSD and "magic mushrooms" can cause a psychotic reaction that usually resolves once the drug has worn off, but may persist for months after use and, in some cases, may be permanent. Some users also experience "bad trips," during which they may be subject to extreme panic and other unpleasant sensations.

In the weeks and months after stopping use, a small percentage of users may experience "flashbacks," where they briefly relive past episodes of drug use. Though vivid and disturbing, flashbacks tend to last only minutes, and diminish in frequency and intensity over time.

RISK REDUCTION

Risk reduction is defined as the attempt to reduce serious risks to health in clients through strategies such as health education, immunization and screening. With the advent of HIV infection, risk reduction strategies should be viewed as an essential component of any alcohol and drug rehabilitation program.

HUMAN IMMUNODEFICIENCY VIRUS (HIV)

The major risks of needle sharing are HIV and hepatitis B and C. Estimates of the prevalence of HIV among injection drug users in Canada vary between one and four per cent, considerably lower than in the United States and Western Europe. Counsellors have a responsibility to inform their clients about the risks of needle sharing and ways to reduce them. Myths are still common in the drug-using population; for example, while most clients are aware of the association between needle sharing and AIDS, some still think it is safe to share needles with sexual partners or close friends. Clients should be reminded that it is unsafe to share any drug paraphernalia such as syringes, spoons and filters.

Clients should be informed about needle exchange programs in their area, and instructed on how to clean needles using household bleach (fill the syringe with bleach twice, then fill with water two or more times). Clients should be reassured that bleach will not enter their veins if this procedure is followed. Bleach is not completely effective in preventing hepatitis transmission, so the use of clean needles is much preferred.

Some therapists express concern that giving such advice encourages or condones drug use. However the message to the patient is similar in intent to that given routinely to alcoholics: Don't drink, but if you do, make sure you don't drive.

Injection drug users should be tested for HIV, with their consent and only after receiving pre-test counselling. Although not curative, medication has been shown to prolong life and delay the onset of symptoms in asymptomatic HIV patients.

(See Chapter 27 for more information about HIV and AIDS.)

HEPATITIS B

Hepatitis B is a virus that causes liver inflammation and damage. It is transmitted by needle sharing, sexual contact, and from mother to newborn. Most patients infected with hepatitis B recover within one to two months, but a small proportion become chronic carriers (that is, the virus persists indefinitely). Some of these patients develop liver cirrhosis later in life; a small number develop liver cancer.

Patients entering a drug and alcohol treatment program should have their blood tested for hepatitis B. Injection drug users whose blood indicates that they have never been infected with hepatitis B should be offered vaccination, which is extremely safe and effective. Hepatitis B carriers should have their sexual partners and household members vaccinated, and should be referred to a liver specialist. Interferon, a powerful antibiotic, can lead to improvement and, in some cases, cure.

HEPATITIS C

This virus is similar to hepatitis B, except that it is transmitted primarily through needle sharing; sexual transmission is rare. It is estimated that 40 per cent of injection drug users are carriers, and up to 40 per cent of carriers will eventually develop cirrhosis.

Blood tests to detect hepatitis C should be ordered by the patient's physician in all current or former injection drug users and whenever hepatitis C is suspected (for example, elevated liver enzymes). No vaccine is yet available to prevent hepatitis C, but it can be treated with Interferon.

SEXUALLY TRANSMITTED DISEASES

Alcohol and drug users have high rates of sexually transmitted diseases such as chlamydia and gonorrhea. This reflects unsafe sexual practices and inadequate health care. Young women should be advised to see their physician or a health clinic for regular STD screenings and Pap tests. Both men and women should be given information on safe sex.

UNWANTED PREGNANCIES

The drug-using population tends to use birth control sporadically. The irregular menstrual periods of women using alcohol or heroin may convince them that they are at little risk of becoming pregnant; with abstinence, however, they usually become fertile again. Both men and women should be counselled on the need for birth control.

SUICIDE

Patients with alcohol and drug problems are at extremely high risk for suicide. Patients who are intoxicated or in withdrawal may be at particular risk for an impulsive suicide attempt, and carefully supervised detoxification is required.

IMPAIRED DRIVING

All patients should be informed of the risks of driving while using any drug. Some patients believe that their driving is not affected if they don't feel intoxicated; they should be informed that even small amounts of alcohol or other drugs impair the ability to react quickly in complex driving situations.

CONCLUSION

Alcohol and drug abuse is associated with a wide variety of serious physical problems. Alcohol abuse can cause gastritis, liver disease, and damage to the brain and nervous system; it is a major factor in motor vehicle accidents and other forms of trauma. Alcohol, heroin and cocaine can harm the fetus. Cocaine has life-threatening cardio-vascular complications. All drugs of abuse can have serious psychiatric complications. Intravenous drug use can transmit bloodborne infections such as HIV and hepatitis.

Counsellors should inform their clients of these health risks, and advise them of preventive practices and services such as immunization and needle exchanges. Counsellors also need to be alert to the symptoms and signs of physical and psychiatric illness in their clients.

ANNOTATED BIBLIOGRAPHY

Andreasson, S., Allbeck, P., and Romelsjo, A. (1988). Alcohol and mortality among young men: Longitudinal study of Swedish conscripts. *British Medical Journal* 296: 1021–1025.

> A prospective study showing that heavy drinkers have a high mortality rate from suicide.

Camargo, C.A. (1989). Moderate alcohol consumption and stroke: The epidemiologic evidence. *Stroke* 20: 1611–1626.

> A review of the relationship between alcohol consumption, hypertension and stroke.

Chasnoff, I.J., Griffith, D.R., MacGregor, S., et al. (1989). Temporal patterns of cocaine use in pregnancy: Perinatal outcome. *Journal of the American Medical Association* 261 (12): 1741–1744.

Chasnoff, I.J., Burns, W.J., Schnoll, S.H., et al. (1985). Cocaine use in pregnancy. *New England Journal of Medicine* 313 (11): 666–669.

Dombroski, M.P., Wolfe, H.M., Welch, R.A., et al. (1991). Cocaine abuse is associated with abruptio placentae and decreased birth weight, but not shorter labor. *Obstetrics and Gynecology* 77 (1): 139–141.

> (The above three papers show that women using cocaine during pregnancy are more likely than normal controls to experience spontaneous abortion, abruptio placentae and decreased birth weight. At birth, cocaine-exposed infants show impaired neurological and behavioral responses.)

Cregler, L.L., and Mark, H. (1986). Medical complications of cocaine abuse. *New England Journal of Medicine* 315 (22): 1495–1500.

> Concise review of adverse physical effects of cocaine.

Finnegan, L.P., et al. (1977). The effects of maternal drug dependence on neonatal mortality. *Drug and Alcohol Dependence* 2: 131–140.

> This study shows that heroin-dependent mothers experience higher infant mortality rates than healthy controls, due to low birth weight and premature labor.

Freed, E.X. (1981). Changes in weekly self-ratings of depression by hospitalized alcoholics. *Journal of Psychiatric Treatment and Evaluation* 3: 451–454.

> In this clinical study, the depression of hospitalized alcoholics is resolved by four weeks of abstinence.

Frezza, M., Padova, C.D., Pozzato, G., et al. (1990). High blood alcohol levels in women. The role of decreased gastric alcohol dehydrogenase activity and first-pass metabolism. *New England Journal of Medicine* 322 (20): 95–99.

> This biochemical study suggests that women are more likely to develop alcoholic liver disease than men because they have lower levels of the enzyme needed to metabolize alcohol.

Fullilove, R.E., Fullilove, M.T., Bowser, B.P., et al. (1990). Risk of sexually transmitted disease among black adolescent crack users in Oakland and San Francisco, CA. *Journal of the American Medical Association* 263 (6): 851–855.

In this cross-sectional survey, the number of drugs used daily was associated with the number of risk behaviors (e.g., failure to use a condom, multiple sex partners).

Gawin, F.H., and Ellinwood, E.H. (1988). Cocaine and other stimulants: Actions, abuse, and treatment. *New England Journal of Medicine* 318 (8): 1173–1182.

Reviews cocaine intoxication and withdrawal.

Griffiths, R.R., and Sannerud, C.A. (1987). Abuse of and dependence on benzodiazepines and other anxiolytic/sedative drugs. In *Psychopharmacology: The Third Generation of Progress*, ed. Meltzer, H.Y. New York: Raven Press.

Excellent review of benzodiazepine dependence and withdrawal.

Loper, K.A. (1989). Clinical toxicology of cocaine. *Medical Toxicology and Adverse Drug Experience* 4 (3): 174–185.

Comprehensive review of adverse effects of cocaine.

Mihas, A.A., and Tavassoli, M. (1992). Laboratory markers of ethanol intake and abuse: A critical appraisal. *American Journal of Medical Sciences* 303 (6): 415–428.

A good review of the effects of alcohol on blood tests.

Naranjo, C.A., Poulos, C.X., Bremner, K.E., and Lanctot, K.L. (1992). Citalopram decreases desirability, liking, and consumption of alcohol in alcohol-dependent drinkers. *Clinical Pharmacology and Therapeutics* 51/6: 729–739.

A controlled study demonstrating that the serotonin reuptake inhibitor citralopram causes reductions in alcohol consumption.

National Institute on Alcohol Abuse and Alcoholism. (1991). Fetal alcohol syndrome. *Alcohol Alert* 13: 1–5.

A readable summary of current knowledge of FAS.

Rosett, H.L., and Weiner, L. (1984). *Alcohol and the Fetus*. New York: Oxford University Press.

A comprehensive review of research findings.

Sellers, E.M., and Kalant, H. (1976). Alcohol intoxication and withdrawal. *New England Journal of Medicine* 294: 757.

Describes the use of diazepam to treat alcohol withdrawal.

Streissguth, A.P., Clarren, S.K., and Jones, K.L. (1985). Natural history of the fetal alcohol syndrome: A 10-year follow-up of eleven patients. *Lancet* 1985: 85–91.

Shows that the physical and cognitive effects of FAS continue into adolescence, causing severe disability.

Williams, C.M., and Skinner, A.E.G. (1990). The cognitive effects of alcohol abuse: a controlled study. *British Journal of Addiction* 85: 911–917.
> Demonstrates cognitive impairment in heavy drinkers compared to light drinkers matched for age, social class and education.

Wright, C., and Moore, R.D. (1990). Disulfiram treatment of alcoholism. *American Journal of Medicine* 188: 647–655.
> Concludes that disulfiram may promote short-term abstinence but has no proven effect on long-term outcome; should not be used as sole treatment.

BOOKS

The following books are recommended because the nonphysician will find them readable, yet informative and comprehensive.

Barnes, H.N., Aronson, M.D., and Delbanco, T.L. (eds). (1987). *Alcoholism: A Guide for the Primary Care Physician*. New York: Springer-Verlag.

Cohen, S., and Kahan, B. (1989). *Treating Alcohol Problems: The Family Physician's Guide*. Regina: Saskatchewan Alcohol and Drug Abuse Commission.

Devenyi, P., and Saunders, S.J. (eds). (1989). *Physicians' Manual for Medical Management of Alcohol- and Drug-related Problems*, 5th ed. Toronto: Addiction Research Foundation.

Royal College of General Practitioners. (1986). *Alcohol — A Balanced View*. London: Authors.

Chapter 11

Ending with Clients: Closure in Counselling

CARL KENT

INTRODUCTION

The last stage of the helping process is the ending of the helping relationship. Although this stage has received little attention in the literature, compared to the beginning or middle stages, it is nonetheless critically important. The way in which the helping relationship and process are concluded greatly influences whether clients can maintain the progress they have made and continue to make further gains. For this reason, it is important that practitioners plan and handle this stage with sensitivity and skill.

This chapter will focus on the ending process and identify relevant tasks, for both practitioners and clients, which are essential to effectively managing the conclusion of the counselling process. No distinctions will be made between concluding the counselling relationship with an individual, a family or a group. The essential dynamics are the same for all modes of intervention, with minimal adaptation required for each treatment context.

CONCEPTUALIZING CLOSURE

To most counsellors, it is obvious that the "beginning" of any treatment contact represents a distinctive and identifiable phase. It makes sense that "starting on the right foot" has implications for the rest of the therapeutic contact.

In treatment, "endings" are as important as "beginnings," though this phase of the treatment contact is not written about with as much clarity or frequency as other stages. Ward (1984) has suggested that this neglect arises out of several sources, including:

(1) normal human tendencies to avoid separation and loss issues
(2) counsellors' inclination to focus on building relationships, rather than on activities aimed at discontinuing relationships
(3) counsellor training overemphasizes skill building to the exclusion of case management issues.

Effective closure of the counselling process must begin with the premise that closure is a process or phase, rather than one point in time representing an abrupt cessation of an activity (Cavanaugh, 1982; Corey, Corey, Callanan and Russell, 1982; Shulman, 1979). Yalom (1975) underlined the importance of the ending process when he wrote: "Termination is more than an act signifying the end of therapy and, if properly understood and managed, may be an important factor in the instigation of change" (p. 365). Hansen, Warner and Smith, (1980) suggest that if the ending process is dealt with inappropriately, it "may not only conclude this experience without effective change ... but also so adversely affect individuals that they may not seek further help when necessary" (p. 539).

There appears to be wide agreement that three main functions are involved in this phase of treatment:

(1) assessing client readiness for ending the counselling process and for consolidating whatever has been learned
(2) resolving remaining affective issues and constructively closing the significant and often intense relationship between the client and the counsellor
(3) maximizing transfer of learning (from the counselling situation and specific problem issues to life in general and other problems) and increasing the client's confidence in his or her ability to maintain change after the counselling contact has ended.

Nelson (1983) has noted that successful closure in a therapeutic relationship parallels the stages people experience when dealing with death. Obviously the parallel referred to here is the death/ending of the counselling relationship. If treatment ends too abruptly, it might be perceived as rejection, which is a difficult issue for clients and practitioners alike. The client who feels rejected might be tempted in turn to reject the whole therapeutic contact and with it all gains and plans for positive action and referral.

Shulman (1984) proposed, as a rule, that the ending process constitute one-sixth of the time of the therapeutic process. In fact, there is general agreement that treatment should not be ended during the session in which it is first mentioned. Not only will this prevent impulsive and premature discontinuance, it allows a clear review of the counselling process to date, an evaluation of the progress made, and planning for future goals.

PROBLEM AND GOAL DEFINITION: HOW TO DETERMINE WHEN TO END

A clear focus of the helping process is a necessary precondition to successful ending. Being specific about client problems and agreeing on goals helps determine how long treatment will continue and how counselling activities will be structured. When goals have been established in the beginning and included in the terms of the treatment contract, their review at the time of closure will allow for a precise measurement of progress and any work yet to be accomplished.

It must be said here that many effective practitioners insist on explicit, specific and *written* contracts that spell out not only mutual expectations and responsibilities, but also goals, sub-goals and the detailed, operationalized steps and time required to meet them. This obviously leads to frequent revisions, with the advantage of client and practitioner always knowing where they stand. Progress and success will be readily apparent, as will stagnation and poor use of therapeutic time.

It is probably best to comment here about the common problem of the chronically relapsing substance abuser who regularly misses appointments. When does the counsellor say: "That's enough; I am ending my involvement with this client"? What does the counsellor do about the chronic alcoholic who, over an extended period of time, does not get better? What about the person who is unlikely ever to improve? Is this issue related to ending alone or to contracting and goal-setting as well? It would seem that as long as specific, if modest, goals are *agreed upon,* and as long as there is discernible movement towards those goals, the counselling contact is useful and worthwhile. Remember that a practitioner can only facilitate change with those clients with whom he or she has contact. Even if there are no observable positive changes in the client, the focus should likely be more on realistic contracting than on ending. Intermittent, supportive follow-up contact might be agreed on to maintain the therapeutic contact, so as to be ready for action when the situation or client allows it. How much change is enough to justify ongoing counselling contact? That is ultimately a question of staff resources and agency policy.

If the client's problems are developmental in nature (i.e., an adolescent who has difficulties with leaving home, or an adult dealing with the pressures of parenting), the closure might well be designed to allow for extensive follow-up as the transitional aspect of the problem continues to unfold. A specific example might be with the teenager, Bill T., who resents parental interference with his choice of friends and his excessive and irresponsible drinking. In this instance, he wants the adult's freedom of decision-making without honoring the other side of the same coin — namely respect for duties and commitments.

On the other hand, if the client's problems are related to specific and concrete issues, a definable end of the treatment contact might suggest itself. In fact, when the expectations of the outcome are shared and based on a thorough assessment, the time of ending will fall into place readily. An example might be to help Jane S. deal with her marital breakdown in a more constructive manner than excessive drinking. When she has learned to stop drinking and grieve the end of her marital relationship, she might be able to pick up the pieces of her life on her own and end the therapeutic contact.

What a client expects to gain from the helping process is maintained both by hopes for specific change and the personal validation he or she receives from the helping relationship. As the counselling work progresses, the practitioner must monitor and maintain an appropriate balance between goal achievement and relationship gratification both for himself or herself and the client.

Certainly it is unrealistic to aim for a complete cure of all the client's problems, although helpers are susceptible to accepting such a global goal. It might be much more practical to focus on some major concerns the client identifies rather than to include all the problems the practitioner can pinpoint. After all, most people (including counsellors) have some problems they either learn to live with or are content to struggle with on their own.

Concepts such as "clinical judgment" about a client's readiness for closure and "working through" such variables as the ending of the client-counsellor relationship and feelings of grief and sadness are important, but they are hard to operationalize and next to impossible to measure. It seems a lot more realistic to choose specific and behavioral goals against which progress in counselling can be measured. Maholick and Turner (1979, p. 588) identified seven areas helpful for evaluating client readiness to end the counselling process:

(1) examining whether initial problems or symptoms have been reduced or eliminated
(2) determining whether the stress that motivated the client to seek counselling has dissipated
(3) assessing increased coping ability
(4) assessing increased understanding and valuing of self and others
(5) determining increased levels of relating to others and of loving and being loved
(6) examining increased abilities to plan and work productively
(7) evaluating increases in the capacity to play and enjoy life.

Practitioners should also evaluate how confident the client has begun to feel about continuing to live competently without the help of counselling.

Further, a number of client behaviors — other than direct and explicit statements — may signal the onset of the ending stage. Among those mentioned in the literature are a decrease in the intensity of the work of counselling, lateness, joking and intellectualizing (Corey et al., 1982). Also mentioned are missed appointments, apathy, acting out, regression to earlier and less mature behavior patterns, withdrawal, denial, expression of anger and mourning (Shulman, 1984). The client might also express feelings of impotence, dependence, inadequacy and abandonment. If the client increasingly displays some of these behaviors or feelings but does not talk about a desire for closure, the counsellor may have to initiate the process.

In any case, the counsellor must initiate and help the client come to terms with both task and relationship issues of ending. A detailed review of the counselling process, an evaluation of the progress made so far, and a subsequent plan for future goals is recommended.

One way to guide clients through the ending process successfully is to point out predictable reactions to loss (including anticipated loss) and to help them to identify those reactions when they are either directly or indirectly expressed. For example, Peter T.'s counselling contact had evidently been coming to a close. He displayed a variety of reactions, including lateness, cancellations, increased digressions into story-telling, and shifting the focus of the session onto the counsellor. When closure was mentioned, however, he would rapidly identify a minor crisis to legitimately prolong the counselling contact. An open discussion of these dynamics allowed the client to face his anxieties about "being on his own." In addition to exploring the issue of confidence and independent functioning, an extended follow-up agreement seemed to be an acceptable compromise solution.

Various authors have written about the predictable stages of the grieving process: denial, anger, sadness, acceptance and disengagement (Germain and Gitterman, 1980; Kubler-Ross, 1969). However, we cannot assume that all clients uniformly pass through all these stages without variation, though it is generally recognized that both clients and counsellors are likely to experience denial. The expression of this denial may take many forms, ranging from general detachment to premature discontinuation of counselling sessions. Regular clinical supervision can help counsellors identify, face, and finally resolve their own denial. Focusing on the client's denial may be instrumental in overcoming it and allows open exchange about the pain and distress associated with loss and separation.

Clients might be encouraged to summarize their personal reactions to the counsellor and the counselling process. They should give feedback about what they found to be helpful or distracting during the treatment process. It is important that the counsellor face this opportunity to receive feedback (including the occasional criticism) without being defensive. It might help to view this situation as an opportunity for learning; the information received should be taken seriously.

Counsellors may feel uncertain about their own capacity to deal with the closure and may encourage clients to remain in denial as a form of self-protection. It is the counsellor's responsibility to guide the ending process through appropriate timing of interventions and use of self-disclosure. The honest expression of the counsellor's own reaction during ending validates the client's feelings triggered by the closure. (Of course, the counsellor's self-disclosure must never be detrimental to the client and his or her feedback must always be tempered by clinical judgment concerning the best interests of the client.) Through this mutual exchange or sharing of reactions, the reality of the ending is verified.

At this stage, the counsellor-client relationship moves from an unbalanced power relationship towards a position of greater equity and balance. The focus may be allowed to shift away from the client towards neutral ground or towards the counsellor. This in turn enhances the client's level of independent functioning, which is appropriate and desirable for the ending stage of counselling.

One major task of the ending experience is to connect treatment to the client's subsequent problem-solving efforts. This may be partly accomplished by a closure review, evaluation of goal accomplishment, and by planning activities and setting goals for the future.

The client needs to be encouraged through the ending process to set out on a self-directed course of action. Of course, the development of new goals or the restating of old, unaccomplished goals must be based on a realistic evaluation of the client's problem-solving capacity.

A constructive use of these closure issues supports client self-esteem and reinforces the client's hope that progress can be achieved. Effective ending also frees up the client to make new efforts at important life tasks and relationships, which in turn enhances his or her problem-solving abilities.

REASONS FOR ENDING

When the decision to end treatment is mutual, working through the ending stage helps clients to consolidate and transfer learning, enhance their level of independent functioning, and bring the client-counsellor relationship to a closer level of balance.

Frequently, however, the client decides to end with little or no prior consultation with the counsellor. The practitioner may be abruptly informed of the client's decision, or more frequently may find out through a series of missed appointments. Mostly the counsellor learns of the decision and not of the reasons behind it.

If the client initiates closure at the beginning of the counselling process, it could mean that he or she doesn't appreciate the techniques or procedures of counselling. Or the client may disagree with the counsellor's theoretical orientation or plainly just dislike the counsellor. The client may feel that he or she will not get the desired help in this context — or may have returned to the use of substances. Active follow-up contact is encouraged to offer alternative counselling arrangements that more closely fit the client's expectations (possibly through referral to another counsellor or treatment setting) or to make renewed efforts to engage the client in treatment.

To avoid attrition at this stage, Zweben and Li (1981) tried to provide new patients with "role induction" information designed to reduce the discrepancy between their expectations of the counselling experience and reality. They speculated that clients with unrealistic expectations of counselling likely need immediate help with their concrete problems as well as "actively engaging 'significant other(s)' or providing them with a 'buddy' at the point of entry, in order to forestall premature termination" (p. 172).

During the middle stage of counselling, some clients will end prematurely if they feel that the counselling process is creating more problems than it is able to resolve. Closure at this stage is often due to the unsettling feeling that the client experiences as a result of changing behaviors. Frequently the client's life and relationships become destabilized and the perceived cost of continued counselling and changing is seen to be higher than maintaining the previously recognized problem. This kind of reaction is often conveniently explained by the practitioner as a "lack of motivation" on the client's part. Here too, early focus on desensitizing the client against the temporary unsettling effects of change may help to prevent early cessation of the counselling process. In spite of this, many clients will still discontinue treatment without specifying the cause.

It is important to examine critically the characteristics, length and type of counselling contact of clients who discontinue treatment prematurely, to identify any commonalities such as family responsibilities, unstable accommodation or length of time on the waiting list. Such analysis may allow the counsellor and/or agency to reach out to clients at risk for early ending and provide support in dealing with such issues. This might include helping the client to better understand the reasons behind the premature ending and also to offer renewed contact or help with referral.

When a client discontinues treatment, or expresses the wish to do so, and significant problems are still unresolved, the counsellor must try to help the client deal with negative reactions and feelings. If the client is willing to engage in an "exit interview," Ward (1984) identifies at least four positive outcomes that may result:

    (a) reduction of as many negative influences as possible before the client resumes life without counselling
    (b) resolution of critical issues to the extent that the client is able to continue counselling with the same counsellor
    (c) preparation of the client for gaining maximum benefit from referral to another "helper"
    (d) increased likelihood that the client will re-enter counselling or some other personal growth experience at some future date.

When the practitioner decides to end the counselling process, it should be presented as a logical and inevitable step in the change process in which the client is engaged. This minimizes the client's feelings of rejection by the counsellor.

The ending of treatment really begins with the first session following assessment. Closure should be treated like any other treatment goal and should regularly be included in treatment planning and goal-setting. This means that the length of the planned counselling contact is constantly reviewed and revised in view of outstanding treatment goals and the rate of progress.

BALANCING THE RELATIONSHIP DURING CLOSURE

When addressing the therapeutic system and the issue of closure, even the most egalitarian counsellor is perceived to be higher in the hierarchy than the client. Thus, the client is held accountable for having the problem, while the counsellor is the source for solution development during which he or she directs the client towards change. In fact, the counsellor is regarded as the source of useful and important information leading to change.

Ward (1984) as well as Haley (1987) write that, at the time of closure, it is desirable for this inequality to end and for the client to be more formally positioned on an equal footing. For example, counsellors might begin to express more of themselves as persons, disclose personal reactions to ending with clients, and respond to clients' inquiries more directly, rather than turning the question back upon the client or making an interpretation. Shifting the relationship onto a more egalitarian footing is believed to bring closure to the real relationship between counsellor and client (Dewald, 1969). If this transformation is not performed, the client may become so dependent on the counsellor so as to believe that only the therapist, and not the client, has the power or resources to solve his or her problems. The result of this dependency can be, at best, unnecessarily prolonged treatment and, at worst, undermined confidence and recurring relapses.

TRANSFER OF THE CLIENT TO ANOTHER COUNSELLOR

The case transfer is a special type of ending that might be called for in a variety of circumstances. Examples are a counsellor leaving his or her agency; a student concluding a field placement; ill-health or changing responsibilities of the practitioner; or sometimes, when carefully considered, the mutually beneficial transfer of a long-term client to a different counsellor or a follow-up/aftercare group. The same rules of ending that were already discussed apply here. Ideally, case transfers work well when the client and the departing practitioner engage in a cognitive and affective review of the previously shared contacts. Included in this are an agreement of the progress accomplished towards explicitly stated therapeutic goals, an acknowledgment of the work yet to be done, and a mutual processing of the counsellor's and client's feelings about the intimate process that has occurred.

In addition, a positive working relationship must be established between the client and the new therapist so that rapport and trust can develop, the client's feelings of loss can be reviewed and the new goals can be confirmed. All of this must be done without loss of the momentum towards change. To achieve these objectives, clearly and openly discuss with the client — during the course of several interviews — the need for and the implications of ending and arranging a transfer.

This transfer might appear even more logical if the mode of intervention is changing as well. When individual or couple/family treatment leads to a transfer to a follow-up or aftercare group, it might be wise to discuss this new mode of treatment. Here are some of the most typical questions that would benefit from clarification: What might the client realistically expect from this new approach? What are the differences and benefits? How much can the client rely on the group leader? What are the issues that remain in need of work? Who is going to take the initiative with these concerns?

No matter what the mode of treatment, the new individual/couple/family or group counsellor must be well informed about the essential and the still unresolved issues of the client to be transferred. At least one transfer interview with the client and both counsellors is suggested, during which the departing therapist and client can share with the new counsellor some of the highlights of their past work together as well as the goals they feel still need to be achieved.

It is common for the new counsellor to feel a bit apprehensive at this time, since he or she will feel a lot of explicit and implicit expectations to be as (or more) helpful, warm, friendly and sensitive as the departing practitioner. If the transfer was well prepared, the comparisons will soon cease and the new relationship will be appreciated by the client in its own right.

Difficulties may arise when the client and departing practitioner did not have enough time to prepare for the case transfer. A client may then feel rejected, sad, hopeless, guilty, worthless or angry. A lot of time, effort and forward momentum will be lost in dealing with these unresolved feelings. It is then left up to the new counsellor to help the client come to terms with these feelings before progress can be made towards identified goals.

CLOSURE IN A GROUP CONTEXT

Though, essentially, the dynamics and issues are the same for all modes of intervention, here are a few considerations as they apply for working with groups. Here, too, an important principle in constructive ending of the counselling process is to treat the ending process as a stage in its own right. In this way, significant issues related to closure gain the attention they deserve. Effective closure of the counselling process in a well-handled ending stage can help to solidify the group members' learning and to maximize their continued success after counselling.

In addition to discontinuing the intimacy established with the counsellor, group members must also deal with their feelings about separating from each other. Guilt over the way the group functioned is common. For example, if previously a group member dropped out prematurely, discussion may return to this event. The predominant concern may be on the group "having let him down." If a client indicates or the counsellor suspects that the client may abruptly discontinue the counselling process before it is completed, Ohlsen (1979) and Hansen et al. (1980) suggest that the subject of ending should be openly discussed. If the client does not return for the next scheduled group meeting and does not contact the counsellor to reschedule, efforts should be made to contact the client. Some clients may be testing the counsellor's concern, may have reached a difficult point in the counselling process, or may be so overwhelmed that they do not have the confidence to continue. A contact may be all that is needed for the group member to rejoin the group. Another client may well have negative feelings and be resistant to continued counselling. Again, the counsellor can then contact the client and, if the client wishes to end counselling, invite and strongly encourage the client to return for at least one more group session to process any unresolved issues, to decide about the need for a possible referral, and to help the counsellor to understand better the reasons for ending the counselling process. If these efforts are unsuccessful, an outreach letter to invite the client to return at any time can be effective. Although less desirable than working with the client in person, it is possible to work on some of these issues during a telephone conversation.

The desire to have functioned more effectively is also prominent in clients' requests for continuation of the sessions. There is often unfinished business related to two of the most important themes, authority and intimacy, that any group invariably has to deal with. Group members need to share with each other not only the angry feelings that emerged through their work together but also the feelings of loss they are experiencing as their mutual support system is being dismantled.

A common aspect of the ending stage is the group members' denial of the imminent end of the group. This may be followed by anger, which emerges in direct and indirect forms. The easily discernible mourning period is usually characterized by apathy and a pervasive tone of sadness. Frequently, the group will experiment and try out the experience of ending counselling. This can frequently be seen when group members operate independently of the group worker or spend a great deal of time talking about new groups or counsellors. Further, it is not unusual for group members to avoid the negative aspects of ending by suggesting a farewell party. Here, an attempt should be made to go beyond the more readily expressed positive feelings and to share negative feedback as well. Since group members will have different reactions, the counsellor should encourage the expression and acceptance of differing views.

As mentioned earlier, counsellor strategies for dealing with endings of groups are similar to those encountered in other modes of treatment. The counsellor should bring the reality of ending to the group members' attention early, so as to familiarize and desensitize them to its inevitability. The typical stages a group encounters should be pointed out as the group experiences them, identifying the indirect cues and naming the processes (denial, anger, mourning) taking place. Neither should the group counsellor hold back his or her personal feelings, since the group ending has meaning for the counsellor as well. Discussion of the feelings generated by the ending process should be encouraged and be made as specific as possible. For example, when a group member states, "It was a great group," the counsellor should inquire, "What was it about the group that made it great?"

The counsellor must also pay attention to the transitional aspect of the ending stage. For example, if group members plan to meet with other counsellors, how can they best prepare to begin the relationship in a positive manner? If group members have finished with counselling for the time being, what have they learned and how can they use their learning in their new life situations? If they have found the group experience helpful, how can they find similar sources of support in their subsequent life? In this way, the counsellor can make sure that the process of ending is also a process of identifying and consolidating gains, resolving affective concerns related to ending the relationship with the counsellor positively, and preparing the client to maintain counselling gains after sessions end.

CONCLUSION

Thanks to the pioneering work of Kubler-Ross on death, dying and the grieving process, it is possible today to deal more effectively with the closure phase of counselling. Specific steps have been identified to evaluate a client's readiness for ending the counselling process. The importance of identifying and consolidating gains made in counselling has been pointed out, as well as the need to resolve affective issues in order to end the relationship appropriately. Specific steps to handle clients' attempts to leave counselling prematurely have also been highlighted.

Effective closure of the counselling process can help reinforce clients' learning and maximize their continued self-efficacy and success after counselling. Whether short or long term, the intent of the helping process is to make a difference in the life of the client. It is through the process of closure that this difference can be understood, evaluated and maintained.

REFERENCES

Cavanaugh, M.E. (1982). *The Counselling Experience: A Theoretical and Practical Approach.* Monterey, CA: Brooks/Cole.

Compton, B., and Galaway, B. (1984). *Social Work Processes,* 3rd ed. Homewood, IL: The Dorsey Press.

Corey, G., Corey, M.S., Callanan, P.J., and Russell, J.M. (1982). *Group Techniques.* Monterey, CA: Brooks/Cole.

Dewald, P.A. (1969). *Psychotherapy: A Dynamic Approach.* New York: Basic Books.

Germain, C., and Gitterman, A. (1980). *The Life Model of Social Work Practice.* New York: Columbia University Press.

Haley, J. (1987). *Problem-Solving Therapy,* 2nd ed. San Francisco: Jossey-Bass.

Hansen, J.C., Warner, R.W., and Smith, E.J. (1980). *Group Counselling: Theory and Process,* 2nd ed. Chicago: Rand McNally.

Hepworth, D.H., and Larsen, J.A. (1982). *Direct Social Work Practice, Theory and Skills.* Homewood, IL: The Dorsey Press.

Kubler-Ross, E. (1969). *On Death and Dying.* New York: Macmillan.

Lackey, M.B. (1982). The termination phase in social work with groups. *University of Southern California: Dissertation Abstracts International* 43 (September).

London, M. (1982). How do you say good-bye after you've said hello? *Personnel and Guidance Journal* 60 (March). New Bedford, MA: Southeastern Counselling Association.

Maholick, L.T., and Turner, D.W. (1979). Termination: That difficult farewell. *American Journal of Psychotherapy* 33: 583–591.

Marx, J.A. (1984). An exploratory study of the termination of individual counselling in a university counselling centre. *University of Maryland: Dissertation Abstracts International* 44 (June).

Nelson, J.C. (1983). *Family Treatment: An Integrative Approach.* Englewood Cliffs, NJ: Prentice Hall.

Ohlsen, M.M. (1979). Termination techniques with couples groups. *Journal for Specialists in Group Work* 4: 110–112.

Quintana, S.M., and Holahan, W. (1992). Termination in short-term counseling: Comparison of successful and unsuccessful cases. *Journal of Counseling Psychology* 39 (3): 299–305.

Shulman, L. (1979), (1984). *The Skills of Helping Individuals and Groups.* Itasca, IL: Peacock.

Ward, D.E. (1984). Termination of individual counselling: Concepts and strategies. *Journal of Counselling and Development* 63: 21–25.

Wetchler, J.L., and Ofte-Atha, G.R. (1993). Empowering families at termination: A structural/strategic orientation. *Journal of Family Psychotherapy* 4 (1): 33–44.

Yalom, I.D. (1975). *The Theory and Practice of Group Psychotherapy,* 2nd ed. New York: Basic Books.

Zweben, A., and Li, S. (1981). The efficacy of role induction in preventing early dropout from outpatient treatment of drug dependency. *American Journal of Drug and Alcohol Abuse* 8 (2): 171–183.

MEETING CLIENTS' NEEDS

Chapter 12

Working with Women

SUSAN HARRISON

INTRODUCTION

Bruised, battered, belittled and bewildered, buffeted by societal attitudes and stereotypes are the women who end up in the offices of addictions counsellors. If we, as counsellors, are to help these women recover and develop their potential, we must understand and empathize with each one individually; we must know the treatment issues that pertain specifically to women; and, as much as is possible with our current state of knowledge, match each client to the types of treatment or interventions that meet her needs.

This chapter compiles what I have learned over the years in my work with women who are struggling with problems related to substance use. This includes work with women in mixed-gender treatment facilities, in detox, in residential and day treatment programs, in outpatient and aftercare counselling; with women individually, or with their partners, families and children; and with women in groups, both mixed and gender-specific. Most of what I have learned has come from listening to and working in partnership with my clients — only very recently have research studies started to substantiate many of the things that clinicians working with women with substance abuse problems have come to know from their experience.

Most women with drug-related problems do not present themselves for treatment; those who do have often experienced a range of problems, from physical and psychological health consequences to family, job-related, financial, legal and other problems. Although we are just beginning to see women coming for help earlier — as health promotion, prevention, and early intervention efforts take hold in communities — we can safely anticipate that for some time we will continue to work with women who have been severely damaged by their substance use and abuse (although I will mention Martha Sanchez-Craig's early intervention work for women earlier on the continuum).

This chapter will discuss how attitudes affect women's development of substance use problems, as well as their recovery. Societal attitudes to women in general, to women with alcohol and drug problems in particular, attitudes in research and counsellor attitudes will all be explored. Several barriers that women face will also be highlighted. These include socio-economic status; isolation; unrecognized needs; fear of losing children; and the health and mental health care systems. Some attention will be given to special considerations in female substance use, including physical effects of both alcohol and other drugs, sexual dysfunction and various psychological factors including reasons for use, self-esteem issues, suicide risk, and physical and sexual abuse. The last section will address some major issues in recovery, among them the core components of a treatment program for women, necessary related services, treatment modalities and counsellor characteristics.

ATTITUDES AFFECTING WOMEN'S DEVELOPMENT OF SUBSTANCE USE PROBLEMS AND THEIR RECOVERY

When working with women with alcohol and drug problems, the importance of attitudes cannot be overemphasized. Attitudes within our society toward women in general, and toward these women in particular, have an impact on many levels. Attitudes of significant others in these women's worlds — life partner, other family members, employer, friends, counsellor — and of the client herself may determine when and if a woman decides to seek help and whether she finds supports or obstacles in her road to recovery.

Societal Attitudes to Women in General

As stated earlier, to help female clients, we must understand and empathize with each of them individually. To empathize with them as women is even more basic and important than to understand and empathize with their substance use problems. Because, as Beth Glover Reed (1985) stated so simply and powerfully, "women are women long before they become involved in chemical misuse or dependency." Women's reality is much different from men's reality. We must truly appreciate the fabric woven from the various threads in women's lives.

Women still hold secondary status in our society, and minority women even more so if they are of a race, ethnic group, language or sexual orientation other than the white anglophone heterosexual majority. Women devalued this way often become victims of violence and have lower self-esteem and lower aspirations than do men.

A few statistics from *Women in Canada: A Statistical Report 1995,* on various women's social, health and economic conditions, are illustrative:

- Although the percentage of women who smoke has declined over the past 15 years, smoking among female teenagers has increased. In 1994, 29 per cent aged 15–19 smoked, up from 21 per cent in 1990.
- Women continue to make up the large majority of lone parents in Canada. In 1991, over 80 per cent of all single-parent families were headed by women.
- The education gap between men and women is narrowing in general. However, at all levels of educational attainment, women's earnings are lower than those of men.
- In 1993, the average annual pre-tax income from all sources of women aged 15 and over was $16,500 — just 58 per cent of the average income of men.
- Employed women (working full-time) in 1993 earned, on average, $28,400 — just 72 per cent of the figure for men.
- 52 per cent of all women aged 15 and over are employed; 63 per cent of women with children under age 16 are employed.
- 69 per cent of all part-time workers in 1994 were women; 34 per cent of them indicated that they wanted full-time employment but could only find part-time work.
- Even when employed, women are still largely responsible for looking after homes and families. In 1992, employed women with a spouse and at least one child under age five spent 5.3 hours a day on household activities — about two hours a day more than men.
- One-third of all homicide victims in 1993 were female (208). However, women made up 59 per cent of all homicide victims killed in domestic relationships.
- In 1993, there were 151 incidents of personal crimes such as sexual assault, robbery, attempted robbery and assault for every 1,000 women aged 15 and over, compared with 136 personal crimes for every 1,000 men.
- In 1993, six per cent of Canadian women reported being sexually assaulted; three per cent were physically assaulted that year by dates or boyfriends, other known men or strangers; three per cent of married women reported experiencing wife assault.
- In 1993, 75 per cent of violent attacks against women were not reported to police and 90 per cent of sexual assaults were not reported.

Studies have documented the detrimental effects of these social conditions on the mental and physical health of women (Lowe, 1989; Thomas, 1988; MacLeod, 1987). Researchers in the fields of women's health and women with addictions have found that stress resulting from social conditions such as violence and poverty may lead to drug and alcohol abuse as a coping mechanism (Groeneveld, 1989).

Attitudes Toward Women with Alcohol and Drug Problems

Women's use of alcohol has always been judged more harshly than that of men. In ancient Rome, drinking by a woman was punishable by death. In modern times, although there appears to be a veneer of acceptance of women with substance abuse problems, less tolerant attitudes linger just below the surface. It was well known that Winston Churchill "enjoyed a drink" and no one at the time seemed to question his judgment or his ability to run the government of the day. Had Margaret Thatcher "enjoyed a drink" during her years as British Prime Minister, would she have been judged as dispassionately?

I hope I am wrong, but the pendulum appears to be swinging back again in the direction of harsher public opinion toward people with alcohol or drug problems, whether male or female; media coverage, both print and electronic, has shown less tolerance in the last few years. Because women have always been more stigmatized in this regard than men, we might expect the situation to go from bad to worse (i.e., that women with alcohol and drug problems may be judged even more harshly in the future than they are now).

The greater stigma that surrounds women with substance abuse problems delays or prevents their seeking assistance — they actually integrate society's negative attitudes and feel extremely guilty and responsible for their situation. Mothers with drug problems are terrified of losing their children if anyone discovers their problem. Because of alcohol's greater physiological effects on women than men, any delay in seeking help because of negative attitudes puts women at higher risk than men. These physiological effects will be discussed later in this chapter.

Attitudes in Research

Clinicians working with women should keep in mind that what we read is rarely free of attitudinal bias. Except for a few beginning theoretical formulations about female psychological development (Miller, 1976; Belenky, Clinchy, Goldberger and Tarule, 1986) and the development of women's moral reasoning (Gilligan, 1982), theories of human development, therapeutic models and techniques, and even what are considered acceptable research models, were developed predominantly by and for men. These may be valid for male populations but they are usually generalized to apply to female populations. Women have always been measured with a male yardstick and been found lacking. Women are not lacking; they are just different.

Jellinek knew that alcoholic women were different from alcoholic men. As a pattern began to emerge from all the data he was collecting (mostly from men), he noticed that the women were not fitting the pattern (Jellinek, 1946 and 1952). He therefore set aside the women's data — he never pretended it applied to women. So what became the famous "phases chart" had some accuracy for the development of male alcoholism, but did not apply to women. But as his chart became more and more widely disseminated, the assumption that it applied to both genders went with it. This was not unusual. The same thing happened and still happens with other addiction research and research in any other field. When reading studies, be skeptical and question whether they apply to women. Be aware of whether research studies include both males and females. If both sexes are included, are the data for women analysed separately to see if there are any gender differences?

Counsellor Attitudes

Addiction workers have widely held several stereotypes of women with substance use problems, none of which I have found to be true. It was felt that women were sicker and less motivated than men and therefore harder to treat. It is a lot easier for program administrators to come to this conclusion than it is to wonder whether their program might not be designed to meet women's needs. If you find that women are dropping out, try to find out which women and why — maybe they all have family responsibilities or share other concerns that your program could address.

It has been my experience, particularly with regard to motivation, that there is generally less denial among women than men. If anything, women carry an exaggerated sense of guilt and responsibility. This can be a two-edged sword: it may produce the anxiety and discomfort necessary to motivate them toward change (although it may also serve as a barrier to the woman's seeking help initially); but at times it can overwhelm the client, whose level of despair then makes her more vulnerable to self-destructive behaviors, including suicide. Psychological denial is evident more often in people who are in a position to help than in the women themselves: helpers often "deny" that the women in their lives may be experiencing drug-related problems.

Counsellors, clinicians, therapists — anyone who works in a helping capacity with women with substance problems — must take a good look at her or his own attitudes. We are not unaffected by the society in which we live or the biases that were part of our own professional training. Those of us who work in the addictions field are not immune from stigmatizing women. We need to begin by asking ourselves the most basic question: "Do I even like women, let alone value and respect them?" In other words, do I have a "positive regard" for women, or have I internalized negative societal attitudes toward them? Did it matter to me, for example, whether my first-born child was a boy or a girl? If, after a soul-searching examination of whether we value and respect women, we answer in the affirmative, we may be able to work effectively with women.

Then we need to ask ourselves more specific questions related to situations we will definitely face if working with women. Could you work effectively with a woman who:
- told you she had abused her children either physically or verbally
- was neglecting her children
- had given up her children or was expressing disinterest or hostility toward them

223

- revealed heavy drinking and/or drug use during pregnancy
- you felt had totally inadequate parenting skills
- wishes to end a marriage where there are school-age children, and where she is well taken care of
- has been married several times
- insists on staying in an abusive relationship
- talks about the difficulties in the relationship with her female lover
- tells you she has had or is contemplating an abortion
- spends most of her time with you in tears
- makes a pass at you
- is grieving the death of a child/spouse/parent
- has killed someone or assaulted someone
- is just starting to acknowledge being a lesbian
- earns a living through prostitution
- has begun to have memories of childhood incest
- has divulged plans to commit suicide
- is totally contented being a housewife
- is often angry in interviews
- is obese
- is HIV-positive or has AIDS?

Visualize yourself working with a client in one of these situations — how do you feel toward her? Could you be supportive, and create a therapeutic environment conducive to client growth? Or do you recognize in yourself personal values or biases that would affect your feelings toward her?

I will return to further discussion of counsellor attributes at the end of the chapter, examining one's ability to empathize with the woman as the primary ingredient in helping her recover. Attitudes and empathy are two key ingredients — the parentheses within which all other knowledge and skills are held.

BARRIERS THAT WOMEN FACE

We have already discussed attitudes — often the greatest barrier a woman faces in recovering from drug problems. In fact, many of the barriers that will be highlighted here are the result of attitudes and women's status in our society.

Socio-Economic Status

Women do not generally have the same economic resources as their male counterparts. Some of the statistics cited earlier point to the differences. It is generally understood that a range of social, psychological and physical consequences arise out of being poor or having a low income. Most important for our purposes here is the inverse relationship between income levels and symptoms of psychological distress (Turner and Beiser, 1987; D'Arcy, 1982). Many women are poor; many women become depressed.

It is among society's economically disadvantaged groups that the highest use of many of the mood-altering prescription drugs occurs. Women with the highest use of tranquillizers, sleeping pills and antidepressants share low income as a common variable (Canadian Centre on Substance Abuse and Addiction Research Foundation, 1995). Women predominate in many low-income groups. A lot of women are poor — undereducated, unemployed or underemployed, underpaid, retired and widowed. The chronic stress of attempting to live on a low income often leads to depression — as does the loneliness and isolation so characteristic of many subgroupings of women, such as elderly widows and single women with children.

Isolation

The loneliness and isolation so common to these groups of women point out the lack of a support system (which is the reality for most of the female clients with whom I have worked, whether poor or not). The catalysts that often connect a man to the help he needs to recover commonly do not exist for a woman. Women less frequently have a life partner; and if they do, he or she often does not support her recovery efforts. Some partners may even sabotage these efforts if they feel the woman will be more compliant, less angry, etc., if numbed by substance use. Or the lack of support may be due to her partner's fear of losing a "drinking buddy."

The isolation that women with alcohol and drug problems experience can be seen not only as a barrier, but as a major health risk. In his classic work on suicide, Durkheim (1951) pinpointed several common elements among those who take their own lives: alienation, no sense of belonging, not feeling valued or useful, and low self-esteem. A more recent review of several studies involving 37,000 people in the United States, Finland and Sweden has found that individuals cut off from others, either close friends or family, are much more likely to die prematurely than those with a strong social network (House, Landis and Umberson, 1988).

Ironically, as we become more aware of the importance of relationships, they seem to be more and more elusive in our fast-paced society. So much of what goes on in the late 20th century emphasizes and reinforces distance between people, and pits one individual against another. The concepts of extended family and community in their broadest interpretation are barely recognizable as the support systems they used to be. A sense of belonging, of being valuable, respected, cared for and caring of, of relying on and being relied on is crucial to the health of human beings. We are social animals. People who feel good about themselves, who feel connected to other people, valuable and whole, have much less need to seek these feelings — or numb the lack of them — through substance use.

Unrecognized Needs

Although still the primary nurturers, women rarely benefit from the reciprocal aspects of this role — they do not feel valuable, respected and cared for. How does the nurturer get nurtured? She is socialized and skilled in attending to the needs of others but not good at identifying her own needs. In fact, a woman with substance use problems rarely feels that she has legitimate needs. She will delay or avoid seeking help because it might temporarily inconvenience or disrupt her family and she believes that their needs come first — even (in some cases) when her survival may be at stake.

She is not alone in her belief. Her family, partner, children, friends, employer and doctor may explicitly or implicitly convey the same message. I have worked with many women who were emphatic in their need to schedule appointments around hockey practices, their partners wanting to bring people home from work, children needing help with a project, etc. Even as they became stronger in their recovery and more able to acknowledge their right to have their own needs met, they still felt very guilty over the one evening a week they came for their support group (said guilt often reinforced by a partner or children who felt inconvenienced and wanted things the way they were). A woman's connection with her treatment program may always remain somewhat tentative because of this dynamic — guilt is one of the last destructive (in this case) emotions to go.

Child Care Responsibilities and Concerns

Some elaboration on women's child care responsibilities and concerns as a barrier would be useful at this point. Consider a widely quoted idea from a 1970 article by Curlee: "No one likes to think that the hand that rocks the cradle is a shaky one." It encapsulates the essence of the difficulty faced by mothers who might need help for drug problems (although a more basic and practical reality may be that her own financial limitations may prevent her getting appropriate treatment unless the program provides child care). Because of the greater stigma attached to women with alcohol and other drug problems, it is easy to leapfrog from one idea to another: she has substance use problems — she has children — she is an unfit mother! There is no denying that some children experience, in varying degrees, the consequences of their mothers' substance use. But there is a world of difference between that and the concept of "unfit mother."

Their fear of having their children taken from them keeps many women from seeking help. The guilt a woman feels because of real and perceived effects of her substance use on her children, and her perception of the quality or lack of her parenting skills, often make her reluctant to arrange for child care, even if she admits that she needs help. She fears that the substitute care-giver may take better care of her children; the children may not want to come back to her; she is terrified of the separation she may face if she seeks help. Many treatment program staff, in my experience, have not acknowledged these genuine concerns on the part of their female clients. Instead they have accused them of "defocusing," of not taking their recovery seriously, of being in denial, etc. To say that this is not helpful to female clients is an understatement!

Health and Mental Health Care Systems

At first glance it seems bizarre, but the health care and mental health care systems often prevent women from getting appropriate help for substance abuse problems. Far too many of the women I assessed had spent years seeing one mental health professional after another, getting one psychiatric diagnosis on top of another before she, on her own — from reading or seeing something that "clicked," or from having a family member or friend suggest she might have a drinking problem — would come in for assessment.

The mental health system's negative consequences for a woman include sexual exploitation by therapists, drug side-effects, and victim-blaming treatments, according to Susan Penfold, a feminist psychiatrist in British Columbia (Penfold and Walker, 1983). My own clinical experience confirms that much extra therapeutic work is often necessary to undo the damage produced by mental health professionals. Some psychiatrists and psychologists still attribute any mental health problems a client is experiencing to her individual deficiencies. Little, if any, attention is paid to interpersonal, social or environmental factors. Few psychologists and psychiatrists have learned that long-term psychoanalysis can do little to help a client recover from substance abuse. The impact on self-esteem, the increased guilt and internalizing of a feeling of personal responsibility for the problems she is experiencing cannot be overstated.

This may be a good point to say something about antidepressants, in particular the newer generation of antidepressants, such as Prozac. Prescribing of these medications to women has increased. Any minimal levelling off of prescribing of benzodiazepines to women has been offset by prescribing of antidepressants. At least one-quarter of the women I have worked with had been taking antidepressants, usually prescribed by their family doctors. An Australian article suggests that this is also a trend there. The article quotes a *Medical Journal of Australia* (October, 1989) article in which general practitioners claim that "they were either prescribing fewer psychotropic drugs overall or were prescribing more antidepressant agents in place of minor tranquilliser agents" (Butt, 1991, p. 16).

227

Women were not included in early tests on antidepressants that looked at therapeutic benefits and side-effects. So is it any surprise that, even though women receive more prescriptions for antidepressants than do men, men seem to respond more to this type of medication and women suffer more side-effects (Rodin and Ickovics, 1990)? And among these side-effects are symptoms that may lead to a diagnosis of depression, which prompts some doctors to prescribe even more medication (Penfold, 1987). So even though addictions counsellors rarely consider antidepressants a problem because they do not produce physical dependence, they are a serious concern. I am not saying they are never appropriate. I have, on occasion liaised with and referred suicidal women to trusted psychiatric colleagues when I felt antidepressants might be the only alternative to impending need for hospitalization or high potential for suicide.

SPECIAL CONSIDERATIONS IN FEMALE SUBSTANCE USE

Chapter 10 of this book goes into detail about the physical effects of substance use. For our purposes here, I will highlight a few things that are important to know in working with women.

Physical Effects

SUBSTANCE USE

Most women who come to you will have been using multiple substances — usually alcohol in combination with benzodiazepines and/or narcotic painkillers (usually codeine) and perhaps an antidepressant. Some combinations may also include illicit substances, predominantly cannabis and cocaine. It is also likely that your clients will have been taking the prescribed drugs legally, their prescriptions filled repeatedly by a family doctor; only a small percentage would have been "double-doctoring." In fact, the same family doctor may prescribe two benzodiazepines for a woman, one for anxiety and one to help her sleep. Patients have no idea of the potential risk of becoming dependent on these medications; they know about the dangers of Valium (diazepam), but they do not know that taking Xanax (alprazolam) for anxiety and Halcion (triazolam) for sleep over an extended period of time is as dangerous. Neither are women routinely told of the dangers of abrupt cessation of these drugs after taking them for a long time.

ALCOHOL USE

Although women's use of alcohol and drugs in general has been lower than that of men (the exception being prescribed medications, which are still prescribed at twice the rate of men), it appears that young women (ages 18 to 29) are drinking more — and more like men. In a 1995 student survey, Adlaf et al. found no significant differences between adolescent males and females in the number who drank: 60 per cent of the males; 57.6 per cent of the females (Adlaf, Ivis, Smart and Walsh, 1995).

In a comparative study of university student drug use from 1988 to 1993, Gliksman et al. (1994) report that, in 1993, almost 44 per cent of female students reported engaging in heavy binge drinking (often defined as more than five drinks per occasion). Binge drinking often results in problems faster than other drinking patterns. Further, about the same number of males and females said they engaged in binge drinking in the week before they were surveyed (although males did so on more than one occasion in that period).

If this trend continues, it should alarm us. Women are more vulnerable to the effects of alcohol. Given the same amount of alcohol, women get drunker, get drunk faster, and stay drunk longer than their male counterparts. These effects are due to a number of factors such as percentage of body fat (women have a higher percentage and therefore have less body water to dilute the alcohol's effects); hormones (alcohol generally has more effect on women premenstrually); and metabolism (including diminished activity of the stomach enzyme that breaks down alcohol, as reported by Frezza, Di Padova, Pozzato, Terpin, Baraona and Lieber [1990]). A woman who drinks two-thirds as much as a man probably gets the same effect. So if you have been assessing all clients' quantity and frequency of alcohol use according to what is hazardous for males, you need to know the facts about females. Women who drink two to three drinks a day have significant risk for developing cirrhosis.

Women also develop other types of alcoholic liver disease at a faster rate than men (Saunders, Davis and Williams, 1981); prevalence of auto-immune diseases and of auto-antibodies is more common in women (Hill, 1984); they are more susceptible to alcohol-related brain damage than men (Jacobson, 1986). Women are also particularly vulnerable to cancer of the lips, tongue, pharynx and esophagus. They are, however, less prone to peptic ulcers and pancreatitis. It is also important to note whether your female clients have been taking birth control pills. This medication slows the metabolism of central nervous system depressants so that drugs (particularly lipid soluble drugs) accumulate more rapidly with continued use (Jones and Jones, 1984).

Studies have also been finding a connection between alcohol consumption and breast cancer (i.e., that there is a significantly elevated risk of developing breast cancer at even moderate levels of consumption [Schatzkin et al., 1987]). A few studies question these findings. More research is needed but there appears to be some level of risk.

Sexual Dysfunction

Stephanie Covington, an expert in the area of women, sexuality and addictions, reported at a conference in Winnipeg in 1990 that she had found 74 per cent of women in recovery to be sexually dysfunctional and, interestingly, that they often reported having these difficulties before developing substance use problems. The types of sexual dysfunction reported included infertility, miscarriages, lack of interest in sex, lack of lubrication, preorgasmia, vaginismus, anorgasmia and dyspareunia. This becomes a recovery issue that will be mentioned again later in this chapter and is covered in detail in Chapter 24.

I am not going to discuss the risk to the fetus of a pregnant woman from her use of substances. Ample information is accessible elsewhere, and there has been an unfortunate tendency to focus more on the potential damage to the fetus than on the welfare of the woman in her own right (health promotion messages are frequently examples of this).

Psychological Factors

Women seek nurturance and support from alcohol and drugs where there is often none from other people. The combination of causal and contributing factors — biological, psychological, social and environmental — varies with each individual. However, there are several factors I have seen in all the women I have worked with.

REASONS FOR USE

Whether they are taking alcohol, prescription or illegal drugs (and they are usually smoking as well), women use mood-altering substances to cope, to deal with stress, to nurture themselves, to escape from and numb the pain of past events or of their current status, or to allow them to continue functioning in their social roles. This applies to young women and elderly women, financially secure women and women living on limited incomes.

SELF-ESTEEM

It has now been widely documented that women alcoholics have lower self-esteem than their male counterparts (Beckman and Amaro, 1986). Not only do they have very low self-esteem, many have little or no sense of self and no sense of purpose in life (Schlesinger, Susman and Koenigsberg, 1990). They feel powerless, with no control over their lives, and yet they take total responsibility and blame for anything that is wrong in their lives. Their problem (as Covington so succinctly put it at the Winnipeg conference "Women and Substance Abuse: Strategies for the 90s") is not grandiosity, but invisibility.

SUICIDE RISK

Considering the social factors affecting women's lives and the attitudes toward women with alcohol and other drug problems, it is not surprising that they experience an affective disorder (depression) more often than their male counterparts. Although a combination of abstinence and nonpharmacological interventions is usually sufficient for these problems to improve, some women remain depressed for several months despite maintaining abstinence (Goldman and Bander, 1990). Alcoholic women are at greater risk of suicide than females generally — as much as five times so (Gomberg, 1989). At least half of the female clients I have worked with attempted suicide and 30 per cent had tried more than once.

You will come across other forms of self-destructive or self-injurious behavior, such as head-banging, hair pulling, slashing, burning, etc., as well as a variety of eating disorders; bulimia more often than anorexia (see Chapter 25 for more details). Although the dynamics of these behaviors are complex, they share the common element of a woman's desperate attempt to have control over something, often to bury memories, particularly of childhood sexual abuse.

PHYSICAL AND SEXUAL ABUSE

Physical or sexual violence, experienced as a child or an adult, is common among women entering addictions treatment. In fact, if you assume your clients have been abused, you will be right much more often than wrong. A conservative estimate based on my clinical experience would be that two-thirds of these clients have experienced some combination of childhood incest and/or other sexual abuse, physical abuse as a child, physical and/or sexual abuse as an adult. Anyone working with women in recovery must have a reasonable level of expertise in this area.

Although history of abuse should form part of every assessment, working on the abuse issue in depth should not, in my opinion, be initiated by the therapist too early in recovery. It is a different situation if the client initiates exploration of the abuse. If she, for example, in the absence of her mind-numbing drugs, is starting to have memories of abuse, they cannot be ignored. They will cause her to relapse and may place her at higher risk of suicide. I will never forget the director of a 28-day residential treatment program who asked: "How do you keep your clients from defocusing onto their incest issues? They're here for addiction treatment; we can't help them with all their other issues!" He was displaying not only insensitivity to the recovery needs of his clients, but also incompetence, in my opinion, in understanding the lives of his female clients. How much more helpful it would be if he were to understand that recovery issues involve a person's life experiences.

I have met very few addiction counsellors who feel they have the knowledge and experience needed to work effectively with women around the trauma of early childhood sexual abuse. Regression is common, often to preverbal stages of their childhood. Clients' memories can terrify them. If you do not have the expertise to help your clients work through these issues, refer them to someone who does — or develop the expertise but do not rationalize that your only job is to help your client stay sober! In the meantime, while you gain expertise and competence, you can help by using the basic steps one uses when a child discloses sexual abuse. Communicate the messages: "I hear you; I believe you; you are not to blame for what happened to you; I will support you while we get you the help you need."

MULTIPLE PERSONALITY DISORDER

Multiple personality disorder (MPD), although rare, occurs quite frequently among those who have experienced sexual abuse in childhood (Wilbur, 1984). I have known four, a high number given the frequency of this disorder across a population. In all cases, these women were treated by a therapist who had particular expertise in this area. However, the sequencing of the treatments can probably vary: regression therapy for the MPD followed by addiction treatment; the reverse; or the two overlapping for part of the course of therapy/treatment — it will vary depending on the situation of the individual client (and, sometimes, the length of time it takes to get to see a qualified therapist).

SOME MAJOR ISSUES IN RECOVERY

Tasks in Recovery

The first task for a counsellor is to help his or her client stay sober and avoid other compulsive behaviors, such as bingeing on food. The client also needs to learn to feel better about herself — this in itself is a journey that usually begins with confronting her self-hate, moving through despair to hope, to beginning to develop a sense of self, upon which self-esteem will be built slowly over the rest of her life. At the same time, she must begin to identify her own needs, not just the needs of others, finding a new balance. Even the basic needs of health — nutrition, sleep and exercise — can be difficult when she is so accustomed to attending to others' needs. She needs, too, to learn how to seek nurturance from other people and not substances. Because this involves elements like relationships, sexuality, and spirituality, it cannot be rushed. She needs some sense of self and how to relate to that new self before she focuses on significant relationships in her life. Finally, she needs to learn to express anger. Healthy anger in women in our society is barely tolerated, let alone encouraged. But the client must learn ways to express it if she is to develop strength, self-esteem, some sense of control over her life, and perhaps, most of all, to avoid depression.

Accomplishing these tasks is not easy in the best of circumstances; the attitudes already discussed compound the difficulty, as do the lack of services needed by women in recovery and the rigidity of many traditional treatment programs that offer standard components through which a client flows, no matter what his or her individual circumstances.

CORE COMPONENTS/SERVICES OF
A TREATMENT PROGRAM FOR WOMEN

My suggestions here will focus on those services most likely needed by women whose problems have taken them beyond the point where they could consider moderation: women whose goal is abstinence. As community prevention and health promotion efforts improve, some women may prefer to discuss and ultimately alter their use of substances before they have resulted in serious problems. The early intervention techniques developed by Martha Sanchez-Craig are being found to be particularly effective with women (Sanchez-Craig, 1990). Her self-help book *Saying When* is particularly useful for this group.

Assessment

An effective treatment plan or program must begin with a comprehensive assessment. Any instruments should be checked for their reliability, validity and appropriateness for use with women. In order to know what services a client will need, the assessor should ask more than the standard questions about substance use. He or she should also explore:

- any consequences she may experience after even low amounts
- circumstances under which she uses
- whether she uses and shares needles
- whether she smokes
- medical problems (remember to ask specifically about gynecological problems and any previous psychiatric diagnosis, even though it may prove to be wrong — the symptoms of a drinking problem are often misdiagnosed as depression)
- history of violence/abuse
- suicide attempts
- other kinds of self-destructive or injurious behavior, including eating disorders
- partner's substance use
- what, if any, social supports she already has in place
- whether the client has children or other dependants for whom she will need care arrangements
- financial resources — does she even have enough for public transit (do not assume this applies only to low-income women; I have worked with wealthy women who had no access to money without going through their husbands)
- educational/vocational background (there might be a need for upgrading or retraining).

Environment

The environment in which the assessment and core services take place is rarely thought to have any bearing on whether the client enters or stays in treatment. It has been my experience, however, that surroundings play some part in whether a client feels comfortable enough to come back a second time (obviously a less important part than the person doing the assessment). Women, I think, are more field-dependent than men — more attuned to and affected by details in their environments. Because of the violence issues for this population of women, an immediate sense of safety in and around the environment is crucial. Consider the following factors:

- Is public transit very close by?
- Are streets well lit?
- Is her privacy assured — are meetings with her counsellor structured to protect the confidentiality of their discussions?
- Are her personal belongings accessible only to her?
- Is there (in the case of mixed programs) adequate physical separation from male participants? One client told me why she left a mixed residential program prematurely: she had been placed initially in a stabilization unit in which she was the only woman, with only a fabric screen separating her bed from the men. She was terrified of falling asleep and left after three days.

Essential Services

In addition to a comprehensive assessment and attention to the physical and emotional environment, the following are essential ingredients in any treatment program, whether outpatient or day treatment, or short- to long-term residential:

- substance abuse education following a biopsychosocial model (Donovan and Marlatt, 1988), including discussion of possible contributing factors, consequences and effects
- relapse prevention (see Chapter 8)
- skills training to develop self-esteem and coping (Reed's 1987 list seems complete to me in this regard): assertiveness training, financial management education, instruction in personal goal setting, education in stress and crisis management, assistance in developing communication skills and a support system, discussion of gender and socialization issues, and instruction in basic survival skills.

Also essential are education on nutrition, exercise and other leisure activities; family (in its broadest sense); and discussions on sexuality, including attention to sexual abuse issues, body image, eating disorders and performance expectations.

I should clarify what I mean here: there should not be any performance expectations. With the high incidence of sexual dysfunction, many sex acts, such as intercourse and other forms of two-person sexual activity, need to be delayed or postponed for some time while clients work on other issues. If there is a life partner in the picture, he or she may expect their sex life to resume or improve immediately. It is quite possible, however, that the client has never engaged in any sexual activity without being under the influence of a mood-altering substance. Or she may be retrieving memories of sexual abuse that need attention, etc. In other words, it is not only her right, but a necessary part of recovery in some cases, to proceed slowly in resuming or exploring her sex life with a partner.

Not all clients will need all the essential components and services. Clients will have different needs. The same comment applies to the following related services.

Related Services

Other necessary services could be offered as part of the treatment program itself or through referral elsewhere in the community. These include:

- medical services
- vocational services
- services for eating disorders
- appropriately sensitive psychiatric consultation and/or treatment
- services for the children of clients, including child care, prevention/ education and treatment programs
- other types of family (again in its broadest sense) programming, including educational and support groups for partners, parenting education, family therapy and couples' groups (these should not occur too early in recovery — women usually need at least several months of self-focused recovery elements first)
- legal services
- and probably most important, services for recovery from the trauma of sexual abuse.

TREATMENT MODALITIES

Because of the constellation of factors usually found among women seeking treatment — low self-esteem, guilt, social isolation, and history of physical and sexual abuse — I prefer gender-specific group treatment, at least in early recovery. Let me begin by describing some of the problems women face in mixed-gender groups.

I have built this list over the last 10 years, adding from my own group experience and every study I have found that looked at the issues: interaction in mixed groups reinforces traditional role stereotypes; women speak less often and for less time than men; women are often interrupted; women do not defend their ideas vigorously; issues of body image and sexuality are not discussed; women compete and do not develop closeness with each other; women are passive, talk softly and tend to withdraw; women overtly and covertly defer to men and encourage male participation and interactions; men's language patterns predominate.[1]

If the ultimate goal of a treatment plan is that a woman develop her potential — that she achieve and maintain abstinence or control over her use of substances, discover a sense of self, build self-esteem, develop social supports and recover from the trauma of abuse — common sense alone should lead us to conclude that these objectives can best be met with the help of other women. All-women groups facilitated by female leaders allow clients to develop a sense of self through validation of one's experiences and perceptions; attempt personal, behavioral and attitudinal changes; express difficult feelings like anger and shame; share the social determinants of problems special to women; please themselves instead of others; learn to trust and value women. And for almost all women (the exception sometimes being those who have been abused by mothers or lesbian partners), these groups provide the safety necessary to take risks. Some women may be reluctant to engage in an all-women group because they dislike other women. Despite the potential benefits of a woman's participation, you may have to accept that she may reject your advice in this regard: in other words, keep your options open. Women can now access all-women Alcoholics Anonymous and Women for Sobriety groups, as well as all-women groups within some treatment programs and services.

After a woman is progressing well in her recovery, has begun to develop some sense of herself and some self-esteem, there can be some specific benefit to participation in mixed-gender groups, co-led by male and female therapists. Skilled facilitators, themselves fully aware of different interaction patterns between men and women, and healthy in their own gender roles and interactions, can model for participants. Women clients can practise what may be new assertive interactions with men in what should be, with good facilitators, a safe setting.

Except for women whose particular combination and quantity of substances would likely result in withdrawal requiring close monitoring (e.g., to watch for seizures), or those who need to remove themselves from their living situation or the influence of their significant others, day treatment or outpatient treatment is just as effective and much less costly and disruptive than residential treatment. Although there has not been a lot of good outcome research, in general there has been enough to demonstrate that nonresidential treatment is usually preferable. And for women, with all of the other responsibilities in their lives, this is probably even more true.

I realize that my preference for all-women groups, though based on clinical experience, perpetuates what Vanicelli (1984) describes as the "unsubstantiated, but dearly held, beliefs of care providers." I stand by it, however, awaiting more research in the area of treatment outcome and matching clients to treatment modalities.[2] The most ground I will give on this point is that, at the very least, women be given a choice of treatment modalities and sex of therapist.

COUNSELLOR CHARACTERISTICS

In discussing gender of therapist, I have almost come full circle. I began this chapter by stating that if we are to help women recover and develop their potential, we must understand and empathize with each one individually. I truly believe that many components of a treatment program could vary and not greatly affect outcome, as long as there is the essential relational bond between the client and her therapist. Put another way, I hope treatment outcome research in the substance abuse field eventually confirms what psychotherapy research has — that one of the key prognostic variables in treatment is the empathic qualities of the therapist. Empathy means profoundly valuing and understanding the client's reality. It also involves knowing yourself intimately so you can be with your client every step of the way and not lose yourself in the process. I offer the following list of questions, based on those used by the authors of *Women's Ways of Knowing,* for some self-exploration from a perspective you may not have considered:

- How do you express your anger?
- What are your deepest fears? How do you deal with them?
- Do you seek nurturance for yourself? How, in what ways, from whom?
- Have you experienced intimate group sharing with other women/men?
- Have you been through your own therapy?
- Do you know who you are — could you describe yourself to someone?
- In your own family, how are roles assigned; how are finances handled; who makes money decisions? How are household duties handled?
- If you have children, how are they growing up vis-à-vis traditional male/female roles, ways of interacting, etc.?
- What would you (or did you) look for in a helping person?
- What stands out for you in your life over the last few years?
- What kinds of things have been important?
- What is your life like right now? What do you care about, think about?
- Is the way you see yourself now different from the way you saw yourself in the past? What led to the changes? How do you see yourself changing in the future?
- What does being a woman/man mean to you?
- Do you think there are any important differences between women and men?
- How has your sense of yourself as a woman/man been changing?

- What relationships have been really important to you in your life? Why? How would you describe those relationships? How would the other person describe them?
- Have you had a relationship with someone who helped you shape the person you have become?
- Have you had a really important relationship where you were responsible for taking care of another person? How would you describe this? How important was that in your life?

I hope you can see some connection between your own answers to these questions and your ability to walk in step with your women clients.

Again it seems common sense to me that women therapists would generally be more likely than male counterparts to empathize with women clients. Men and women have very different realities, very different experiences of the world. They develop differently, think differently, develop different kinds of moral reasoning, have different experiences of intimacy and sexuality and on and on. The odds are that a woman therapist will understand the world her female client describes better than a male therapist. This is not to say that a male therapist can never empathize with the experiences of his female clients. A study reported by Kaplan (1985) found that very experienced males could achieve the same rate of therapy outcome as moderately experienced or experienced female therapists. I have selectively referred clients to male therapists but never for sexual abuse or other abuse issues, and not in early recovery while a woman is just beginning to develop a sense of self and a support network.[3]

CONCLUSION

In preparing for a workshop a few years ago, I wanted to describe to participants the essence of the relationship between a woman recovering from substance use problems and her counsellor. I used the following analogy, thinking I had developed it, only later discovering that it been used years before in relation to teaching, probably by Paulo Freire. Rather than being disappointed by my lack of originality, I was reassured by the fact that others had conceptualized it in a similar way.

Accompanying an addicted woman on the long journey to recovery — through self-loathing, guilt and despair to self-understanding, self-acceptance, self-respect and control over her own life — is like being a midwife. The client sets the pace, and you move forward with her when she has the strength; sit quietly beside her while she catches her breath, encouraging her, guiding her to push again, telling her the pain won't last, that the destination is worth it, that you've seen many other women go through this, that you know she has the strength to push again. And, ultimately, she has given birth to herself, to the beginning of her potential finally becoming reality.

ACKNOWLEDGMENTS

I would like to express my gratitude to current colleagues within the Addiction Research Foundation for their feedback on this chapter, but especially to former clients and colleagues at Amethyst Women's Addiction Centre for giving me their input on the first draft — thank you Lynn, Ellen, Pierrette and Jane.

ENDNOTES

[1] It was a delight to read a sociolinguist's analysis and validation of what had been my own observations of mixed and gender-specific groups. Deborah Tannen (1991) describes many of the above conversational dynamics between men and women, as well as others, as "cross-cultural communication, prey to a clash of conversational styles" (p. 42).

[2] Copeland and Hall's 1992 study found that a specialist women's service, in comparison with traditional mixed-sex services, attracted significantly more women with dependent children, or who were lesbian, or who had a maternal history for drug or alcohol problems, or who had suffered sexual abuse in childhood. The Women's Program at the Addiction Research Foundation found that retention rates for women were higher in that program than in the mixed program.

[3] A large multi-site study, Project MATCH, is beginning to produce results for publication. One of the areas it should be able to say something about is the relationship of gender of therapist to treatment outcome.

REFERENCES

Adlaf, E.M., Ivis, F.J., Smart, R.G., and Walsh, G.W. (1995). *Ontario Student Drug Use Survey.* Toronto: Addiction Research Foundation.

Annis, H., and Davis, C. (1989). Relapse prevention. In *Handbook of Alcoholism Treatment Approaches,* eds. Hester, R.K., and Miller, W.R. New York: Pergamon Press.

Beckman, L.J., and Amaro, H. (1986). Personal and social difficulties faced by women and men entering treatment. *Journal of Studies on Alcohol* 47: 135–145.

Belenky, M.F., Clinchy, B.M., Goldberger, N.R., and Tarule, J.M. (1986). *Women's Ways of Knowing.* New York: Basic Books.

Brody, C. (1987). *Women's Therapy Groups.* New York: Springer Publishing Co.

Butt, L. (1991). Antidepressants: Beyond benzodiazepines. *Connexions* (March/April): 14–18.

Canadian Centre on Substance Abuse and the Addiction Research Foundation. (1995) *Canadian Profile: Alcohol, Tobacco and Other Drugs 1995.* Toronto: Authors.

Copeland, J., and Hall, W. (1992). A comparison of women seeking drug and alcohol treatment in a specialist women's and two traditional mixed-sex treatment services. *British Journal of Addiction* 87: 1293–1302.

Curlee, J. (1970). A comparison of male and female patients at an alcoholism treatment centre. *Journal of Psychology* 74: 239–247.

D'Arcy, C. (1982). Prevalence and correlates of nonpsychotic psychiatric symptoms in the general population. *Canadian Journal of Psychiatry* 27: 316–324.

Donovan, D.M., and Marlatt, G.A. (eds.). (1988). *Assessment of Addictive Behaviors*. New York: The Guilford Press.

Durkheim, E. (1951). *Suicide*. New York: Free Press.

Frezza, M., Di Padova, C., Pozzato, G., Terpin, M., Baraona, E., and Lieber, C.S. (1990). High blood alcohol levels in women: The role of decreased gastric alcohol dehydrogenase activity and first-pass metabolism. *New England Journal of Medicine* 322 (2): 95–99.

Gilligan, C. (1982). *In a Different Voice*. Cambridge, MA: Howard University Press.

Gliksman, L., Newton-Taylor, B., Adlaf, E., DeWit, D., and Giesbrecht, N. (1994). *University Student Drug Use and Lifestyle Behaviors: Current Patterns and Changes from 1988 to 1993*. Toronto: Addiction Research Foundation.

Goldman, D.S., and Bander, K.W. (1990). Six-month course of depression in female alcoholics. *Journal of Substance Abuse* 2: 375–380.

Gomberg, E.S. (1989). Suicide risk among women with alcohol problems. *American Journal of Public Health* 79: 1363–1365.

Groeneveld, J., and Shain, M. (1989). *Drug Use among Victims of Sexual Abuse*. Toronto: Addiction Research Foundation.

Guberman, C., and Wolfe, M. (eds.) (1985). *No Safe Place: Violence Against Women and Children*. Toronto: The Women's Press.

Health and Welfare Canada. (1990). *National Alcohol and Other Drugs Survey (1989): Highlights Report,* eds. Eliany, M., Giesbrecht, N., Nelson, M., Wellman, B., and Wortley, S. Ottawa: Minister of Supply and Services Canada.

Hill, S.Y. (1984). Vulnerability to the biomedical consequences of alcoholism and alcohol-related problems among women. In *Alcohol Problems in Women,* eds. Wilsnack, S.C., and Beckman, L.J. New York: The Guilford Press.

House, J., Landis, K., and Umberson, D. (1988). Social relationships and health. *Science* 241: 540–545.

Jacobson, R. (1986). The contribution of sex and drinking history to the CT brain scan changes in alcoholics. *Psychological Medicine* 16: 547–559.

Jacobson, R. (1986). Female alcoholics: A controlled CT brain scan and clinical study. *British Journal of Addiction* 81: 661–669.

Jellinek, E.M. (1946). Phases in the drinking history of alcoholics. *Quarterly Journal of Studies on Alcohol* 7: 1–88.

Jellinek, E.M. (1952). Phases of alcohol addiction. *Quarterly Journal of Studies on Alcohol* 13: 673–684.

Jones, M.K., and Jones, B.M. (1984). Ethanol metabolism in women taking oral contraceptives. *Alcoholism: Clinical and Experimental Research* 8: 24–28.

Kaplan, A.G. (1985). Female or male therapists for women patients: New formulations. *Psychiatry* 48 (May).

Lowe, G.S. (1989). Women, paid/unpaid work, and stress: New directions for research. Background Paper. Ottawa: Canadian Advisory Council on the Status of Women.

MacLeod, L. (1987). *Battered But Not Beaten: Preventing Wife Battering in Canada*. Ottawa: Canadian Advisory Council on the Status of Women.

Miller, J.B. (1976). *Toward a New Psychology of Women*. Boston: Beacon Press.

Moore, M. (1987). Women parenting alone. *Canadian Social Trends* (Winter): 31–36.

Penfold, P.S., and Walker, G.A. (1983). *Women and the Psychiatric Paradox*. Montreal: Eden Press.

Penfold, S. (1987). Antidepressants. Proceedings of a national consultation on women and drugs. Ottawa: Minister of Supply and Services.

Reed, B.G., and Leibson, E. (1981). Women clients in special women's demonstration programs compared with women entering co-sex programs. *The International Journal of the Addictions* 16: 1425–1466.

Reed, B.G. (1985). Drug misuse and dependency in women: The meaning and implications of being considered a special population or minority group. *The International Journal of the Addictions* 20 (1): 13–62.

Reed, B.G. (1987). Developing women-sensitive drug dependence treatment services: Why so difficult? *Journal of Psychoactive Drugs* 19 (2): 151–164.

Rodin, J., and Ickovics, J.R. (1990). Women's health review and research agenda as we approach the 21st century. *American Psychologist* (September): 1018–1034.

Sanchez-Craig, M. (1994). *Saying When: How to Quit Drinking or Cut Down*, 2nd ed. Toronto: Addiction Research Foundation.

Sanchez-Craig, M. (1990). Brief didactic treatment for alcohol and drug-related problems: An approach based on client choice. *British Journal of Addiction* 85: 169–177.

Saunders, J.B., Davis, M., and Williams, R. (1981). Do women develop alcoholic liver disease more readily than men? *British Medical Journal* 282: 1140–1143.

Schatzkin, A., Jones, D.Y., Hoover, R.N., Taylor, P.R., Brinton, L.A., Ziegler, R.G., Harvey, E.B., Carter, C.L., Licitra, L.M., DuFour, M.C., and Larson, D.B. (1987). Alcohol consumption and breast cancer in the epidemiologic follow-up study of the first national health and nutrition examination survey. *The New England Journal of Medicine* 316: 1169–1173.

Schlesinger, S., Susman, M., and Koenigsberg, J. (1990). Self-esteem and purpose in life: A comparative study of women alcoholics. *Journal of Alcohol and Drug Education* 36 (i): 127–141.

Statistics Canada. (1995). *Women in Canada: A Statistical Report,* 3rd ed. Ottawa: Statistics Canada, Social and Economic Studies Division.

Stoppard, J.M. (1988). Women and the mental health system: Mental health policy as though women mattered. Paper presented at the Symposium on Women and Mental Health, Section on Women and Psychology, Canadian Psychological Association Annual Convention. Montreal, June 1988.

Tannen, D. (1991). *You Just Don't Understand.* New York: Ballantine Books.

Thomas, E. (1988). *Issues and Priorities for Women's Health in Canada.* Ottawa: Health Promotion Directorate, Health and Welfare Canada.

Turner, R.J., and Beiser, M. (1987). Major depression and depressive symptomatology among the physically disabled: Assessing the role of chronic stress. Paper presented at the meeting of the American Public Health Association. New Orleans, October 1987.

Vanicelli, M. (1984). Treatment outcome of alcoholic women: The state of the art in relation to sex bias and expectancy effects. In *Alcohol Problems in Women,* eds. Wilsnack, S.C., and Beckman, L.J. New York: The Guilford Press.

Wilbur, C.B. (1984). Multiple Personality and Child Abuse. *Psychiatric Clinics of North America* 7 (1): 3–7.

ADDITIONAL RESOURCES

Addiction Research Foundation. (1996). *The Hidden Majority: A Guidebook on Alcohol and Other Drug Issues For Counsellors Who Work with Women.* Toronto: Author.

British Columbia Ministry of Health and Ministry Responsible for Seniors. (undated). *Women's Day Treatment Manual.* Victoria: Authors. (Contact: Adult Clinical and Addictions Services Branch, 3rd Floor, #1810 Blanshard Street, Victoria, BC V8T 4J1. Telephone: 604-952-0800.)

Centre for Substance Abuse Treatment. (1994). *Practical Approaches in the Treatment of Women Who Abuse Alcohol and Other Drugs.* Rockville, MD: CCAT. (Rockwall, IL, 5600 Fishers Lane; Rockville, MD 20857.)

Cambridge and Somerville Program of Alcoholism Rehabilitation (CASPAR). (1990). *Getting Sober, Getting Well. A Treatment Guide for Caregivers Who Work with Women.* Cambridge, MA: The Women's Alcoholism Program of CASPAR. (Address: 6 Camelia Avenue, Cambridge, MA 02139. Telephone: 617-661-1316.)

You can contact INFO-ARF at the Addiction Research Foundation (1-800-463-6273) to obtain lists of resources (books, manuals, videos) on women and substance use.

Chapter 13

Working with Men

EVA INGBER

INTRODUCTION

It is commonly believed that substance abuse programs have been designed primarily by men for male clients. Despite this, a question remains as to whether treatment adequately identifies and addresses gender issues for men. Gender-focused research has tended to concentrate on women's patterns of use and unique treatment issues such as trauma, physiological effects and the stigma for women who use substances. Women's substance use is explored with clients by acknowledging their gender roles, oppression and socio-political issues. "The alcoholic" is sort of a generic person — an apparent male, but a male out of the context of maleness (van Wormer, 1989).

With an increasing number of women's treatment programs becoming available, more mixed-gender programs may be evolving into men's programs (this pattern may be changing with current budget cuts, downsizing and the restructuring of services). In the substance abuse field, the issue of single-sex treatment groups has been controversial and often unsupported. Many in the field have tended to view alcohol and drug problems as similar for men and women. When developing treatment for men, an opportunity exists to consider what it means to provide a service that is unique to men's gender issues as they relate to substance use problems.

This chapter will identify and explore the following topics: the characteristics of male substance use; the reasons for men's substance use and the role of substances in men's lives; creating a working environment in a men's treatment group; issues for work in recovery (assertiveness, men as perpetrators and victims of violence, expressing anger); and the gender of the therapist.

CHARACTERISTICS OF MALE SUBSTANCE USE

In our society, men are more likely than women to drink and to use illicit drugs. A recent national survey (Health and Welfare Canada, 1992) found that 84 per cent of men compared with 72 per cent of women were current drinkers. Similarly, men are twice as likely as women to report using marijuana and cocaine. However, men are less likely to use psychoactive medications.

In terms of drinking patterns and associated problems, men consume more drinks per occasion, per week and per year, and are far more likely than women to report heavy episodic drinking occasions (more than five drinks on a single occasion). Men are also more likely to report alcohol-related problems, drinking and driving, and contact with the police resulting from their alcohol use (Health and Welfare Canada, 1992; Weisner and Schmidt, 1992). Men are over-represented in substance abuse treatment settings compared to women, and, in terms of substance abuse care in nonspecialized settings, men are more likely to use criminal justice settings, while women are more likely to use mental health settings (Weisner and Schmidt, 1992). Male problem drinkers are more likely to describe their problems as explicitly alcohol- or substance abuse-related, while women are more likely to interpret their symptoms as depression or anxiety (Weisner and Schmidt, 1992).

REASONS FOR SUBSTANCE USE AND
THE ROLE OF SUBSTANCES IN MEN'S LIVES

The Social Context

A socialization experience that encourages hard drinking while mandating achievement and toughness for men is a precarious experience. Those who fail to achieve according to the norms of the society may turn to alcohol to numb the pain of despair. Achievement of the prescribed masculine role, in turn, is hindered as the drug or alcohol takes its toll — sexually, behaviorally, financially, and emotionally. Three areas then — the male drinking culture, pressures to excel and produce, and sexual orientation — may affect men's risk for alcoholism. Certain events that involve loss or conflict in areas of traditional masculine role performance (such as unemployment, powerlessness, sexual conflict) are highly associated with excessive drinking in the male (van Wormer, 1989).

By the time many men seek treatment, they have often learned to associate socializing with substance use. A man may be quite isolated, although his social network may be connected to others with similar patterns of use. Men commonly express concerns about not knowing how or where to socialize, and fear losing friends. However, a man with a substance use problem is less likely than a woman to lose a partner, and concern by a partner or fear of losing one's family can be a strong motivator for many men to seek help.

Risk Situations for Substance Use

Substantial evidence shows that for moderately to severely dependent drinkers of both sexes, the highest risk situations involve negative emotional states, interpersonal conflict and social pressure to drink (Annis and Graham, 1995; Annis et al., 1996), although heavy substance use is less likely to be associated with unpleasant emotions and conflict for men than for women (Annis et al., 1996). In Annis's 1996 study (Annis et al., 1996, in press) these three risk areas, together with urges/temptations, accounted for 90 per cent of the relapse crisis situations reported by clients of both genders. The study also suggests that men are less successful in abstaining in the presence of other drinkers. (In contrast, women are less successful in abstaining in negative affect situations.) Consequently, one of the highest risk situations for men is social pressure to drink or to use. When seeking treatment, men may benefit from addressing issues related to socializing without substance use. Related to this, some areas for work may include developing a support system; undergoing social skills training (including communicating with intimate partners); developing new leisure activities; and practising refusal strategies while enhancing self-esteem.

CREATING A WORKING ENVIRONMENT IN A MEN'S TREATMENT GROUP

For most men, talk is primarily a means to preserve independence and negotiate and maintain status in a hierarchical social order. This is done by exhibiting knowledge and skill, and by holding centre stage through verbal performance such as story-telling, joking or imparting information. From childhood, men learn to use talking as a way to get and keep attention. So they are more comfortable in larger groups made up of people they know less well — in the broadest sense, "public speaking." But even the most private situations can be approached like public speaking, more like giving a report than establishing rapport (Tannen, 1990).

In a men's group, clients may initially communicate mainly with the therapist. Often, little eye contact and disclosure occurs among the male group members, unlike in a women's group, where women begin supporting each other with empathetic comments such as: "I know how you feel. I have felt the same." In a mixed group, men will often communicate to the female group members. As discussed by van Wormer (1989), "the most difficult challenge in leading a men's group is to get the men to talk about their feelings. The typical alcoholic male reaction is to describe a situation of dire circumstances and then to say, 'I can handle it.'"

Consequently, a men's group must acknowledge and discuss men's gender issues and make the connection to the function of substance use in their lives. Yet men have not been socialized to connect with one another by sharing feelings. As discussed by Doyle (1989), men are socialized to hide their feelings, especially from other men. He writes that when males disclose, it is usually to women with whom they are close, and that men typically view other males who are self-disclosers with some skepticism, if not disdain. As a result, the challenge of expressing personal feelings must be acknowledged, particularly in a group with other men. Furthermore, men may need help in identifying their feelings. They also need to know that they may experience a flooding or numbing of feelings when stopping substance use and that this experience is common, particularly if there is any history of trauma.

It can sometimes be useful to facilitate exercises that encourage men to talk with one another, while creating group norms and ownership for the group. One way of developing comfort in the group is to introduce discussion on the topic of similarities and differences that may arise in a group of men with a history of substance use. It is important to give men permission to share varied life experiences. This issue can be introduced by asking the men to list possible differences that may arise in such a group. These differences may include the following: reasons for seeking help, family support, history of substance use, employment status and financial situation. The facilitator can include issues that the men may feel are more challenging to identify, such as race, culture, religion, health issues (e.g., HIV status) and sexual preference. The second part of this process involves discussing and recording ways to respect these differences. This list could include ways that members can support and constructively challenge each other, such as by listening, respecting confidentiality, being nonjudgmental, being open to learning from each other, avoiding labelling people's behaviors, and discussing how to give constructive feedback (using "I" messages, the option of asking for or refusing feedback). This exercise will allow men to discuss and become aware of what to expect in the group, which will reduce uncertainty and can increase comfort. By recording this list, clients can review the group norms if required (i.e., if a client makes a racist, homophobic or sexist comment or joke). This exercise can be helpful in giving men permission to share experiences while reducing the fear of being judged.

To encourage the men to communicate directly with each other, clients can be asked to facilitate a peer check-in during each session. In this peer check-in, the volunteer facilitator may ask the following types of questions: Have group members experienced thoughts or cravings for substances? Has there been any substance use? Are people concerned about upcoming risk situations? What is going better? Through these interactions, clients learn coping strategies, share strengths and vulnerabilities, and help one another. In this way, the interaction becomes less therapist-centred and more group-focused.

ISSUES FOR WORK IN RECOVERY

Expressing Feelings through Assertive Communication

Identifying feelings, coping with feelings, and learning to express these feelings without substances are important parts of recovery. When teaching assertiveness skills to men, there is often discussion about language and effective communication (assertive versus aggressive communication). Men in our society are more likely to learn that aggressive behavior is equated with success, especially in the workplace.

The traditional male role attributes both the power and the burden of material responsibility on the male. The ideal image of a man in our culture portrays the stereotype of a physically dominant "macho" male who makes all the decisions and gets his needs met through the women in his life. In the media, the man who dominates through force is often depicted as strong and desirable (Addiction Research Foundation, 1995).

Consequently, men may benefit from learning and practising assertive behavior. It is often helpful to address issues of assertive communication early in a program, including teaching and practising "I feel" messages, so that the men can use these skills in a safe place, as well as receive constructive feedback. It is important to normalize and validate the challenges of men expressing their feelings, and also to give them permission to share feelings.

Linking Violence and Substance Use

Men in treatment for substance abuse may also have a history of violence, as either the perpetrator, the victim or both. This may be particularly true for men referred from the criminal justice system. While drinking itself does not cause violence, studies show that problem drinkers are far more likely than abstainers to abuse their partners. A positive association between alcohol intake and aggression has been documented in areas such as spouse assault, child abuse and general physical violence (Potter-Efron and Potter-Efron, 1991a). "Men make choices about whom they use violence against, and how much violence they use. It is men who use violence most often and do the most damage" (Miedema, 1996). One study suggests that, in comparison with abstainers and moderate drinkers, the rate of violence is about 15 times higher among problem drinkers (Strauss et al., 1980). Problem drinkers who abuse their partners are also more likely than other abusers to use violence when they are intoxicated. Statistics show that 90 per cent of reported spousal violence is male against female. Most male abusers have themselves been the object of abuse, the witness to abuse, and emotionally or physically deprived in childhood. In fact, most abusers believe they are victims themselves. For them, violence is a means of gaining control and power in their lives.

249

When men are using substances, particularly at high levels, or when they are in withdrawal, there may be increased risk for violence. However, power and control are factors with or without substance use. To work with a man on these issues, the substance use must be addressed first so that he can decide to explore his attitudes and take responsibility for his behavior.

A study that examined power and marital violence found that men enrolled in either substance abuse treatment programs or anger management programs had similar levels of egalitarianism and violence in their relationships (Crossman et al., 1990). These results suggest that the belief in traditional sex roles may be a meaningful indicator for spouse abuse. The study also recommends that treatment programs address alcohol abuse and violence for both batterers and substance abusers.

Traditional gender differentials promote a sense of entitlement at the expense of social and emotional responsibility in men. In the context of abusive behavior, these gender-based differentials fail to promote the acceptance of responsibility for abusive behavior by the perpetrator of that abuse (Jenkins, 1990).

It is not enough to stop abusing substances; further education and support are necessary to stop the emotional, verbal, psychological and/or physical violence. Education about the "cycle of violence" is essential, while connecting it to the fact that men choose when and whom they violate, including when they are under the influence of substances. In discussing this cycle, it is also important to educate men that their partners may use substances to cope with the emotional and physical pain of the abuse. Education linking power and control to violence is also necessary, as well as offering information about the "cycle of equality" in order to provide men with new means of communicating in relationships. Referrals to groups for men who are violent may be necessary, due to limited time and resources in substance abuse treatment settings to address this issue.

According to Jenkins (1990), the models of helping men who are violent to cease their abusive behavior and relate respectfully to others is based on the assumption that these goals can be best achieved if the perpetrator of violence accepts full responsibility for his abusive actions.

He must acknowledge fully the existence and significance of the abuse and understand the potential impact of his abusive actions upon the victim and others. He must accept his culpability for his actions and bear the full onus for ceasing his abuse and changing his behavior. For the counsellor, the challenge is to derive an approach that will engage the man in a way that facilitates his taking responsibility for his participation in therapy and encourages an active interest and motivation for changing his own behavior (Jenkins, 1990).

At the same time, it is important to link violence and substance use, so that men learn that violence is not an alternative coping mechanism.

Learning about Expressing Anger

Whether or not a man has a history of violence, the topic of communicating anger may need to be explored. It is important to discuss with a client the possible connection between how his style of communicating feelings of anger may be a trigger to substance use, such as hiding feelings of hurt or disappointment, or feeling powerless in a conflict with his employer. A man may have learned that substance use has helped him to cope with feelings of anger or that it has allowed him to express these feelings, in both constructive and/or destructive ways. Yet some clients may be uncomfortable discussing the topic of anger. For a person from a family with a history of substance use problems, anger may have been a forbidden emotion. Potter-Efron and Potter-Efron (1991b) discuss the idea of anger avoidance, which is defined as a pattern of thinking, acting and feeling in which individuals attempt to ignore, avoid and suppress their anger. These authors state that people who avoid anger may seldom notice the physical and cognitive cues that indicate anger. The expression of anger may have been feared due to past experiences that threatened the functioning of the family, such as violence. A man may be unable to identify feelings of anger and may feel disconnected or threatened by discussion of the topic.

For men with a history of post-traumatic stress disorder (PTSD), treatment settings have found that participation in treatment appears to increase symptoms of irritability, anger and mood lability, leading to both relapse and outbursts of anger and violence (Reilly et al., 1994). Consequently, anger management has been increasingly incorporated into the treatment of PTSD and substance abuse (Zweben, Clark and Smith, 1994). The objectives of anger management treatment are twofold: to teach clients to identify the specific cues and triggers to anger, and to help them develop strategies for controlling their anger in the form of individualized, control plans (Reilly et al., 1994). The therapist's role is to give men permission to communicate feelings of anger, to provide education on ways to constructively express anger, and to teach conflict-resolution strategies.

It is useful to help men identify their warning signs when they are feeling anger build by identifying self-thoughts, behavior and physical warning signs (such as shaking or an increased heart rate). Using these techniques, men can learn to avoid relapse or inappropriate behavior. Examples of cognitive-behavioral strategies suggested by Meichenbaum (as cited in Reilly et al., 1994) to teach clients to think and plan before they act include self-monitoring feelings, time-out strategies, relaxation training, exercise and talking to a supportive person. Men often enter a substance abuse treatment program convinced that the only ways to handle conflict are with violence or total avoidance, yet in group counselling they participate in conflict resolution and experience intimacy that does not prove to be emotionally or physically devastating (Seidel, Gusman and Abueg, 1994).

Many clients experience difficult periods of anger and rage during or shortly after treatment when other issues begin to emerge (Potter-Efron and Potter-Efron, 1991b).

Addressing issues of expressing and coping with feelings of anger requires ongoing work that can be continued during the aftercare phase of treatment as issues arise. Patricia Evans (1992) refers to the cycle of anger addiction in which the verbal abuser releases his anger at his partner through angry outbursts. The cycle involves the build-up of tension, the verbal explosion and the release of tension. The abuser's anger arises from his sense of personal powerlessness. Evans states that although alcohol does not make him angrier, it does make him feel freer to vent his anger. By being empathic, a man can envision how his expression of anger can affect those around him. Through this experience, he can consider his partner's feelings and ultimately develop relationships based on mutual respect.

Coping with Trauma

Individuals suffering from syndromes related to childhood trauma are at increased risk for substance dependence (Sullivan and Evans, 1994). In the past 10 years, increased awareness, education and research have emerged regarding the connections between substance use and trauma. Although most of the research has pertained to women, clinicians are increasingly aware that this may also be an issue for their male clients. Thus, it is important that in the assessment phase of treatment, clients are asked about trauma history. In a study by Harvey, Rawson and Obert (1994), the rate of reported childhood sexual assault among inpatient substance abusers was eight per cent when patients were not routinely asked about assault history. The rate increased to 30 per cent when routine inquiry regarding assault was conducted for all patients.

The research literature contains minimal information on the trauma histories of men with substance abuse problems, and their needs in treatment. The trauma literature for men focuses on PTSD in relation to veterans. According to the National Vietnam Veterans Readjustment Study, 22 per cent of male Vietnam veterans with a current PTSD diagnosis suffered from alcohol abuse and dependence and six per cent suffered from drug abuse and dependence (Reilly et al., 1994). Although no data are currently available on the rates of PTSD for male civilians seeking substance abuse treatment, a large-scale general population study indicates that substance abuse-PTSD co-morbidity cuts across gender (Brown and Wolfe, 1994).

Clinicians seem to be working more toward integrating and connecting the issues of trauma and substance use, viewing substance use as a coping strategy to deal with the emotional and physical pain from abuse, particularly for women. Men continue to face the stigma of discussing their histories of being physically or sexually abused, though as previously noted, men who are violent to women and children often suffer from their own traumas of the past, including child abuse (Addiction Research Foundation, 1995). It is important for men to receive education and support on coping with issues related to trauma, in particular, information about symptoms commonly experienced and strategies to cope with these feelings and reactions.

In Judith Lewis Herman's book *Trauma and Recovery* (1992), she describes the stages of recovery for the trauma survivor, which include establishing safety, reconstructing the trauma story, and restoring the connection between survivors and their community. In establishing an environment of safety, it is valuable for clients to learn what symptoms they may experience when stopping substance use if a history of trauma exists. According to Herman, trauma robs the victim of a sense of power and control; the guiding principle of recovery is to restore power and control to the survivor. By educating men about the symptoms of PTSD, and providing them with grounding techniques to cope with flashbacks and nightmares, they learn that others have had similar feelings. This can reduce some of the fear experienced during the recovery process. Grounding techniques that have been found to be helpful in coping with flashbacks include helping a person create safety in the present by focusing on breathing techniques and strategies that create comfort and safety.

When providing this information in a men's group setting, it will not be relevant to all. Thus, it is important to explain that although this information may not be connected to the life experience of all group members, the strategies can be used to cope with both unpleasant feelings and cravings to use substances. One of the goals of providing this information is so that clients will have ways to cope with issues related to trauma, which will aid in preventing relapse. It is important to communicate to the clients who have experienced trauma how and where they can seek support, including individual counselling or referrals to specialized counselling. It is very challenging for a man to discuss trauma issues in a group setting, not knowing if he will receive support from other group members. A man may feel shame that he has experienced trauma and may feel increased vulnerability when disclosing his story. In my experience, the reaction to information about trauma and grounding techniques has been mixed. At times there may be silence in a group, and occasionally there may be questions and/or some disclosure. However, by providing education on this topic, there will be increased awareness about trauma, and permission to seek support. When these connections are not made for clients, the men will lack the strategies to cope with trauma issues. A disclosure by one man may trigger flashbacks for another. Without education, a man may not understand what he is experiencing and will be at increased risk for relapse.

Counsellors should also be aware that some men may be in relationships where they are experiencing violence. As with women, discussing safety plans, counselling options and providing resources/referrals is very important.

GENDER OF THERAPIST

The research is inconclusive in terms of the usefulness of matching therapist and client by gender (Bowman, 1993); however, some research suggests that female therapists are more effective with both female and male clients. A review by Nelson (1993) revealed that male and female therapists rated same-gender clients as having a better prognosis and indicated greater enjoyment when working with same-gender clients. In addition, clients seemed to speak more freely with same-gender counsellors, and counsellors appeared to identify and name feeling and content more easily with same-gender clients. Female counsellors are also more optimistic than male counsellors that incest survivors could overcome their problems (Adams and Betz, 1993). Findings are inconclusive regarding the best gender for male clients (Nelson, 1993). From a clinical perspective, it seems that for certain issues in treatment, it may be helpful to have male and female co-facilitators, such as when addressing topics on anger and violence. The co-therapists need to have open and egalitarian communication and can role-model communication between the genders. Men may feel more comfortable having a male therapist present to discuss issues relating to male gender roles, sexual health and sexuality. Obviously, more research is required to assess what is most helpful to men seeking treatment.

CONCLUSION

When working with men, it is important to acknowledge current challenges, as well as to help men make connections to issues of their past that influence choices and patterns in coping with various life situations. We need to explore issues with the male client in the context of what it means to be male in his family of origin, his culture, his larger community, his society and in connection with his life experiences. By discussing what it means to be male, the client receives support and validation that both positive and challenging experiences are associated with being male. By working from a feminist model with women, there is recognition of gender roles, the influences of socialization and oppression, which influence how women use substances to cope. By using this model with men, there is recognition of the benefits and costs of being male, which gives men permission to make connections regarding the role of substances in their lives in the context of being male.

Consequently, when beginning the process of counselling men, counsellors can work to anticipate and identify the issues that may be barriers to men engaging in a program. Some of the emotional barriers may include a feeling of discomfort in sharing personal experiences, a lack of experience in expressing emotions, and in being in a group setting, particularly with other men.

The counsellor is responsible for acknowledging these issues, normalizing the feelings and helping men to feel a sense of comfort that will allow for the exploration of substance use triggers and the development of coping strategies.

By working to see the male client through understanding and empathy, given his particular life experiences and socialization as a male, we can help him explore other issues that are connected to his recovery. These inter-related issues include the following: health issues, the effects of substance use on the body, nutrition and healthy eating, sexual health and sexuality, intimacy, isolation, developing a support system, his role as a parent, relaxation techniques to cope with stress, spirituality, self-care and self-esteem.

It is hoped that through treatment, a man may experience a connectedness to self and an understanding of the role that substances have played in his life. It is also hoped that treatment will provide opportunities for developing alternative ways of coping that will contribute to his overall confidence and well-being. A man learns he is not alone and that change is possible.

ACKNOWLEDGMENTS

I would like to thank Robert Murray and Carolynne Cooper, both of the Addiction Research Foundation, and Scott MacPherson, of the Donwood Institute, for reviewing my work. I would also like to acknowledge Carole Neron, M.S.W., for her initial development of the differences exercise.

REFERENCES

Adams, E.M., and Betz, N.E. (1993). Gender differences in counselors' attitudes toward and attributions about incest. *Journal of Counselling Psychology* 40 (2): 210–216.

Addiction Research Foundation. (1993). *An Educational Package LINK Violence Against Women and Children in Relationships and the Use of Alcohol and Drugs. Searching for Solutions.* Toronto: Addiction Research Foundation.

Annis, H.M., and Graham, J.M. (1995). Profile types on the inventory of drinking situations: Implications for relapse prevention counselling. *Psychology of Addictive Behaviors* 9: 176–182.

Annis, H.M., Turner, N.E., and Sklar, S.M. (1996). *Inventory of Drug-Taking Situations: User's Guide.* Toronto: Addiction Research Foundation.

Annis, H.M., Sklar, S.M., and Moser, A.E. (1996). Gender in relation to relapse crisis situations, coping and outcome among treated alcoholics. In Press. Toronto: Addiction Research Foundation.

Bowman, D. (1993). Effects of therapist sex on the outcome of therapy. *Psychotherapy* 30 (4): 678–684.

Brown, G.R., and Wolfe, J. (1994). Substance abuse and post traumatic stress disorder co-morbidity. *Drug and Alcohol Dependence* 35: 51–59.

Crossman, R., Stith, S., and Bender, M. (1990). Sex role egalitarianism and marital violence. *Sex-Roles* 22 (5/6): 293–304.

Doyle, J. (1989). *The Male Experience,* 2nd ed. Dubuque, IA: Wm. C. Brown Publishers.

Evans, P. (1992). *The Verbally Abusive Relationship, How to Recognize It and How to Respond.* USA: Bob Adams, Inc. Publishers.

Harvey, E.M., Rawson, R.A., and Obert, J.L. (1994) History of sexual assault and the treatment of substance abuse disorders. *Journal of Psychoactive Drugs* 26 (4): 361–367.

Health and Welfare Canada. (1992). *Alcohol and Other Drug Use by Canadians: A National Alcohol and Other Drugs Survey (1989) Technical Report.* Prepared by M. Eliany, N. Giesbrecht, M. Nelson, B. Wellman and S. Wortley.

Herman, J.L. (1992). *Trauma and Recovery.* USA: Harper Collins.

Jenkins, A. (1990). *Invitations to Responsibility, The Therapeutic Engagement of Men Who Are Violent and Abusive.* South Australia: Dulwich Centre Publications.

Miedema, J. (1996). *Changing Ways Counsellor's Manual: Challenging Men Toward Safety and Equality in Their Primary Relationships.* London, ON: Changing Ways.

Nelson, M.L. (1993). A current perspective on gender differences: Implications for research in counseling. *Journal of Counseling Psychology* 40 (2): 200–209.

Potter-Efron, P.S., and Potter-Efron, R.T. (1991a). Anger as a treatment concern with alcoholics and affected family members. *Alcoholism Treatment Quarterly* 8 (3): 31–46.

Potter-Efron, P.S., and Potter-Efron, R.T. (1991b). *Anger, Alcoholism and Addiction: Treating Individuals, Couples and Families*. New York: W.W. Norton and Co.

Reilly, P.M., Westley Clark, H., Shopshire, M.S., Lewis, E.W., and Sorensen, D.J. (1994). Anger management and temper control: Critical components of post-traumatic stress disorder and substance abuse treatment. *Journal of Psychoactive Drugs* 26 (4): 401–407.

Seidel, R.W., Gusman, F.D., and Abueg, F.R. (1994). Theoretical and practical foundations of an inpatient post-traumatic stress disorder and alcoholism treatment program. *Psychotherapy* 31 (1): 67–78.

Strauss, M.A., Gelles, R.J., and Steinmetz, S.K. (1980). *Behind Closed Doors: Violence in the American Family*. Garden City, NJ: Anchor Books.

Sullivan, J.M., and Evans, K. (1994). Integrated treatment for the survivor of childhood trauma who is chemically dependent. *Journal of Psychoactive Drugs* 26 (4): 369–377.

Tannen, D. (1990). *You Just Don't Understand*. New York: Ballantine Books.

van Wormer, K. (1989). The male-specific group in alcoholism treatment. *Small Group Behavior* 20 (2): 228–242.

Weisner, C., and Schmidt, L. (1992). Gender disparities in treatment for alcohol problems. *Journal of Medical Association* 268 (14): 1872–1876.

Zweben, J.E., Westley Clark, H., and Smith, D.E. (1994). Traumatic experiences and substance abuse: Mapping the territory. *Journal of Psychoactive Drugs* 26 (4): 327–344.

Chapter 14

Clients with Physical Disabilities

DOUG BULLOCK

INTRODUCTION

Only since the early 1980s have attention and resources been directed to understanding and helping persons with addiction problems and disability issues (Boros, 1989). Increased attention to these issues has come mostly through a concerted lobbying effort on the part of individuals with disabilities, and passage in the United States of the Disabilities Rights Legislation (de Miranda and Cherry, 1989). As with many groups who find themselves outside the mainstream of North American cultural reality, they have gained addiction services only through hard-fought efforts. Those gains, especially in Canada, are small indeed at this time. Research on addiction and disability issues is scant, and what little exists has been done in isolation. There are as yet few common definitions or a solid base of knowledge on which to build a consensus for developing therapeutic guidelines or training opportunities.

This situation presents a clear challenge for the clinician working with a person with a disability. You will need to spend more time building the therapeutic relationship and advocating on behalf of the client. This chapter explores these issues and suggests some therapeutic approaches to meet the challenge.

DISABILITY: DEFINITION AND MEANING

Defining disability is a complex issue and very much depends on who does the defining. Various studies of disability issues focus the definition to include only a particular type of disability and generally examine a selected sample, often within an institutional setting. Statistics Canada (1992) completed the second Canada-wide survey of disability; the Health and Activity Limitation Survey used the following definition of disability:

> Disability was assessed through an internationally standardized set of questions known as "Activities of Daily Living." This is a practical series of questions designed to identify any difficulties people have in performing their daily routines. For example, respondents were asked if they had difficulties in moving from room to room, carrying objects 10 metres, dressing themselves, reading a newspaper, following a conversation, or being understood while speaking.... Six types of disabilities were identified, namely, disabilities relating to mobility, agility, hearing, seeing and speaking, and mental disabilities.

Using this definition, the Canadian survey estimated that 4.2 million Canadians (15.5 per cent of the population) reported some form of disability.

For planning and lobbying purposes, it is important to have a broad sense of the types and numbers of persons with disabilities. However, without more complete research, formal survey definitions of disability have limited therapeutic use. Little is known about the personal meanings of disability, and this information must be sought from clients directly. According to Hart and Trotter (1977), how the individual defines and views his or her disability is most important to recognize. It is often not the fact of disability (as formally defined) that concerns the individual but the "handicaps" it creates for them. Robert Christie (1992) summed this notion up perfectly in a letter to the *Ottawa Citizen*:

> Many disabled people, especially those born with their disability, don't see themselves as being disabled, although everyone else does. Rather they think of themselves as being "normal." They have always been the way they are and they are used to being that way.

These thoughts are important. Self-acceptance in the face of society's negative attitude towards disability is often a major issue to be resolved as part of recovery from addiction.

DRUG USE: PREVALENCE, PATTERNS AND TREATMENT UTILIZATION

Many studies, especially in the United States, have tried to determine the rate of drug use and abuse among persons with a disability (Moore and Polsgrove, 1989). I will not attempt an exhaustive review of these studies but point to a few patterns that emerge on review. Individuals with spinal cord and head injuries seem consistently to record higher levels of pre-injury drug/alcohol use than the general population; many were actually injured while under the influence of drugs or alcohol (Heinemann, Doll and Schnoll, 1989). Adlaf, Smart and Walsh (1990), in examining the connection between alcohol/drug use in those with work limitations due to disability, found problems with alcohol were highest among those with moderate work-role limitations and that the use of prescribed psychoactive medication rose with increased disability.

U.S. studies have found higher rates of alcohol and street drug use than Canadian studies. Canadian studies, however, find higher rates of prescription drug use among persons with a disability, possibly reflecting the lower cost to users for medically prescribed drugs.

Tyas and Rush (1990), reporting on the use of addiction treatment services in Ontario by persons with disabilities, found that 3.7 per cent of clients were considered to have a mobility impairment, 2.3 per cent a developmental handicap, 1.5 per cent impaired vision, and 1.4 per cent impaired hearing, with an overall total of approximately 16 per cent of clients in treatment having a disability. According to Statistics Canada (1992), of the general population in Ontario between the ages of 15 and 64, seven per cent report a mobility impairment, one per cent a vision impairment, and three per cent a hearing impairment. Except for the comparative rates for those with seeing disabilities, it is consistent with care-giver observations that persons with disabilities are underrepresented in the treatment population if we assume that the prevalence rate for alcohol and other drug problems among them is the same as in the general population. Since these surveys did not use exactly equivalent methods or definitions of disability, this analysis should be seen as suggestive only.

Tyas and Rush (1990) also report that six per cent of addiction services have specially tailored services for those with physical or sensory disabilities. Respondents, however, indicated a wide variation in what constituted a specially tailored service. Most services reported physical accessibility modifications within their program or access to sign language interpreters, but very little in the way of specialized training for staff. Only half the respondents felt that specialized training was even necessary for their staff to respond to the needs of persons with disabilities.

Moore and Polsgrove (1989), in analysing a series of U.S. studies, conclude that:
> Existing research has frequently been compromised by sample or design problems which are associated with limited resources. There needs to be a closer factoring of the nature of the disabilities being studied, whether the disabilities were congenital or traumatic in origin. Also the need to look at drug use pattern evolution, age of onset, etc. ...to assist in mounting effective prevention, intervention or treatment efforts (p. 82).

In conclusion, a review of drug use and treatment program utilization studies gives us little clinical guidance. The main lessons are that drug use among persons with disabilities probably parallels that of the general Canadian population; the most notable exception is a higher rate of prescribed drug use among those with severe work-role limitations and alcohol use among those with disabilities resulting from trauma. Given that drug use rates are generally similar, why do we find proportionally only half as many persons with physical and hearing limitations participating in treatment?

The only conclusion is that existing treatment programs and methodologies are not meeting the needs of this community.

RISK FACTORS

To succeed at intervention, we must understand the unique risk factors for drug abuse identified for persons with a disability. They face many of the same risk factors as others, including relief from anxiety and frustration, low self-esteem, sensation-seeking, drug and alcohol availability, poverty, genetic influences, etc. However, these influences can take on unique meanings. They are often magnified in significance because of general social attitudes to disability.

Several authors have described and corroborate unique risk factors influencing persons with disability (Boros, 1989; Kelly, 1991; Schaschl et al., 1989). They are listed below:
- more sensitivity to alcohol and other nonprescribed drugs because of drug interactions and medical conditions resulting from the disability
- chronic pain, spasticity, etc., can lead to self-medication
- lower self-esteem related to the disability and to architectural or physical barriers preventing participation in activities that provide social contact and development of social skills
- vicarious excitement and sensation-seeking when normal activity and mobility are limited
- people with disabilities, especially those with a disability from a young age, are taught to comply with medical and professional advice, institutional rules, etc.; this can result in low self-esteem
- unemployment leads to low economic status, increases isolation and removes people from situations where drug and alcohol problems might be identified and help offered
- society's negative attitudes give messages that people with disabilities are incapable and dependent, and this leads to low self-esteem
- care-givers, family members and health care professionals may feel that the person with a disability has enough to cope with without having to address a drug- or alcohol-related problem
- physical and attitudinal barriers prevent access to community programs and services that could provide early intervention for alcohol and other drug problems
- heightened vulnerability to physical abuse and consequent emotional issues that increase risk of drug abuse.

Case Studies

The case studies presented by de Miranda (1995) illustrate some of these factors at work. He notes, for example, the case of Mary. During the early years of her arthritis,

Mary was haunted by a fear of abandonment. A subject of much discussion was whether Mary should be sent to a "crippled children's school." This early threat of rejection and being sent away caused Mary to be compliant and not rock the boat by asserting her independence or rebelling against parental authority. To her, drug use was particularly attractive because it helped boost her energy levels and allowed her to maintain an activity pace that probably would not have been otherwise possible. For her recovery to be successful, she needed to accept the functional limitations her disabilities created.

Another case discussed by de Miranda is that of Lois, who developed late onset deafness. Lois recalled the frustration of being in a hospital-based addiction program that did not have any special provisions for deaf clientele.

"I complained bitterly, but I don't think that the staff really understood the level of my difficulties," explained Lois (p. 23). She was eventually helped by a hearing man who had been through three previously unsuccessful treatment episodes. He took notes for her and acted as an interpreter. This important example of self-help in action not only helped Lois in her recovery, but her "interpreter" was helped in his recovery.

The two examples above demonstrate how some of the special risk factors for people with disabilities can play out. The list highlights the fact that many of the unique risk factors are social and attitudinal in nature. They may not have originated within the individual, but are imposed by cultural and social values.

Other Risk Factors

These risk factors could apply to all persons with a disability. However, other unique risk factors associated with particular disabilities should be noted. Sinclair (1992) in describing his experience with deaf culture states:

> ...many deaf people do not consider themselves to be an 'impaired' population (since they communicate perfectly well with signs) but rather an ethnic population... and includes a strong moral opposition to addiction, as well as a strong enabling (us against the world) attitude.

Traumatic head injury is often associated with alcohol abuse (Parkinson, Stephensen and Phillips, 1985) and the consequences of brain injury for alcohol or drug abuse treatment can be complex. As with developmental handicaps, cognitive deficits may require slowing the pace of treatment and more reliance on supportive interventions and short-term, goal-oriented approaches. Burganowski (1992) describes a risk factor particular to persons with traumatic brain injury. Common symptoms of this type of injury include slowed speech or unsteady gait. These behaviors are often accepted in bars and taverns but not in everyday society. People with brain injuries may feel much less anxiety and negative judgment in such environments. Once again, this risk factor is not intrinsic, but precipitated by cultural values and expectations.

These factors must be carefully assessed in treatment planning. Often, the therapeutic role will have to include a strong element of advocacy and systems work. These issues are explored in more detail in the next section.

TREATMENT AND RECOVERY ISSUES

As noted earlier, there is no standard model of treatment for persons with disabilities. A few programs exist in the United States, but to date there is no formal body of research to guide us on what works best and for whom. Most information is anecdotal, and your own intervention work must be guided by your own instincts, and most importantly, by your client's experience. Knowing the risk factors and the treatment issues discussed in the next section should help you understand your client's needs and factors involved in developing and following a treatment plan.

Conditions that enable or support drug abuse are highly relevant for people with disabilities and these conditions should be of clinical concern. Enabling conditions go far beyond the immediate family situation: friends, the legal system, health care providers, etc., all inadvertently work together to maintain an addiction. Two attitudes on the part of care-givers contribute to this situation. One is sympathy and "hero" biases, where those around the abuser feel the struggles and difficulties caused by the disability justify the use of drugs or alcohol — he or she has enough to cope with without worrying about the drug use. This attitude may reflect the feeling that "the drug use is the only pleasure in the person's life and it would be wrong to take that away."

Society's negative attitudes towards both disability and addiction also enhance enabling. "Physically impaired" persons often are perceived as hopeless, helpless, fragile and sick (Schaschl and Straw, 1989). Attach a further label of "alcoholic" or "drug addict" and we can see why those around the individual will go to great lengths to deny a drug problem, preferring instead to attribute consequences of drug abuse to the disability itself. Thus typical signs of drug abuse — lack of motivation, low energy levels, increased physical problems, etc. — are easily seen as a consequence of the disability, not of drug abuse. Both these attitudes work closely but tragically in tandem: thus the individual may have easy access to drugs from sympathetic friends and care-givers, while the inevitable consequences of abuse are attributed to the disability. A person with a disability and growing addiction will often understand these forces at a sophisticated level, making effective intervention a real challenge for the inexperienced.

PRACTICAL INTERVENTIONS IN A SERVICE VACUUM

Working with people having a disability requires a unique type of creativity, especially for therapists without prior experience in this area. You will need an accessible location for meetings; flexibility around scheduling because of less predictable access to public transportation; and possibly technical aids or interpreters for communication purposes. Although Tyas and Rush (1990) found that six per cent of Ontario's addiction treatment services reported specially tailored services for the physically disabled, anecdotal evidence suggests that these provisions are often partial, requiring a greatly modified treatment protocol for the client. This can make it difficult for him or her to identify and bond with other clients. Programs that require complete abstinence from all psychoactive drugs may deny access to a person with a disability who legitimately uses a prescribed psychoactive drug to control spasms or epilepsy. Finally, most staff in existing treatment programs have not been trained to understand the particular cultural and psycho-social factors that accompany disability — few training opportunities exist.

Since little formal research has been done to clarify these unique treatment issues and give guidance on what works best (Moore and Polsgrove, 1989; DiNitto and Webb, 1995), we are exploring new territory when first counselling the client with a disability. Treatment programs for the physically disabled — both inpatient and outpatient — exist in the United States (Schaschl et al., 1989; Boros, 1992). A poll of the provincial addiction agencies in Canada, completed with the cooperation of the Canadian Centre on Substance Abuse (Hawley, 1993), indicates that no provincially funded programs are specifically tailored to the needs of persons with a disability. Private counselling or counsellor services may exist, but would need to be determined at a local level.

For most counselling situations, outpatient treatment is probably the most practical choice, involving a combination of professional and peer support interventions. Those requiring inpatient care would have to go to the United States, at least until suitable programs are developed in Canada. Outpatient models, however, provide a number of advantages for treating all but the most severely addicted individual, with or without a disability. The advantages include:

- flexible location — anywhere from a traditional office setting to the client's home (this allows the client a greater sense of anonymity and allows the service to exist in smaller communities without formal addiction services)
- flexible scheduling (the pace and duration of treatment can be tailored to suit the client)
- opportunity to work with the unique goals of the client, not necessarily enforcing abstinence as a criterion for providing assistance; the client is very much in charge of the treatment direction and resources employed
- may not require the client to accept the label of "alcoholic" or "addict," which deters many persons concerned about their alcohol and other drug use from contacting traditional services
- draw on a variety of social service resources to meet the unique needs of a client; not restricted to providing a standard set of interventions to all clients, regardless of their utility

- treatment progress is constantly tested against the backdrop of the client's day-to-day life, thus real life difficulties are continually being addressed and incorporated into the treatment plan.

A central feature in outpatient treatment approaches is the comprehensive and ongoing assessment of client needs and progress during treatment. Modifications are made as new information is gathered while the client progresses through self-discovery and a series of behavior changes. This feature is a real advantage when working with a person with a disability. Without clear directions from previous experience, we must constantly listen to our clients to understand the issues, and try a variety of creative approaches to understanding and solving problems. Many existing resources now support the use of outpatient approaches. Training in outpatient and early identification approaches is available through organizations like the Addiction Research Foundation, and publications detailing these methods are available, e.g., Hester and Miller (1989). Many communities have excellent resources to help a person with a disability with practical issues, such as housing, transportation, technical devices, advocacy, and social and psychological support. With outpatient approaches, these can be used as required to address problems contributing to drug use. These resources can be discovered through local organizations serving persons with a disability.

Case Studies

John de Miranda (1990) provides interesting examples of creative interventions that have worked for people with disabilities.

Lois (noted earlier) had difficulty achieving sobriety until she finally accepted her late onset deafness. She relied on a combination of AA and psychotherapy to achieve recovery. She did not meet many deafened individuals in recovery, but she developed a unique network of hearing persons to assist her in recovery. She was also greatly assisted by reading the wide range of recovery literature and selected books. She also found that participating in a local university alcohol and drug certificate program was helpful to her recovery.

The case of Hank is another success story described by de Miranda. Hank was a heavy alcohol and drug user who was rendered quadriplegic (C-6) following an alcohol-related car crash. He continued to use drugs and alcohol during his rehabilitation and after moving back to the community with the help of a full-time attendant. Hank began taking courses in a community college, moved on to university studies, and eventually became trained as a computer programmer despite continued heavy drug use. He found employment and began a romantic involvement following his training. It was here that he began a gradual transition out of heavy drug use and changed his lifestyle. He eventually became a Christian and gave up drug use altogether. He occasionally drinks alcohol socially, and will use diazepam to cope with headaches caused by blood pressure increases due to his quadriplegia. Through Hank's many achievements, alcohol and drug abuse became incompatible with his newfound skills and interests. Hank's story is one of recovery without use of the traditional addiction treatment network.

These case studies illustrate the varied routes that people with disabilities followed in regaining control over their lives. Each individual employed a unique combination of resources, depending on life circumstances. As in all successful recovery stories, these people eventually took charge of their own recovery and were able to make choices that were right for their own needs.

The Independent Living Movement

Of particular relevance to addiction issues is the independent living movement, a relatively new development in Canada. Twenty-one centres that base their programs on this philosophy are now funded in Canada and several others are in developmental stages. These centres are guided by the following mission statement:

> To promote and enable the progressive process of citizens with disabilities taking responsibility for the development and management of personal and community resources (CAILC, 1985).

As this statement implies, Independent Living Centres (ILCs) are consumer-controlled and encourage the development of independent living both in terms of accessing services and in the development of self-esteem. Many ILCs have concerns about addictions, as they severely hamper the development of personal responsibility and independence. The Canadian Association of Independent Living Centres (CAILC) has published a pamphlet on addiction warning signs for persons with disabilities, and presented a brief to the Canadian Centre on Substance Abuse (CAILC, 1992) recommending ways to provide addiction treatment to this population.

Independent Living Centres should be seen as a prime resource in finding appropriate service options in your community. Independent Living Centres have regional mandates. If a centre does not exist in your community, contact CAILC at (613) 563-2581 for the centre closest to you.

ACKNOWLEDGMENT

I wish to express my appreciation to Nancy Kelly and Sue McKay, staff of the Ottawa Carleton Independent Living Centre, for their review and helpful critique of this manuscript.

REFERENCES

Adlaf, E.M., Smart, R.G., and Walsh, G.W. (1990). *Substance Use and Work Disabilities*. Toronto: Addiction Research Foundation.

Boros, A. (1989). Facing the challenge. *Alcohol Health and Research World* 13 (2): 101–103.

Boros, A. (ed.) (1992). *AID Bulletin*. Kent, OH: Kent State University, Sociology Department.

Burganowski, D. (1992). Disabilities and drug abuse: The avoided issue. Conference presentation at the Rehabilitation Centre. Ottawa, June 1992.

Canadian Association of Independent Living Centres (CAILC). (1992). Brief on substance misuse and persons with disabilities. Ottawa, March 1992.

Canadian Association of Independent Living Centres. (1992). Taking control. (pamphlet). Ottawa: Authors.

Canadian Association of Independent Living Centres (CAILC). (1985). First National Independent Living Centre meeting. Kitchener, Ontario, 1985.

Christie, R. (1992). as quoted in *Contacts* 4 (3). The newsletter of the Ottawa-Carleton Independent Living Centre (December 1992).

de Miranda, J. (1992). *Final Report: Case Studies Project. An Investigation of Alcohol and Other Drug Problems and Recovery among Five Persons with Disabilities*. San Mateo, CA: Peninsula Health Concepts.

de Miranda, J., and Cherry, L. (1989). California responds: Changing treatment systems through advocacy for the disabled. *Alcohol Health and Research World* 13 (2): 154–157.

DiNitto, D.M., and Webb, D.K. (1995). Compounding the problem: Substance abuse and other disabilities. In *Chemical Dependency: A Systems Approach*. Englewood Cliffs, NJ: Prentice Hall Inc.

Frieden, A. L. (1990). Substance abuse and disability: The role of the independent living centre. *Journal of Applied Rehabilitation Counselling* 21 (3): 33–36.

Hart, L., and Trotter, A. (1977). Alcoholism – disability versus handicap: An important distinction. *Journal of Studies on Alcohol* 38 (7): 1443–1446.

Hawley, M. (1993). *Poll of Canadian Provincial Addiction Organizations*. Ottawa: Canadian Centre on Substance Abuse.

Heinemann, A.W., Doll, M., and Schnoll, S. (1989). Treatment of alcohol abuse in persons with recent spinal cord injuries. *Alcohol Health and Research World* 13 (2): 110–117.

Hester, R.K., and Miller, W.R. (1989). *Handbook of Alcoholism Treatment Approaches: Effective Alternatives*. New York. Pergamon Press.

Kelly, N. (1991). Personal communication, Ottawa-Carleton Independent Living Centre. Ottawa, 1991.

Moore, D., and Polsgrove, L. (1989). Disabilities, developmental handicaps and substance misuse: A review. *Social Pharmacology* 3 (4): 375–408.

Parkinson, D., Stephensen, S., and Phillips, S. (1985). Head injuries: A prospective, computerized study. *Canadian Journal of Surgery* 28 (1): 79–83.

Schaschl, S., and Straw, D. (1989). Results of a model intervention program for physically impaired persons. *Alcohol Health and Research World* 13 (2): 150–153.

Sinclair, J.R. (1992). Counselling the hearing-impaired. Paper prepared for presentation to the Community Addiction Network. Ottawa, 1992.

Statistics Canada. (1992). 1991 Health and Activity Limitation Survey — highlights. In *The Daily*. Ottawa: Tuesday, October 13, 1992.

Tyas, S.L., and Rush, B.R. (1990). *Treatment Issues for Disabled Clients: Results of a Survey of Alcohol and Other Drug Services in Ontario*. Toronto: Addiction Research Foundation.

Chapter 15

Substance Abuse and Older Clients

JANE BARON AND VIRGINIA CARVER

Evidence suggests that alcohol is the foremost substance of abuse by the elderly, followed by drugs obtained legally through prescriptions or over the counter (NIAAA, 1982).

INTRODUCTION

Can you imagine someone close to you — a parent or grandparent, an elderly friend or neighbor — having an alcohol or drug problem? If we think at all about the older person with such a problem, it is usually the older skid row alcoholic.

However, in recent years substance use problems among older people have been receiving increasing attention in the literature. A National Library of Medicine Literature Search of publications between 1980 and 1985 produced nearly 50 citations concerned with substance misuse or abuse among older people (Kenton, 1985). Federal and provincial governments have also identified the misuse or abuse of pharmaceuticals by older persons as a concern, (e.g., Baker, 1992; Health and Community Services, New Brunswick, 1991; Lankin, 1992).

There are a number of reasons for this interest in substance use problems among older people. One may be our increasing lifespan and aging population. By the year 2036, approximately one-quarter of Canadians will be aged 65 or over (Health and Welfare Canada, 1989). Also, since the 1960s, many new psychoactive medications have come on the market, particularly the benzodiazepines (Valium, Xanax, Halcion, etc.). It has taken some time to recognize that they may be a mixed blessing, particularly for the older person. Finally, there is increasing understanding of the effects of various substances on the body and how certain groups such as the elderly or women may be more vulnerable to these effects.

EXTENT OF SUBSTANCE USE AMONG OLDER ADULTS

Patterns of substance use change as people age. Older adults are less likely than people in other age groups to drink, but more likely to use psychoactive medications, particularly central nervous system depressant medications such as tranquillizers and sleeping pills. Use of illicit drugs in this age group is very low to non-existent.

Just over half of older Canadians (65 years and older) are current drinkers (46 per cent of women and 66 per cent of men) (Health and Welfare Canada, 1992). The proportion of older Canadians who are frequent drinkers (22 per cent drink four or more times a week) and infrequent drinkers (31 per cent drink less than once a month) is higher than proportions for other age groups. Older Canadians also consume less per drinking occasion (1.7 drinks versus 2.8 drinks) than other age groups (Health and Welfare Canada, 1992).

In Ontario, the percentage of older drinkers has increased over the last two decades from 53.5 per cent in 1977 to 67.0 per cent in 1994 (Adlaf, Ivis and Smart, 1994). To some extent, the drinking patterns of the current generation of older Canadians may reflect the drinking mores with which they grew up. This may be particularly true for those older women who grew up at a time when public drinking was less acceptable for women than it is now. As younger people with more exposure to alcohol age, there may be an increasing number of older heavy drinkers.

Consistent with their pattern of lower alcohol consumption, older adults also report low rates of problem use. Only four per cent of older adults report experiencing problems as a result of their alcohol use (Health and Welfare Canada, 1992). However, these low rates of reported problems may not reflect the numbers of older adults whose drinking puts them at risk.

In contrast to use of alcohol, use of prescribed and over-the-counter central nervous system (CNS) depressant medication generally increases with age. A recent survey of older adults in one Ontario community found that 30 per cent were taking one or more depressant medications and 27 per cent were taking one or more prescribed depressant medications (Graham et al., 1995). Other Canadian studies using provincial drug plan data have found rates of use ranging from one in five to one in two older adults using a CNS depressant drug (usually a sleeping pill/tranquillizer) (New Brunswick Health and Community Service, 1991; Quinn, Baker and Evans, undated; Tamblyn et al., 1994.) Use of depressant medication has been associated with multiple use of psychoactive drugs, poorer health, more stress, and lack of support from family and friends (Bergob, 1994; Graham, Carver and Brett, 1996).

WHY SUBSTANCE USE MAY BE A PROBLEM FOR OLDER ADULTS

Substance use problems among older adults may occur both for those who are drinking at low levels or using prescribed or over-the-counter medication at therapeutic dosages, as well as for those with a long-term pattern of heavy alcohol use or dependence on medications or other drugs. As people age, they become more sensitive to the effects of substances. This has been well described by a number of authors (e.g., Baker, 1985; Lamy, 1985; McKim and Mishara, 1987; and Sellers, Frecker and Romach, 1983). At the same time, symptoms of problem substance use may be mistaken for signs of aging or other health problems. Identification of a problem may also be hampered by the attitudes of those around the older person who is using alcohol or other drugs.

With age, changes in body composition (reduced body water and lean body mass but increased body fat) may mean that water-soluble drugs, such as alcohol, are more concentrated, and drugs that are stored in the fat, such as benzodiazepines, stay in the body longer. At the same time, older people may experience a decline in kidney and liver functions resulting in higher concentrations and slower elimination of some drugs from the body, or they may have some other health problems that impair the functioning of their liver or kidneys. Because women are generally smaller and have less body water and more fat than do men, they are more vulnerable to the effects of substances.

Counsellors need to know that even low levels of drinking or using medication as prescribed may be hazardous for an older person. For instance, two to three drinks a day for women, or three to four drinks a day for men over a number of years may result in serious health consequences, including liver or neurological damage. In the study of an Ontario community described above (Graham et al., 1995), there were significant differences in reported use of alcohol for symptom relief between those drinking less than one drink a day and those drinking more than one drink but less than two. The results indicated that, even at very low levels of alcohol use, older adults may be at risk of problems.

This same study found that those who were using depressant medications were also more likely to be using alcohol for personal effects reasons (e.g., to relax, to relieve anxiety/tensions, to forget worries and to relieve pain). It also found that current drinkers who were using depressant medications were more likely than current drinkers who *weren't* using depressant medications to report concerns about their drinking (Graham et al., 1995).

Therapeutic dosages of prescribed depressant medications that are appropriate for a younger person may result in over-medication in someone older because of physiological changes noted above. Over-medication may result in difficulties in motor functions (e.g., falls, co-ordination problems), confusion and forgetfulness, etc.

The variety of prescribed and over-the-counter medications used by older adults may have additive effects when used together. For instance, an older adult may be simultaneously using several drugs that depress the central nervous system. These might include alcohol, a prescribed sleeping medication, and an over-the-counter painkiller containing codeine, such as 222s, increasing the risk of experiencing problems. Older adults should also be particularly careful about driving or using complex machinery when they are using alcohol or depressant medications.

EXAMPLE

A 70-year-old woman is being treated by her physician for high blood pressure. The physician has prescribed two medications, a minor tranquillizer (a benzodiazepine) as a mild sedative and an anti-hypertensive. In addition, she frequently takes over-the-counter pain medication containing codeine for tension headaches. She uses the maximum recommended daily dosage and occasionally exceeds it. She has not told her doctor about taking this over-the-counter medication. Several times a week she consumes two to four standard drinks in the course of an afternoon bridge game. The minor tranquillizer, codeine and alcohol have an additive effect, because they are all central nervous system depressants. She has experienced occasional dizziness, confusion, and recent memory loss. She has also had several unexplained falls, the most recent of which fractured her wrist.

IDENTIFICATION OF SUBSTANCE USE PROBLEMS

It may be difficult to distinguish between problems attributable to substance use from those that may be assumed to be signs of aging. The health care professional should be alert to the extent of alcohol or medication use when the client is confused, depressed, has memory or other cognitive problems, frequent falls or fractures, or is neglecting himself or herself and the environment.

Difficulties in identification are compounded by the fact that standard measures or criteria for dependence or problem use may not be relevant for older people. Not only will risk levels of substance use (e.g., number of drinks per occasion) be set higher than appropriate for older people, but also indicators of problem use, such as work, family or legal difficulties, are often not relevant to the older person's life (Beresford, 1996; Bucholz et al., 1996; Graham, 1989). Because of their own attitudes to heavy drinking and sometimes poor memory for events, older people may not report problems when asked about their drinking or other drug use (Graham, 1986).

Even if a family member or health professional recognizes that an older person's problems may be caused by alcohol or medications, they are sometimes reluctant to raise the issue. They may believe that the older person has only a few more years to live — why not leave the person to drink in peace? Or that the drug is prescribed, therefore it must be okay. This is misleading, since reducing or stopping drinking or some medications can improve the person's quality of life (e.g., more interest in socializing, less confusion or memory problems, less depression or anxiety, and improved physical health).

In an effort to increase identification and better understand the issue of substance use problems in older adults, researchers and clinicians have developed descriptions of different stages of a substance use problem as follows:

Early: beginning to move from light or moderate social drinking to using alcohol to cope with the stresses of life; may experience increased alcohol consumption or mild adverse consequences; may increase or extend use of other mood-altering drugs.

Acute: experiencing acute symptoms directly associated with current alcohol or other drug consumption; i.e., intoxication, withdrawal, severe depression, suicidal ideation or problematic behavior changes.

Chronic: experiencing ongoing consequences associated with alcohol or other drug use such as physical (cardiovascular, gastrointestinal, neurological), psychological (memory loss, low self-esteem, lack of coping skills) or social (loneliness, isolation).

Recovering: abstinent or decreased (nonhazardous) alcohol or other drug use, and attending to other adverse consequences associated with use.

As well, experience has shown that substance use problems among older adults differ somewhat based on patterns of use and age of onset. One of the earliest and simplest alcohol dependence typologies was done by Rosin and Glatt (1971). Two different groups were identified:

Early Onset: long-term alcohol use associated with personality or mental health difficulties.

Late Onset: the development of problems associated with use later in life and usually in reaction to stresses associated with aging.

A number of other studies (Carruth, 1973; Dunham, 1981; Graham, 1989) have also grouped older persons' problems into three, four or five categories, according to age of onset and pattern of use.

For the purpose of this discussion, we use two categories: *early onset,* meaning persons whose alcohol or drug problems developed early in life and continued into old age; and *late onset,* for people who developed dependencies later in life, often in reaction to stresses associated with aging, mainly losses or illnesses.

Intermittent problem users may form a fairly large group. These are people who have abused substances periodically throughout their adult life but the problem becomes more serious or consistent as they age. This group can be addressed within the early or late onset groups, depending on the symptoms with which they present.

SCREENING

Counsellors working with older adults should take a careful history of all substances used by the older client. This initial screening can provide an opportunity to give information or education to the older client who may be having difficulty managing his or her medications, or may be unaware that they are drinking more than age-specific low-risk drinking guidelines recommend. Responses at this level may include information on safe drinking guidelines; exploring alternative ways of coping with stress, anxiety or sleep problems (e.g., relaxation techniques, exercise, nonchemical sleep aids, diet); referral to a pharmacist or physician to discuss medication management issues.

Screening also provides an opportunity to explore for potential problem use and make a decision about whether a more in-depth assessment is required.

The following lists provide some sample questions that can be used to ask about alcohol or mediation use.

Medications
(prescription and over-the-counter)

QUESTIONS

Are you currently taking any medications to help you sleep, for anxiety or depression, or for pain?

How long have you been taking these medications? How often do you take them?

Do you usually take the prescribed amount of medication or do you sometimes take less than or more than the amount prescribed by the doctor?

Do you take any other prescribed medications?

Do you ever take medication that has been prescribed for someone else (e.g., a family member, friends)? Do you ever share your medication with someone else?

Have you ever obtained a prescription for the same drug from more than one doctor, without the other doctor knowing?

Does one doctor know all the medications you are taking, even if you are prescribed medications by several doctors?

Do you ever have difficulty remembering when to take your medication?

Do you sometimes put your medication in a different bottle from the one given to you by the doctor or the pharmacy and then forget to label the bottle?

What over-the-counter medication do you take? Do you take this medication on the advice of a doctor?

Do you ever drink alcohol while you are also taking medication without checking with a doctor?

WARNING SIGNS OF PROBLEMS WITH MEDICATION MANAGEMENT

- forgetting to take medication or getting confused about which medication is in the container
- not having one doctor who knows about all the medication a person is taking (e.g., over-the-counter medication and medication prescribed by another doctor).

WARNING SIGNS OF INAPPROPRIATE MEDICATION USE

- not taking medication as prescribed (particularly taking more than prescribed)
- regularly taking over-the-counter medication without the advice of a doctor
- using medication (e.g., benzodiazepines to help her sleep or for anxiety) regularly for several months or longer
- drinking alcohol while taking medication without checking with a doctor
- using medication that has been prescribed for someone else
- driving (or operating other machinery) while using depressant medications.

Alcohol

Make sure you and the client define a "drink" in the same way:
340 mL (12 oz) beer = 140 mL (5 oz) wine = 40 mL (1.5 oz) liquor

QUESTIONS

Have you ever had a drink containing alcohol (e.g., beer, wine, liqueur, whisky)?

How often do you have a drink containing alcohol?

How many drinks containing alcohol do you have on a typical day when you are drinking?

Are there days or times of the week when you drink more than usual?

Do you ever drive (or operate other equipment) after having one or more drinks during the previous hour?

WARNING SIGNS

• drinking more than two standard drinks on any day
• drinking more than nine standard drinks per week for women or 14 standard drinks per week for men
• drinking and driving (or operating other machinery)
• drinking while using medication when this is contraindicated.

Adapted from: *The Hidden Majority: A Guidebook on Alcohol and Other Drug Issues for Counsellors Who Work with Women,* Addiction Research Foundation, 1996. These are warning signs for the general population. Given the information outlined in this chapter, older adults may want to set lower limits for themselves.

REFERRAL

Because many older people do not consider their alcohol or other drug use a problem, they may not always be accepted by substance abuse treatment programs that require them to be motivated to stop using substances upon entry. For a number of other reasons, traditional substance abuse programs are often not appropriate for older people:

• Most programs require clients to travel to or be in residence to participate.
• Some older persons are not ready or able to leave their homes because of physical or emotional problems such as depression.
• The kinds of issues discussed in many programs may not be relevant to the lives of older people; they may be uncomfortable participating in a group that requires them

to talk about themselves.
• They may have difficulty in following group interaction because of hearing or sight problems.

Thus, older people with substance use problems benefit from services geared to their special needs and life circumstances. These needs and circumstances are related to the physical, emotional, mental, social and spiritual effects of substance use and society's attitude to older people, particularly those with a substance problem.

Depending on the resources available in a community, referrals are made to individual practitioners or programs that are best able to respond to alcohol or other drug problems within the context of the older person's life circumstances.

ASSESSMENT

Whether an in-depth assessment is conducted by addiction-specific personnel or general health or social work practitioners, the following elements should be considered:

• The assessment may require a number of contacts, rather than a structured, time-limited interview. This is because the initial presenting problem, or in some cases a crisis, may have to be dealt with first. Also, an older person may have a shorter attention span or tire easily.
• The initial focus is on the person's presenting problem — which is often not alcohol or drug use or abuse. It is important to attend to their concern in order to engage the person in a process of change. The substance use issue is best introduced when the person is most receptive; often after the initial concern is attended to and a therapeutic and caring relationship has been developed.
• Older people need time to tell their story and may not be willing or able to complete forms or other structured tests.
• The assessment may focus on different areas than would an assessment of a younger person. In older people it is important to assess such areas as sensory functioning, mobility, living environment and lifestyle, losses, diet, mental condition, physical health, social support, literacy and speech. If information on some of these areas is already available from other involved health professionals, don't repeat a questioning process that may feel invasive or tiring for an older person.
• The level of functioning in the above areas determines the older person's ability to make changes in their lives. Someone who is in poor health, cannot get around, is living in unhealthy circumstances or is confused will not be able to deal with alcohol and drug use until these immediate problems are addressed. In contrast, the younger person who presents for treatment, once he or she has stopped drinking or using drugs, is more likely to be in good health and have the energy and motivation to develop a healthy lifestyle.

The following section details the areas that may be addressed in a comprehensive assessment of an older person:

Sensory function: How well does the person hear or see (e.g., read labels on medication containers, books, newspapers)? Has sense of taste been lost?

Mobility: Can the person move about inside and outside, walk without aids, bathe/dress independently, shop for himself or herself?

Living environment and lifestyle: Is the person happy in her or his living situation? Have there been housing problems because of substance use? Can the person maintain his or her living environment? Are there fire hazards or sanitation problems? Is it close enough to stores, buses, etc.? Does the person go out? How often does he or she see other people?

Losses: Has she or he lost family, friends, physical health (hearing, sight), a job or home?

Diet: What are the person's eating habits (i.e., does he or she eat alone)? Does the person have a good appetite/enjoy food? How is food prepared and stored?

Mental condition: Is the person experiencing confusion, memory problems or psychiatric problems?

Physical health: Ask about sleeping patterns, weight change, disabilities and illnesses, medical supervision, dizziness, vision, hearing, foot care, digestion/elimination and dental problems.

Social support: Is there contact with family and friends? How much contact with other people? Does the person have close support vs. acquaintances?

Literacy and speech: Are there reading or writing problems?

Alcohol and other drug use: How often and how much does she or he drink? Has the pattern of drinking changed (increase, decrease, periods of abstinence)? Has drinking affected other areas of functioning? What medications (prescribed and over-the-counter) are being used? How often, for how long, and why?

The above in-depth assessment will help both the client and the practitioner to determine the next steps for intervention/treatment.

INTERVENTION/TREATMENT

Intervention with older adults often entails outreach activities. Outreach may mean working with the client in his/her own home or neighborhood or places where the person is most comfortable. Outreach can also mean psychologically reaching out (i.e., offering help in a way that accommodates the older person's needs), addressing the problems that are of most concern to the client, and not having unrealistic expectations. In other words, adjust the program, or efforts to help, to the client and do not expect the client to adjust his or her needs to the program or the help that is offered.

Once a person's problems and strengths have been identified through the assessment process, initial interventions are often aimed at engaging the person in a process of change aimed at reducing or alleviating the substance use problem(s) and their effects.

Much of the work done at this level will be motivational (i.e., encouraging and supporting the individual and helping to remove barriers to change).

More in-depth interventions are part of a treatment process aimed at helping the individual make behavioral, environmental and attitudinal changes that will result in less hazardous use of problem substances and enhanced overall health.

In order to develop effective treatment interventions, the needs of early and late onset users will be addressed separately.

Early Onset

People with early onset substance abuse problems usually present in the chronic stage. Those who still use addictive substances often use less and fewer times per week than younger people, or than they did when they were younger. This can mislead the users and others to believe that the severity of the problem has decreased, while in fact, they are still using at hazardous levels for their age and physical condition.

Some older people may be abstinent for one reason or another when they enter treatment, often in response to some acute injury or illness associated with their substance use. However, many of the physical, psychological and social problems associated with long-term use are still acute. These range from physical illnesses such as diabetes, arthritis, digestive disorders and heart disease to the social and psychological problems of depression, isolation, loneliness and low self-esteem.

The early onset person may enter treatment in his or her fifties but present with problems usually associated with the elderly (i.e., chronic illness, isolation and multiple

losses). Housing, financial constraints and inadequate social support are often problems. (Most specialized substance abuse programs for older adults accept clients from
aged 55 and older when, as indicated above, they have such a profile.)

Thus, these people often require a specialized intervention, one that responds
to issues associated with the person's physical, psychological, emotional and
spiritual needs.

PHYSICAL

Alcohol affects every system of the body. It adversely affects the appetite and diges-
tion of food, sleep patterns, and nerve, muscle and joint functioning. Thus, poor
nutrition, inadequate sleep and lack of exercise over many years weaken the person's physical condition and predispose him or her to chronic illnesses. Some of the
major effects of chronic alcohol problems are diseases such as hypertension, diabetes, arthritis and disorders of the digestive system. Other psychoactive substances
can also harm the physical system, and it is important to treat the chronic physical
condition while also focusing on withdrawal from the drug. The older person may
have to withdraw under the supervision of a physician rather than in a nonmedical
detox setting.

PSYCHOLOGICAL

The person with a substance use problem may present with a particular psychological picture. Often the earlier tasks of development have been interfered with or have
not been completed because of substance use. Such tasks include becoming an individual with adequate ego strength; developing one's life work and becoming productive in a job; developing intimacy with a partner and learning to be interdependent;
becoming responsible to others in a family or similar situation; and finding one's
place in society.

The older person with inadequate ego strength may have poor coping skills and lack
of assertiveness accompanied by feelings of anger, frustration, helplessness and inadequacy. Empathetic understanding and acceptance of the person's feelings, seeking
out and supporting his or her strengths, as well as new training in coping and
assertiveness skills will help the individual develop a higher level of ego strength.

Failure to fully develop one's potential and the loss of many jobs as a result of substance use also add to psychological problems associated with failure, insecurity, and
condemnation from family, friends and society. Poorly developed work habits and
skills are accompanied by feelings of low self-esteem and inadequacy. In most cases,
the older person will not be returning to the workforce; treatment should focus more
on leisure activities and helping the person rediscover earlier skills and interests or
develop new ones.

Throughout the years, as alcohol or drug use became the main focus of life, these clients may have failed to do the work necessary to develop intimate relationships. Problems associated with developing relational skills were solved by the use of substances. The result is poor social skills, inability to relate to others at a deep-feeling level and loss of family and friends due to behavior associated with alcohol and drug use.

Treatment that includes an opportunity to socialize, and helps a person become comfortable expressing his or her feelings, will help to alleviate loneliness. Though many older people will initially prefer individual counselling, a goal of the intervention should be to help them feel comfortable joining a group. This can often be a key to developing new friendships and a stepping stone to assisting the person to move out into the wider community.

People with long-term substance use problems have usually not developed the ability to be interdependent — to be responsible to and for others, and to have others be responsible to and for them. This may present in various ways: not showing up for appointments, demanding behavior, or over-dependence on the care-giver. The client may fluctuate between angry feelings of "I don't need anyone, leave me alone," to clinging to the care-giver. It is often necessary to allow a person the opportunity to depend on the care-giver for a period of time. The goal, of course, is to broaden the base of support gradually and help the person interact with others in a give-and-take relationship.

SOCIAL

Social isolation is a major problem for the early onset client, and the physical and psychological limitations mentioned above affect the person's ability to form and maintain friendships. Compounding this is the loss of family and friends because of addictive behavior.

Social isolation can be a problem for many older people as they lose the company of work colleagues, children leaving home, and partners or other close friends who have died. For the early onset person, these changes often occur earlier in life and are more extensive than for others of a similar age. Friends and family have been replaced with "drinking friends" and places. The long-term effects of substance use may have decreased the ability to actively participate in relationships; communications are blurred. Energy for social activities is also decreased.

Social isolation promotes feelings of loneliness and fear, as well as anxiety when with people. It must be attended to gradually in treatment. As mentioned above, a relationship with one caring person is often a good place to start, followed by encouraging the client to gradually extend his or her circle of contacts.

Spiritual

The spiritual issues attendant on long-term alcohol and other drug use usually revolve around the meaning of life and feelings of guilt and remorse. Freedom to talk about these issues is a necessary part of treatment. Recent understanding about and more acceptance of the process of addiction can help a person relieve the guilt and accept the personal strengths that have allowed him or her to survive the ravages of abuse.

Finally, it is important to consider the effect of society's attitude toward the person with a substance use problem. Frequently this attitude is pessimistic. Family and care-givers have observed many years of substance abuse, promises made and broken, efforts to stop using followed by even greater use. Many attempts at control are brief, then the cycle begins again. The family reaches the end of its coping ability and moves away in an effort to reclaim its own health. Eventually friends and colleagues look on from a distance and it is left to the professional care-giver to offer support and to try once again.

Without a good understanding and acceptance of the chronic relapsing nature of the problem, even the health care professional may give up. If this happens, the client's feelings of hopelessness and helplessness are reflected by all those around him or her. This impasse must be broken by using creative interventions to engage a person with a chronic substance use problem in a process of change. It is essential to find areas of change that are important to the client and in which he or she feels some confidence for success. Often this is not initially in the area of substance use. However, as people become stronger both physically and emotionally, and with support, they can change their use of alcohol and other drugs.

The best approaches (Kola, 1980; Zimberg, 1978; Olsen-Noll, 1989; Kinney, 1983; Hogstel, 1990; Graham, 1989) to intervening with the person with an early onset substance use problem include:

- an individual approach focusing on areas for change that the client sees as both important and achievable (e.g., a relationship with a counsellor can be the first step toward alleviating loneliness, to be followed later by other social activities; basic needs such as food and shelter can be addressed as well)
- a supportive one-to-one relationship, which is nonconfrontational and nurturing, recognizing the possible initial need for dependence
- outreach — working with the client in his or her own home, allowing for physical and emotional comfort; reach out to offer help instead of waiting for the person to seek help
- group activities that offer support and social interaction with peers; this may take the form of a supportive counselling group, as well as recreational activities undertaken by the group
- a thorough knowledge and use of available health and social services in the community.

Late Onset

As mentioned earlier, the person who develops a substance use problem later in life is grouped as late onset. Often this problem develops as a reaction to stresses associated with aging or stage in life. The person usually enters treatment at a later age, commonly 65 to 75 or older, with fewer years of substance abuse and fewer losses associated with it. Thus the late onset person presents quite a different picture than the early onset person. Often they have lived a full life, having successfully managed a career and family. Skills and interests have been developed during the adult years and family ties are more likely to be intact.

A substance problem can develop through two routes. Some people may have been social drinkers all their lives. After retirement, with more leisure time and drinking-related social activities and fewer work-related constraints, drinking may escalate. Combined with increased physical sensitivity to the effects of alcohol and other drugs as people age, this is sufficient to initiate major health and possibly other problems related to substance use.

The second route occurs when an older person self-medicates with alcohol or other psychoactive drugs, or is prescribed psychoactive drugs to alleviate stress caused by physical ill-health or loss of someone close to them.

As with early onset, late onset problems may occur in many dimensions of people's lives — physical, psychological, social and spiritual. However, late onset problems may present somewhat differently.

In some ways, the late onset person resembles the younger substance abuser. Recognition and acceptance of crossing the line from social to harmful use is difficult. As well, symptoms or problems associated with heavy alcohol or drug use (e.g., confusion, disorientation, recent memory loss, tremors, inflammation of joints, gastritis, hypertension, depression, heart disease and sleep disturbances) are often erroneously accepted as normal signs of aging. Thus, the client, the family and care-givers may fail to identify the problem in its early stages.

The late onset person is often dealing with a crisis and it is important to identify the stressor and attend to it along with the substance use problem. Crises in later years most often pertain to loss. As one client aptly described it, after reading about the stages of grief in a popular magazine, "I am perpetually in several stages of grief at the same time. I never get out of it." Care-givers must be aware of the impact of multiple losses on the older person. These losses and the resulting grief are best responded to by interpersonal means rather than by using drugs (Harrison, 1987).

Understanding the normal grief reaction and facilitating its appropriate response is a key element in addiction treatment for the elderly. Grief is the personal response to loss, real or symbolic. This response often affects the person both physically and emotionally. In the older person, grief may occur in response to losses associated with role change, physical and mental illness, death or separation from meaningful persons in one's life, financial changes, and changes in living arrangements. Grief can be understood through an adaptation-to-loss model as described by Harrison (1987) which includes four tasks:

ACCEPTING THE REALITY OF THE LOSS

To accept a loss, a person must experience it. To experience it often means allowing painful physical and emotional responses to occur. Physical responses may include shortness of breath, a physical feeling of emptiness, changes in bowel and bladder habits, and changes in appetite and sleep patterns.

Feelings of acute fear, anger, sadness and anxiety often accompany the experience of loss. Cognitively, the person may fluctuate between preoccupation with the object of loss and denial of it. Careful listening with empathetic responses will allow the person to feel and express his or her grief safely.

EMANCIPATION EMOTIONALLY FROM TIES WITH THE PERSON OR OBJECT

Freeing oneself emotionally from the loss occurs gradually as one feels and expresses one's emotions. It is important to have these feelings validated by recognition and caring from another person who can provide a touchstone to reality for someone who is still experiencing overwhelming feelings of loss. People experiencing acute grief often say that they feel they are losing their minds. Tranquillizers, sedatives and alcohol only serve to mask, repress and delay these normal feelings of grief, which resurface when the drug is withdrawn. A careful history with attention to life's losses will help the care-giver understand and respond to a client's emotional and physical needs.

ADJUSTING TO THE ENVIRONMENT WITHOUT THE PERSON OR THING THAT HAS BEEN LOST

This means making active choices that emphasize other parts of one's life, establish new roles or relationships, or rearrange one's life pattern to deal with the loss. For example, an older person whose eyesight begins to fail might have to adjust to not being able to drive, fill out forms, read directions or see price tags, or to enjoy a good book. Support is needed at this time when change is necessary but the desire and emotional fortitude are low. Groups can sometimes help at this stage by offering support, new ideas for adaptation and opportunities to meet new people.

REINVESTMENT IN A NEW RELATIONSHIP OR ACTIVITY

This fourth task occurs when one redirects one's time, energy, activity and emotions into a different person or area. It means developing new relationships as important as the old; putting time and energy into new activities to replace the ones that have been lost; and enjoying and developing new roles. The care-giver in this stage can encourage and validate the person's efforts toward reinvestment. For example, a person reinvesting in a new relationship may feel guilt over betraying the person he or she has lost. The care-giver can validate these as natural feelings, while supporting the person in the new relationship.

In helping older persons deal with life changes, it is important to understand how their responses differ from those of younger people:
- The tasks of grief generally take longer to complete. This may be related to diminished energy to perform the grief work.
- Responses appear to be less emotional than in younger persons, but there are more physical symptoms.
- There is a greater tendency to idealize the lost person, object or physical or mental ability.
- Significant losses lead to greater social isolation than would occur in a younger person. Older people have less physical and emotional energy to reinvest in a new lifestyle.
- There appears to be greater hostility to living persons, often specific family members. This hostility is common in many grieving persons. Its increased intensity in the elderly is not clearly understood.
- There is some evidence that the elderly person "gives up" or "withdraws" from completing the adaptation process. For some, the task appears overwhelming; for others, the internalization of emotions leads to a decrease in the energy needed to complete the grief work.

Two further factors must be considered in working with both the early onset and late onset older person. These are: (1) the high incidence of concurrent disorders — i.e., substance abuse and mental illness; and (2) the developmental tasks of aging.

Though there are no estimates of the prevalence of concurrent disorders in the elderly, professionals working with them know that the combination of mental illness and alcohol or other drug dependence is a major treatment challenge. Depression is particularly common, though it is often unclear whether the depression preceded or was the result of substance use. Also the extent of the depression may be unclear until the person is fully detoxified. Both need to be investigated and treated.

Finally, anyone working with older people should know the normal developmental tasks of aging. The major tasks are to resolve one's life's conflicts successfully; to review and integrate one's past events with a personal value system that reflects the achievement of life satisfaction; the emergence of a developed life philosophy; and the acquisition of wisdom (Birren and Renner, 1981). Older people need to both face their mortality and accept, understand and value their life as it has been lived. Success in achieving this personal integration is highly influenced by the successful completion of earlier developmental tasks (as discussed previously). For the older client, attention to developmental tasks is a necessary part of treatment and recovery. It is particularly important to either resolve or accept one's life conflicts that were related to alcohol or drug use. This can be positively influenced through an understanding of the addiction process. Thus, education is an element of treatment. Reminiscing is another way an older person sorts through the events and meaning of his or her life in order to understand and achieve self-acceptance. This process often involves the expression of feelings and some problem solving. The care-giver can facilitate this process of integration by recognizing its importance; lending support and validation through careful listening and affirmation of the person's life achievements; helping clients understand traumatic issues, including those associated with the addiction; and helping them solve, where possible, remaining issues.

In conclusion, the older person in treatment covers a wide age range and presents at all stages of problem use. The early and late onset substance users form two fairly distinct groups. They share some similarities in terms of the developmental tasks of aging, but also have different needs and require different treatment approaches.

Early onset clients suffer more widespread physical, psychological, social and spiritual losses. As a result, they present for treatment with major problems such as chronic illness, loneliness, poor self-esteem, poor coping mechanisms, isolation, depression and loss of meaning in life. These problems often create a sense of helplessness and hopelessness. A treatment approach that attends to these problems, as well as to the drinking or drug use, is most effective for this group.

On the other hand, the late onset client usually suffers fewer overall losses. He or she may develop a dependence on alcohol or other drugs through two different routes: (1) social drinking becomes hazardous to the person because of increased amounts, decreased ability to metabolize the substance, or interactions with other medications or (2) a person experiences a crisis or severe stress associated with later years, often loss, and alleviates the symptoms through chemical means. Education about substance use, attention to the crisis, fostering healthy ways of dealing with distress and support are important treatment approaches for this group.

For both the early and late onset person, attention to tasks of aging and a knowledge and use of community resources are essential for successful treatment.

REFERENCES

Adlaf, E.J., Ivis, F.J., and Smart, R.G. (1994). *Alcohol and Other Drug Use among Ontario Adults in 1994 and Changes Since 1977*. Toronto: Addiction Research Foundation.

Baker, M.J. (1992). Saskatchewan's patient profile release program: A province-wide drug monitoring program. Paper presented at the Canadian Association on Gerontology Pre-Conference Workshop on Medications and the Elderly. Alberta, October 2, 1992.

Baker, W.W. (1985). Psychopharmacology of aging: Use, misuse, and abuse of psychotropic drugs. In *The Combined Problems of Alcoholism, Drug Addiction and Aging,* eds. Gottheil, E., Druley, K.A., Skolada, T.E., and Waxman, H.M. Springfield: Charles C. Thomas.

Beresford, T.B. (1996). Alcoholic elderly: Prevalence, screening, diagnosis, and prognosis. In *Alcohol and Aging*, eds. Beresford, T., and Gomberg, E. New York: Oxford University Press.

Bergob, M. (1994). Drug use among senior Canadians. *Canadian Social Trends* (Summer 1994): 25–29. Statistics Canada Cat. 11-008E.

Birren, J.E., and Renner, V.J. (1981). Concepts and criteria of mental health and aging. *American Journal of Orthopsychiatry* (April 1981): 51.

Bucholz, K.K., Sheline, Y.J., and Helzer, J.E. (1996). The epidemiology of alcohol use, problems and dependence in elders: A review. In *Alcohol and Aging*, eds. Beresford, T., and Gomberg, E. New York: Oxford University Press.

Carruth, B. et al. (1973). Alcoholism and problem drinking among older persons: Community care providers and the older problem drinker. Paper presented at the Alcohol and Drug Problems Association of North America, New Brunswick, NJ, Sept. 28, 1973.

Dunham, R.G. (1981). Aging and changing patterns of use. *Journal of Psychoactive Drugs* 18 (2): 40–41.

Eliany, M., and Clarke, J. (1992). *The Use of Alcohol and Other Drugs by Older Canadians and Its Consequences*. Ottawa: Health and Welfare Canada, Minister of Supply and Services Canada. Cat. No. H39-259/1992E.

Graham, K., Carver, V., and Brett, P. (1996). Women aged 65 and over: Alcohol and drug use. In *Women's Use of Alcohol, Tobacco and Other Drugs in Canada*, eds. Adrian, M., Lundy C., and Eliany, M. Toronto: Addiction Research Foundation.

Graham, K., Clarke, D., Bois, C., Carver, V., Dolinki, L., Smythe, C., Harrison, S., Marshman, J., and Brett, P. (1996). Addictive behaviour of older adults. *Addictive Behaviours* 21 (3): 331–348.

Graham, K., Clarke, D., Bois, C., Carver, V., Marshman, J., Brett, P., Dolinki, L., Smythe, C., and Harrison, S. (1995). Alcohol use, depressant medication use, and reasons for drinking among older people. Preconference draft of paper to be presented at the 21st Annual Alcohol Epidemiology Symposium of the Kettil Bruun Society of Social and Epidemiological Research on Alcohol. Porto, Portugal, June 5–9, 1995.

Graham, K., Saunders, S., Flaver, M.C., Birchmore Timney, C., White-Campbell, M., and Zeidman, A. (1989). Evaluation of the COPA Project: A description of client characteristics, interventions and outcomes. Unpublished draft report. Toronto: Addiction Research Foundation.

Graham, K. (1986). Identifying and measuring alcohol abuse among the elderly: serious problems with existing instrumentation. *Journal of Alcohol Studies* 47 (4): 322–326.

Harrison, M.K. (1987). Loss, grief and adaptation. In *Psychogeriatrics: A Practical Handbook,* ed. Wasylenki, D. Toronto: Gage Educational Publishing Co.

Health Canada. (1995). Partners for action: A Canadian workshop on seniors and medication, alcohol and other drugs. Ottawa, Government Conference Centre. January 9–11, 1995.

Health and Welfare Canada. (1989). *Charting Canada's Future.* Ottawa: Minister of Supply and Services.

Health and Welfare Canada. (1990). *National Alcohol and Other Drug Survey 1989: Highlights Report,* eds. Eliany, M., Giesbrecht, N., Nelson, M., Wellman, B., Wortley, S. Ottawa: Minister of Supply and Services Canada.

Hogstel, M.O. (1990). *Geropsychiatric Nursing.* Toronto: The C.V. Mosby Company.

Kenton, C. (1985). Drugs and the elderly. National Library of Medicine Literature Search, No. 85-2, November 1980 through March 1985.

Kinney, J., and Leaton, G. (1983). *The Elderly. Loosening the Grip.* Toronto: The C.V. Mosby Company.

Kola, L.A., Kosberg, J.I., and Wegner-Burch, K. (1980). Perceptions of the treatment responsibilities for the alcoholic elderly client. *Social Work in Health Care* 6 (2): 69–76.

Lamy, P. (1985). The aging: Drug use and misuse. In *The Combined Problems of Alcoholism, Drug Addiction and Aging,* eds. Gottheil, E., Druley, K.A., Skolada, T.E., and Waxman, H.M. Springfield: Charles C. Thomas.

Lankin, F. (1992). Looking towards the future. Speaking notes of the Honourable Minister of Health, Frances Lankin, at the ADRAO Annual Conference and General Meeting. June 7, 1992.

McKim, W.A., and Mishara, B.L. (1987). *Drugs and Aging.* Toronto: Butterworths.

National Institute on Alcohol Abuse and Alcoholism. (1982). Alcohol and the elderly. In *In Brief* RPO 254: 1/82.

New Brunswick Health and Community Services. (1991). *Study of the Application of a Drug Utilization Review Model to Benzodiazepine Use in the Senior Citizen and Income Assistance Population in New Brunswick.* Fredericton, NB.

Olsen-Noll, C., and Bosworth, M. (1989). Alcohol abuse in the elderly. *American Family Physician* 39: 173–179.

Quinn, K., Baker, M., and Evans, B. (Undated). *Who Uses Prescription Drugs? Results from a Population-wide Study in Saskatchewan.* Regina: Saskatchewan Health.

Rosin, A., and Glatt, M.M. (1971). Alcohol excess in the elderly. *Quarterly Journal of Studies on Alcoholism* 32: 53–59.

Sellers, E.M., Frecker, R.C., and Romach, M.K. (1983). Drug metabolism in the elderly: Confounding of age, smoking and ethanol effects. *Drug Metabolism Reviews* 14 (2): 225–250.

Tamblyn, R., McLeod, P.J., Abrahamowicz, M., Monette, J., Gayton, D.C., Berkson, L., Dauphinee, W.D., Grad, R.M., Huang, A.R., Isaac, L.M., Schnarch, B.S., and Snell, L.S. (1994). Questionable prescribing for elderly patients in Quebec. *Canadian Medical Association Journal* 150 (11): 1801–1808.

Zimberg, S. (1978). Treatment of the elderly alcoholic in the community and in an institutional setting. *Addictive Diseases: An International Journal* 3 (3): 417–425.

RESOURCES

Action on Women's Research and Education. *Drug Wise: A Book for Older Women about Safe Drug Use* and *Drug Wise: A Book about Safe Drug Use for Older Women Who Are Caregivers.* Both published by Action on Women's Research and Education, Aware Press, Kingston, ON.

Addiction Research Foundation. *Alcohol and the Older Adult* and *Sleeping Pills, Tranquillizers and Pain Medication and the Older Adult* are two helpful brochures that are available from the ARF.

Beresford, T., and Gomberg, E. (1996). *Alcohol and Aging.* New York: Oxford University Press.

Centretown Community Health Centre. *LESA: A Program of Lifestyle Enrichment for Senior Adults with Alcohol and Other Psychoactive Drug Problems.* This manual is available from the Centretown Community Health Centre, 340 MacLaren Street, Ottawa, ON K2P 0M6. It provides a comprehensive description of the components of the treatment program as well as addressing administrative issues.

Graham, K., Saunders, S.J., Flower, M.C., Birchmore T.C., White-Campbell, M., and Pietropaolo, A.Z. (1995). *Addictions Treatment for Older Adults: Evaluation of an Innovative Client-Centred Approach.* New York: The Haworth Press Inc.

Health Canada Seniors Medication and Alcohol Use Internet Site:
http://www.hwc.ca/datahpsb/seniors/index.htm

Lifestyle Enrichment for Senior Adults (LESA) et al. *Alternatives.* An educational package including print materials and a video developed by LESA, the Addiction Research Foundation of Ontario (ARF) and the Community Older Persons Program, Toronto (COPA). It includes a presentation for persons working with seniors on how to identify and intervene with seniors with substance abuse problems, as well as a presentation for seniors on common stresses of aging, ways seniors may cope by using alcohol or other drugs and alternatives to using drugs to cope with these stresses. Available in English or French from the ARF Marketing Department, 33 Russell Street, Toronto, ON M5S 2S1 or by calling 1-800-661-1111 (in Toronto, call 416-595-6059).

Chapter 16

Working with Lesbians and Gay Men

BETTY-ANNE M. HOWARD AND BLAIR EDWARD COLLINS

INTRODUCTION

Very little is known about how, and indeed whether, lesbians and gay men differ in their substance use compared to the general population, since most research studies rarely ask people about their sexual orientation. Consequently, their data would be assimilated into the results of whatever particular target group was being focused on. However, self-identifying lesbians and gay men are found in about 10 per cent of any and every population, whether ethnic, cultural, socio-economic or religious.

Working with lesbians and gay men may prove to be particularly challenging for counsellors, as many of the issues pertaining to this group require close examination of commonly held attitudes, beliefs and assumptions that go deep inside all of us. This chapter will offer assistance with a process of self-examination; provide a better understanding of the factors involved in dealing with lesbian and gay alcohol/drug problems; and offer suggestions on how to serve this population better. To do this, we will discuss various definitions, examine myths and misconceptions, address addiction-related issues pertaining to both the community service organization and the counsellor, and review some of the limited research that has been conducted to date on the needs of lesbians and gay men with alcohol or drug problems. We also contend that, by taking what one already knows about substance abuse and combining this with the wealth of contemporary lesbian and gay resource material that is available, the counsellor will be empowered to deal with lesbians and gay men in a sensitive and understanding way.

We will begin by providing information on the definitions of sexual continuum/sexual orientation, lesbians, gay men, coming out, and heterosexism/homophobia/homohatred. This section will lay the groundwork for understanding the issues presented in subsequent parts of this chapter.

DEFINITIONS

Sexual Continuum/Sexual Orientation

It is easy to separate ourselves from the plight of others when we draw a dividing line between us and them. It's much easier not to identify with the struggles and challenges that a particular group of people must face. It is much safer to rest easy with the illusion that we are in no way like those other people. This also touches on the belief that, in some way, whatever misfortune befalls a particular group, they got what they deserved for being different or "other than" the predominant group. When counsellors look at sexual orientation from a dichotomous perspective, they fall into the trap of drawing a very rigid dividing line. This is not to say that being identified as heterosexual is the same as being identified as gay or lesbian; there are big differences.

It is widely believed and accepted that sexual orientation falls on a continuum — with exclusively heterosexual at one end and exclusively homosexual at the other (Kinsey, 1948). Kinsey's sexuality continuum is a seven-point scale with the middle point representing a sexuality that includes the same amount of sexual thoughts, feelings and behaviors towards both men and women. As Lewis and Jordan (1989) point out in their review of the literature on sexuality and sexual orientation, there are multiple components of sexual orientation — including sexual activity, primary affectional relationships and fantasy — and sexual feelings can be expressed in many different ways, not exclusively through genital sex. When all these factors are considered, most people's sexuality falls somewhere around the middle of the continuum, with relatively few existing exclusively at either end. In addition, this less rigid and more accurate concept of sexuality recognizes that most individuals will, throughout their lives, exist at various points on the continuum. On the other hand, our society operates exclusively on the basis of the two opposite ends of this spectrum, insisting that most individuals identify as either gay (homosexual) or straight (heterosexual). As a result, one end is socially acceptable and the other is not; one is good and the other is bad.

Adolescence, a time for establishing sexual identity, is a particularly vulnerable time for young lesbians and gay males and, perhaps, it is a confusing time for those who are uncertain about their sexual orientation.

Many myths and misconceptions regarding lesbians and gay men have been perpetuated in order to maintain hatred, fear and mistrust, and to justify discriminatory practices. In order to dispel many of the myths, it is important to look at who lesbians and gay men really are and their experience of being put in the "bad" category.

It is important to keep in mind that lesbians and gay men are a remarkably heterogeneous group. They can be found in all ethnic groups and all occupations (Lewis and Jordan, 1989).

Recognizing that homosexuality exists along a continuum, definitions are difficult to create (Israelstam and Lambert, 1986). However, to begin to understand what it means to be a lesbian or gay man in our society and to begin addressing the needs of this special population, one must understand lesbians and gay men.

Lesbians

Lesbians define themselves in many different ways and live their lives in ways that fit their own definitions. For example, there are lesbian separatists who prefer to separate themselves from all men and male influence; lesbian feminists who are committed to achieving the goals of the women's movement; and gay women who don't identify as different from other women beyond the fact that their sexual partners are women.

The following definition embraces the multidimensional nature of lesbianism: "A lesbian is a woman who *prefers* other women on many levels: sexually, emotionally, intellectually, psychically — and who defines herself as a lesbian" (our emphasis), (Hughes et al., 1984). Part of our society's way of defining a woman is through her relationship to men (i.e., Miss or Mrs., an engagement ring to indicate that she is "taken" but no such symbol of a man's engagement, fathers "giving away" their daughters to future husbands, etc.). Women whose primary sexual, emotional and intellectual relationships are not with men do not fit society's definition of women. Here we begin to see the basis for many of the myths about lesbians. Lesbians, in varying degrees, defy the standards set out for proper/normal female behavior. As a result, lesbians are punished and oppressed. One thing that all lesbians have in common is their love for women. This, by itself, is a threat to many people in our society.

Oppression is a frequently used term, so it is important to establish exactly what is meant by the oppression of lesbians.

The oppression of lesbians shows itself in many different ways. We are invisible and invalidated. History books make no mention of us and we rarely appear in fiction. When we are mentioned in psychology or sociology, we are seen as deviant or ill. The media rarely give us images of ourselves, and never positive images. A young woman growing up has no chance of receiving the information and support she needs in order to see lesbianism as a valid life choice.

Images of lesbianism in both popular myth and "objective" scholarly writings portray us as evil, sick, shameful, corrupting and exclusively sexual. We are presented to ourselves — even from the more "enlightened" viewpoints — as tragically doomed to promiscuity, alcohol, drugs, violence, despair and suicide.

These stereotypical images reinforce negative attitudes about lesbianism and sanction more overt forms of oppression. Lesbians are ridiculed, harassed, verbally abused, shunned. As lesbians we are disowned by our families, evicted from our homes, fired from our jobs. Our children are taken from us. We are sexually assaulted, beaten, raped. We are incarcerated in mental hospitals and psychiatric institutions (Hughes et al., 1984, p. 17).

No matter how much a lesbian may try to "pass" as heterosexual (and it certainly must be tempting under the circumstances!), and no matter how privileged she may be in this society (economically, educationally, racially, etc.), every lesbian lives with this oppressive environment. Any counsellor working with lesbians must be aware of this oppression and respect the strength it takes to function under these conditions.

Gay Men

Just as there are many different kinds of lesbians, there are many different kinds of gay men who live a variety of lifestyles appropriate to the personal sense they have made of their gay identity. For example, some gay men have chosen roles contrary to the socially limited and stereotypic masculine roles as defined in contemporary society with its patriarchal privilege. They are willing to explore fully the gamut of those emotional feelings and practical ways of relating and functioning in our society that have traditionally been limited to the arena of the "feminine" or "female role." Still others are more hesitant to challenge and renounce the masculine social privilege they enjoy as males in our society, and prefer to limit the meaning of their gayness to the emotional and sexual/genital aspects of their lives; and, in some instances, solely to the genital expression of their sexuality.

As a result, an adequate, all-encompassing definition of a gay man is extremely difficult to offer, but for the purposes of this discussion, let us borrow from Hughes et al.'s (1984) definition of "lesbians" cited earlier and apply it to the gay male: A gay man is a man who *prefers* other men on a number of levels: sexually, emotionally, intellectually, psychically — and who defines himself as a gay man.

This definition must, however, be further qualified with caution. Here one already encounters one of the ramifications of living in a homophobic, and in many instances, homo-hating society:

> Many researchers no longer believe that people can be clearly divided into groups of homosexual (lesbians, gay men), heterosexual, and bisexual by simply asking about the sex of past or present sexual partners. When it comes to labelling one's sexual orientation identity (not sexual behavior), the best judge is the individual himself or herself. And often you cannot predict behavior accurately from the label a person has selected (Reinsch and Beasley, 1991, p. 144).

Consequently, it is well worth considering that, even in terms of self-definition, there are many men who, while engaging almost exclusively in same-sex genital activity and/or emotional relationships, would still hesitate to define themselves as "gay" because of the contemporary social climate of homophobia and/or homo-hatred. Thus, even the process of self-definition is affected by such discrimination.

Because of the social privilege traditionally enjoyed by men, gay males have endured still other forms of oppression that are both similar to and different from the oppression of lesbians.

As with lesbians, gay men are invisible and invalidated. Their historical achievements or contributions have often been recorded, but what *has* been consistently overlooked, or even blatantly denied (especially regarding those historical male figures whose contributions have been valued as "outstanding"), is their gay sexual orientation. It is as if recognizing their gay sexuality would somehow lessen their contributions. Thus, the myth is maintained and perpetuated: "Gay men are misfits who have nothing to contribute to society." And the world continues to believe that there are no positive gay role models.

Contemporary media images of gay men (if they are presented at all) continue to perpetuate the stereotype of the overtly effeminate male who is emotionally "weak" and laughably comic in appearance and demeanor. In fact, only a small minority of gay men can be identified as such by this stereotype. Other men who are wrestling with homosexual feelings, but who do not fit the stereotypic definition, will continue to feel confused — one explanation for the discrepancy between an individual's self-determined label and sexual/emotional activity.

Both the gay man and the lesbian pay the same emotional price for living in such an oppressive environment. Both must live with socially sanctioned acts of violence and discrimination, ridicule, harassment, verbal and emotional abuse and ostracism. The act of declaring one's sexual identity or having it discovered carries with it a number of possible penalties: loss of family, employment, friends, children, social status and religion. As stated earlier, this may be even more problematic for adolescents, who depend on their families and friends for support and validation.

The result: many gay men prefer to "pass" themselves off as heterosexual in this heterosexual male-privileged society, and pay a heavy emotional price: the destruction of self-image, a sense of alienation, and incredible stresses and burdens on any attempts at intimacy and committed relationships. A counsellor must be aware of both the psychic energy it takes to stay closeted, and the emotional cost of trying to live openly and authentically as a gay male or lesbian in our society — a "Catch-22" situation.

Coming Out

The phrase "coming out" has its origins in the term "coming out of the closet." This comes from the idea that homosexuality is one of those "skeletons in the closet" (i.e., something to be ashamed of and kept hidden). "Coming out" can take two forms: acknowledging to yourself that you are lesbian or gay, and telling someone else. Both are ongoing processes that can be problematic. Even individuals who have felt since birth that they were lesbian or gay have to deal with family expectations that they be heterosexual (Rothblum, 1989). It is especially difficult for adolescents whose parents are totally unprepared to be told by their child that he or she is gay.

"Many gays are in a state of stress caused by stigmatization and the fact that their upbringing by no means prepares them for what they have to cope with from the time they first realize they are homosexual on" (Israelstam, 1986, p. 27). No matter how many times a lesbian or a gay man comes out, they must daily combat both society's assumption that they are heterosexual and the many negative responses when this assumption is addressed. As Sarah Pearlman so aptly put it in *Invisible Lives* (1990), "Throughout life there is a decision of whether to come out or not to come out, and that always is either a major or a minor crisis" (p. 47).

The healthy "coming out" process for an individual involves the removal of the negative attitude/belief about homosexuality implanted by a homophobic society and the development of a positive gay/lesbian identity in its place.

Heterosexism/Homophobia/Homo-Hatred

Heterosexism is the belief that everyone is, or should be, heterosexual:

> Just as a *sexist* perspective is one that uses male behavior and experience as the norm, a *heterosexist* perspective uses heterosexual behavior and experience as the norm by which to measure all human social and sexual activity [and] ... can shape an individual's language, concepts, values and fundamental ways of thinking about human relations and society. Heterosexist viewpoints can bias research on lesbians and gay men, in the way research questions are formulated, in the methodology and in the interpretation of results. Another serious outcome of a heterosexist viewpoint is the invisibility of lesbians and gay men: the language, meanings and concepts in popular usage often fail to recognize gay and lesbian existence (Toronto Board of Education, 1992).

According to Pearlman (1989), "a primary demand of the dominant heterosexual culture is that lesbians [and gay men] participate in their own invisibility through 'passing'" (p. 84). Because of this, many positive role models that could be found in all areas of society are missing because many lesbians and gay men are in hiding (Israelstam, 1986). This passing/hiding represents another form of oppression for lesbians and gay men who fear that discovery could lead to job loss, denial of housing, and loss of friends and family support (Schwartz, 1980).

As stated earlier, other stressors include a society that sees lesbians and gay men as inferior (Lewis and Jordan, 1989), unable to cope with heterosexual responsibilities of marriage and family — as deviants who need help (Schwartz, 1980).

The context of development for gay and lesbian youth is profoundly different from that of their "straight" peers, and usually difficult. Prevailing social sentiments leave many feeling uncomfortable about themselves generally and their sexuality in particular. They have difficulty finding adequate information and support. In our culture, which invests heterosexual youth with highest sexual value, gay and lesbian youth often feel worthless.... Stress levels may be high for gays as a consequence of having a more complex adolescence (Health and Welfare Canada and the Addiction Research Foundation, 1991, pp. 1–19).

In their work *After the Ball* (1989), Kirk and Madsen contend that much of what is defined as "homophobia" is not based on individual and group fear of gays but rather on "hating." They continue:

> Fear need have nothing to do with it.... Clearly when we call our enemies "homophobes," we run the risk of underestimating them, which is a big mistake. Worse, the specious "diagnosis" suggests an equally specious "cure": that if straights just got to know us, they'd necessarily get over their fear — which, as with fear of tarantulas, is simply not true (p. xxii).

Furthermore, this underestimation of heterosexual discrimination suggests that lesbians and gay men are in a position of power in that they evoke fear from many heterosexuals. Fear doesn't kill gay men and lesbians or put them at risk of physical violence and bashing — hatred does. For Kirk and Madsen (1989), it is essential that we call hatred by its real name if society is to come to grips with the seriousness of this issue.

MYTHS/MISCONCEPTIONS

A number of myths and misconceptions — stemming from a lack of awareness, and from homophobia and homo-hatred — impinge on our attitudes and practices pertaining to lesbians and gay men. It is imperative for counsellors working with lesbians and gay men to examine and dispel these myths embedded in their own belief systems, and often in their clients' belief systems as well (i.e., internalized homophobia).

Some myths or assumptions revolve around sexual issues. These are illustrated in comments such as: "It's only what you do in bed," or "Your whole life is nothing but sex." To address the first, lesbians and gay men do not leave their identity and their lives in their bedrooms! If you are a lesbian or gay man, you are that 24 hours a day, seven days a week. It is not something that miraculously happens to you upon entering a bedroom. The second comment implicitly denies the public aspects of heterosexuality: it is present in sex scenes in movies, television programs, books and magazines, and in advertisements. It is also displayed by heterosexual couples holding hands and kissing in public, and in family photos in the workplace, implied by discussions about pregnancy, and anything public having to do with weddings and marriage, to name just a few.

These myths reflect a narrow view of lesbians and gay men and sexuality itself. They also serve to negate the day-to-day reality of lesbians' and gay men's lives, as partially discussed in the definitions section of this chapter. Counsellors who believe they can work comfortably with a lesbian or a gay man by limiting their understanding of lesbian and gay sexual identity to the arena of the bedroom run the risk of trying to "heterosexualize" the client. To judge, on the other hand, a lesbian or gay client's need to process sexual issues denies her or him the same heterosexual need, which is taken for granted as a more "acceptable" or "normal" enterprise.

The next myth, which is perhaps the most insulting, is that lesbians and gay men are child molesters. This myth serves to further isolate and degrade lesbians and gay men and is simply not true. "More than 85 per cent of all child molestation in schools involves heterosexual males and is directed at females" (Thayer, 1993). In fact, many lesbians have been the "vanguard of social change" (Rothblum, 1989), addressing issues of sexual abuse/sexual violence, helping establish rape crisis services and lobbying for changes at all levels of government and society to make the world a safer and more respectful place in which to live.

Another common belief is that there is something unnatural about lesbians and gay men, that somehow heterosexuality is the natural way to be, and that anything different is by definition unnatural. Many authors have disputed this assumption in a variety of ways. Lewis and Jordan (1989) cite literature that establishes homosexual behavior as part of the natural order within other species in the animal kingdom, and considered quite normal and acceptable in many other cultures, present and past. These authors also place friendships on the continuum of sexuality, pointing out that the many forms of caring and affection expressed within these relationships are entirely acceptable to our society. Since friendships can naturally lead to romantic relationships, this should, in turn, lead to the acceptability of homosexuality. Lewis and Jordan (1989) further report that studies examining lifestyles and functioning find that lesbians and gay men can be fully functioning, well-adjusted, healthy human beings. Other authors cite literature that asserts that lesbians are more self-confident than female heterosexuals, and that gay men are less defensive than male heterosexuals (Rothblum, 1989).

A belief that comes up particularly among religious people is that homosexuality, especially the inter-male sex act, is immoral. Biblical scholars addressing this issue have examined the original references and have repeatedly corrected this assertion, which has arisen from misconceptions and misrepresentations of ancient words and phrases (Lewis and Jordan, 1989; Bullough, 1979). They conclude that the genital act of homosexuality is not in and of itself immoral.

Another common misconception is that homosexuality is a psychological disorder; not until 1987 was it finally removed as a diagnostic category by the American Psychiatric Association. Unfortunately, this categorization has led to the belief that homosexuals are pathological, less happy than heterosexuals, less responsible, and less capable of mature and loving relationships (Rothblum, 1989). Historically this has meant that, when a lesbian or gay man sought treatment of any kind, the approach was to treat or eradicate the homosexuality and not the presenting problem (Israelstam, 1985).

Although, as stated earlier, we do know that many lesbians and gay men lead happy, fulfilling lives despite the heavy doses of homophobia levied each and every day, we won't know exactly how healthy (or unhealthy) lesbians and gay men really are until more research is conducted in this area. Homophobia has been cited as the reason why more research has not been done with this population and why gays are left out by most writers (Israelstam, 1985).

Myths/Misconceptions Regarding Lesbians

Some beliefs pertaining specifically to lesbians are ridiculous. For example: "Lesbians are not real women.... lesbians want to be men... lesbians hate children," etc. Lesbians are not perceived to be "real women," because they often do not perform traditional female roles. Because lesbians are sexual with other women, they are *ipso facto* considered to be "man-haters" and because some lesbians defy what is considered to be appropriate female behavior, they are believed to be men or at least wanting to be men.

Hughes et al. (1984) examine the whole range of myths as they pertain to lesbians, refuting them in both a factual and humorous way. They suggest there are four groups of myths in circulation: male/female roles, causes and explanations (of lesbianism), sex and sexual functioning, and myths within the women's movement. What stands out about all of these myths is that lesbians are depicted as "different" or "other" or "not women"; they also establish a belief that "unacceptable female behavior constitutes lesbian behavior" (p. 20) and that with these myths we are also being taught what constitutes *acceptable* female behavior.

Myths/Misconceptions Regarding Gay Men

Perhaps the most insulting and ridiculous belief about gay men is that they are "inferior" and emotionally weak men made so by domineering mothers who, if still alive, will always control their sons' lives. There are no data to support this belief, nor any data to suggest that any one kind of family situation results in the formation of gay male children (or lesbians for that matter).

Another equally disdainful myth is the belief that gay men are interested in, and intent on, having sex with every other man they encounter. Again, there is no research whatsoever to suggest that gay men, in general, are any more promiscuous than their heterosexual counterparts. This common belief has been suggested as one explanation for the high levels of discomfort so many heterosexual men feel around self-proclaimed gay males. This heterosexual male discomfort is worth considering because it surfaces a very interesting phenomenon. Heterosexual males have traditionally enjoyed the privilege of being able to pursue or discourage sexual interaction without much personal fear or discomfort, whereas women in our society have experienced much less freedom and comfort in this same pursuit; they have always had to live with the fear of continued aggressive male sexual advances, even when they have made their lack of interest very clear, and too often the result is sexual assault or even rape. A heterosexual male being pursued by a gay male, on the other hand, has much less privilege in this kind of interaction, and possibly for the first time experiences a lack of safety as it relates to his own sexual choices. The power balance is completely different and, although he may not experience the same vulnerability as a woman might, he suddenly experiences an interaction that is, perhaps for the first time in his life, more equal in terms of power and safety.

Another common belief is that "most gay men really want to be women." Some men do feel that they are "females trapped inside male bodies" and seek sex-change operations to correct their internal struggle. Such men are defined as transsexual, and have nothing to do with homosexuality. Many gay men rejoice in and celebrate the experience of their masculinity, and the masculinity of the other gay men they may find themselves attracted to. They have no desire to be women, and feel happy and comfortable relating to other men both genitally and emotionally in the context of their own "maleness." As mentioned earlier, only a small percentage of the gay male population may be readily identified by the stereotype of the "effeminate male." While some gay men have chosen to explore living alternative roles to those traditionally assigned to men in our society, it must be stressed that there is no limit to the ways in which gay men choose to live out their sexual identities.

Yet another common belief is that men choose to be gay: "If that's what he's chosen, it's okay for him, but I don't want him flaunting it around me!" While lesbians and gay men can and do choose to identify themselves as homosexual, individuals do not make the personal internal choice of who they are or are not sexually, emotionally, physically and psychically attracted to. Individuals can only decide what to do with the feelings they have discovered. For the gay male, then, sexual identity has nothing to do with choice, and everything to do with acceptance or denial of the identity one discovers. For those men who struggle to deny their same-sex attractions, counsellors should recognize that most often this is a direct result of homophobia. Who, after all, would choose to be something frowned upon (to say the least) by society? There is also a marked difference between the notion of choice between the lesbian and gay male: for lesbians, the concept and notion of choice to self-identify can be empowering. It can be a step toward gender equality in a patriarchal society that has always tried to impose definitions and positions on females. But for gay males, the concept of choosing to self-identify also involves giving up some of the gender-privilege they have enjoyed simply by being male in our society.

Another common but ridiculous belief is that, if only the gay male "met the right woman, he would be okay; namely, he would become heterosexual." The success or failure of any individual's sexual or relational history with a member or members of the opposite sex has nothing to do with one's sexual identity. Indeed, continued failure to develop sexual or emotional heterosexual intimacy can be attributed to the fact that such a male is desperately trying to live something that he is fundamentally incapable of, because it does not reflect his true self.

All of these myths point to similar themes running through the false beliefs associated with lesbians; namely, that such men are less than their heterosexual counterparts; that they are strange, inferior and different.

These myths are perpetuated by the fact that the media are always quick to identify the criminal, the psychopath or any other individual in any kind of negative media coverage as being "gay." The "heroes" of our world who also happen to be gay get little of the same kind of recognition regarding their gay self-identification.

ADDICTION ISSUES

Incidence/Prevalence

In most of the literature that looks at alcohol and drug problems among lesbians and gay men, a frequently cited statistic is a 30 per cent rate of alcoholism or a significant drinking problem among homosexuals: a rate three times that of the general population (Zigrang, 1980; Glaus, 1989; Schwartz, 1980; Lewis and Jordan, 1989; Israelstam and Lambert, 1986). Unfortunately, there is no consistency regarding the definition of alcoholism or even drinking problems in either this or the mainstream literature. In light of this, and given that the estimates for alcohol-dependent males in North America are five to seven per cent, and the estimates for nondependent alcohol abuse (problem drinking) are between 15 and 35 per cent (Skinner and Horn, 1984), it would be safer to assume that the extent of the alcohol problem in the lesbian and gay population is the same as in the general population. Also, heterosexist bias in research methods and fear of oppression keeps most "ordinary" lesbians and gay men hidden from researchers. Until more broadly based lesbian and gay male populations are studied, and until the criteria for alcoholism and alcohol problems are agreed upon and used consistently, we cannot truly argue that lesbians and gay men have significantly greater alcohol problems than the general population. It is important, however, to acknowledge the significance of whatever research has been done on the incidence/prevalence of alcohol problems in the lesbian/gay population; until recently, this particular population was largely ignored.

Factors contributing to alcohol and drug problems among lesbian and gay populations may differ from those of the general population. The reason most often cited for the high rate of alcoholism among lesbians and gay men is homophobia and the emotional difficulties that result from experiencing it (Zigrang, 1980; Schwartz, 1980; Lewis and Jordan, 1989). Thus, lesbians and gay men may use alcohol or other drugs as a way to cope with living in a world where hatred and oppression are daily occurrences. Others may drink or use drugs to block out this reality. This, in turn, may increase the possibility of suicide attempts among gays and lesbians, especially during adolescence (Tremblay, 1995).

The second most frequently cited factor contributing to alcohol and drug problems among the lesbian/gay population is the "gay bar scene," with suggestions that gay people spend most of their time in bars and have few alternatives for "out" socializing (Zigrang, 1980). However, other researchers such as Ziebold (1978) refute this assertion, reporting that gays do not spend any more time in bars than do single heterosexual Americans. This particular factor may only be relevant in urban communities where gay bars are able to operate. Lesbians and gay men who live in rural communities and don't have access to gay bars are probably underrepresented in these studies and are likely to present some different factors contributing to their drinking behavior. Another factor to consider may be that the lesbian or gay man is using alcohol or other drugs as a disinhibitor, to allow that person to act on his or her desires, and because of internalized homophobia, that person may be unable to do so without the chemical.

Current Treatment Climate

What treatment options exist for lesbians and gay men with an alcohol/drug problem? How are lesbians and gay men treated if and when they "come out" to their counsellors? Are the needs of lesbians and gay men being addressed in treatment agencies? These are but a few of the questions we now intend to address. The picture is rather bleak in many ways.

First of all, Israelstam (1986) acknowledges that research on lesbians and gay men and related interventions is only now being done and is rather sparse. At the same time, he points out that there is little to no work on this in Canada; most has taken place in the United States. There are indeed many reports that discuss needs of "special populations" (blacks, youth, women, the elderly), and yet rarely are lesbians and gay men mentioned (Israelstam, 1985; Westermeyer, 1990; Zigrang, 1980) — a glaring omission that speaks to the invisibility of this group. One could reasonably argue then that the needs of lesbians and gay men are not being effectively met. Israelstam (1985) noted that therapists, counsellors and researchers looking into the alcohol and drug problems of lesbians and gay men report that there has been both inappropriate treatment delivered and a lack of facilities to meet the needs of this group. Service providers largely ignore the needs of lesbians and gay men, with some clinicians seeing little if any relevance of a person's sexual orientation to their drinking (Zigrang, 1980). This attitude is probably an "over-correction" of the old belief that homosexuality itself needed to be cured. Schwartz (1980) recognizes that little has been done in the way of treatment for lesbians and gay men and that some professionals in treatment facilities are not facing their own homophobia, their own fears about being homosexual, or their own unresolved sexuality issues. In a more recent study conducted by the Addiction Research Foundation in Ontario, Israelstam (1986) found that staff at ARF who intervened in alcohol and drug problems felt that sexual orientation should be taken into account, but also recognized that the current climate does not encourage lesbians and gay men to come forward for treatment. Israelstam clearly considers identifying the special problems of this group an important aspect of intervention, along with reducing hostility and homophobia in society, taking into account the special problems of lesbians who are even more overlooked, educating the gay community about alcohol issues and the intervention community about gay issues, and forging links between the two communities.

What Is Being Done?

There has been some significant effort put forward by particular groups in an attempt to address the special needs of lesbians and gay men. It is beyond the scope of this chapter to cover all that has been done in both the United States and Canada. We will highlight four particular initiatives.

ALCOHOLICS ANONYMOUS

AA has been acknowledged as the first and by far largest organization to intervene in gay alcohol problems (Israelstam, 1985; Kus, 1987; Zehner and Lewis, 1984; Zigrang, 1980). Literature, special groups for lesbians and gay men, and workshops at annual AA conferences are examples of the types of efforts made by this group. However, it is also acknowledged that homophobia still exists within the brotherhood of AA, which poses a problem for lesbians and gay men seeking help for an alcohol problem.

THE NATIONAL ASSOCIATION OF LESBIAN AND GAY ALCOHOLISM PROFESSIONALS (NALGAP)

This group was formed in the United States to help alcoholism agencies and professionals better serve the needs of alcoholic lesbians and gay men. According to Schwartz (1980), the goals of NALGAP are to:

... encourage everyone in the alcoholism field to create a safe and supportive atmosphere for both gay staff members and gay clients and to ensure that every workshop, seminar, conference, newsletter and journal that deals with alcoholics and their families addresses the needs and problems special to gay alcoholics and their families (p. 11).

It would be most encouraging if all addiction agencies shared these goals. Perhaps many of the barriers to lesbians and gay men receiving appropriate treatment would then begin to be addressed.

The Donwood

A treatment service in Ontario is beginning to address the needs of lesbians within the framework of sensitizing its services to the needs of women. This is truly an encouraging effort.

In response to a Key Informant Survey on Issues and Priorities for Women's Health in Canada (Thomas, 1986), conducted by the Health Promotion Directorate of Health and Welfare Canada, the Donwood established a focus group on women with the purpose of recommending a program that would better meet the needs of women. Their recommendations included providing training and education for all staff regarding gay sexuality issues, resources in the community, and homophobia, as well as offering therapy groups for lesbians and their partners.

Training materials have been developed by the Women's Alcoholism Program of CASPAR — the Cambridge and Somerville Program of Alcoholism Rehabilitation (Finkelstein, Duncan, Derman and Smeltz, 1990) — to address the issue of lesbians with alcohol problems.

WHAT CAN AGENCIES AND COUNSELLORS DO?

An important question to consider is whether existing treatment programs can also serve the special needs of particular groups. Should separate facilities be established to address the needs of lesbians and gay men? Many authors suggest that, despite the homophobia among some treatment service providers, education and training can begin changing the services now offered (Schwartz, 1980; Zigrang, 1980).

Internal

Within organizations, it is important to educate staff to create a safe environment where lesbians and gay men can acknowledge the reality of their lives and be treated respectfully. This will begin to make existing services more available and accessible (Westermeyer, 1990) to this often neglected "special population."

Homophobia on the part of the counsellor will have to be addressed. What Glaus (1989) so aptly expressed in reference to working with lesbians can be applied to working with gay men as well:

> It is unfortunate but true that persons reared in this culture cannot escape the inculcation of at least some homophobia attitudes and beliefs and the therapist is no exception. A readiness to deal with the client's lesbianism requires that the therapist surface and deal with her own homophobia (p. 141).

This homophobia acts as a barrier to lesbians and gay men receiving appropriate treatment (Finkelstein et al., 1990).

Homophobia is also evident in agencies where lesbian and gay staff members are not "out" in their own work setting. The fear that they will be avoided by homophobic colleagues, and by clients who are not lesbian or gay, contributes to their reluctance to "come out" (Rothblum, 1989). Clearly an environment where it is safe for counsellors to "come out" would make for a safer environment for lesbian and gay clients. Zigrang (1980) and Israelstam (1986) indicate that many lesbians and gay men do not reveal their sexual orientation in treatment. This leads to silencing and hiding parts of oneself, which inhibits and interferes with recovery, while disclosure may result in rejection, isolation, derision and humiliation.

Israelstam (1985) offers the Gay Client's Bill of Rights (Department of Public Health in San Francisco, 1983) when discussing working towards prejudice-free treatment and intervention. This bill of rights clearly establishes the responsibility of providers to offer services that promote the dignity and respect of lesbians and gay men and the opportunity to request a counsellor who is either gay-identified or at least sensitive to and knowledgeable about gay lifestyles.

One way of exploring many of the long-held stereotypes about lesbians and gay men is by asking counsellors who aren't gay to answer these questions as though they themselves were in the minority (Schwartz, 1980): "Why are you heterosexual? Isn't it out of fear of rejection? We have read heterosexuals like you have histories of failures in gay relationships; isn't it possible that you are just going through a phase and that sooner or later you'll get over it and be gay like the rest of us? Why would anyone want to hire a heterosexual? Why do you feel like you have to tell everyone you are heterosexual? Can't you just keep quiet?"

These questions, along with additional training and education regarding lesbian and gay issues and ongoing supervision, will help counsellors meet the needs of this population. However, the bottom line still remains that "if the counsellor's morals, values, or belief system places him or her in conflict with those of the client, it will be extremely difficult if not impossible to intervene effectively in the addictive process" (Lewis and Jordan, 1989, p. 175).

Israelstam (1986) suggests that agencies dealing with alcohol problems need to decide if their programs benefit or are relevant to the lesbian and gay community. (The CASPAR training manual offers a tool for evaluating organizational attitudes and practices for homophobia [Finkelstein et al., 1990]). If not, then these agencies need to decide if this is the situation they want. Clearly, there is room for improvement on many fronts, including increasing workers' knowledge of gay issues and addressing homophobia as it affects the staff, their services and the agency.

External/Outreach

In order to begin providing effective and appropriate services to the lesbian and gay community, outreach is required and will serve several functions. First, becoming aware of the lesbian and gay organizations and services in your community will enable you to recommend ways in which clients can overcome their isolation and become a part of this network/community (Rothblum, 1989). Second, outreach opens your service to the lesbian/gay community by sending a message that you are making an effort to meet its needs. Third, it gives you an opportunity to become more familiar with and knowledgeable about gay/lesbian lifestyles, which is imperative to your work with this client group.

One final suggestion offered by Israelstam (1985) in the area of prevention involves alleviating homophobia among gays themselves, and in society at large. He proposes that any health professional who agrees that homophobia is dysfunctional should be involved in initiating "public health campaigns aimed at changing the social, psychological and ultimately the physical environment to a more honest and safe one as regards homosexual-homophobic issues" (p. 25).

TREATMENT ISSUES
PERTAINING TO LESBIANS AND GAY MEN

Clearly, some of the reasons lesbians and gay men have for excessive drinking or drug taking are different from those of the general population (Israelstam, 1986). In addition, certain factors need to be considered with this population.

Assessment

It is important to ensure that assessment instruments incorporate value-free questions. For instance, when conducting an assessment, instead of assuming (as most people do) that the client is heterosexual, ask questions that leave the door open to either possibility. For example, you can ask, "Do you have a current partner/significant relationship with a woman or man?" (Finkelstein et al., 1990). Even if the client is a lesbian or gay man and is not yet comfortable disclosing this to you, you have left the door open to discuss the issue later on.

The CASPAR training manual (Finkelstein et al., 1990) offers the following advice. If a client "comes out" to you, it is important not to reassure him or her that "That's not an issue for you" and/or "We are only dealing with your drinking/drug problem and not your sex life." These comments will only serve to silence the client, sending the message that you are really uncomfortable with this issue. Instead, a more appropriate response would be to ask how it feels for him or her and what fears or concerns he or she may have regarding "coming out" to you. It is also extremely important to treat this information respectfully — always allow the client to judge when and to whom he or she comes out.

Another phrase we have often encountered among counsellors is: "If you are comfortable with your sexuality and it's not a problem, then I don't/won't address it." No matter how "out" a person (client or otherwise) may be, there is no escaping the homophobia in our society. As such, experiencing "problems" that result from identifying as lesbian or gay is inevitable so long as we live in a homophobic/heterosexist world. A recent publication, *Invisible Lives: The Truth about Millions of Women-Loving Women,* by Martha Barron Barrett (1990), looks at what it is like to be a lesbian in today's world. Based on her interviews with "invisible lesbians," she came to understand that "even the benign attitude (in our society) of 'live and let live' is in fact discriminatory. That toleration, even acceptance, is a far cry from genuine empathy..." (p. 17). Her understanding came from gaining a deeper level of understanding of lesbian life based on hearing the stories of the women she interviewed.

If your client has decided to acknowledge the reality of his or her life and is "out" to you, it is important to determine where he or she is in the coming out process. Is he or she "out" at work, school, with parents, friends? If he or she has a partner/lover, how "out" is that person? A great deal of stress in relationships can come from one person being severely closeted and the other being very "out." It is very difficult to maintain this balance because the more closeted person may fear being discovered by being associated with his or her partner.

The client may also be uncertain about his or her sexual orientation. In this case, it is important for the counsellor to remain as neutral as possible (Finkelstein et al., 1990), supporting the client by providing information on community services that could help the client better understand her or his sexual feelings.

Someone who is just beginning to question his or her sexual orientation may be in more distress than a person who has already come to identify himself or herself as gay/lesbian. People may use alcohol or other drugs to deal with their confusion or to stop the process of "coming out," if they are terrified of what being gay will mean in this world.

It is not uncommon for a person who is beginning to address an alcohol/drug problem to start feeling the conflicts and homophobia that were once masked by alcohol/drugs (Finkelstein et al., 1990). These feelings may correspond with a "desire" not to be lesbian or gay in order to escape having to deal with issues that arise from being a member of a despised and degraded group. Helping clients by trying to cure or dissuade them from their sexual orientation is unhelpful and unethical (Finkelstein et al., 1990). Becoming familiar with the resources in your community for lesbians and gay men and linking your client with these resources is helpful.

When acknowledging the existence and role of a partner or extended family (friends and/or members of the lesbian/gay community), it is important to ensure they are acknowledged and treated as would a heterosexual client's partner/spouse and family members, and that they are educated about alcoholism and chemical dependency (Glaus, 1989).

Treatment Considerations

When individuals have been rejected by their family or friends because of their sexual orientation, the focus needs to be on finding alternative support systems. In addition, discussing the advantages and disadvantages of "coming out" to friends, family, employers, etc., needs to be considered (Zigrang, 1980).

Making a referral to self-help groups such as Alcoholics Anonymous or Narcotics Anonymous can pose particular problems for the lesbian or gay man. Schwartz (1980) suggests that the total honesty required as part of the AA program may present a conflict because lesbians and gay men may be forced either to be open and therefore possibly face ostracism, or to hide behind a "false heterosexual front," which can create a great deal of stress. Fear of encountering homophobia — and the presence of so many men — may lead some gays and lesbians to resist attending AA meetings. Glaus (1989) recommends that the counsellor be aware of alternatives, such as gay-positive AA groups or lesbian/lesbian-positive Women for Sobriety Groups.

Individuals who come from a highly religious background that emphasizes that homosexuality is immoral and unnatural have to deal with particular issues (Zigrang, 1980). One solution might be to acquaint the client with various lesbian/gay-positive church-related groups, such as DIGNITY, the Roman Catholic organization of lesbians and gays; AFFIRM, the Anglican organization of lesbians and gays, etc.; or the Metropolitan Community Church, a lesbian/gay-positive church with communities in many cities in Canada and the United States. Yet such a referral assumes that the solutions to the client's religious or spiritual issues lie in some form of organized religion, which isn't always the case. Fortunately, there are also a number of good references dealing with the spiritual dilemmas of lesbians and gay men from various perspectives. It would be a good idea to acquaint yourself with the resource list of books and publications dealing with spiritual issues at the end of this chapter.

The CASPAR training manual proposes a treatment strategy for lesbians (which can be applied to gay men as well). It takes a positive view toward lesbians and lesbianism, which in turn can prove to be greatly beneficial to the well-being of your clients:

> The most helpful treatment strategy will be founded on the perspective that sees a lesbian as a whole person, and her lifestyle as one which fits within the definition of a healthy and viable option. The main goal of treatment in this perspective is to help a woman live to her fullest potential, and have healthy and affirming relationships with the people in her life (Finkelstein et al., 1990, p. 473).

Lesbians and Addiction Issues

Lesbians who have an alcohol or drug problem experience a triple oppression (Lewis and Jordan, 1989; Glaus, 1989; Swallow, 1983): that of being an alcoholic/drug addict, a woman and a lesbian. Very little has been written regarding lesbians and addictions as lesbians continue to remain a fairly invisible group (Barrett, 1990; Israelstam, 1986), and addiction workers tend to be unaware of any differences that may exist when it comes to the treatment needs of lesbians versus gay men (Israelstam, 1985).

According to Lewis and Jordan (1989), and their review of the literature regarding the needs of lesbians who have an addiction problem, several factors need to be considered. Recognizing society's expectations for appropriate female behavior, these authors forewarn counsellors to be aware of the possible prejudice against women who display independent and autonomous ideas and behaviors. The temptation may be to counsel the client to become less assertive, and to behave in a manner that is more in line with the roles expected for women.

Anthony (1985) has also reported that the most common presenting problem of lesbians seeking counselling is difficulty with a lover relationship; some of these difficulties stem from a lack of social and personal support systems available to lesbians, who often remain closeted to varying degrees because of societal oppression. A clear understanding of this oppression, as discussed earlier, is needed to work effectively with lesbians.

According to Glaus (1989), who refers to the literature on women and addictions, women are more likely than men to be depressed and have low self-esteem; this factor needs to be addressed with lesbians. The counsellor also needs to acknowledge that, for lesbians who are severely closeted and isolated from the lesbian community and are therefore missing out on positive role models, these negative affective states may be more pronounced.

One final factor to consider, which is addressed by Loulan (1984), is sexual functioning. Many of the women in her study experienced significant difficulties in their sex lives, especially in early sobriety, with a general trend for sexual satisfaction to improve over the course of recovery. Included in her book, *Lesbian Sex* (Loulan, 1984), is a chapter on Sex and Sobriety, which contains helpful procedures a woman can follow to regain full and satisfying sexual experiences.

Keep in mind when working with lesbians that "emotional bonding, social and friendship networks, and a lifestyle with a strongly woman-identified emphasis is also part of a lesbian's existence" (Finkelstein et al., 1990, p. 468). And, that "the strength of a lesbian relationship is often cited to be the level of intimacy, uniqueness, and equality that can be achieved by two women" (Rothblum, 1989, p. 8).

Gay Men and Addiction Issues

Gay men who have an alcohol or drug problem also deal with a number of oppressions: that of being an alcoholic or drug addict, and a gay male, and of being considered inferior in a male-dominated society that tolerates little or no diversity in terms of the roles assigned males and females. This adds another complication absent from the lesbian experience. Many gay men who have tried to assume traditional societal male roles have paid the price of repressing many "sensitive feelings," and may lack the ability to process and self-reflect and thus have great difficulty dealing with internal feelings and emotions — traits more acceptable to traditional feminine social roles. As a result, it might take the gay male considerably longer to come to terms with his inner feelings and emotions. Indeed, it is common knowledge that far more women than men take advantage of the various levels of psychiatric services. This is not to suggest that women have more problems than men, but rather that women generally have a better understanding of themselves, and are more willing to engage in the process of personal growth and self-reflection. A gay male who has attempted to identify with the traditional male model has yet to learn this.

As with lesbians, there are also possible prejudices against gay men that counsellors must watch out for. An important starting point is for the counsellor to take a courageous personal inventory of his or her own areas of homophobia and homo-hatred. This self-awareness will enable the counsellor to guard against trying to direct the gay male to assume roles and traits according to the former's personal definition and/or level of comfort of what might be considered appropriate or acceptable. For example, the heterosexual male counsellor may have difficulty relating to the gay male who is comfortable exhibiting many qualities traditionally defined as "feminine," or have trouble accepting the self-definition of a gay male who exhibits extremely masculine and virile qualities.

As with lesbians, counsellors must have a clear understanding of the emotional and psychological burden of being a gay male in a homophobic world. They must be conscious of the fact that heterosexual men have — and take for granted — many "free choices" that are not available to the gay male because of consequences of oppression, lost job security, family relationships and other factors discussed earlier. In short, a counsellor must understand the institutionalized and socialized discrimination that compromises the freedom of the gay male client. In his book *Growing Up Gay in a Dysfunctional Family* (1991), Rik Isensee discusses those elements of institutionalized homophobia that limit freedom of choice, and thus may prevent the gay male from successfully completing some levels of healthy emotional and psycho-sexual development.

It is extremely important that the therapeutic community at large begin to understand that many of the emotional issues brought to them by the gay male are a direct result of the ramifications of oppression in a homophobic culture and society, and not a result of any particular individual's inability to cope with various issues. Otherwise, there is the danger of "blaming the victim" for experiencing the results of such oppression.

CONCLUSION

This chapter has attempted to introduce the counsellor to many of the issues pertaining to this group by close examination of commonly held attitudes, beliefs and assumptions that go very deep inside all of us. It is imperative that the counsellor engage in such a process of self-examination and be honest about his or her own attitudes, misconceptions about and prejudices towards lesbians and gays. It is by far the better option for a counsellor to recognize his or her own limitations of prejudice or discomfort and responsibly choose not to engage in a therapeutic relationship with a lesbian or gay male than to pretend that these issues simply do not exist or affect treatment protocol: they do. And they will manifest themselves in countless ways that the client will pick up and interpret as disapproval, judgment, etc.

For the counsellor who is genuinely interested in pursuing a better understanding of the issues involved, it is not only acceptable but also helpful to ask your clients about their own experience; to invite your clients to help you better understand them. This will assure clients that you care, and are genuinely interested in understanding and validating their personal experiences as influenced by their lesbian or gay sexual orientation. You need not be an "expert" in this area: the most important thing you can offer is a genuine caring and acceptance of your clients just as they are — including (not in spite of) their homosexuality. Take what you know about treatment protocol for any individual and contextualize these with the issues raised in this chapter, and you will be moving in the right direction.

REFERENCES

Addiction Research Foundation. (1986). Internal Document No. 75. Toronto: Author.

Anthony, B. (1985). Lesbian client — lesbian therapist: Opportunities and challenges in working together. In *A Guide to Psychotherapy with Gay and Lesbian Clients,* ed. Gonslorek, J. New York: Harrington Press.

Barrett, M.B. (1990). *Invisible Lives: The Truth about Millions of Women-Loving Women.* New York: Harper and Row Publishers.

Bullough, V.L. (1979). *Homosexuality: A History.* Scarborough, ON: The New American Library of Canada Ltd.

Clunis, D.M., and Green, G.D. (1988). *Lesbian Couples.* Seattle, WA: Seal Press.

Department of Public Health, City and County of San Francisco. (1985). *Gay Bill of Rights.* San Francisco: Division of Alcohol Programs, Alcoholism Evaluation and Treatment Centre.

The Donwood Institute. (1989). *The Focus Group on Women's Issues: The Emerging Self.* Toronto: Author.

Finkelstein, N., Duncan, S.A., Derman, L., and Smeltz, J. (1990). *Getting Sober, Getting Well: A Treatment Guide for Caregivers Who Work with Women.* Cambridge, MA: Women's Alcoholism Program of CASPAR, Inc..

Glaus, K.O. (1989). Alcoholism, chemical dependency and the lesbian client. In *Loving Boldly: Issues Facing Lesbians,* eds. Rothblum, E.D., and Cole, E. New York: Harrington Park Press.

Health and Welfare Canada and the Addiction Research Foundation. (1991). *Youth and Drugs: An Education Package for Professionals, Workbook, Unit 1, Adolescent Development.* Toronto: Authors.

Hughes, N., Johnson, Y., and Perreault, Y. (1984). *Stepping Out of Line: Workbook on Lesbianism and Feminism.* Vancouver: Press Gay Publishers.

Isensee, R. (1991). *Growing Up Gay in a Dysfunctional Family.* New York: Prentice Hall Press.

Israelstam, S. (1985). Alcohol and drug problems of gay males and lesbians: Therapy, counselling and prevention issues. Internal Document No. 48. Toronto: Addiction Research Foundation.

Israelstam, S. (1986). Knowledge and opinion of alcohol workers at the Addiction Research Foundation of Ontario regarding issues affecting gay males and lesbians. Internal document No. 75. Toronto: Addiction Research Foundation.

Israelstam, S., and Lambert, S. (1986). Homosexuality and alcohol: Observations and research after the psychoanalytic era. *The International Journal of Addictions* 21 (4/5): 509–537.

Kent, D. (ed.) (1990). *The Kinsey Institute New Report on Sex*. New York: St. Martin's Press, 1990.

Kinsey, A.C., Pomeroy, W.B., and Martin, C. (1948). *Sexual Behavior in the Human Male*. Philadelphia: W.B. Saunders.

Kinsey, A.C., Pomeroy, W.B., and Martin, C. (1953). *Sexual Behavior in the Human Female*. Philadelphia: W.B. Saunders.

Kirk, M., and Madsen, H. (1989). *After the Ball: How America Will Conquer Its Fear and Hatred of Gays in the 1990s*. New York: Doubleday.

Kus, R.J. (1987). *Alcoholics Anonymous and Gay American Men,* Chapter 5: Special Problems. Binghamton, NY: Haworth Press Inc.

Lewis, G.R., and Jordan, S.M. (1989). Treatment of the gay and lesbian alcoholic. In *Alcoholism and Substance Abuse in Special Populations,* eds. Lawson, G.W., and Lawson, A.W. Maryland: Aspen Publishers, Inc.

Loulan, J. (1984). *Lesbian Sex*. San Francisco: Spinsters/Aunt Lute Book Company.

Loulan, J. (1987). *Lesbian Passion: Loving Ourselves and Each Other*. San Francisco: Spinsters/ Aunt Lute Book Company.

National Association of Lesbian and Gay Alcoholism Professionals. P.O. Box 376, Oakland, NJ 07436. Phone (201) 666-0600.

Pearlman, S.F. (1989). Distancing and connectedness: Impact on couple formation in lesbian relationships. In *Loving Boldly: Issues Facing Lesbians,* eds. Rothblum, E.D., and Cole, E. New York: Harrington Park Press.

Pearlman, S.F. (1990). Quoted in *The Truth about Millions of Women-Loving Women: Invisible Lives,* by Barron Barrett, M. New York: Harper and Row.

Reinsch, J., and Beasley, R. (1991). *The Kinsey Institute New Report on Sex*. New York: St. Martin's Press.

Rothblum, E.D. (1989). Introduction: Lesbianism as a model of a positive lifestyle for women. In *Loving Boldly: Issues Facing Lesbians,* eds. Rothblum, E.D., and Cole, E. New York: Harrington Park Press.

Rothblum, E.D., and Cole, E. (eds.) (1989). *Loving Boldly: Issues Facing Lesbians*. New York: Harrington Park Press.

Schwartz, L.R. (1980). *Alcoholism among Lesbians and Gay Men: A Critical Problem in Critical Proportions*. Phoenix, AZ: Do It Now Foundation, Box 5115.

Skinner, H., and Horn, J. L. (1984). *Alcohol Dependence Scale (ADS) User's Guide*. Toronto: Addiction Research Foundation.

Swallow, J. (ed.) (1983). *Out from Under: Sober Dykes and Friends*. San Francisco: Spinsters Inc.

Thayer, P.A. (1993). Attitude quiz: Empirical data and relevant facts associated with homosexuality. In *Sexual Orientation: A Resource Guide for Teachers of Health Education in Secondary Schools*. Toronto: Toronto Board of Education.

Thomas, E. (1986). *Issues and Priorities for Women's Health in Canada, 1984*. Ottawa: Health Promotion Directorate, Health and Welfare Canada.

Toronto Board of Education. (1993). *Sexual Orientation: A Resource Guide for Teachers of Health Education in Secondary Schools*. Toronto: Author.

Tremblay, P.J. (1995). The homosexuality factor in the youth suicide problem. Paper presented at the Sixth Annual Conference of the Canadian Association for Suicide Prevention. Banff, Alberta, Oct. 11–14, 1995.

Westermeyer, J. (1990). Treatment for psychoactive substance use in special populations: Issues in strategic planning. *Advances in Alcohol and Substance Abuse* 8 (3/4).

Zehner, M.A., and Lewis, J. (1984). Homosexuality and alcoholism: Social and developmental perspectives. In *Homosexuality and Social Work*. Binghamton, NY: Haworth Press Inc., 1984.

Ziebold, T.O. (1978). *Alcoholism and the Gay Community*. A publication of Blade Communications Inc. Washington, DC: Whitman-Walker Clinic.

Zigrang, T.A. (1980). Who should be doing what about the gay alcoholic? Paper presented at the National Alcoholism Forum, National Council on Alcoholism Inc. Seattle, Washington, May 4, 1980.

RESOURCES

There are hundreds of lesbian/gay publications, organizations, bookstores and groups across Canada and the United States. To find them, try the telephone book under "Lesbian," "Gay" or "Women." Most larger communities also have lesbian/gay-sponsored information telephone services, usually listed under "Lesbian and/or Gay Information." Your local women's bookstore may also have information on local groups and activities.

SUGGESTED READINGS

Many of the books listed in the references section of this chapter might interest to you. Here are some additional readings, and/or ones we believe will be especially helpful.

Becker, C.S. (1988). *Unbroken Ties: Lesbian Ex-Lovers*. Boston: Alpon Publications Inc.
    This book covers the gamut when it comes to lesbian break-up. It explores what it feels like to go through separation and how to cope with the loss.

Clunis, D.M., and Green, G.D. (1988). *Lesbian Couples*. Seattle: Seal Press.

> A guide for lesbians dealing with the pleasures and challenges of being a couple. Written by two experienced lesbian therapists, who pay attention to issues of race, class, age, physical ability, and the problems when one or both partners are recovering from substance and/or sexual abuse.

Finkelstein, N., Duncan, S.A., Derman, L., and Smeltz, J. (1990). *Getting Sober, Getting Well: A Treatment Guide for Caregivers Who Work with Women*. Cambridge, MA: Women's Alcoholism Program of CASPAR, Inc.

> An excellent hands-on treatment guide for caregivers who work with alcohol- and drug-abusing women. For price, or to order, write: The Women's Alcoholism Program of CASPAR, Inc., 6 Camelia Ave., Cambridge MA 02139, or phone (617) 661-1316.

Isensee, R. (1991). *Growing Up Gay in a Dysfunctional Family: A Guide for Gay Men Reclaiming Their Lives*. New York: Prentice Hall.

> This books describes the chaotic and traumatic family histories of millions of gay men, and provides an excellent guide for healing and recovery from the effects of growing up in a homophobic world. It is written sensitively in the spirit of a 12-step recovery program, and can provide useful information for any gay male struggling with his sexual identity, and/or counsellor working with such a client.

Loulan, J. (1984). *Lesbian Sex*. San Francisco: Spinsters Inc.

> Written by a lesbian counsellor who has pioneered work in the area of female child sexual abuse, this book includes a chapter on sex and sobriety.

Money, J. (1988). *Gay, Straight, and In-Between: The Sexology of Erotic Orientation*. New York: Oxford University Press.

> In this book, John Money explores the continuum of human sexuality dealing with such topics as the evolution of the term "homosexuality," and the issue of gender identity and bisexuality. He explores the diverse historical, cultural and psychological influences that affect sexual orientation.

Sang, B., Warshow, J., and Smith, A.J. (eds.) (1991). *Lesbians and Midlife*. San Francisco: Spinsters Inc.

> This is an anthology by and about lesbians from 40 to 60, with personal stories, poems and insights, covering such diverse topics as sex after menopause, changing body image, re-emerging creativity, being single at mid-life, retirement and more.

Schneider, M.S. (1988). *Often Invisible: Counselling Gay and Lesbian Youth*. Toronto: Central Toronto Youth Services, 27 Carlton Street, 3rd Floor, Toronto, ON M5B 1L2. (Copies may be ordered directly from their address as listed)

> This textbook is written for counsellors dealing with lesbian/gay youth.

Toronto Board of Education. (1993). *Sexual Orientation: Homosexuality, Lesbian and Homophobia, A Resource Guide for Teachers of Health Education in Secondary Schools*. Toronto: Author.

> In this ground-breaking manual for teachers, a specific program of education and sensitization is set up for the understanding of lesbian and gay sexual orientation, and challenges homophobia and intolerance. It also contains a chapter with a complete list of the lesbian/gay resources in the Greater Toronto Area. An excellent resource guide for any counsellor or agency.

SPIRITUAL ISSUES

Boyd, M. (1984). *Gay Priest*. New York: St. Martin's Press.
>   Malcolm Boyd, an Anglican priest, explores his own journey of coming to terms with his sexual identity and commitment to Christian ministry, and offers sound advice for lesbian or gay Christians in understanding their spiritual commitment.

Edwards, G. R. (1984). *Gay/Lesbian Liberation: A Biblical Perspective*. New York: Pilgrim Press.
>   Written in the context of Roman Catholic liberation theology, this books explores lesbian and gay spirituality from the biblical perspective. A good rebuttal to the fundamentalist abuse of scripture to condemn homosexuality.

Guindon, A. (1986). Gay fecundity or liberating sexuality. Chapter 7 in *The Sexual Creators: An Ethical Proposal for Concerned Christians*. New York: University Press of America.
>   Rev. André Guindon, a Roman Catholic priest and theologian from Ottawa, Ontario, explores the validity of lesbian and gay sexuality as well as the contribution lesbians and gay men can make to the understanding and meaning of human sexuality in the Christian context.

Fortunato, J.E. (1983). *Embracing the Exile: Healing Journeys of Gay Christians*. New York: Seabury Press.
>   John Fortunato, a gay psychotherapist, explores the faith dimensions of lesbian and gay Christians seeking hope and encouragement as they struggle to make sense of their spirituality in the context of their sexual orientation.

MacNeil, J.J. (1985). *The Church and the Homosexual*. New York: Next Year Publications.
>   This is a key Christian theological treatise on homosexuality written in the Jesuit tradition of Roman Catholic theology. Rev. John J. MacNeil is co-founder of the New York chapter of DIGNITY, the Roman Catholic organization for lesbians and gay men.

Chapter 17

Assessment and Outpatient Counselling for Adolescents and Young Adults

DARRYL N. UPFOLD

INTRODUCTION

This chapter focuses on assessment, treatment planning and outpatient counselling for substance-abusing young people from a cognitive-behavioral approach. This approach is compatible with the "stages of change" model (Prochaska, DiClemente and Norcross 1992), which is used as the framework for outpatient counselling described in this chapter. The assessment, treatment planning and counselling strategies described apply to middle and late adolescence, and young adulthood (approximately ages 16 to 24). A discussion of early adolescence would involve an extensive review of family assessment and family therapy methods, which exceeds the scope of this chapter.

PART 1 reviews the key concepts in assessment and treatment planning to "match" client needs to the appropriate treatment level on the "continuum of care." This includes methods to determine problem severity, and the importance of age, predisposing risk factors, personal strengths, client preferences, mental health and social stability in assessment and treatment planning. The use of self-monitoring instruments, brief screening instruments and comprehensive assessment instruments is discussed. Guidelines to assist in "matching" the client to the appropriate level of treatment are suggested. The issue of abstinence and non-abstinence goals is also discussed.

PART 2 covers a model of outpatient counselling, based on the stages of change and cognitive-behavioral techniques, with an emphasis on how this model is used to develop counselling strategies in individualized treatment plans.

It is important to note that counsellors working with young people must have a thorough knowledge of the physical, emotional and cognitive changes that occur, and the psychological challenges that must be resolved, during this developmental period (e.g., see Sprinthall and Collins [1995], *Adolescent Psychology: A Developmental View)*. The characteristics of each stage of development have a significant impact on the assessment protocol, treatment plan and treatment strategies that would be appropriate for a client. This includes the level of abstraction that can be used in counselling (e.g., cognitive interventions might be more appropriate for young adults than for middle-stage adolescents); the assessment instruments used; and the recommended counselling modalities (e.g., family therapy may be more appropriate for middle adolescents; individual or group counselling may be more appropriate for older adolescents and young adults). Assessment protocols, treatment strategies and treatment goals must be relevant to the client's age and stage of development.

PART 1
ASSESSMENT AND TREATMENT PLANNING ("MATCHING")

The addictions field and its most widely available treatments were developed without a research basis (e.g., Pattison, Sobell and Sobell, 1977). Early concepts proposed that "alcoholism" was a homogeneous phenomenon with a biologic or genetic etiology and a progressive course, like a disease. Abstinence from alcohol was considered to be the only possible treatment goal, and one treatment method — self-help — was used to achieve and maintain abstinence. Little emphasis was put on assessing individual differences in alcohol problems, because it was assumed that problems were all the same. The nature of the problem and the appropriate treatment were implicitly understood as a function of the assumed homogeneity of "alcoholism."

Subsequent research, however, has suggested that alcohol (and other drug) problems are heterogeneous in nature, and have multiple causes and variable courses of development and outcome. Conclusions from this research have important implications in assessment and treatment planning:

- Alcohol and other drug problems can be conceptualized as existing on a continuum of problem severity from mild to serious rather than as a dichotomous problem ("alcoholism") that one "has" or "does not have."
- A non-abstinence treatment goal can be appropriate for some individuals.
- Many treatment options are possible, and matching the client to the appropriate treatment is a key variable in determining outcome.
- The client's characteristics (e.g., gender, coping styles) and problem (e.g., severity) should be considered in the selection of the appropriate level of treatment.

Alcohol and other drug problems need to be carefully assessed on an individual basis to help determine the most appropriate type of treatment and treatment goal.

ASSESSMENT OF ALCOHOL AND DRUG USE

Assessment is a process of systematically collecting information regarding the characteristics of the client and of the client's use of substances. This information is used to make treatment planning decisions about treatment goals and the course of treatment that are likely to be effective. The initial assessment information is gathered in one or more interviews with the client and, if appropriate, with family members. For example, it may be important to include family members with an adolescent, but not with a young adult who is living independently.

Brief or comprehensive assessment instruments are also commonly used to collect and analyse information. The amount and type of information collected and the use of assessment instruments will vary based on each client's circumstances and needs.

The first treatment planning decision is to determine the most appropriate level of treatment for the client on the "continuum of care" — ranging from less intrusive interventions such as outpatient counselling to more intensive, structured day treatment, residential treatment and detoxification programs. This is referred to as "matching." Information collected in assessment interviews is also used to develop an individual treatment plan and specific treatment strategies after the client has been referred to the appropriate treatment resource. (This is discussed in Part 2.)

In selecting the appropriate level of treatment, counsellors should consider the following seven factors: (1) problem severity; (2) age; (3) predisposing risk factors; (4) personal strengths, support systems and preferred change strategies; (5) the role of client preference; (6) mental health; and (7) social stability.

PROBLEM SEVERITY

Problem severity is determined by two variables: the quantity and frequency of consumption of alcohol and other drugs; and the extent of negative psychosocial consequences that result from the consumption (e.g., school/work, family and social relationships, physical and mental health, legal status, leisure/recreation activities).

Measuring Quantity and Frequency of Consumption

The quantity and frequency of consumption can be measured by self-monitoring or by using a structured instrument such as the Timeline Followback (Sobell and Sobell, 1992).

SELF-MONITORING

Self-monitoring, which is used in most programs of behavior change, usually continues throughout the assessment and counselling process. The objective of self-monitoring is to generate an accurate picture of the quantity and frequency of substance use on a daily basis over a given time period. This can be done for current use if the client is continuing to use, as well as retrospectively for a given period of time.

Self-monitoring has several purposes. It is used to gather consumption data to determine problem severity, make treatment planning decisions based on identified patterns of consumption, monitor progress in reducing consumption, and increase motivation by raising the client's awareness of his or her consumption levels. Most young clients look at their use over a relatively short timeframe (such as a weekend or during a school break), and even excessive use can be rationalized if it is interpreted as an isolated incident. Clients are often surprised to see the consumption levels and patterns of use that are revealed during a longer period of self-monitoring.

The counsellor can work with the client to develop a method of self-monitoring that is appropriate to the client's level of cognitive development, personal circumstances and preferences. This can range anywhere from keeping a detailed journal to jotting down figures on a wallet-sized card. It is important for accuracy that the client record the amounts used as soon as possible after the episode.

In terms of its utility in determining problem severity, data gathered during the self-monitoring period can be used to place the client's use on the following continuum of problem severity that is often used to describe adolescent and young adult substance use.

Stage	Pattern	Negative Consequences
Experimental	• Used once or twice	• None
Recreational	• Use is infrequent, restricted to recreational activities and special occasions	• None or minor • Can result in intoxication • Not preoccupied with getting and using
Regular	• Predictable pattern to use • Not restricted to recreational activities and special occasions • Use during week	• Preoccupied with getting and using • Negative consequences present • Intoxication/hangovers frequent
Dependent	• Daily/near daily use	• Clear negative consequences • Continues to use even when aware of the problem • Physical addiction/withdrawal symptoms

(Source: modified from Tupker [ed.], 1991)

TIMELINE FOLLOWBACK (TLFB)

The TLFB is an excellent instrument to measure the consumption of alcohol or other drugs. Like self-monitoring, it can be used to assess problem severity, develop a treatment plan and increase motivation. It is a structured instrument that helps a client retrospectively construct a detailed picture of his or her consumption over a past period of time. It is available in both paper-and-pencil and computer formats. Research on the TLFB indicates that most clients are able to provide an accurate picture of their past consumption for periods up to one year. The TLFB yields a description of the pattern of the client's consumption as well as information on a number of other variables related to consumption (e.g., the approximate amount of money spent on and number of calories consumed from alcohol during a given time period can be calculated automatically with the computer version). The pattern of consumption, including the average number of drinks per day, week or month can be calculated. The results of the TLFB, presented in graph form, provide visual, objective feedback that can increase the client's awareness of his or her substance use and increase his or her motivation to change. The TLFB was developed initially to measure alcohol consumption. The TLFB manual also includes instructions on how to use the TLFB with other drugs, including tobacco. The TLFB is designed specifically to increase the accuracy of recalling consumption retrospectively. If a picture of past use is the goal, the TLFB is recommended.

Issues in Measuring Consumption

There are several issues to keep in mind when measuring and assessing problem severity based on adolescents' consumption of alcohol and other drugs. First, adolescents' patterns of consumption often vary considerably over time. A changing pattern of use might be related to variables over which the adolescent may not have much control, such as availability of money or the substance itself, the opportunity to use, and the day-to-day influence of peers. It is important to determine if a low frequency of use is due to situational factors or a deliberate decision to reduce substance use.

A second issue in using consumption level as a factor in assessing problem severity is that most adolescents who present for treatment use more than one substance, usually alcohol and cannabis. Multiple drug use presents some difficulty in assessing problem severity. For example, how does the moderate use of two substances compare in problem severity to the excessive use of one?

Wilkinson and Lebreton (1986) developed the following criteria to rate multiple drug problem severity.

Low
Alcohol — no more than 20 drinks per week and no associated problems
Cannabis — no more than four joints per week, no more than two joints in any one day, no associated problems
Other drugs — no more than one use per month

Intermediate

Alcohol — no more than 10 drinks per day and no more than 42 drinks per week
Cannabis — no more than 10 joints per week
Other drugs — more than one use per month but less than one use per week

High

Alcohol — more than 10 drinks per day and more than 42 drinks per week
Cannabis — 10 joints per week or more
Other drugs — one use per week or more.

Some counsellors may find the "low" threshold to be too high, and other factors, such as age, need to be considered when using any set of consumption criteria to determine problem severity. This framework is presented to sensitize the counsellor to the complexity of assessing multiple drug use. However, there is no standard approach to quantifying multiple drug use.

In terms of planning treatment based on problem severity, serious problems often require increased structure and intensity of treatment. For example, clients who have a "regular" pattern of use may need a day/evening treatment program. Clients who are "dependent" may need the level of structure provided by a detoxification and/or residential program. However, in addition to consumption level, the consequences of consumption — which will vary from client to client — need to be considered in recommending the appropriate level of treatment.

Measuring Negative Psychosocial Consequences of Consumption

In the assessment interview, the counsellor should carefully review how each psychosocial life area (e.g., school/work, family and social relationships, physical and mental health, legal status, leisure/recreation activities) may have been affected by substance use. In addition, the counsellor should explore for other high-risk behaviors, such as drinking and driving, engaging in unprotected or unplanned sex, and behaving aggressively while using alcohol or other drugs.

Conventional treatment planning practice suggests that the least intrusive intervention (i.e., a schedule of outpatient counselling) is typically recommended unless the client is clearly at serious risk of harm. If a client has many compromised life areas and there are serious consequences of substance use, such as depression, risk of suicide, and continually engaging in high-risk behaviors while intoxicated, residential treatment is usually recommended.

The Use of Assessment Instruments to
Measure Negative Psychosocial Consequences

Assessment instruments are used to supplement information that is collected by the counsellor in the interview. The advantage of standardized assessment instruments is that they provide an objective evaluation of the variable(s) they were designed to measure. A review of screening and assessment instruments for addiction and other psychosocial areas is provided in the *Directory of Client Outcome Measures for Addictions Treatment Programs,* published by the Addiction Research Foundation. The reader is also referred to George and Skinner (1991) for a thorough review of addiction assessment instruments for adolescents.

The counsellor needs to know what and how much substances, and psychosocial information is required in order to be able to select the most appropriate instrument for treatment planning. Information needs will vary from case to case, depending on the client's ability to self-report, the availability of other collateral sources of information, the complexity of the case, and so on. The counsellor also needs to determine if the circumstances are appropriate to administer a questionnaire. For example, a client should not be asked to complete a questionnaire if he or she is intoxicated, in crisis or hostile to the assessment process.

THE PERSONAL EXPERIENCE INVENTORY (PEI)

The PEI (Winters and Henly, 1989) is a comprehensive, self-report addictions assessment instrument that can be used to measure a variety of negative consequences and other psychosocial variables associated with adolescent substance use. It has been tested for validity and reliability, and is widely regarded by counsellors and behavioral scientists as an excellent instrument for use with adolescents aged 12 to 18.

The PEI has two sections:
1. Chemical Involvement Problem Severity (the term "chemical" is commonly used in the United States); and
2. the Psychosocial Section.

The first part features 13 scales that measure various aspects of the severity of the substance use problem, including degree of psychological involvement with the drug, effects of use, and personal consequences of use. The second part features 14 scales that measure various aspects of psychosocial functioning like self-image, psychological disturbance, deviant behavior, and peer involvement with alcohol and other drugs. Scales in each part are designed to detect "faking bad," "faking good," and inattentive responding. The PEI must be scored by computer, and therefore purchase of the PEI software is required.

Each PEI scale has a computer-generated narrative report. The client's responses on each scale are also presented as T-scores, which are compared to two groups: a sample of adolescents in treatment for substance use; and a high school sample. Using the T-scores, which are presented as bar graphs, the client can compare his or her score on each scale to both samples. This information can have a powerful influence on the client's awareness and acceptance that there is a problem and, consequently, on motivation to change.

BRIEF SCREENING QUESTIONNAIRES FOR YOUNG ADULTS

A number of brief questionnaires that yield objective but less comprehensive information on problem severity can be used with young adults, but not adolescents. The Michigan Alcoholism Screening Test (MAST), the Short Alcohol Dependence Data (SADD), and the Drug Abuse Screening Test (DAST) are commonly used questionnaires. They can be completed in five to 10 minutes and can be scored manually and interpreted quickly by the counsellor. Guidelines are provided for each questionnaire to interpret the client's score in terms of problem severity. The appropriateness of using these and other instruments with young adults is reviewed in the *Directory of Client Outcome Measures for Addictions Treatment Programs.*

AGE

Developmental theorists hypothesize that substance use during adolescence may impede psychosocial maturation and the successful resolution of the psychological challenges of adolescence. Some research suggests that a later onset of regular use of tobacco, alcohol and cannabis is predictive of less involvement with those substances (Jessor, 1982). This research suggests that the younger user may be at greater risk of developing a serious problem than an older adolescent, even if each has a similar level of consumption. This has implications for the modality, intensity and length of treatment that is appropriate, as well as for the treatment goal. For example, a treatment plan for a 14-year-old recreational user might emphasize a goal of abstinence and recommend intensive family therapy until the goal is achieved. A treatment plan for an 18-year-old recreational user might recommend a less intensive program of individual counselling with a goal of preventing increased use while continuing to assess the appropriateness of a non-abstinence goal.

PREDISPOSING RISK FACTORS

Researchers have identified numerous hereditary, environmental and developmental factors that may increase an adolescent's vulnerability to alcohol and other drug problems (e.g., Hawkins, Lishner, Catalano and Howard, 1986). Perhaps the most commonly cited predisposing factor is a family history of substance abuse. Statistically, adolescents who have a parent with a substance use problem may be at greater risk of developing a similar problem (Goodwin, 1981).

There is no clear agreement among researchers regarding the predisposing factors that contribute most to an adolescent's vulnerability. The following factors are reported in *Youth and Drugs* (Tupker, 1991) as "primary risk factors":

- developmental lags
- learning difficulties and disabilities
- deficiencies in interpersonal and social competencies
- a history of behavioral difficulties
- family circumstance, including substance abuse.

Forney, Forney and Ripley (1989) also note that having peers who use alcohol or other drugs is a "predictive factor" for the initiation of substance use among adolescents.

Counsellors should screen for the presence of predisposing factors in assessment. It may be advisable to have ongoing but not necessarily frequent contact over a longer period of time for adolescents with several predisposing factors, even if the young clients are not currently using alcohol or other drugs at high levels.

PERSONAL STRENGTHS, SUPPORT SYSTEMS AND PREFERRED CHANGE STRATEGIES

The assessment and treatment planning process involves exploring the client's strengths and support systems as well as the problem. A discussion of the problem alone is not likely to result in any behavior change. The client's strengths and the nature of his or her support system will determine the specific change strategies that are most likely to work for that individual.

The importance of acknowledging and using client strengths can be illustrated by referring to commonly used weight-loss strategies. Adults who engage in a program of weight loss can choose from several strategies that are designed to reduce caloric intake. One person might choose to continue to eat the same number of meals each day but reduce the quantity of food they consume at each meal; another might choose to eliminate one meal a day; and a third might choose to substitute high-fat foods with low-fat foods. After selecting a strategy, one person might enlist the support of a spouse or friend; another might proceed independently without seeking support from others. All strategies can work, but not all are likely to work for each person, because the strengths and coping skills required for each strategy are different. The first individual must be able to resist further eating once a certain portion has been consumed. The second must be able to tolerate the feeling of being hungry if he or she is to skip a meal. The third person must deal with the psychological loss of eliminating favorite foods. One person might find a friend's reminder of his or her goal to be energizing and motivating, another might find it to be intrusive and not motivating.

The success of the change process in counselling depends to a large extent on identifying and using the strengths, preferred change strategies and support systems that the client either brings to counselling or develops over the course of treatment.

Adolescents are often unaware of how they typically go about solving problems and may need help to identify both their strengths and the people who comprise their support system. Counsellors can use several techniques to help young clients identify their strengths and coping skills. Counsellors can review previous problem situations at home, at school or with friends to identify and make explicit what the adolescent has done in the past to deal with problems. A second technique is to ask the client: "What could you have done to have a better ending?" to a particular situation. Clients will analyse the situation from their own unique perspective, which creates the opportunity to frame the discussion in terms of the strengths and strategies that could lead to a better ending. A third technique is to analyse a situation in which the client did not consume alcohol or other drugs. The client may have used his or her strengths and strategies without being aware of it. The counsellor should catalogue the identified strengths and strategies to use in individual treatment planning.

Families often have a strong "problem orientation" in relation to an adolescent's substance use. Counsellors will have to identify this and shift the family perspective to developing family-based strategies that are not based solely on prescriptive expectations (usually in relation to curfews, friends, etc.) and punishment for violating expectations.

ROLE OF CLIENT PREFERENCE

As the literature on adult assessment indicates, the client's preference for the level of treatment and the treatment goal should be considered (e.g., Miller and Hestor, 1986). Client preference, however, can sometimes conflict with the treatment decisions that are suggested by assessment data. For example, assessment data might suggest that a goal of abstinence and residential treatment is indicated, but the client might prefer a goal of reduced use and outpatient counselling.

A direct challenge of the client's treatment preferences often results in the client becoming more firmly entrenched in his or her views and less interested in negotiating a treatment plan and goals. One alternative is to accept the client's preferences and design a treatment plan to work toward that goal. This approach highlights the necessity for continuously reassessing the initial assessment findings and evaluating progress and outcome. Accurate, objective feedback regarding problems with progress may lead to the client's re-appraisal of treatment decisions that were based on his or her preference rather than clinical experience. Objective results from self-monitoring and assessment instruments are usually more persuasive than counsellor observations alone.

The client's age is a factor in determining the appropriateness of this approach. With younger adolescents, it may be more appropriate to work with the family to develop family-based strategies that are designed to prevent *any* use of substances, even though the adolescent may prefer to keep using.

MENTAL HEALTH

Recent epidemiological studies (e.g., Boyle and Offord, 1991) have indicated that many adolescents with substance use problems also have co-existing psychiatric disorders such as mood disorders (depression, anxiety), bipolar disorders or conduct disorders. Counsellors should be familiar with the description and symptoms of these disorders. A period of abstinence from substance use is usually required in order to conduct an accurate evaluation of a psychiatric disorder. If a psychiatric disorder is suspected and the client is unable to achieve a period of abstinence on an outpatient basis, a residential program might provide the best opportunity for a complete evaluation.

SOCIAL STABILITY

Social stability involves factors such as accommodation status (Does the client have a stable, supportive, appropriate living situation?); work or school status (Does the client work or attend school?); and social support system (Does the client have a supportive family and a peer network that will support the change process? Is the client engaged in community activities such as sports, clubs or a church?). Clients with sufficient social stability and structure may be good candidates for a less intrusive level of treatment — even if their substance abuse problem is serious. On the other hand, clients with low social stability may require a more structured level of treatment — even if their substance abuse problem is *less* serious.

SETTING TREATMENT GOALS

The issue of abstinence and non-abstinence treatment goals has been hotly debated by researchers and counsellors. Recent reviews of the research literature (e.g., Miller, 1983; Marlatt, 1983; and Peele, 1992) have suggested that, in some cases non-abstinence (also referred to as reduced use, moderate use or controlled use) can be an appropriate goal for *some* individuals. It should be noted that this research was conducted with adult clients, and the findings may not apply to adolescents.

However, other research with adolescents (e.g., Wilkinson and Martin, 1991) indicates that reduced use is a common outcome of treatment. In summary, there appears to be sufficient research and evidence from clinical practice to suggest that some young clients can achieve non-abstinence goals. As discussed, the age of the client is a significant variable to consider in setting treatment goals.

Research and clinical practice suggest that the following variables should be considered in determining the appropriateness of a non-abstinence treatment goal.
• Problem severity: less severe problems of shorter duration
• Dependence history: no evidence of physiological dependence, characterized by tolerance and withdrawal symptoms
• Family history: no evidence of severe dependencies in biological parents or grandparents
• Mental health: no evidence of a major psychiatric disorder; no symptoms of psychological disturbance emerge while using (e.g., mood changes)
• Physical health: no health contraindications (e.g., liver functioning)
• Substance use history: some prior evidence of consumption without intoxication
• Effect of substance use on behavior: no evidence of risk-taking or aggressive behavior while using alcohol or other drugs
• Client preference: the client has a strong preference for a non-abstinence goal.

Young clients are frequently unwilling to initially accept a goal of abstinence, even when assessment data indicate that abstinence is appropriate. It is also common for young clients to frequently shift goals — from reduced use to abstinence and back to reduced use. An adult generally has a longer drug-taking history, so there is usually persuasive evidence to promote setting a long-term abstinence goal. But with young clients, there is usually only a short history of problem behavior to review in deciding on the most appropriate treatment goal. As a result of this relative inexperience with their problem, some young clients are uncertain about the necessity of abstinence. Counsellors may get greater commitment to a treatment goal if they set short-term goals (e.g., week-to-week goals) for their young clients, regardless of whether the goal is abstinence or non-abstinence. It is important to continuously monitor progress and to use outcomes to confirm or revise goals and strategies.

There is a legal issue involved in goal setting, because many adolescent clients are under the legal drinking age. In addition, adolescents may prefer a goal of non-abstinence for other drugs (usually cannabis) that are illicit. From a legal perspective, the use of all illicit substances needs to be discouraged. However, the reality seems to be that young clients usually do not endorse a goal of abstinence just because there is a legal reason to do so.

A compromise that is often acceptable to young clients who will not endorse a goal of abstinence is to negotiate a goal of "reduced use working towards abstinence." This approach serves two key functions: it encourages young clients who do not want to abstain to engage in a counselling process that is acceptable to them at that point in time; and it addresses the legal dilemma by including abstinence as a (longer-term) treatment goal.

Some adolescents are unwilling to initially accept abstinence goals because they have beliefs that inhibit the change process. Adolescents often believe that if they stop using, they will not be accepted by their friends, and they will not be able to tolerate any loss of pleasure that is derived from substance use in social settings. These beliefs may discourage young clients from engaging in the change process if abstinence is required in counselling. The young person who engages in counselling to reduce use will learn new behavioral skills and experience new reinforcement contingencies (i.e., there will likely be some intrinsic or external reward for reducing substance use) that promote change. As the client becomes skilled in and confident with new coping skills, he or she may become more open to discussing additional goal setting. Positive experiences that occur during occasions of no use or little use can be used to confront the client's beliefs concerning anticipated losses. Usually the reality is that young people will still have friends, and can still enjoy social activities without excessive substance use.

In summary, it seems more productive to help clients achieve goals that they themselves identify and are willing to work toward than to insist that they work toward goals that are imposed by others. Clients are not likely to seriously work toward goals that they do not support. On the other hand, even minimal reduction in drug use can create confidence and therapeutic momentum, which can be used to work toward more significant behavior change. The reader is reminded that this approach may not be advisable for younger adolescent clients for whom family-based prevention strategies may be necessary.

The initial assessment and treatment planning process results in a recommendation for the appropriate level of treatment on the continuum of care. Initial treatment goals may be identified during treatment planning and referral. For example, if a referral to a residential program is made, abstinence is usually the goal. A referral for outpatient counselling is often made without a goal being specified; goals often emerge gradually during the course of outpatient counselling.

PART 2
OUTPATIENT COUNSELLING

This section covers the following: the importance of structure; maintaining a focus on treatment goals; case management; an outpatient counselling model based on stages of change research (Prochaska and DiClemente, 1992); and cognitive-behavioral techniques.

STRUCTURE

Some adolescents and young adults have little structure in their day-to-day lives. For example, they may not attend school or work, have limited contact with family members and family rituals, and have little community involvement (such as sports or church).

A certain level of structure for adolescent clients is a requisite component of an effective outpatient treatment plan. Without sufficient structure, young clients often have difficulty implementing counselling strategies in a social environment that may not support the treatment goal.

Day-to-day structure can be increased by using some easy-to-implement strategies, including:
• scheduling homework or job hunting at the same time every day
• having regular meals
• setting times to get up in the morning and go to bed at night
• exercising regularly
• planning leisure/recreational activities for free time.

Counsellors can also increase structure by making several appointments at a time, calling to remind the client of the appointments, not easily accepting cancellations, and assigning behavioral "homework" between appointments. The client may initially resist attempts at increasing structure, and may present his or her own compromise in response to the counsellor's suggestions. If sufficient structure cannot be established to support effective outpatient counselling, a residential treatment program might be considered.

MAINTAINING A FOCUS ON TREATMENT GOALS

The counsellor must maintain a focus on the treatment goals. Teenagers often experience events that they perceive as "crises," but it is difficult to maintain a focus on treatment goals when counselling deals with parental conflict one week, with boyfriend or girlfriend problems the next, and with a school problem the following week.

Although crises may occasionally emerge, during each session the counsellor must maintain a focus on reviewing and confirming treatment goals, progress toward goals, barriers to achieving those goals, and preferred strategies to initiate and maintain changes. This focus brings structure, predictability, commitment and positive expectation to counselling.

CASE MANAGEMENT

Structure and focus on treatment goals can be more easily maintained through effective case management and the use of community resources.

Young clients frequently have other psychosocial problems in addition to substance abuse — particularly family, leisure, school or employment problems. Treatment for the substance use problem will be more effective if a comprehensive treatment plan that addresses all of the client's needs is developed and co-ordinated among all the service providers. Each service provider needs to have a clear idea of what is expected of the client and what is expected of the service provider. Although it can be time-consuming to co-ordinate, it is effective to have all service providers meet occasionally with the client to review treatment goals, progress towards achieving them, any barriers that the client has experienced, and what could be done to overcome the barriers. In this way, the client will receive positive reinforcement from the service providers and, at the same time, avoid or solve problems by having regular access to key helpers. As a result of such co-ordination, the client will likely view the counselling relationship as helpful and supportive, and he or she will be more likely to experience successes.

AN OUTPATIENT COUNSELLING MODEL: THE STAGES OF CHANGE

The outpatient counselling approach described in this chapter uses the stages of change (Prochaska, DiClemente and Norcross 1992) as the basic framework and integrates techniques from cognitive-behavioral intervention. This approach is used to develop an individualized treatment plan and counselling strategies that take into consideration the unique characteristics of the client and the problem. The assessment issues that were presented in Part 1 are re-introduced in the appropriate stage of the model.

The stages of change model has had significant impact on the treatment of addictive behaviors. Five stages of change were identified in research on "self-changers," from the time at which individuals were giving no thought to changing (the "precontemplation" stage) to the point when they had successfully changed ("maintenance"). Because progress through the stages correlates to the client's increasing level of motivation to change, this model is often referred to as a "readiness to change model" or a "motivational model." The stages of change model provides the counsellor with an alternative to immediately "confronting denial" for clients who are not yet prepared to change.

The researchers also identified various strategies that self-changers used in each stage. This research has several major implications for the treatment of addictive behavior.

Stage of Change at the Time of Counselling

Clients can be in any stage when they first attend for assessment or counselling, so it cannot be assumed that a client is ready to change his or her substance use. It is essential to recognize the stage of change that the client is in, and to apply the stage-appropriate strategies that are most likely to promote progress to the next stage. For example, the first step a counsellor might take with a new client is to conduct an assessment. However, it might be inappropriate to conduct an assessment with a client who is in the precontemplation stage. This model suggests that it is not the counsellor's responsibility to "make the client change" if the client is not yet prepared to do so.

Setting Goals

It is appropriate to set behavioral goals to reduce or abstain from alcohol or other drugs for clients in the preparation or action stage. But in precontemplation and contemplation, cognitive goals to increase awareness of the dimensions of the problem behavior are appropriate.

Client Progress through the Stages of Change

Although the stages of change model is presented here as a linear model, which clients move through from one stage to the next, in reality it is common for clients to sometimes regress to an earlier stage during counselling. For example, clients who have initiated change in the action stage sometimes begin to rethink (contemplate) whether they really do have a problem, sometimes because they have underestimated the effort required to sustain the changes they are making.

The stages are described here as if they are well defined and discrete, but they are more continuous than categorical. A client can be, for example, partially contemplative and partially preparing to change.

Relapse

In the original research, most of the individuals who were eventually successful had several relapses as they attempted to change. From this finding it was concluded that relapse can be expected in many cases, even cases that might ultimately succeed with long-term abstinence. The possibility of relapsing should be discussed rather than ignored, and strategies to deal with it developed. Relapse should be considered as an opportunity for the client to learn about relapse factors and to improve strategies to prevent further relapse.

Using this model as a framework for counselling involves identifying the client's stage of change and using the strategies that are appropriate for that stage.

PRECONTEMPLATION

The precontemplation stage is characterized by people's lack of awareness of the extent of their substance use and the consequences of their substance use for themselves and others — they do not think that they have a problem. Others may believe an individual has a substance use problem, but the individual expresses no concern and no interest in changing. The individual in precontemplation is likely still using alcohol or other drugs.

Young clients frequently focus on the positive aspects of substance use (e.g., enhancing pleasurable emotions, relieving boredom, gaining status with friends, etc.) and often do not consider the negative aspects. They may acknowledge that they are using, but they aren't concerned about it. They often report that they "don't use any more than anyone else," usually in reference to their peer group.

Many young clients enter counselling in the precontemplation stage because someone — often parents, school counsellors or the legal system — is concerned about their substance use and has insisted that they see a counsellor. Often the referring person expects that some change will occur — usually through some form of direct confrontation — even when a young person is not interested in changing. Counsellors must apply the appropriate counselling strategies with precontemplative clients — strategies designed to increase awareness rather than decrease substance use — even when there is external pressure to have a client's substance use immediately changed.

The objective of counselling precontemplative clients is to increase their awareness of the extent of their substance use and its consequences. In the process, counselling should prompt clients to think about whether aspects of their substance use are problematic. Cognitive change (increased awareness and understanding) — and not behavior change with respect to reduced use or abstinence — is targeted in precontemplation.

Examples of counselling techniques to increase awareness and promote progress toward the contemplation stage include the following:

Acknowledge and support the client's feelings.
A precontemplative client is likely to feel angry or frustrated about "having to be in counselling." The counsellor's efforts to legitimize the client's feelings and offer support enhance the therapeutic relationship (Miller and Rollnick, 1991), which can lead to open discussion of the client's substance use.

Acknowledge the positive reinforcement associated with substance use.

Some counsellors tend to avoid acknowledging that there is some form of positive reinforcement derived from the client's substance use. However, focusing only on the negative aspects of alcohol or other drugs is likely to increase the client's resistance. The counsellor should elicit the client's perception about the specific positive aspects of substance use (e.g., "I become more outgoing"; "I feel more like I belong"). This encourages discussion about the role of alcohol or other drugs in the client's life, and it usually leads to an exploration of the negative consequences and an opportunity for the client to become more aware of these consequences.

Explore the client's self-concept.

Value clarification techniques can be used to increase awareness and concern when there may not be significant negative consequences to motivate the client. Exploring the client's self-concept can create a discrepancy between how the client wants others to perceive him or her, and how he or she might actually be perceived by others as a result of substance use. The counsellor can help clients explore the following: personal qualities they value in themselves and in others, and how these qualities are affected by substance use; if they want substance use to be a part of their identity; and if they want others to see them as "a user." If a discrepancy is created between the ideal self-concept and the actual self-concept, the counsellor can encourage the client to develop his or her ideal self by considering changes.

Reinforce the client's internal locus of control.

Because they are not convinced of the necessity of making changes, precontemplative clients will be very sensitive and resistant to any directives from the counsellor. Therefore, the position needs to be taken that the counsellor will not make decisions for the client; it is assumed that the client is capable of taking responsibility for his or her own decisions.

To promote an internal locus of control, the counsellor can make statements such as: "It's your opinion I'm interested in," "It's up to you to decide what's best for you," and "You're the one who is responsible for your life, not me." This approach decreases resistance and increases clients' sense of personal responsibility to manage their lives effectively. This is always a principle of effective helping relationships, but it is particularly important to be clear about this with precontemplative and contemplative adolescent clients, who may be quite sensitive to what they perceive to be adult attempts to "control." Clients who are more motivated to make changes are usually more receptive to counsellor observations.

Include self-monitoring.

Precontemplative clients can often be persuaded to self-monitor if it is clear that there is no requirement to change their substance use.

Example: "Perhaps you're right — maybe you don't have a problem. I don't know enough about your situation to help you make any decisions about that right now. Maybe what you could do is keep track of your use for a couple of weeks, then we could take a look at it. That could help both of us find out a bit more about your situation."

The motivational value of self-monitoring is that it makes patterns of behavior more explicit, often increasing awareness of frequency and quantity of use. Anyone who has ever "counted calories" as part of a weight-loss program will likely confirm that they became more aware of their food intake if they kept a record. The counsellor must maintain a nonjudgmental position with self-monitoring, or the client will self-monitor defensively, looking for opportunities to minimize.

Provide objective feedback.

Miller and Rollnick (1991) have demonstrated the effectiveness of objective feedback, particularly from standardized questionnaires, as a technique to increase client awareness. Some precontemplative clients may be willing to complete questionnaires, while others may not. (The use of objective feedback also helps clients in the contemplation stage commit to change.) Most brief screening instruments have been designed for adults (e.g., MAST, DAST, SADD), but can be used with young adults. Part 1 of the PEI can be used for this purpose with adolescent clients (ages 12–18).

Try the Inventory of Drug-Taking Situations.

The primary utility of the Inventory of Drug-Taking Situations (IDTS) (Annis and Graham, 1991) is in developing an individual treatment plan in the preparation and action stages by highlighting high-risk situations that require intervention. It can also be effective in raising awareness of the frequency with which the client has used alcohol or other drugs in various situations. It is introduced to the client as a measure of situational use rather than a test of problem severity, although there is some correlation between high frequencies on the IDTS and problem severity. The IDTS is a 50-item questionnaire that measures the frequency of substance use in eight situations: unpleasant emotions, physical discomfort, pleasant emotions, testing personal control, urges to use, conflict with others, social pressure, and enhancing pleasant times. It is available on computer or as a paper-and-pencil test that can be manually scored. Most precontemplative clients are willing to complete the IDTS, possibly because it is not introduced as a test to determine if the client has a "problem."

The above-noted techniques are intended to increase awareness about some aspect of the young client's substance use, perhaps regarding consumption levels that are higher than he or she initially believed, or the negative consequences that he or she previously ignored. An emerging concern creates ambivalence in the client's mind about substance use. At this point, the client begins to "contemplate" whether there may be a problem.

Some Cautions in Working with Clients in the Precontemplation Stage

Counsellors must ensure that in their efforts to be supportive of feelings and to acknowledge the positive reinforcement associated with substance use, that counselling sessions are not simply used by the client as an opportunity to recount episodes of substance use without taking responsibility for them. In addition, counselling sessions should not be used by the client solely to elicit sympathy from the counsellor for his or her circumstances, or to reduce guilt associated with substance use without considering ways to change it. The counsellor must be mindful that the objective is to increase awareness of the level of consumption, the role of substance use in the client's life and the consequences of that use. In the process, counselling is meant to create ambivalence in the client's mind about continuing to use alcohol or other drugs. If progress toward this objective is not made (e.g., within four sessions over four to six weeks) the counsellor might consider terminating counselling. There is a distinction between a nonjudgmental relationship and a relationship that allows the behavior to continue without consequence.

Some clients may initially appear to be in the precontemplation stage because they do not want to make any changes to their substance use, thus suggesting that they lack awareness of the extent and consequences of their substance use. However, there is a difference between individuals who are truly unaware of the consequences of their substance use, and other individuals who are *very* aware of their substance use and its consequences but who have made an informed decision to continue to use — despite negative consequences. The latter type of person often attends counselling to alleviate pressure from people in positions of authority. They are not likely to increase their motivation to change through a counselling process that is designed to increase an awareness that they already have. Counsellors and program managers should consider what is a reasonable response for these individuals.

Other individuals who continue to use alcohol or other drugs despite serious negative consequences that are clearly evident may have a psychiatric disorder, which should be evaluated.

CONTEMPLATION

Increased awareness of substance use creates ambivalence between what the client perceives to be the *benefits* of reducing substance use or abstaining and the client's *concerns or fears* about reducing or abstaining (while the fears inhibit change, the client's new ambivalence promotes change). The objective of counselling in this stage is to reduce the fears about changing and to emphasize the benefits of changing, which will move the client toward making definite plans to change.

Decisional Balance

This is the key concept in working with clients in the contemplation stage. The decisional balance is a method to help the client identify the specific benefits of reducing or abstaining, and the specific fears the client will need to deal with. The benefits and fears can be identified by completing a chart comprised of the pros and cons of changing substance use, and the pros and cons of *not* changing. As the fears of change are worked through and reduced or eliminated, the decisional balance is "tipped" in the direction of acknowledging the benefits of changing, which moves the client closer to a decision to reduce or abstain. (See Chapter 2 of this book for more information about completing a "decisional matrix.")

With young clients, it is particularly important to deal with the issues that are identified as the "cons of changing." This is where the client will identify his or her fears of change that will inhibit the counselling process. As discussed in the section on setting treatment goals, these fears are usually related to the anticipated loss of acceptance from friends, and a perceived inability to get along without using alcohol or other drugs, particularly in social situations. These issues can be barriers to change if they are not thoroughly worked through and accepted by the client.

Assessment

A comprehensive assessment of the client's substance use, as described in Part 1, is appropriate in the contemplation stage for clients who may now want a more detailed picture of the role that substances play in their lives. Objective feedback of the assessment results, particularly from standardized questionnaires, can motivate the client to accept the necessity and benefits of change. The counsellor can introduce treatment planning decisions (matching) at this point or in the next stage, preparation. The counsellor needs to be sensitive to the client's reaction to the assessment process and the feedback of results.

If the client shows some resistance to the assessment process, it suggests that the client is not resolving the ambivalence in the direction of pursuing the benefits of change, but rather is focusing on the fears of change. The counselling process may be moving too quickly toward treatment planning and setting goals, which implies to the client that he or she will now have to stop using alcohol or other drugs. In this case, the client will need to continue to review the benefits and the fears that are identified in the decisional balance chart.

Self-Monitoring

Self-monitoring (which might have been introduced to the client in the precontemplative stage) can be used to highlight the benefits of not using if occasions of abstinence or reduced use have occurred. These occasions can also be used to explore the fears of changing (the "cons") — most of which are exaggerated in the client's mind until they are identified and re-evaluated.

In the contemplation stage, the work is often cognitive, with the counsellor looking for opportunities to work through fears, emphasize benefits and provide feedback. A client can stay in the contemplation stage for a considerable time as he or she re-evaluates substance use from a more aware and open perspective — as if the client is noticing some of the "negatives" of his or her substance use for the first time.

Clients move from contemplation into the preparation stage when they have worked through their fears of change, and are now focused on the benefits of making changes to their substance use. Clients in contemplation may still be using, and may not yet know what kind of treatment or treatment goal is best for them (although they probably have begun to explore these issues with their counsellors). Client statements such as "I'm not sure how my friends will handle it if I give up drugs" or "I don't know how I'll handle weekends without drinking" are indications that the client is resolving his or her fears of changing and is moving into the preparation stage.

PREPARATION

In the preparation stage, the client has made a decision to work toward a goal of reducing or abstaining. Appropriate tasks at this stage are assessment, treatment planning, and conducting a functional analysis to develop counselling interventions and strategies.

Assessment and Treatment Planning

Most clients will be receptive to completing an assessment in order to make treatment planning decisions (matching). Referrals can be successfully made in this stage if the identified treatment cannot be provided by the counsellor. Most clients will not follow through on referrals made before this stage.

Identify Client Strengths, Coping Skills and Support System

In this stage, the client's strengths, skills and support system are reviewed (strengths and skills may have been identified in an earlier stage). Also reviewed are skills that need to be developed and any barriers to the change process. This discussion is a prelude to developing interventions, and will increase the client's confidence to change.

Functional Analysis of Behavior

This is the core concept in developing an individualized treatment plan for outpatient counselling. Based on social learning theory (Bandura, 1977), functional analysis has been widely applied in behavior therapy. Functional analysis means that substance use serves a "function" for the individual — that there is a reason why the individual uses alcohol or other drugs in certain circumstances. Conducting a functional analysis leads to an understanding of the following:

(1) the "antecedents" that "trigger" an episode of substance use;

(2) the pattern of substance use that resulted in that situation; and

(3) the positive consequences of the substance use that maintains the use.

The changes that clients eventually make are predicated on an understanding of the antecedents and consequences of their substance use.

To conduct a functional analysis, the counsellor reviews the client's recent episodes of alcohol or drug use to identify the antecedents and consequences of each episode. It is often easiest to proceed by:

(1) exploring several recent incidents of substance use first;

(2) identifying the positive reinforcement that followed the use; and

(3) identifying the antecedent condition(s) that triggered each incident.

An individual treatment plan is developed based on the results of the functional analysis. The treatment plan can involve interventions for any of the three areas of the functional analysis:

(1) to avoid or neutralize antecedent conditions so they do not trigger an episode of substance use;

(2) to learn new responses (not involving substance use) to an antecedent (often referred to as "refusal training") if the antecedent is not avoided; and

(3) to acquire alternative positive reinforcement instead of substance use in response to an antecedent if the antecedent is not avoided.

1. Interventions for Antecedents

Most antecedents fall into one of three categories:

• thoughts (e.g., "I'll have more fun if I'm drinking")

• feelings (e.g., anger, anxiety, boredom)

• situations (e.g., being at a party where drug use is encouraged).

Interventions can be developed to modify thoughts, cope with feelings, or avoid situations that are antecedents to substance use, so that the antecedent is either eliminated or no longer triggers an episode of substance use (i.e., it is "neutralized").

Antecedent	Example of an Antecedent	Examples of Interventions
Thoughts	I'll have more fun if I'm drinking.	Cognitive modification: I'll have more fun at first, and then I'll probably get sick.
Feelings	Anger	Anger management Psychotherapy
	Boredom	Leisure skills Learning to tolerate low levels of stimulation
Situations	Drug use at party	Avoidant strategy Cognitive modification
	Conflict with parents	Problem-solving skills Family therapy

2. Interventions to Develop Alternative Responses to Antecedents

This refers to developing strategies to respond to antecedents — if the antecedent is not avoided — without using alcohol or other drugs.

REFUSAL SKILLS

Most clients will have to develop refusal skills for situations that the client chooses not to avoid, or that cannot easily be avoided. For example, a client may choose to attend a party (a situational antecedent) rather than avoid it, but will learn skills to abstain from alcohol. Clients need to develop refusal skills need so that they feel comfortable using them. Clients are more likely to use these skills if they have been rehearsed, for example, in role-play situations with counsellors.

PEER PRESSURE AND PEER SUPPORT

Most adolescents in treatment are reluctant to avoid their friends even if their friends are heavy substance users, at least until later in the change process. Specific attention needs to be paid to how the client is going to deal with substance-using peers. Peer "pressure" can be turned into peer "support" if the client communicates a genuine desire to their friends that they are trying to change their behavior, and that they are asking for their help. Peers can be asked to recognize and support occasions when the young client does not drink, rather than rewarding incidents of heavy use. This is an example of changing a "reinforcement contingency." The client is now rewarded (by peer support and recognition) for not using; this is in contrast to the previous reward of, for example, being applauded for excessive substance use. Even heavy users often recognize the healthy nature of reducing or eliminating substance use and frequently are supportive of friends who are attempting to do so. If that support is not forthcoming, the client often begins to recognize the necessity of developing an avoidant strategy, instead of a refusal strategy, for situations in which their friends are using alcohol or other drugs.

3. Interventions to Acquire Alternative Positive Reinforcement

There is usually some immediate positive consequence to the client's substance use that the client is seeking. There may be other activities that can provide the client with positive reinforcement that is similar to the reinforcement provided by alcohol or other drugs. If the young client can acquire similar positive reinforcement, the substance use can be framed as a choice rather than as the only option. For example:

Positive Consequence	Examples of Interventions
Increased sense of belonging when smoking cannabis with friends	Improve self-esteem Develop other group activities
Feels relaxed when drinking	Relaxation training
Becomes more outgoing	Social skills training

Using the IDTS in Functional Analysis

The IDTS was introduced in the discussion on precontemplation as an instrument to increase awareness of situational use. Its primary utility, however, is in developing an individual treatment plan. As an adjunct to functional analysis, the IDTS produces a profile of the frequency with which the client used alcohol or other drugs in each of eight situations (antecedents). Interventions can be developed for the situations that evoke the most frequent episodes of substance use.

Some interventions that can be recommended for clients are general, commonly used strategies, like anger management, relaxation therapy, and problem-solving skills. Others are designed specifically for the client's unique circumstances regarding his or her substance use goal (e.g., strategies to refuse peer pressure to use cannabis after school).

The shift into the action stage often happens during the functional analysis and development of the client's individual treatment plan. In some cases, the client continues to develop strategies for some situations while abstaining or reducing in others — in essence, being in both preparation and action at the same time.

ACTION

The action stage begins when the client actually begins to abstain or reduce his or her substance use by employing the interventions and strategies that were developed in the individual treatment plan in the preparation stage. In most cases, new strategies are developed as the effectiveness of each intervention is evaluated (i.e., Did the refusal strategy work, or is an avoidant strategy required?) and the treatment plan modified.

"Action" with many clients is a gradual process that begins with using techniques to gain control of their behavior. The action stage may include some occasions when the client successfully reduced or abstained, along with some incidents of substance use. Each occasion should be reviewed to learn what worked for the client, and what did not work. The following are cognitive-behavioral techniques that are effective in helping clients in the action stage improve their ability to change.

Verbal Rehearsal

A verbal rehearsal can improve the effectiveness of a strategy, particularly if it involves a cognitive technique to modify an antecedent (e.g., "I'll have fun for a while if I drink, and then I'll probably continue to the point of where I'll get sick and make a fool of myself") or a refusal strategy (e.g., "I'm not drinking tonight... I'm trying to go a week without drinking"). Rehearsing the strategy increases the likelihood that the client will use it when it is required.

Mental Imagery

The client is asked to develop a mental picture of the desired outcome of a particular high-risk occasion. Mental imagery can be described as a movie with the client controlling the story, making all the necessary changes so that the client achieves his or her goal. Envisioning the desired process and outcome increases commitment to the goal. The client will also be able to identify any aspects of the strategy that he or she does not feel comfortable with, indicating that the strategy needs to be modified before it is likely to be effective.

Written Reminders

The client's goals and strategies are written on a small pad of paper and given to the client to keep handy. Cues can be developed to indicate when it should be reviewed (e.g., once an hour in a high-risk situation). This technique can be helpful for many clients who are committed to their goal but who have a difficult time using their strategies in high-risk situations.

A variation of this technique is to help the client generate a list of reasons for abstaining or reducing his or her use. The client is then asked to review the list when in a high-risk situation, and to rank the reasons, from the ones that had the most impact on his or her commitment to the treatment goal to the reasons with the least impact. The most powerful reasons are kept and the others are eliminated. New reasons can be added to the list and evaluated as counselling progresses.

Practising Behavior Change

Some young clients will have little experience with planned, deliberate behavior change. These clients may struggle with using their strategies, even when they are appropriate to their strengths. It can help to practise change skills in ways that are less challenging than actually changing substance use. The client can identify a routine behavior and plan to change it in some way (e.g., a client could plan to take a different route to school or a counselling appointment, or change his or her normal routine after school). This will help the client understand that it is normal for behavior change to require some effort, because it does not happen by itself. Ideally, the client will realize that change may include some initial uneasiness, but that he or she was capable of change in one area and, therefore, can apply change strategies in other areas.

The action stage of change begins when the client has initiated reduction or abstinence from alcohol or other drugs After the client has achieved his or her goal for a period of time — often thought of as approximately six months — the client moves into the maintenance stage.

Brief Example of an Individual Treatment Plan

A functional analysis of a 19-year-old male client's substance use revealed several antecedents that often resulted in alcohol or cannabis use, as well as several specific positive consequences that promoted continued use.

Antecedents: peer pressure from two friends; being in two particular bars; boredom (especially on weekends); sports activities; thinking about drinking (especially in the afternoons).

Pattern of substance use: still using alcohol (15 drinks per evening) and cannabis (two joints per evening), both on a daily basis.

Positive consequences: enhanced pleasure in bars; sense of status, acceptance from friends and other acquaintances while drinking; becoming more outgoing, talkative, happy.

Substance use goal: abstinence from all substances.

Client preferences: client did not want to consider avoidant strategies to deal with most situational antecedents; wanted to learn how to continue with social activities without using alcohol or cannabis.

Interventions for antecedents: cognitive modification to change his thinking in the afternoon about the anticipated excitement of drinking, from "I always have a great time when I drink" to "I have a good time for the first one or two hours, and then my mood turns ugly and I usually offend someone I care about."

Interventions for response to antecedents: refusal training using verbal rehearsal, mental imagery, and written reminders of refusal strategies to be reviewed once an hour in high-risk situations; developed peer support from one friend who previously had expressed concern over the client's drinking; developed specific behavioral strategies to counter offers to drink in bars and other social situations (e.g., purchase a soft drink before anyone can buy him a drink; going to parties with his supportive friend).

Interventions to acquire positive consequences: registered for an instructional course to be a hockey referee, which gave him a sense of enjoyment and acceptance in a group that does not promote substance use; group therapy was suggested to help improve social skills to become more "outgoing and talkative" without using substances, but the client declined this recommendation.

Revisions to Treatment Plan

New interventions for antecedents: After several months, the client recognized that there were several high-risk situations (one bar where he was known as a "regular," and one friend who continued to pressure him to drink) in which he was not confident that he would be able to continue to effectively use his refusal skills. At this point, he began to consider avoidant strategies. The counsellor helped the client deal with the sense of loss he would feel in avoiding these situations.

New interventions in response to antecedents: Client expanded his peer support network by disclosing to several other friends and family members that he was attempting to abstain, and asked for their support.

Other Psychosocial Goals

Employment: During the maintenance stage, the client decided that a job change might be necessary to maintain abstinence.

Relationships: He decided that a relationship with a female who did not drink, or drank very little, would be necessary if he were to maintain his goal.

Leisure: He withdrew from a sports team that he associated with heavy alcohol use.

MAINTENANCE

In this stage, the client often identifies other changes that can be made that will help to prevent relapse. With young clients this often involves identifying certain situations (antecedents) that the client might have been initially reluctant to avoid (e.g., certain friends or certain bars) that he or she now recognizes constitute a high risk for relapse, and require an avoidant strategy.

Relapse Prevention

Research (e.g., Prochaska and DiClemente, 1992) clearly suggests that the process to achieve stability from a substance abuse problem often involves a relapse. Relapses should be anticipated and discussed, rather than ignored as if they are not going to occur. If a relapse occurs, it should be used as an opportunity to identify new strategies rather than labelled as a "failure." Taking the perspective that a relapse is an opportunity to learn new skills tends to increase the client's self-confidence that he or she will be able to prevent a relapse in the future.

Evaluating Progress in Action and Maintenance

There are several possibilities to explore if relapses occur frequently in the action or maintenance stage. The counsellor should reassess the stage of change to ensure that the client was in the preparation and action stage of change when behavior change goals were set and action toward them initiated. Consistent effort to reduce or abstain will occur only in the action (or maintenance) stage.

The strategies that were developed to initiate behavior change should be reviewed to ensure that they are consistent with the client's skills. Strategies cannot be successfully used if the client does not have the requisite skills. For example, a client with poor communication or assertiveness skills may have difficulty with refusal strategies. Assertiveness training would be required first, and in the meantime avoidant strategies might be more successful. The counsellor should also check to ensure that the client actually tried to implement the strategy when a relapse occurred, rather than "seeing how it goes." In this case, the reason for not using the strategy needs to be explored.

It is difficult to make definitive statements about what constitutes "success" and the optimum length of counselling with young clients. The potential impact of predisposing risk factors and the role of developmental factors on the client's long-term substance use are difficult to evaluate on an individual basis. George and Skinner (1991) concluded that most adolescent alcohol abusers will "mature" out of their excessive alcohol use without treatment. Other research has indicated that even clients who have achieved a goal of abstinence will frequently "lapse" in the future, and that reduced use seems to be a more common outcome of treatment than abstinence (Wilkinson and Martin, 1991).

ACKNOWLEDGMENT

The author would like to thank Coba Moolenburgh, MSW, CSW, Clinical Supervisor, St. Mary's Counselling Service, for her review of this chapter.

REFERENCES

Annis, H.M., and Graham, J.M. (1991). *Inventory of Drug-Taking Situations (IDTS): User's Guide (Draft)*. Toronto: Addiction Research Foundation.

Bandura, A. (1977). *Social Learning Theory*. Englewood Cliffs, NJ: Prentice Hall.

Boyle, M., and Offord, D. (1991). Psychiatric disorder and substance use in adolescence. *The Canadian Journal of Psychiatry* 36 (10): 699–705.

Forney, M.A., Forney, P.D., and Ripley, W.K. (1989). Predictor variables of adolescent drinking. *Advances in Alcohol and Substance Abuse* 8 (2): 97–113.

George, G.S., and Skinner, H.A. (1991). Assessment. In *Drug Use by Adolescents: Identification, Assessment and Intervention,* eds. Annis, H.M. and Davis, C.S. Toronto: Addiction Research Foundation.

Goodwin, D.W. (1981). Adoption studies of alcoholism. *Progress in Clinical and Biological Research* 69 (C): 71–76.

Graham, K., Price, B., Brett, P., Baker, A., Bois, C., Boyle, B., Chapman, L., Eliany, M., Gaskin, J., Martin, G., Sobell, L., and Thompson, J. (1993). *Directory of Client Outcome Measures for Addictions Treatment Programs*. Toronto: Addiction Research Foundation.

Hawkins, J.D., Lishner, D.M., Catalano, R.F., and Howard, M. (1986). Childhood predictors of adolescent substance abuse: Toward an empirically grounded theory. In *Childhood and Chemical Abuse: Prevention and Intervention,* eds. Griswold-Ezekoye, S., Kumpfer, K.L., and Bukoski, W.J. New York: Haworth Press.

Jessor, R. (1982). Critical issues in research on adolescent health promotion. In *Promoting Adolescent Health: A Dialogue on Research and Practice,* eds. Coates, T.J., Peterson, A.C., and Perry, C.L. New York: Academic Press.

Marlatt, A.G. (1983). The controlled drinking controversy. *American Psychologist* (October): 1097–1110.

Miller, W.R. (1983). Controlled drinking: A history and critical review. *Journal of Studies on Alcohol* 44 (1): 68–83.

Miller, W.R., and Hestor, R.K. (1986). Matching problem drinkers with optimal treatments. In *Treating Addictive Behaviors: Processes of Change,* eds. Miller, W.R., and Heather, N. New York: Plenum Press.

Miller, W.R., and Rollnick, S. (1991). *Motivational Interviewing: Preparing People to Change Their Addictive Behavior*. New York: The Guilford Press.

Pattison, E.M., Sobell, M.B., and Sobell, L.C. (1994). Emerging concepts of alcohol dependence. In *Options: Guidelines for Outpatient Treatment of Alcohol and Drug Problems*. Toronto: Addiction Research Foundation.

Peele, S. (1992). The diseased society. *The Journal* (October/November): 7–8.

Prochaska, J.O., and DiClemente, C. (1984). *The Transtheoretical Approach: Crossing the Traditional Boundaries of Therapy.* Homewood, IL: Dow Jones/Irwin.

Prochaska, J.O., DiClemente, C.C., and Norcross, J.C. (1992). In search of how people change. *American Psychologist* (September).

Sobell, L.C., and Sobell, M.B. (1992). Timeline Followback: A technique for assessing self-reported alcohol consumption. In *Measuring Alcohol Consumption: Psychosocial and Biological Methods,* eds. Litte, R.Z., and Allen, J. New Jersey: Humana Press.

Sobell, L.C., Toneatto, T., and Sobell, M.B. (1994). Behavioral assessment and treatment planning for alcohol, tobacco, and other drug problems: Current status with an emphasis on clinical applications. *Behavior Therapy* 25: 533–580.

Sprinthall, N.A., and Collins, W.A. (1995). *Adolescent Psychology: A Developmental View,* 3rd ed. New York: McGraw-Hill Inc.

Tupker, E. (ed.). (1991). *Youth and Drugs: An Educational Package for Professionals.* Toronto: Addiction Research Foundation.

Wilkinson, D.A., and LeBreton, S. (1986). Early indicators of treatment outcome in multiple drug users. In *Treating Addictive Behaviors,* eds. Miller, W.R., and Heather, N. New York: Plenum Press.

Wilkinson, D.A., and Martin, G.W. (1991). Intervention methods for youth with problems of substance abuse. In *Drug Use by Adolescents: Identification, Assessment and Intervention,* eds. Annis, H.M., and Davis, C.S. Toronto: Addiction Research Foundation.

Winters, K.C., and Henly, G.A. (1989). *The Personal Experience Inventory Manual.* Los Angeles: Western Psychological Services.

Chapter 18

Street-Involved Youth

Dennis Long

Street-involved youth, or "street youth" as they are often known, are an all-too-common phenomenon in most Canadian cities. While most of us recognize this, few people — even addictions professionals — understand who street youth are or what their lives are like. Confounding this is the fact that few studies have been conducted of this population in a Canadian context. This chapter will use recent Canadian data (drawn primarily from two Addiction Research Foundation studies by Smart et al., 1990 and 1992) and experience (as executive director of a treatment agency working with such youth) to paint a picture of street-involved youth in a city in Ontario.

PROFILE OF STREET-INVOLVED YOUTH

Although these youth are often called "street kids," this term has recently fallen out of favor, primarily because it is often used in a derogatory way. The term is also inexact and tends to oversimplify the situation of many young people. The preferred term, "street-involved youth," includes *all* youth who are involved in street activities ("hanging out," prostitution, panhandling, petty crime and so on). While some youth are truly homeless, many have some type of shelter, albeit inadequate and transient. They find themselves in these circumstances because they have run away from, or been "thrown away" by, their families of origin.

The first group, runaway youth, are kids who have run away from home several times before leaving permanently. Some began leaving as young as age 10, while most left between the ages of 11 and 15. Few came from intact families, and most had been physically abused; as well, many (more females than males) had suffered sexual abuse (Smart et al., 1990 and 1992). The second group, "throwaway youth," refers to young people who have been forced out of their families of origin, either through the application of "tough love" principles or by parental will. Case workers indicate that these kids are older (age 15 to 16) when they first find themselves on the street. A third group, sometimes called "curbsiders," are those who are on the street intermittently. These youth have varying degrees of unsatisfactory home environments, but still spend some time there, appearing on the street mostly on weekends and in the evenings (Lowery, Lee and Ward, 1996).

Many street-involved youth are frequently depressed, and not surprisingly have a significantly high incidence of attempted suicide (43 per cent). It is more difficult to determine if these youth have a higher incidence of psychiatric complaints. One study reported a high incidence of "psychotic" thoughts (Smart et al., 1992), although without a full examination, which was not possible, these thoughts are not reliable as indicators of psychiatric illness. Despite the prevalence of these types of problems, most street-involved youth showed a surprisingly high level of self-esteem. In fact, their feelings of self-esteem are positively correlated with identifying themselves as street people (Smart et al., 1990 and 1992). Those who so identified themselves also had less frequent episodes of depression. Despite this, however, it is safe to say that street life is not conducive to stable mental health, and that street-involved youth have higher-than-average mental heath needs.

Little data are available regarding the physical health status of these youth; however, based on information about the general street population and anecdotal information from workers, it is safe to assume that street-involved youth are at high risk for infections such as HIV/AIDS, Hepatitis A, B and C, and tuberculosis. They are also at risk for frequent minor traumatic injuries requiring medical intervention.

In terms of drinking and drug use, street-involved youth are heavy consumers, with 95 per cent indicating that they drink (compared with 59 per cent of the general youth population), and over 30 per cent reporting very heavy drinking. Drug use is also pervasive, with over 80 per cent reporting regular drug use. It is important to note that the two studies we are using recorded some decline in drug and alcohol use between the first and second studies (Smart et al., 1990 and 1992). However, since those reports were completed, increased drug use has been indicated among all youth, and specifically an increase in the use of particular drugs, notably heroin (Addiction Research Foundation, 1995; Metro Toronto Research Group on Drug Use, 1995). Anecdotal evidence indicates similar increases for street-involved youth. Predictably, these youth report high levels of both drug and alcohol problems, with about one-third reporting a drug problem and the same number reporting problems with alcohol. There is also significant overlap, with about one-quarter reporting both problems.

Consequently, the picture emerges of a group that has either chosen or been forced into a lifestyle that is stressful, difficult and dangerous. These youth experience far more than their share of physical and emotional problems and have significant problems meeting their financial and shelter needs. Nonetheless, they take great pride in their identity as street-involved youth and gain significant self-esteem from their ability to manage their lives and survive on the street. At the same time, this lifestyle is highly stressful, and produces youth with a high incidence of affective disorders, some indications of a likelihood of more serious psychiatric disabilities, and who are at high risk for infection and physical injury.

SERVICES FOR STREET-INVOLVED YOUTH

Simply put, the problem in providing services to these youth is determining how to approach them in a manner that respects their self-image, provides for their needs, and allows them to enter structured treatment programs or establish themselves in stable, non-street-related living situations.

The first priority is to try to keep street-involved youth relatively safe and healthy even if they are unwilling to alter their living situation or drug use. To do this, harm reduction services need to be provided, and the agencies dealing with these youth must adopt a harm reduction approach to delivering their services.

"Harm reduction" is a frequently misunderstood term that is often viewed as a synonym for drug legalization or for focusing only on reducing the spread of HIV/AIDS. In fact, harm reduction is a public health-based approach to drug use that emphasizes the minimization of the harm associated with that use, without requiring the cessation of use (Erickson, 1995). While it is true that the most effective way to avoid drug-related harm is to not use, and therefore it is possible to view total abstinence as "harm reduction," in fact, true harm reduction approaches view enforced abstinence as counter-productive, and instead adopt an approach that assumes that drug use will not only continue, but also that it serves a function in the lives of most users.

This is true for street-involved youth, who frequently describe drug use and, for that matter, excessive alcohol consumption, as part of the street lifestyle. For them, it is an environmental or normalizing factor rather than an example of aberrant behavior. Many also point out that drug use plays a role in their ability to deal with the stress and other emotional challenges of their lifestyle. Attempting to "cure" street-involved youth of drug use or abuse would be a futile goal, as it would likely be viewed as an attempt to impose values on them, rather than as a true attempt to help. Consequently, workers must be prepared to accept drug use as an endemic part of the lives of these youth.

Notwithstanding this, however, some street youth will identify their drug use as a problem. The dilemma is that it is so connected to and integrated with their current living situation and peer culture that to address the problem of drug use, even when identified as a separate issue, is extremely difficult, if not impossible.

353

It must be emphasized that street-involved youth are, for the most part, youth who struggle with many problems and who have, for legitimate reasons, learned to distrust adults — particularly those who hold positions of authority or who claim to be "on their side." For this reason, those who work with street-involved youth must adopt the following principles.

Outreach

Workers must go to where the youth are. This means providing service on the street and in other settings where they are found. The model of a mobile service operating out of a van can obviously be effective, but it is important to note that this approach is limited to areas where there is a concentration of street life (e.g., downtown Toronto). Another drawback is that a van service can be intimidating to youth and can serve to separate workers from their clients. Outreach must also be provided in other settings such as youth centres, pool halls, video arcades and so on. As well, many youth are frequently involved in the legal system. The same workers who do street work can provide outreach at the local detention centre, providing a continuity of care that would otherwise be impossible. This service also allows workers to be accessible for clients at times of high stress and anxiety.

Street work must also be provided at times that are sensitive to the needs of the youth. While it is obvious that "9 to 5" hours are inappropriate, thought must be given to the ways in which youth support themselves. For example, youth involved in the sex trade will not want workers around during their working hours, usually the late evening, but may be more receptive to contact in the late afternoon or early evening. Likewise, youth who are panhandling may be more approachable after rush hour. Workers must also develop sensitivity and a solid understanding of the social structure of the street and the etiquette of approaching someone.

The use of cellular phones is particularly effective. Cards distributed with workers' cell phone numbers and hours of availability make it easier for kids to call them and arrange meetings of mutual convenience, even when the workers are out of their offices. This system is particularly effective in providing needle exchange or other harm reduction services where a quick response is helpful.

Provision of Immediate Needs

Street-involved youth have certain basic needs: money, food and shelter, in roughly that order, followed by clothing and employment (Smart et al., 1990 and 1992). It goes without saying that most people will find it difficult to relate on any meaningful level if they are cold, hungry and lack shelter. Consequently, workers should identify these needs at the outset, and provide the appropriate assistance. Besides these basics, other needs are equally important. Most of these youth will need condoms, and many will need access to clean needles. Youth on the street seldom receive regular health care, and often find formal health care facilities less than welcoming. Thus, connection to sympathetic and easily accessible health care is often important. Finally, support and emotional empathy should also be available, although most street-involved youth will report that they have support from their own social links, and thus may be resistant, at least initially, to support from outsiders.

Trust

As noted above, most street-involved youth distrust others, particularly adults. The ability to "walk the walk and talk the talk" is less important than credibility. Youth on the street are members of a culture that, like other cultures or communities, maintains an efficient communications system. Any hint that a worker has betrayed a client's trust, broken confidentiality or, worse still, co-operated with the police or other authorities, will seriously damage or destroy the effectiveness of that worker.

Informality

Services must be, and must appear to be, informal. Rules and procedures should be minimal, and staff dress and the physical environment (where relevant) should be specifically intended to increase the comfort level of clients.

Respect

All of us like to be respected as individuals; these youth are no different. Agency policies, structures and culture must reinforce this as a primary objective. In particular, workers must avoid labelling, since most youth do not like to be labelled as "street kids" (despite their need to self-identify as street people). Workers and agencies should avoid labels and diagnoses in their dealings with clients, and in describing their services.

Consistency

Street-involved youth live in a transient world where people come and go, and things are always changing. There are few constants in their lives, and they expect all relationships to be brief and temporary. For this reason, workers and programs must ensure that once a relationship has been established, a deliberate effort is made to maintain contact with clients. With this population, it is ineffective to apply the office-based model of equating a client's failure to attend with a lack of interest or motivation. Failing to maintain contact with clients simply replicates their street experience and reinforces their belief that adults and professionals are not trustworthy or committed to them.

Adopting a case management model where contact is maintained with clients throughout their involvement with other agencies and programs is key to ensuring progress and responding effectively to setbacks.

Although the immediate goal of working with street-involved youth must be primarily harm reduction, the ultimate goal is to move youth into a more stable non-street-involved life. While in some cases this can be achieved without additional help, most youth will require other services such as vocational training, supportive housing, addictions treatment or mental health treatment. Preparing street-involved youth for these services is a key role for outreach workers. As indicated above, the most important part of this role is to develop and maintain a supportive, respectful and enduring relationship with the client. In most cases, this will be a long-term process. Most of these youth will find it extremely difficult to establish trust, and will behave in ways designed to test the relationship. Workers will require great skill, perseverance and patience.

If street-involved clients seek help on their own (and only a few do), they often find integration into structured programs difficult. The studies by the Addiction Research Foundation report that few street-involved youth actually sought addictions treatment, and those who did, did not find most programs particularly helpful (Smart et al., 1990 and 1992). Notably, clients seem to prefer residential programs, which raises the point that a stable environment and housing is one of the key needs of these clients. More traditional programs such as Alcoholics Anonymous were rated extremely low by most clients.

While this section deals primarily with services to youth before they enter more structured programs, the accessibility and acceptability of such programs is an important issue. Most treatment programs are not designed to meet the needs of street-involved youth. Programs must consider the primary needs stated above. Outpatient services that do not provide for the housing and other needs of these clients, or that are not prepared to work closely with services that do, will not be successful. Day programs with too high a "threshold," requiring complete and immediate abstinence and perfect attendance, will likewise fail. Residential services must be youth-focused, and must provide a community that supports the needs of street-involved clients, including their ongoing housing needs.

While we have described the factors that will lead youth into a street-involved life, these are not the same as those that keep them on the street. Factors making it difficult for youth to leave the street, in addition to the emotional issues discussed above, are a severe lack of appropriate housing that will accept them and a general downturn in the economy, making entry-level employment highly competitive. In Ontario, street-level services have been severely reduced in recent years, and welfare rates and rules have changed, compromising the ability of youth to survive autonomously without resorting to street activities.

Innovative programs such as the Ambassador Project of the City of Toronto Public Health Department are promising, as they use peer counsellors, most of whom are former street-involved youth, to deliver services to street youth. But other innovative approaches are desperately needed. The problem of street-involved youth will not go away, and shows every indication of worsening.

Street-involved youth are a population that has been poorly studied and about whom we are just beginning to build adequate data. However, what we do know raises serious concern. These young people have experienced, and continue to experience, a complex mix of problems. They have adopted a difficult and challenging lifestyle that, on one level, provides them with an identity and self-esteem while at the same time is severely damaging and dangerous. Providing services to these youth requires approaches that respect and respond to their immediate needs. While some innovative models have been and are being developed, both the youth and the services that work with them are facing serious challenges from our changing fiscal and social environment.

REFERENCES

Addiction Research Foundation. (1996). *Innovative Strategies When Working with High-Risk Youth: Harm Reduction; Early Intervention; Engaging Youth.* Teleconference. Toronto: Addiction Research Foundation.

Addiction Research Foundation. (1990). *Proceedings of the Youth and the Street Forum.* Toronto: Addiction Research Foundation.

Adlaf, E.M., Ivis, F., Smart, R.G., and Walsh, G.W. (1995). *Ontario Student Drug Use Survey, 1977–1995.* Toronto: Addiction Research Foundation.

Erickson, G.E. (1995). Harm reduction: What it is and is not. *Drug and Alcohol Review* 14.

Lowery, G., Lee, T., and Ward, J. (1996). *A Situational Analysis of Services to Concurrent Disorder Street Youth in Metropolitan Toronto.* Health Canada.

Metro Toronto Research Group on Drug Use. (1995). *Drug Use in Metropolitan Toronto.* Toronto: Author.

Smart, R.G., Adlaf, E.M., Porterfield, K.M., and Canale, M.C. (1990). *Drugs, Youth and the Street.* Toronto: Addiction Research Foundation.

Smart, R.G., Adlaf, E.M., Walsh, G.W., and Zdanowicz, Y.M. (1992). *Drifting and Doing: Changes in Drug Use among Toronto Street Youth, 1990–1992.* Toronto: Addiction Research Foundation.

Chapter 19

Counselling Culturally Diverse Clients[*]

BERYL TSANG

INTRODUCTION

Canada has always been a multicultural, multi-ethnic and multi-racial society, but it is becoming even more so every day. In Ontario alone, one-third of all Canadians will be "new" Canadians[1] — European, Asian or African in heritage. One thing is certain — all Canadians will need access to sensitive and caring health and human services.

The objective of this chapter is to provide health and human service providers working in the addictions treatment field with some of the knowledge, resources and skills they will need to work with different clients. It has been developed from the experiences of service providers who work with diverse communities. Their recommendations, ideas and guidelines will augment the expertise that service providers already have, so that they can be even more effective in meeting the needs of a pluralistic society.

WHAT DO WE MEAN BY AN INCREASINGLY DIVERSE CLIENT BASE?

When we speak about an increasingly diverse client base, we are not only speaking about people with cultures, ethnicities, languages, races, religions and spiritualities other than those of the Anglo-Celtic/Anglo-Saxon mainstream, but also of people whose *experiences* are different from those of the mainstream. These people include:

---

[*]This chapter is an abridged version of a more comprehensive handbook, *Cultural Diversity: A Handbook for Addiction Service Providers,* published by the Addiction Research Foundation (1994).

- **immigrants,** who have chosen to leave their homes and resettle in Canada
- **refugees,** who have fled to Canada out of a well-founded fear of persecution[2]
- **ethnic and linguistic minorities,** who have chosen to identify themselves as having ethnic or linguistic heritages distinct from those of the mainstream groups
- **in-settlement populations,** who emigrated to Canada several decades ago but, because of lack of opportunity, have not been able to fully integrate and settle in to the mainstream society
- **racial minorities,** who see themselves as racially different from the mainstream racial groups
- and **religious or spiritual minorities,** who view their religious and spiritual beliefs, practices and values as distinct from those of mainstream religious or spiritual groups.

HOW DO CULTURE, ETHNICITY AND RACE AFFECT SUBSTANCE USE AND MISUSE?

Almost all cultures, ethnic groups and races will use psychoactive substances. They will, however, use them in different social contexts. Some may use them as recreational stimulants, (e.g., chewing khat, a vegetable with stimulant effects, after a dinner with friends) while others may use them as part of religious or spiritual ceremonies (e.g., wine during communion). Some will use them as performance enhancers (e.g., chewing coca leaves to improve speed and agility while hunting) while others will use them as medicines (e.g., a hot toddy to treat a cold). Some will use them to celebrate (e.g., a toast at a wedding), while others will use them as part of an everyday meal.

Every culture, ethnic group and race attaches symbolic meaning to a particular substance or set of substances. Among some groups, for example, red wine is thought to symbolize the blood of Jesus Christ and is therefore seen as life-giving. Every culture, ethnic group and race also applies logic or a rationale to using substances. Among some groups, for example, cannabis is regarded as a holy substance and is intended for use during religious or spiritual reflection. Along with this logic and rationale, there are rules, both articulated and not articulated, that govern substance use. These rules include who may consume what substances (men, women, youth, elderly, etc.); when substances may be consumed (with lunch, after work, on weekends, during holidays, etc.); where (at home, in a bar, at a social club, outdoors, indoors, etc.); why (for relaxation, as a stress reliever or thirst quencher, etc.); and how (alone, with family, with friends, etc.). These rules also dictate which effects of substance use will be tolerated and the penalties (e.g., being cut off, isolated from the group, physically restrained, etc.) for displaying non-sanctioned effects.

Culture, ethnicity and race are factors in determining patterns of substance use, but not necessarily the patterns of misuse. Members of diverse communities misuse substances for many of the same reasons that members of mainstream communities do: trauma, stress, social isolation, poverty, life change and family breakdown.

Experiences with migration and discrimination may also affect the way in which diverse populations misuse substances.

As with mainstream communities, ability, age, class background, gender and sexual orientation will influence patterns of misuse and help-seeking behaviors.

Service providers in Metropolitan Toronto's Chinese-Canadian community, for example, have found that immigrants from Hong Kong smoke more in Canada than they did in Hong Kong, although cigarettes are more expensive and less available in Canada.

HOW DO CULTURE, ETHNICITY AND RACE AFFECT THE WAY IN WHICH GROUPS AND INDIVIDUALS SEEK AND RESPOND TO ADDICTION TREATMENT SERVICES?

Culture will often determine the type of help that people seek. People who come from cultures where the family is of great importance, for example, may seek help that includes the family and meets a number of its needs. Culture will also influence the timing of one's help-seeking behavior. For example, people who value privacy may only seek help once they have failed to resolve an issue on their own — which may mean that the problem will be compounded by the time they find help. Lastly, culture may affect the frequency and range of help that people seek. Someone from a very social culture may seek services often, look for different services to meet different needs, and regard different service providers as friends or part of an important social network.

Ethnicity or race, meanwhile, will often determine the quality and type of service people receive. People who belong to a non-Anglo-Celtic or Anglo-Saxon ethnic group, for example, may need mental health services that take into account their culture, language, race, religion or spirituality. If most mental health services are designed for people of Anglo-Celtic or Anglo-Saxon heritage, people of other ethnic groups may have to use another service — one that speaks their language but doesn't necessarily offer the specific service they need. Ethnicity or race may likewise determine how service users are treated and ultimately how they respond to a service. People who are part of a racial minority, for example, often experience racism (e.g., hostility, negative judgments, denial that discrimination exists) when seeking services, and may not be receptive to services or service providers who are not of the same background.

UNDERSTANDING OTHERS AND
HELPING THEM UNDERSTAND YOU

When providing service to culturally diverse clients, it is important to be aware of the following differences that can lead to miscommunication.

Common Areas of Difference That Can Lead to Miscommunication

Attitudes towards feelings and emotions
Acceptability of expressed/non-expressed feelings, what feelings can or cannot be expressed (e.g., anger, joy, etc.), how they are expressed.

Body language, personal distance, use of touch
Eye contact, greetings, handshakes, placement of chairs.

Forming of relationships
Period of time it is considered appropriate to take to develop rapport, make friends, discuss an issue.

Gender and sex roles
What roles do men and women play? Are they equitable? How are men and women expected to relate to each other? How are gays and lesbians viewed? What is their relationship to their larger social group?

Importance placed on age, family and social group
What privileges or limits do people have at certain ages? Why? What is the role of the family? Who has what responsibilities within the family? How do family members interact with each other? How do they interact with the larger social group? What is the role of the social group? What are its components? How are group members expected to relate to one another?

Personal and social boundaries
Definitions of private and public, rules governing what may or may not be discussed, with whom and in what context. For example, sexuality may be openly discussed with members of both sexes within a family but not with members of the same sex outside the family.

Regard for things such as education, material goods, money relationships and self
What things are valued? (e.g., friendships, success at work) To what extent are they valued? For example, is a PhD considered the ultimate accomplishment? Why are they valued? For example, is it because a particular group of people have historically been marginalized that they feel the need to have their children and grandchildren succeed?

Time

What kind of time is valued? (e.g., punctuality, flexibility)

Use of intonation, humor, language and metaphors

Why are certain tones stressed? Why is something funny? Why are certain words or descriptions chosen? Why are certain things evoked?

Providing service to culturally diverse clients may seem like a difficult task at first. You may be concerned that you can't fully understand your clients' needs, because you are unaware of their experiences. You may worry about inadvertently offending them, because you are unaware of their norms, values and practices. You may worry about not being able to provide them with adequate or appropriate services, because you are of a different background. Your task, however, won't be difficult if you follow this basic checklist.

Checklist for Effective Communication

☐ Remember that everyone has cultural, ethnic and racial assumptions and biases. Be aware of your own and try to "check them."

☐ Remember that different people have different ways of expressing themselves. Be patient. Expect and anticipate different forms of self-expression and self-presentation. If in doubt, observe how clients interact with you and follow their lead.

☐ Think about how you express yourself. How do you make others feel comfortable or safe? How might you inadvertently confuse or alienate others?

☐ Learn to actively listen when someone speaks to you. Take all comments and concerns seriously even if they have no apparent relationship to the issue at hand. Try to hear what they are saying. Be sure to check your interpretation of what they are saying or not saying in a concerned or validating manner. (For example: "So you believe that you need...." "Your concern is...." "I understand that...." "You feel that...." "What can I do to make you more comfortable?") Allow them to correct you.

☐ Learn to hear what your client is *not* saying. Observe body language. Be sensitive to silences — they may be a time for absorbing information or reflecting on issues.

☐ When communicating any sort of information, ask yourself the following questions:
  • Can they hear me properly?
  • Am I using any words they do not understand? (e.g., jargon)
  • Am I using gestures or body language that may make them uncomfortable?
  • How familiar am I with their day-to-day life?
  • How well do they understand English or French?

- How familiar are they with the issues we are discussing?
- How much can they remember at once?
- Are they too shy or nervous to ask questions?

☐ If possible, ask clients to explain their values, practices and norms to you.

☐ If there is a language barrier, do not be afraid to use innovative means of communicating with your clients (e.g., draw, refer to pictures in magazines, use props).

☐ If difficulties arise, stop the situation or conversation for a few minutes and rest.

☐ Remember that providing service to clients from diverse communities will become easier with practice.

☐ Remember that you could be the one who is different and needing service.

Adapted by Beryl Tsang from: Sue, D.W., Arrendondo, P., and McDavis, R.J., Multicultural counselling competencies and standards: A call to the profession. In *Journal of Counselling & Development,* March/April 1992, Vol. 7, pp. 477–486.

GENERAL HEALTH AND HUMAN SERVICE ISSUES IN CULTURALLY, ETHNICALLY AND RACIALLY DIVERSE COMMUNITIES

While culture, ethnicity and race play an important role in anticipating consumption patterns and help-seeking behaviors, they are not the only factors that determine the type of help that community members need. The life experiences that groups share may also play a role. Some common experiences include being an immigrant or refugee; being in settlement (living in Canada but never fully completing the settlement process); and being of minority status. These experiences often play a significant role in determining the type or the variety of services required. The following sections illustrate some of the common health and human service needs of immigrants, refugees, in-settlement populations and minority groups.

The Immigrant Settlement Process

The ways in which groups of immigrants or individual immigrants settle in Canada will vary. Age, class, education, gender, occupational group, etc., all play a role in the settlement process.

Not all of the things listed in the description below are experienced by all immigrants with the same intensity. Some of the immigrants you serve, however, may experience some of the following issues.

Please note that different immigrants settle at different rates and that these timelines may vary. Also note that if the health and human service needs of immigrants are not met in the earlier stages of settlement, the resources required to meet their needs later will usually be greater.

TIME PERIOD

■ **six months prior to arrival at destination**
☐ 0 to 6 months after arrival
☐ 6 months to 3 years after arrival
☐ 3 to 5 years after arrival
☐ 5 years and onwards

Thoughts and Feelings	Issues and Needs	Resources Required	Potential Resources Required
• anticipation of the move • disengagement from existing life • enthusiasm and excitement • expectations of happiness and success in new country • sadness at leaving friends and family behind • stress over the logistics of moving.	• logistical preparation • total focus on the move • inability to think clearly about what will actually happen once the move is complete.	• information about what to expect in new country (re: housing, transportation, employment, health and human services, education, child care, values, norms, practices, weather, etc.).	• names of groups or individuals to contact in the new country.

The Immigrant Settlement Process

TIME PERIOD
☐ six months prior to arrival at destination
■ **0 to 6 months after arrival**
☐ 6 months to 3 years after arrival
☐ 3 to 5 years after arrival
☐ 5 years and onwards

Thoughts and Feelings	Issues and Needs	Resources Required	Potential Resources Required
• sense of being on holiday • delight in new things • fascination with things unique to new home • favorable comparison of new home to old • culture shock • sense of displacement • lack of context for understanding new home • lack of desire to get to know new home • desire to avoid and criticize things unique to new home • stress and anxiety about being in new environment • unfavorable comparison of new home to old.	• physical orientation to institutions and services in new home • getting professional or vocation accreditation, learning English or French, looking for work and skills development • changes in socio-economic status • creation of a home or "nesting" • establishing a peer group • contacting people of the same background for support and mutual aid.	• assistance meeting basic physical needs (e.g., the need for work, shelter, food, clothing, transportation, etc.) • information on professional or vocational accreditation • language training • "life skills" training • information on skills development • orientation to basic health and human services (e.g., hospitals, health centres, senior or youth groups, etc.) • orientation to religious institutions, lifestyles, educational facilities, food and child care • recreational opportunities.	• interpretation services • help accessing financial institutions, receiving legal aid or setting up a business • information on ethno-specific social clubs • information on heritage programs.

The Immigrant Settlement Process

TIME PERIOD
☐ six months prior to arrival at destination
☐ 0 to 6 months after arrival
■ **6 months to 3 years after arrival**
☐ 3 to 5 years after arrival
☐ 5 years and onwards

Significant changes in lifestyle occur during this stage.

Thoughts and Feelings	Issues and Needs	Resources Required	Potential Resources Required
• sense of being in a "honeymoon" phase • happiness over move • remembering original reasons for move • anxiety over separation with what is familiar • fear of further change • sense of isolation • suppressed anger and depression over inability to cope in a new environment • mourning of old life • loss of self-esteem • feeling that no one is interested in the person, his or her accomplishments, and country of origin • sense of disillusionment or embarrassment at not being able to achieve something or meet expectations.	• desire to achieve something in new home • desire to contribute to new home • frustration and sense of helplessness over inability to contribute in a meaningful way • desire to bring friends and family to new home • negative coping mechanisms developed (e.g., withdrawal from friends and family, substance use, idealization of former home). • positive mechanisms for coping with change (e.g., joining heritage groups, making new friends, getting involved in community groups, etc.) • family roles change and reinforce — or undermine — the family structure (e.g., parents and children become "experts" on different things) • reasons for move are now unclear • experience of having self and accomplishments rejected by host community.	• connection with achievements in previous life • information on how to establish ties to former achievements • new challenges and activities • assessment of skills, resources and knowledge • help identifying unsettling thoughts and emotions • help learning to express thoughts and emotions • validation of loss • information on how to sponsor friends and family members.	• counselling or help dealing with mourning process • help finding or creating mutual aid or support groups • information on how to take care of self and family.

The Immigrant Settlement Process

TIME PERIOD

☐ six months prior to arrival at destination

☐ 0 to 6 months after arrival

☐ 6 months to 3 years after arrival

■ **3 to 5 years after arrival**

☐ 5 years and onwards

Thoughts and Feelings	Issues and Needs	Resources Required	Potential Resources Required
• sense of permanent disassociation from old life • realization that there has been a shift in values, practices and norms (i.e., a permanent shift in lifestyles) • sense of resolution about move • identification and familiarity with new home • desire to "go back," to make sure that leaving was the right thing to do • uncertainty about self and future • reluctant resolution to stay • loss in self-esteem • ongoing questioning of reasons for leaving.	• pursuit of permanent connections to new home (e.g., development of long-term career plans, plans for children, involvement in the community, establishment of peer groups, etc.) • return to old home for a visit • ongoing negative coping mechanisms.	• assistance making connections that bind individuals and families to communities • help establishing goals and objectives • ongoing help establishing ties to former achievements • ongoing help assessing skills, resources and knowledge • ongoing help finding new challenges and activities • ongoing help identifying unsettling thoughts and emotions • help learning to express thoughts and emotions.	• ongoing counselling or help to deal with mourning • ongoing help finding or creating mutual aid or support groups • ongoing provision of information on self-care.

The Immigrant Settlement Process

TIME PERIOD

☐ six months prior to arrival at destination
☐ 0 to 6 months after arrival
☐ 6 months to 3 years after arrival
☐ 3 to 5 years after arrival
■ **5 years and onwards**

Thoughts and Feelings	Resources Required
• sense of belonging.	• person becomes a resource for others.

Refugee Integration Process

The ways in which groups of refugees or individual refugees integrate may vary greatly. In addition to age, class, education, gender, etc., other factors play a role in the integration process, including whether a person arrives alone or as part of a group, whether he or she is accepted, is still awaiting disposition of his or her claim, has spent time in refugee camps or is a torture survivor. The section below illustrates some of the common experiences that refugees may share.

Not all of the things listed in the description below are experienced by all refugees with the same intensity. Some of the refugees you serve, however, may bring some of the following issues to your service.

Please note that refugees, like immigrants, integrate at different rates. The timelines given here may therefore vary. Also note that if refugees' health and human service needs are not met in the earlier stages of the integration process, the resources required to meet their needs later on will be greater.

TIME PERIOD
■ **0 to 6 months after arrival**
☐ 6 months to 3 years after arrival
☐ 3 to 5 years after arrival
☐ 5 years and onwards

Thoughts and Feelings	Issues and Needs	Resources Required	
• conflicting thoughts and feelings (e.g., sense of excitement and happiness but also preoccupation with safety and well-being) • relief at escaping persecution and torture or fear • disorientation and confusion.	• fulfilment of basic physical needs (e.g., the need for work, shelter, food, etc.) • orientation to new institutions and services in new home • contact with those who share the person's culture, ethnicity, language, race, religion, spirituality or experiences • being cared for by "someone who knows."	• assessment of pre-arrival experience (e.g., time spent in refugee camp, family and friends left behind, experiences with violence or torture, etc.), to determine type and scope of health and human services required • determination of need for mental health services • legal assistance (if person is refugee claimant) • assistance meeting basic physical needs (e.g., the need for work, shelter, food and clothing)	• language training • "life skills" training • vocational or professional accreditation • orientation to basic health and human services (e.g., hospitals, health centres, senior or youth groups, etc.) • support groups.

Refugee Integration Process

TIME PERIOD

☐ 0 to 6 months after arrival

■ **6 months to 3 years after arrival**

☐ 3 to 5 years after arrival

☐ 5 years and onwards

Thoughts and Feelings	Issues and Needs	Resources Required	Potential Resources Required
• anxiety over separation from home • guilt about leaving friends and family behind • guilt about being safe when others at home may still be in danger • ongoing fear for personal safety and well-being • fear of further change • depression or disappointment over the indifference of host country about events at home (e.g., Canadians may not care about civil war in Somalia) • unexpressed anger and depression over inability to cope in a new environment.	• desire to achieve something in new home • desire to contribute to new home • desire to do something about what is happening in old home • rising expectations • sense of disillusionment at not being able to achieve something or meet basic expectations • frustration over inability to contribute in a meaningful way • desire to bring friends and family to new home — sadness at not being able to do so.	• connection with achievements in previous life (e.g., practising old profession in new home) • information on how to establish ties to former achievements • new challenges and activities • assessment of skills, resources and knowledge • introduction of new ideas and opportunities • assistance identifying unsettling thoughts and emotions (e.g., thoughts of suicide or violence) • help learning to express thoughts and emotions • validation of anger and depression • information on how to sponsor friends and family members.	• counselling or help to deal with anger and depression • if alone, help finding or creating mutual aid or support groups to serve as surrogate families • information on self-care.

Refugee Integration Process

TIME PERIOD

☐ 0 to 6 months after arrival
☐ 6 months to 3 years after arrival
■ **3 to 5 years after arrival**
☐ 5 years and onwards

Thoughts and Feelings	Issues and Needs	Resources Required	Potential Resources Required
• realization that there has been a permanent shift in values, practices and norms • sense of social dislocation • stress • uncertainty about self and future • withdrawal from friends, family and community • search for stability, control and new coping mechanisms • questioning of self and resources • possible loss of self-esteem • mourning what was left behind • desire to return to what is familiar.	• physical manifestations of uncertainty, stress and dislocation (e.g., colds, aches, pains, difficulty eating and sleeping) • negative coping mechanisms (e.g., withdrawal from friends and family, substance use, idealization of former home) • conflict with friends, family and community • generational conflicts with children.	• assistance dealing with symptoms of social dislocation • help establishing realistic goals and objectives • ongoing help establishing ties to former achievements • ongoing help finding new challenges and activities • ongoing help assessing skills, resources and knowledge • ongoing introduction of new ideas and opportunities • monitoring of psychosocial status • referral to appropriate services • assistance and advocacy accessing services.	• ongoing counselling or help to deal with loss • ongoing help finding or creating mutual aid or support groups • ongoing provision of information on self-care.

Refugee Integration Process

TIME PERIOD

☐ 0 to 6 months after arrival
☐ 6 months to 3 years after arrival
☐ 3 to 5 years after arrival
■ **5 years and onwards**

Thoughts and Feelings	**Issues and Needs**	**Resources Required**	**Potential Resources Required**
• sense of belonging, happiness • sense of resolution about new life and new home • realistic expectations • hope.	• person has friends, interests and structure in life.	• ongoing orientation to services and society • person becomes a resource for others.	• orientation to rights and responsibilities as member of a larger society.

In-settlement Community Profile

The ways in which communities experience being in settlement will vary. A community's socioeconomic background, its age and gender biases, and the age of its members all influence the community's issues and needs. The resources available to deal with the issues and needs may also vary. The following section illustrates some of the experiences that members of in-settlement communities may share. The profile of in-settlement communities is presented in generational terms to illustrate how the history of these communities in Canada has shaped their health and human service needs.

In-settlement Community Profile

First generation:
- emigrated to Canada between 1920s and 1960s
- integrated economically into mainstream but not politically or socially (i.e., worked in mainstream filling particular job niches such as building trades, high-tech industries, restaurants, hospitality sector)
- developed own service organizations, recreational clubs and mutual aid groups
- health and human service needs traditionally met within the community (communities often close-knit, often difficult to move outside of community)
- heavily dependent on professionals (e.g., medical) in the community (few services available to community)
- retained or revived institutions and practices from original home (e.g., alcohol consumption patterns), but the values and beliefs governing those practices no longer exist (e.g., social controls over alcohol)
- most had little access to language training and have limited fluency in English or French
- live parallel existence to mainstream but with fewer resources.

Issues	Needs	Resources Required
• aging • in some groups and families, loss of status as a result of aging (e.g., opinions are no longer considered valid because they are grounded in different life experiences) • fears around aging (e.g., older person doesn't want to burden the family) • in other groups and families, increase in status with age (e.g., experiences are finally considered important) • happiness over aging process (e.g., getting the respect one deserves).	• adjustments to changing roles in both cases • loss of family, friends and peers becomes a reality • development of coping mechanisms to deal with grief • isolation from family or community • smothering by family or community • shifting family responsibilities • illness • development of substance use or increase in substance use.	• recognition by family, friends and community of emotional and physical changes associated with aging • recreational and social activities or the expansion of existing recreational and social activities • opportunities to explore and develop skills and interests • reinforcement of relationships with peers • connection with past self.	• assistance seeking or developing services • opportunities to participate in recreational activities, socialize and talk about life • support in a family or community setting where programs are culturally and linguistically appropriate • therapy for those suffering from depression, grief and loss of status • help dealing with medical professionals.

In-settlement Community Profile

Second generation:
- children of immigrants who came between the 1920s and 1960s
- may see themselves as belonging to two worlds
- are also integrated economically and, to a certain extent, politically, but may choose not to be integrated socially (parents' cultural practices and values are often very strong)
- may still remain tied to own service organizations, recreational clubs and mutual aid groups
- dependence on professionals (e.g., medical) in community remains
- often want to remain in community (community is a source of identity and prestige, and it is a place of upward mobility)
- active in supporting the development of health and human services in own community so that needs can be met within traditional structures
- have retained many of their parents' values, practices and beliefs, but may have also taken on new ones
- most often fluently bilingual.

Issues	Needs	Resources Required
• feeling of being caught between two worlds sometimes; at other times, happy with the duality	• community support for those in "sandwich" role	• assistance seeking or developing services
• responsibility for parents as well as children ("sandwich generation"); stress over this role	• information on self-care	• opportunities to participate in recreational activities, socialize and talk about life
• guilt over not being able to care for aging parents or other family members, especially in communities where this is expected	• health and human services not traditionally provided within community	• support in a family or community setting where programs are culturally and linguistically appropriate
• grief over loss of parents and other family members	• new programs provided by existing community services (e.g., stress reduction, health promotion, etc.)	• therapy for those suffering from stress, frustration and anger
• depression over inability to cope with guilt and grief	• opportunities to explore and develop interests and skills outside of family and community	• help dealing with medical professionals.
• suppressed anger and frustration over lack of resources	• new and different recreational activities.	
• development of positive and negative coping mechanisms to deal with stress and lack of service (e.g., spending more time with friends and peers, substance use or increased substance use).		

In-settlement Community Profile

Third generation:
- grandchildren of those who emigrated between the 1920s and 1960s
- similar to parents but economically, politically and socially integrated
- may retain strong recreational ties to their communities but also have recreational ties to the mainstream
- may retain cultural practices of grandparents but not the values attached to them.

Synopsis of Ethnic, Linguistic, Racial, Religious and Spiritual Minority Experiences

The ways in which groups and individuals experience being a minority will vary. Ability, age, class, gender, education, geographic origin, etc., all play a role in shaping the experience. The section below illustrates some of the experiences that members of minority groups may share.

TIME PERIOD

■ **early childhood (1 to 7 years)**
☐ late childhood (7 to 13 years)
☐ adolescence
☐ adulthood

Thoughts and Feelings	Issues and Needs	Resources Required
• development of sense of self • identification of ethnicity, language, race, religion or spirituality as an asset or barrier • understanding of self as unique or different.	• positive image of self reinforced • education about ethnic, linguistic, racial, religious or spiritual background • recreational and social activities reflective of a variety of values, practices and norms.	• role models of same ethnic, linguistic, racial, religious or spiritual background • opportunities to get to know others who are the same or different • discussion of the value of difference.

Synopsis of Ethnic, Linguistic, Racial, Religious and Spiritual Minority Experiences

TIME PERIOD
☐ early childhood (1 to 7 years)
■ **late childhood (7 to 13 years)**
☐ adolescence
☐ adulthood

Thoughts and Feelings	Issues and Needs	Resources Required
• developing understanding of how the dominant group views ethnic, linguistic, racial, religious and spiritual minorities • desire to identify with these views, whether they are positive or negative • experiences with being the "other" or with discrimination (may result in the internalization of the experience or an expressed reaction) • lowering (or reinforcement) of self-esteem at being "other" or different.	• validation of experiences • positive reinforcement of self-image • outlets to express anger, frustration, joy, pride, etc. • help identifying talents, skills, resources and individuality • assistance learning to assert self in positive way.	• people in authority who understand how it feels to be a minority and can facilitate discussion around it (e.g., teachers, family, friends, counsellors, etc.) • adult approval, love and support • more exposure to peers who are the same • more education around the value of diversity • corrective action when incidents of discrimination are encountered.

Synopsis of Ethnic, Linguistic, Racial, Religious and Spiritual Minority Experiences

TIME PERIOD
☐ early childhood (1 to 7 years)
☐ late childhood (7 to 13 years)
■ **adolescence**
☐ adulthood

Thoughts and Feelings	Issues and Needs	Resources Required
• direct challenge to discrimination or denial of its existence • desire to identify with — or separate from — own ethnic, linguistic, racial, religious or spiritual group • unexpressed anger and frustration with self or society • sense of social dislocation at not being able to cope or sense of power at being able to cope.	• need to take control of life • need to be recognized as an individual • need to assert oneself • experimentation with coping mechanisms, both positive and negative (e.g., over-achievement, acting out) • systemic discrimination may be encountered (e.g., streaming in the school system, "trouble" with authority, not having religious or spiritual holidays recognized at work or school) • conflict with parents over identification or lack of identification with dominant cultural values.	• opportunities to change environment (e.g., organizing a human rights day) • reinforcement of positive self-image through popular culture (e.g., television, music, magazines, etc.) • social activities that increase self-esteem • validation of individuality • support or peer groups to discuss experiences • corrective measures when discrimination is encountered.

Synopsis of Ethnic, Linguistic, Racial, Religious and Spiritual Minority Experiences

TIME PERIOD

☐ early childhood (1 to 7 years)
☐ late childhood (7 to 13 years)
☐ adolescence
■ **adulthood**

Thoughts and Feelings	Issues and Needs	Resources Required
• increasing sense of self • desire to recognize and live with being an ethnic, linguistic, racial, religious or spiritual minority • ability to challenge or accept one's "otherness" or differences.	• development of negative coping mechanisms for dealing with discrimination (e.g., withdrawal from society, deviant behavior, substance abuse, etc.) • barriers to self-fulfilment • unexpressed frustration and anger • positive coping mechanisms, (e.g., demonstrations of racial pride, getting involved in mosque, temple or community centre, etc.) • desire to educate others about one's "otherness" or differences • resources to deal with barriers to self-fulfilment in larger society.	• help understanding discrimination • help identifying and changing negative coping mechanisms • help identifying personal and social resources • help assessing personal assets and skills • empowerment through education, political and social action • counselling • support groups • participation in activities where anger, frustration, joy, etc., may be expressed.

DEVELOPING PARTNERSHIPS WITH CULTURALLY, ETHNICALLY AND RACIALLY DIVERSE COMMUNITIES: STRATEGIES FOR SUCCESS

At this time, few addictions treatment agencies can provide culturally appropriate services, and few diverse communities can provide addictions treatment. It is therefore important that the two groups work together to ensure that those who need addictions-related services have access to them.

Community Resources

Before you can begin developing partnerships with cultural, ethnic and racial communities, you must be aware of the resources that are available to these communities. Such resources are usually listed in service directories, phone books and information centres in nearly every community. Here are some services you may consider reaching out to:

Social and Recreational Clubs offer social and recreational activities to their members, but also act as mutual support groups and community mobilization and action centres for the populations that they serve.

Settlement Services provide support, language training, information, family and individual counselling, and general assistance to groups and individuals during the settlement process, which usually lasts from three to five years.

Reception Centres serve the immediate social, psychological and physical needs of newcomers to Canada. Many are actual hostels or shelters for newcomers.

Multicultural Associations are usually umbrella groups active in developing and disseminating information, programs and services that can be used by their member agencies.

Ethno-Specific Agencies are specifically geared to meet the social service needs of a particular ethno-cultural or ethno-racial community. There is a great deal of variation in ethno-specific agencies. Some serve large populations, and may be established and well resourced with large staffs; others serve smaller communities, may be continually fundraising, have limited staff and depend on volunteers.

Multi-Ethnic Agencies are specifically geared to meet the social service needs of many ethno-cultural and ethno-racial communities. Some may exclusively service ethno-cultural and ethno-racial groups with a common geographic origin, language or race (e.g., a francophone health centre) while others may try to serve as many populations as they can.

Literacy and English/French as a Second Language Services provide ESL/FSL services to newcomers, but also act as meeting places where knowledge, information and friendship can be exchanged.

Training and Development Centres provide life-skills and professional training for the unemployed or underemployed, many of whom are members of culturally, ethnically and racially diverse communities.

Multi-Service Legal Clinics provide legal services, but also help clients obtain workers' compensation, social assistance benefits and housing.

Community Information Centres serve as clearinghouses of information about community-based agencies.

Interfaith Groups and Spiritual Communities provide a variety of social services to members of their faith and others. Many are involved in refugee settlement work and social justice issues.

Cultural Interpreters' Programs facilitate understanding and provide linguistic and cultural translation between non-English-/French-speaking clients and English/French-speaking service providers.

Host Programs match "old" and "new" Canadians for an exchange of friendship and support.

Advocacy and Education Organizations educate society about the social, political and economic issues facing immigrants, refugees, in-settlement populations and minority groups. They also advocate for social changes that will create more equity for these groups.

USING AN INTERPRETER

When working with a diverse client base, you may be called upon to provide service through an interpreter. In some cases you may be able to use "professional cultural interpreters," who are specially trained to work with health and human service providers. These interpreters are usually familiar with your client's heritage, and are able to express your client's needs to you and explain your service models to your client.

More often than not, however, you will be using "volunteer interpreters" — friends or family members of the client. They may be very familiar with your client's heritage but not with your social context or your service models. You may even have to designate a fellow staff person as an interpreter or borrow one from another agency.

Remember that translators may also serve as facilitators who can help your clients understand how your service can help them. They can also help you understand what clients need and why they need it.

Tips for Effectively Using an Interpreter

Whether an interpreter is a professional or a volunteer, keep the following guidelines in mind:

• Acknowledge that the interpreter has a right to be there and that they can help you do your job better.

• Allow adequate time for an interview or counselling session. (The use of an interpreter will often extend the amount of time you will need.)

• Ask the interpreter to explain the client's values, practices, feelings and beliefs if you are unsure about these things.

• Describe your role and your service's mandate to both the interpreter and the client.

• Establish rapport with both the interpreter and the client using the Checklist for Effective Communication.

• Explain terms and concepts to the interpreter, and check the interpreter's understanding of them. Observe the client's reception of the interpretation and check their understanding of the terms and concepts.

• Observe your client's relationship with the interpreter to ensure that the interpreter is actually conveying the client's concerns and not his or her own concerns (which is common when family members interpret) or his or her interpretation of the client's concerns.

• Respond to questions from both the client and the interpreter.

• Stop an interview or counselling session if the interpreter and client seem to be having any sort of a conflict. Try not to get involved in the conflict but encourage its resolution.

• Watch out for the common mistakes (listed below) that service providers make when using interpreters.

Common Problems That Occur When Using an Interpreter

Lack of translatable words/concepts
Some words and concepts that exist in one context do not exist in another. You may need to backtrack and explain to the interpreter the basis of such words and concepts.

Unfamiliar terminology
Interpreters may not be familiar with professional or institutional terminology. Avoid jargon or clearly explain any that you must use.

Linguistic distortion
There may be an inaccurate translation of words. Check to see if both the interpreter and client understand what is being said.

Distortion of meaning/polishing language
Nuances and meanings can be misconstrued or lost if the interpreter "polishes" language. Ask the interpreter not to polish what you are saying. Assure both the interpreter and the client that the interview or counselling session is confidential and encourage the interpreter to fully express what the client is saying. Watch the client's body language and be reassuring when necessary.

Deletion of information
Some elements of speech (e.g., syllables), nuances and anecdotal information may be deleted by the interpreter. In some settings, such as a psychiatric hospital, these may be important. Ask the interpreter not to delete information. Again, encourage the interpreter to fully express what the client is saying, watch the client's body language and be reassuring, when necessary.

Modification/exaggeration of meaning
The interpreter may consciously modify or exaggerate questions and responses on your part or the client's part. Watch your client for any signs of this.

Cultural/ethnic and racial unfamiliarity
Interpreters may not be familiar with specific factors in a client's background or home environment. Once you have established rapport with the interpreter and the client, make sure that you ask questions about their background or home environment.

Blocking
The interpreter may indicate that the client is refusing to participate in the communication process. Try addressing the client directly as best you can.

Adapted from: *Cultural Interpreter Training Manual,* Toronto: Ontario Ministry of Citizenship, page 51.

USING A CARE MAP

A care map is a tool that has been developed to help service providers design a holistic addictions treatment program for culturally, ethnically and racially diverse clients. It has 12 sections, all of which are intended to help service providers determine the thoughts and feelings of their clients, identify their specific health and human service concerns, and match clients to appropriate resources. Service providers may also find care maps useful in managing case loads for clients from different communities.

The cases outlined in each of the following care maps are based on real issues that were encountered by service providers in different settings, but the cases themselves are fictitious.

WHAT A CARE MAP LOOKS LIKE

Name of Client

Status
Immigrant, refugee, in-settlement or minority.

Problems Presented
As determined by the client.

Potential Underlying Causes
As identified by the service provider from his or her interactions with the clients. Use the descriptions of the health and human service needs of culturally, ethnically and racially diverse populations included in this handbook to determine the potential underlying causes.

Significant Relationships
As identified by the client.

Current Life Situation
As identified by the client.

Services Required
As identified by the service provider from his or her interactions with the client. Use the descriptions of the health and human service needs of culturally, ethnically and racially diverse populations included in this chapter to determine the potential services needed.

Type of Service Contacted

Role of Service Provider
As negotiated between the service provider and the client. For example, will the service provider function as a facilitator, an expert or an adviser? If the service provider cannot function in an expected role, can he or she find someone who can?

Wellness Schedule
This is a time-limited counselling program developed by the service provider in consultation with the client.

Referral to Other Agencies
Consult the list of resources available to culturally, ethnically and racially diverse populations in the next section.

Follow-up
None

EXAMPLE OF A CARE MAP FOR AN IMMIGRANT CLIENT

Name of Client
An Li Xing

Status
Immigrant from China. In early 30s. Has been in Canada for two years.

Problems Presented
Argues with husband, children misbehaving at school, has insomnia. Saw a doctor about stress shortly after arriving in Canada, and the doctor prescribed Halcion to help her sleep. Over the last two years, she has become both physically and psychologically dependent on Halcion. She is even "double-doctoring" to get her supply of pills.

Potential Underlying Causes
Left China just before the Tiananmen Square Massacre. Has some guilt about leaving. Expectations of a new and better life in Canada not met. There is a loss in socioeconomic status and an inability to connect with past achievements and positive aspects of former life.

Significant Relationships
Husband and children.

Current Life Situation
Was a chemistry professor in China. Her PhD is not recognized in Canada. She is currently working as a research assistant in a university lab in a largely francophone setting. She is her family's main income provider. Her husband is a post-doctoral fellow working towards a tenure-track job, so he does not have much time for his family. She has few recreational opportunities and does not spend as much time as she would like with her family. She speaks academic French well but is unfamiliar with colloquial French. She therefore spends most of her time with other Chinese immigrants. Most of them, like her, live and work in an academic setting.

Services Required
Assessment of her use of sleeping pills. Discussion of intervention and treatment options. Help choosing an option. Help assessing skills, resources and knowledge. Help re-establishing expectations. Help setting new goals and objectives. Language and life skills training for professionals. New contacts in the Chinese and larger community. Recreational opportunities for self and family. Perhaps couple or family therapy to deal with changing roles.

Type of Service Contacted
Student Health Centre

Role of Service Provider

Facilitator. Begins helping An Li by listening to her family problems and helping her work through them. Refers her to other services but maintains regular contact through phone calls and scheduled visits.

Wellness Schedule

Six-month program. In months one to three, An Li's service provider finds a play therapy group for her and her children, identifies language training and life skills program for her, helps her plan recreational activities, and refers her to social and recreational clubs.

An Li makes a contract with service provider to come in once a month to discuss her life situation, to set aside two weekends a month for social and recreational activities, and to sign up for language training and life skills. With the help of her service provider, she learns some behavioral change techniques to reduce her use of sleeping pills.

In months three to six, An Li continues counselling and language and life-skills training. Now her service provider refers her to a career counselling centre for immigrant women to discuss her future life and work plans, helps her set goals and objectives for upgrading her education, and encourages her to connect with professional associations. As she begins to develop new expectations and hope, her use of sleeping pills stops.

An Li's relationship with her husband, however, does not improve and her service provider suggests marital therapy, which she rejects. Her service provider lets her know that the option is always open to her.

Referral to Other Agencies

FSL/life-skills classes, social and recreational clubs, ethno-specific agencies, training and development centre.

Follow-up

One phone call a month for the next six months to monitor life situation and psycho-social status.

EXAMPLE OF A CARE MAP FOR A REFUGEE CLIENT

Name of Client
Mohammed Omar-Nur

Status
A refugee claimant from Somalia in his mid-40s. Has been in Canada for 10 months and is still waiting to have his claim heard. Has been told it could take up to three years to process. Before coming to Canada, lived in a refugee camp in Egypt.

Problems Presented
Does not feel physically well and is depressed. Expresses anger and frustration towards service providers. Can't sleep and eat. Uses alcohol while socializing with other Somalis, during meals and before bedtime. Does not use much (only one to two drinks per day), but prior to coming to Canada did not drink or believe in drinking. (He is Muslim and Islamic law prohibits drinking.) Feels guilty about drinking but considers it his one pleasure. Has heard about Alcoholics Anonymous but is uncomfortable with their approach. Hears that there is a pill to control alcohol use and wants to know how he can get it.

Has come to your centre with a friend who acts as his translator. His friend, who is also Somali and is upset with Mohammed's drinking problem, keeps interjecting his feelings about alcohol into the dialogue, which makes it difficult to really understand what Mohammed is feeling. The friend also liberally interprets what the counsellor says about treatment.

Potential Underlying Causes
Refugee claimant living in limbo. Left Somalia hoping to send for family but lost touch with family after reaching Egypt. Lived in refugee camp where he was assaulted and possibly raped. Grief and guilt about leaving family behind. Experience in camp created a loss of dignity. Mourning loss of family and self. Constant fear for safety. Uncertainty about present and about future.

Significant Relationships
Few significant relationships. Has connected with other middle-aged Somali men who are alone in Canada.

Current Life Situation
Was a teacher in Somalia, is now driving a taxi. Speaks limited English. Reluctant to socialize but is very lonely. Limited contact with people outside of work and few friends.

Services Required
Accurate information about alcohol use for both Mohammed and his interpreter. Reassurance that alcohol use is considered a health issue (not a moral issue) in Canada. Determination whether alcohol use is problematic. Discussion of intervention and

treatment options. Help identifying level of motivation for dealing with problem, if any. Help choosing an option, if help is desired. Legal assistance. Thorough assessment of pre-arrival experience by mental health service provider who understands post-traumatic stress disorder. Referral to appropriate mental health services. Language and life-skills training. Assistance identifying unsettling thoughts and emotions. Learning to express thoughts and emotions. Validation of anger and depression. Establishment of connection to old life.

Type of Service Contacted
Alcohol and drug assessment and referral centre

Role of Service Provider
Adviser and advocate. Begins helping Mohammed by referring him to a legal aid clinic to discuss his refugee status. Finds him a self-change program at a treatment centre to control his alcohol use and an ad hoc support group for refugees at a reception centre. Offers to provide him with help and information as needed. Intervenes on his behalf with other service providers.

Wellness Schedule
One-year program. In months one to five, Mohammed's service provider refers him to a mental health agency that has experience dealing with refugees suffering from post-traumatic stress disorder. There is a waiting list to get an assessment and a waiting list for the agency's refugee program. His service provider convinces the agency to do an assessment and then helps Mohammed identify some immediate issues he would like to deal with and refers him to a family counselling service for therapy, which he discontinues.

In months six to eight, Mohammed is still waiting to get into the refugee program. He continues with his self-change program and goes to his support group. While he waits, his service provider helps him identify language, life-skills and vocational training he would like to undertake. The service provider helps Mohammed register for training programs (e.g., filling out forms), puts him in touch with an international aid organization that can help him find out about his family, and urges him to participate in the social activities sponsored by his self-change program and support group.

By months eight to 12, Mohammed is in the refugee program and attending a job re-training program. He feels his drinking is under control, but he still feels isolated. His service provider refers him to a "host program," where he is matched with a family that helps him feel more integrated.

Referral to Other Agencies
Legal clinic, addiction service, settlement agency, community counselling centre, mental health service, training and skills development centre, host program

Follow-up
Mohammed is encouraged to check in with service provider periodically.

EXAMPLE OF A CARE MAP FOR AN IN-SETTLEMENT CLIENT

Name of Client
Dominica Arano

Status
Homemaker and homeworker. Second-generation Italian-Canadian in her early 50s.

Problems Presented
Trouble sleeping. Stressed. Difficulty dealing with mother's recent death and father's increasing frailty and alcohol use. Concerned about losing control over her life. Cannot seem to relax and has anxiety attacks. Her husband has just retired and her children are leaving home. Has discussed her issues with her priest, siblings and doctor. No one seems very sympathetic. Doctor has prescribed anti-depressants, but Dominica does not take them. Instead she drinks alone and in secret.

Potential Underlying Causes
Grief over mother's death. Must care for father, who is angry, depressed and verbally abusive, especially when he starts drinking. Guilt over not being able to properly care for father. Desire to have someone else care for him. Tired of being his cook, friend, nurse and translator. Confusion about changes in her roles (wife and mother) as children leave home. Depression over inability to cope; feels that depression will last forever.

Significant Relationships
Husband and children. Relationship with husband has changed significantly since he retired. Places more demands on her attention. Children need her less and less, and are no longer her helpers or allies in the family. At the same time, her father needs more time. This creates conflicts with husband. Husband deals with conflict by drinking and socializing with friends. She deals with conflict by avoiding it.

Current Life Situation
Lives in a small community near a larger urban centre. Leads a comfortable life. Was a garment worker before she married, then became a homemaker, and is now a homeworker, making wedding and bridesmaids' dresses for friends and neighbors when she wants to. She enjoys working and does not feel that she has enough time for this. She is fluently bilingual in English and Italian but feels more comfortable living and socializing in the Italian-Canadian community.

Services Required
Information about emotional and physical changes associated with aging. Information about alcohol use and the elderly. Information about anti-depressants. Culturally appropriate therapy to deal with loss and grief. Culturally appropriate senior support care for father. Regular recreational activities with her husband. Contact with other women in a similar situation.

Type of Service Contacted
Seniors' support service

Role of Service Provider
Expert, mediator and parent. Begins by providing Dominica with information about why she feels the way that she does and why her father and her husband are acting as they do. Sympathizes with her over her difficulties. Refers her to an Italian-speaking doctor who discusses the proper use of anti-depressants and helps her decide whether to use them. (She decides to use them for a limited period of six to eight months and, because she is using them, she stops drinking.)

Wellness Schedule
Eight-month program. Few programs are specifically geared to the health and human service needs of Italian-Canadians in Dominica's community. In months one to five, her service provider arranges to have a senior support worker visit her father. This worker has little experience with Italian-Canadian seniors but, from information Dominica provides, is able to give adequate care. Her service provider then finds a family counselling service in the community, helps her become comfortable with the idea of seeking therapy, and tries to help her therapist understand Dominica's cultural background. Later, her service provider identifies a culturally appropriate service in the nearby urban centre and encourages her to try both services.

In months six to eight, Dominica begins therapy, first with the culturally appropriate service but later (because of the long drive) switches to the local counselling service. She spends a great deal of time explaining her culture to her counsellor, which helps her understand her own behavior. She also starts scheduling time with her husband. Although she still feels out of control, she does not feel she needs to take the anti-depressants any more and her relationships with both her father and husband improve.

Referral to Other Agencies
Family counselling services, Italian-Canadian service, seniors' support group

Follow-up
Monthly phone calls to check on father's welfare and Dominica's well-being. Provision of information and advice on how to deal with seniors and substance use.

EXAMPLE OF A CARE MAP FOR A MINORITY CLIENT

Name of Client
Kurpinder "Kirk" Singh

Status
Sikh-Canadian in mid-20s who identifies himself as a person of color.

Problems Presented
Seeking help for recreational cannabis use. Motivated to stop. Feels he needs to take control of his life and that stopping his cannabis use is one way to do this.

Potential Underlying Causes
Angry at parents for not understanding that he feels caught between the traditional Sikh culture and mainstream Canadian culture. Frustrated with friends who seem to either reject their Sikh heritage or embrace it without question. Outraged at mainstream society for not accepting that he can be both a Sikh and a Canadian. Has experienced racial and religious discrimination throughout his life and feels a sense of social dislocation as a result of it.

Significant Relationships
Few significant relationships. Lives with family in the heart of a suburban Sikh community but feels alienated from family and Sikh friends. Spends most of his time watching television, "hanging out" and attending sports events with co-workers who are also minorities.

Current Life Situation
Graduated from university four years ago with Computer Science degree but was unable to find work with a major company because of his insistence that he be allowed to wear his turban. Instead he found a job in a university computer lab where the work was more stimulating and he seemed to be accepted for himself. It was through his co-workers that he was introduced to recreational cannabis use. While he enjoys the effects of cannabis and does not feel he has a problem, he wants to stop — it costs too much, creates suspicions at home and aggravates an asthma condition.

Services Required
Determination of extent of cannabis use and the interventions or treatment necessary. Forum for expressing anger, frustrations and outrage. Help identifying personal and social resources. Validation of experiences with discrimination.

Type of Service Contacted
Outpatient treatment facility

Role of Service Provider
Fixer and facilitator

Wellness Schedule
None created. Because Kirk was motivated, he uses the outpatient facility he has contacted. His service provider validates his experiences with racism, provides him with information about racism and self-esteem, and advises him to contact a race relations organization to discuss his experiences.

Referral to Other Agencies
Outpatient facility

Follow-up
None

CONCLUSION

The purpose of this chapter was to outline strategies and tactics for addiction service providers working with culturally and racially diverse populations. Since there is no one way of working with these groups, it is important that service providers understand the basic rules of cultural/racial sensitivity; know about the various services that are available to culturally and racially diverse communities; and be aware of the general health and human service needs of immigrants, refugees, in-settlement populations and minority groups.

NOTES

[1] Ontario Ministry of Citizenship. *A Diverse and Changing Society: A Report on Selected Demographic Trends, Ethno-cultural Data Base Materials — Series III,* Special Report Number 5. (Toronto: Queen's Printer for Ontario, 1991), p. 12.

[2] The United Nations has defined refugees as persons who, by reason of race, religion, nationality (citizenship), or membership in a particular social or political group, are outside of their country of nationality or former habitual residence and unable, or by reason of such fear, unwilling, to avail themselves of the protection of that country. Refugees to Canada include government-sponsored refugees, privately sponsored refugees, conventional refugees (those claiming refugee status under the United Nations Convention) and women at risk, who are seeking safety from state-sponsored or social persecution.

SOURCES

Much of the information contained in this chapter has been compiled from interviews with staff at community-based agencies across Ontario. They include:

Ed Graca and Isabel Sales, Abrigo Centre for Victims of Family Violence

Khan Rahi, Access Action Council

Faduma Dirie and Joan Similchik, Canadian Centre for Victims of Torture

Carmelina Losaria Barwick, Clarke Institute of Psychiatry

Odida Quamina Jr., Commission on Systemic Racism and the Criminal Justice System

Robert Cazzola, COSTI Family Services

Beta Leung, Marilyn Porto and Marilyn State, Doctors Hospital Women's Mental Health Program

Dr. Ted Lo, Hong Fook Mental Health Services

Marjan Motezemi and Farnaz Esfanian, Iranian Community of Ontario

Miriam Zeballos, Latin American Community Centre

Margaret Flower, Elly Munn and Anabelle Sabloff,
Metro Addiction Assessment and Referral Services

Moffat Makuto, Multicutural Association of North Western Ontario

Ana Maria Salgueiro, Multicultural Association of Thunder Bay

Elizabeth Cichon, Polish Immigrant and Community Services

Sheila Strong, Scarborough Cultural Interpreters Pilot Project

Baldev Mutta, Tim Weber and Purvi Bering, Punjabi Community Health Project

Ruby Lum, Toronto Board of Education

REFERENCES

Access Action Council. (1992). *Aging in a Multicultural Society.* Toronto: Social Planning Council of Metropolitan Toronto.

Bhaggityia, S. and Brand, D. (1986). *Rivers Have Sources, Trees Have Roots.* Toronto: Cross Cultural Communications Centre.

Casas, J.M. (1989). A culturally sensitive model for evaluating alcohol and other drug abuse prevention programs: A Hispanic perspective. In *Cultural Competence for Evaluators: A Guide for Alcohol and Other Drug Abuse Prevention Practitioners Working with Ethnic/Racial Communities.* Rockville, MD: U.S. Department of Health and Human Services.

City of Toronto Department of Public Health, Health Promotion and Advocacy Section:
  • *The Caribbean Community in Toronto,* 1989.
  • *The Chinese Community in Toronto,* 1989.
  • *The Greek Canadian Community in Toronto,* 1989.
  • *The Italian Canadian Community in Toronto,* 1989.
  • *The Portuguese Canadian Community in Toronto,* 1989.
  • *The Spanish Speaking Community in Toronto,* 1989.
  • *The Sri Lankan Tamil Community in Toronto,* 1989.

Galway, J. (1991). *Immigrant Settlement Counselling.* Toronto: Ontario Council of Agencies Serving Immigrants.

Grace, C.A. (1989). Practical considerations for program professionals working with African American communities. In *Cultural Competence for Evaluators: A Guide for Alcohol and Other Drug Abuse Prevention Practitioners Working with Ethnic/Racial Communities.* Rockville, MD: U.S. Department of Health and Human Services.

James, C. (1991). *Seeing Ourselves: An Exploration of Culture, Ethnicity and Race.* Brampton: Sheridan College Press.

Kim, S., McLeod, J.H., and Shantzis, C. (1989). Cultural competence for evaluators working with Asian-American communities: Some practical considerations. In *Cultural Competence for Evaluators: A Guide for Alcohol and Other Drug Abuse Prevention Practitioners Working with Ethnic/Racial Communities.* Rockville, MD: U.S. Department of Health and Human Services.

Lee, E. (1985). *Letters to Marcia: A Teacher's Guide to Anti-Racist Education.* Toronto: Cross-Cultural Communications Centre.

Ontario Ministry of Citizenship. (1989). *Cultural Interpreter Training Manual.* Toronto: Queen's Printer for Ontario.

Ontario: A Diverse and Changing Society: A Report on Selected Demographic Trends. (1991). Ethno-cultural Database Materials — Series III, Special Report Number 5. Toronto: Queen's Printer for Ontario.

Ontario Ministry of Health. (1989). *Let's Work Together: Guidelines to Promote Cultural/Racial Sensitivity and Awareness in Health Care Programs and Services.* Toronto: Ontario Ministry of Health.

Reeve-Elington, R. (1993). Using cultural skills for co-operative advantage in Japan. In *Human Organizational State.*

Sue, D.W., Arrendondo, P., and McDavis, R.J. (1992). Multicultural counseling competencies and standards: A call to the profession. In *Journal of Counselling & Development* 7 (March/April): 477–486.

Tsang, B. (1994). *Cultural Diversity: A Handbook for Addiction Service Providers.* Toronto: Addiction Research Foundation.

Chapter 20

Cultural Considerations for Native Clients

Audrey Hill

The impact of western acculturation on the family life of a native client is a critical consideration in substance abuse counselling, whether one is working with a client as an individual or in a family setting. This chapter will outline the relevance of systems and structural theory on cross-cultural family counselling. Six cultural considerations will illustrate diverse influences on native family structures. Four native family types will also be discussed in terms of their relevance in counselling native clients.

Family systems theory has made a significant contribution to the field of counselling and has been addressed in literature in the addictions field since 1970. Lawson, Peterson and Lawson (1983) provide a family systems perspective whereby the entire family is seen as the client and the addiction is viewed as a symptom of an entire family system. As a result, assessment and treatment planning for the "family as client" can be facilitated by understanding the dynamics operating in the family structure.

The structural approach is based on the assumption that family interactions provide a focus for assessing family functioning and well-being. Using the systems perspective of "family as client," the structural approach emphasizes three central concepts. The first concept is "family roles," which develop in relation to the family's environment and lifestyle, and provide cohesion and adaptability for the family system. The second concept is "family subsystems," which clarify major areas of family functioning such as the marital subsystem and the sibling subsystem. The third concept comprises "relational boundaries," and addresses the territorial sanctions and limits between members of the entire family systems and those that function for their respective subsystem. An example of how these boundaries function is illustrated by the "incest taboo" — a prohibition of incestuous relations between the marital and offspring subsystems (Goldenberg and Goldenberg, 1985).

Native people, such as Redhorse, Attneave and others, have found the structural and systems perspectives to be philosophically adaptable to cultural views of family functioning. Their relevance to the native family is based on shifting the emphasis to a collective value framework and to resolving concrete, interactional family problems. However, while structural and systems theories provide a conceptual framework for native family functioning, a problem arises when describing the characteristics of a "healthy, functional family system." Attneave (1982) suggests that a "healthy, functional, native family system" would be described by characteristics that emphasized collective values and may not resemble a western definition of family.

It is important to assess the relevance of exploring past and present family dynamics with the native client. Although resistance will be likely, the counsellor must understand the significance of past and present family life, and view the client as a synthesis of experiences that is largely influenced by his or her family of origin. The family structure fundamentally influenced the client's personality development, values, perceptions, socialization, behaviors and so on. For the native client, the counsellor requires at least a general understanding of the family as a natural social system that functions according to a set of values, rules, roles, power structure, communication style and problem-solving strategies (Goldenberg and Goldenberg, 1985).

To help the native client to explore his or her past and present family structure, the counsellor must be aware that the native family is a culturally unique social system with significantly different influences. These differences are contextualized in a historical process of western acculturation (Attneave, 1982; Sue and Sue, 1990). Sue and Sue outline the following six cultural considerations that impact on family structure and emphasize their significance in cross-cultural family counselling.

1. CULTURAL, MINORITY REALITY

Experiences such as poverty, racism and discrimination influence and shape the relational reality of minority family members. As a unit, the family may be structurally defined by its minority status in society. Such experiences may be further defined by the client's culture. For example, the "Oka Standoff" has been described as a racist experience that defines the cultural, minority reality of native people.

2. CONFLICTING VALUE SYSTEMS

Collective values support family interactions based on sharing, generosity and interdependency with the family system. Western values for individuality and the emphasis on independence conflict with a native cultural value framework. The conflict of native and western value systems is experienced in all areas of contemporary native family life, including marriage, parenting and various stages of family life.

3. BICULTURALISM

Social interaction within the educational system, workforce and other areas of western society introduce diverse choices to native people. Compromise, adaptability and change influence the native family structure and perpetuate cultural evolution.

4. MINORITY STATUS

Political and social realities also affect native family structure with past and present losses such as land, language and education. For example, the era of residential schooling of native children created a generation of "institutionalized parents" and many present-day families continue to experience the wounds of institutionalization.

5. LANGUAGE

For native people, the traditional language conveys culture and the true dimension of reality. Adaptation to western language has been described as the most significant loss to native families, creating barriers between traditional wisdom-keepers and new family members.

6. SOCIAL CLASS

Differences in wealth, name, occupation and so on affect the native family structure and the adaptation of family roles and value framework. These differences would also influence the development of the helper-client relationship.

It is important to know these major cultural differences and their potential impact on structural family relationships. In using a structural approach to counselling a native client, it is critical to understand the therapeutic implications for establishing healthy boundaries and alliances according to a cultural view of a "healthy, functional native family system."

The impact of western influences on the native family structure can be viewed along a range, or continuum, of acculturation that provides for four types of native families (Redhorse, Lewis, Feit and Decker, 1978). These family types are reserve-based, migratory, transitional and bicultural native families. It is also important to recognize the cultural diversity among these native family types. For example, one reserve-based family type (Iroquois culture of southern Ontario) will differ significantly from another (Ojibwa culture of northern Ontario). Each native family type in this framework must be viewed with an understanding of the particular cultural society of each client.

The following briefly summarizes each native family type in contemporary Iroquois society and provides commentary on its significance in assessment and treatment planning for the native client.

Reserve-Based Native Family

In contemporary Iroquois society, these families are generally characterized by a large, extended matriarchal family system. Family members have been born, raised, educated and continue to reside on the reserve. Traditional language, cultural knowledge and history have been retained, and have been passed on orally by family members. Traditional Iroquois families continue to adhere to the long house and observe traditional teachings of the "Great Law of the Iroquois Confederacy." This source of knowledge is extremely important to native clients — it is an essential link to the cultural identity of the individual and the family system.

Elder family members retain an integral role in the lives of their extended family members. The primary developmental task of family members is to become an interdependent family system. Individuality is a secondary goal, emphasizing the fundamental group values of sharing, generosity and equality.

Personal and family experiences of reserve life play an important role in the personality dynamics of the addicted native client. Consideration of these early childhood memories is clinically significant in assessing the psychosocial history, and in determining role models, exposure to various childhood traumas, major losses, rules, communication patterns and self-image. The counsellor must understand what the native client perceives to be a healthy, constructive lifestyle. What is a functional native family system? If the client perceives a value for his or her culture, the client's lifestyle must be changed without sacrificing the integrity of cultural identity.

Migratory Native Family

In contemporary Iroquois society, many families frequently migrate from the reserve to nearby urban communities to search for a means of subsistence: employment, housing, health services, educational opportunities and so on. These temporary absences have created a sense of alienation from the traditional family supports of the reserve-based, extended family system. While living in the urban environment, the native family has been exposed to western influences and advanced acculturation. Urban living creates psychosocial stress for each individual. The stressors, often termed "culture shock," have tested the family's ability to adapt to frequent changes. Substance abuse often becomes a dysfunctional coping strategy for the multiple stressors of a migratory lifestyle and alienation from traditional family supports, cultural knowledge and identity.

Assessment of native clients should include an understanding of the childhood influences and experiences of a migratory native family that abused substances in an effort to cope with its lifestyle. Urban experiences would also lead to a "differentness" that would be perceived as a loss of cultural identity. Because of these different experiences and alienation from reserve-based family members, the individual inter-nalizes "differentness" as another psychosocial stressor. It is part of the individual's identity. Treatment planning, from this perspective, should address the native client's motivation to adopt a lifestyle that promotes resolution of a cultural identity crisis and the acquisition of healthy, coping skills for dealing with psychosocial stress.

Transitional Native Family

In contemporary Iroquois society, this native family has adjusted to an urban commu-nity, functions as a nuclear family and has become alienated from the traditional, reserve-based native community and extended native family system. The closed social system that characterizes this family structure tends to deny younger family members access to the reserve's community and family experiences, cultural lan-guage and knowledge. At the same time, adult family members maintain a low level of acculturation with the dominant society. This family may be second- or third-gen-eration "urban," yet may be in transition. If a cultural identity remains, it is based on a western perspective that may range from stereotypical to prejudicial toward the native community.

The counsellor may view a client from this family structure as an individual who is having an identity crisis. Assessment should address the client's perception of the importance of a cultural identity in addiction counselling. The native client may or may not consider cultural identity as a primary issue surrounding his or her addiction. The client may openly acknowledge a sense of loss for the cultural "roots" or may adamant-ly claim that cultural identity is unimportant. Pervasive western influences and the lack of cultural ties and knowledge have led family members to adopt western values that primarily advocate individuality and independence within a nuclear family system. This orientation conflicts with the traditional Iroquois values of collective rights, com-munity development and interdependence within an extended family system.

The substance abuse counsellor must understand the intercultural issues relating to cultural identity and acculturation. For example, some "urbanized" native peoples may be referred to as "apples" (red on the outside, white on the inside), or native peo-ple who demonstrate a bicultural lifestyle may be viewed as "lost" and deserving of tolerance and acceptance. The native client may be aware of — or may even have experienced — such intercultural stigmatism. This situation can pose a barrier to the client's re-integration into the native community. For the native client who is consid-ering repatriation within his or her native family and/or community, counselling sup-ports must be knowledgeable with respect to cultural considerations.

Treatment planning and counselling should help native clients to obtain cultural information and, if possible, referral to an urban native social service or program that may facilitate their return to the native community. Urban native community services are an essential cultural link for the native individual. Some reserves have developed health, social and educational services. It would be helpful for the client and the addiction counsellor to have access to information about each client's reserve community.

Bicultural Native Family

This native family type may reside on the reserve or in an urban community, or may own land and homes in both areas. Generally characterized by higher levels of employment, education and income, family members can function as a nuclear family but have maintained their ties with the extended native family and community. They have successfully adapted to a western lifestyle without sacrificing their cultural identity, knowledge and values, although they may no longer speak their traditional language. In other words, they have bridged the native and western worlds and can function effectively in both. In contrast to the transitional family, this native family type has successfully acculturated toward a harmonious balance of biculturalism.

CONCLUSION

In contrast to the migratory and transitional native family types, the reserve-based and bicultural are the most functional family types, both socially and psychologically. Based on the range of acculturation among native family systems and the four family types outlined here, counsellors must also recognize the cultural diversity that exists. Each family type must be viewed with an understanding of the particular culture of the native client. The native family structure becomes an important cultural consideration in terms of assessment and treatment for the native client with a substance use problem.

Although this chapter has focused on Iroquois family types, it can provide a model for the counsellor to explore the family types of other native clients, since many of the acculturational influences affect other tribes in a similar way.

REFERENCES

Attneave, C. (1982). Native American families. In *Ethnicity and Family Therapy*, eds. McGoldrick, M., Pearce, J.K., and Giordano, J. New York: Guilford Press.

Goldenberg, I., and Goldenberg, H. (1985). *Family Therapy: An Overview*. Monterey, CA: Brooks/Cole Publishing Co.

Hill, A. (1989). Treatment and prevention of alcoholism in the native American family. In *Alcoholism and Substance Abuse in Special Populations*, eds. Lawson, G., and Lawson, A. Rockville, MD: Aspen Publications.

Mohatt, G., McDiarmid, W., and Montoya, V. (1988). Societies, families and change: The Alaskan example. In *Behavioral Health Issues Among American Indians and Alaska Natives*. American Indian and Alaska Native Mental Health Research, Monograph No. 1: 325-365.

Redhorse, J., Lewis, R., Feit, M., and Decker, J. (1978). Family behavior of urban American Indians. *Social Casework* 59: 67–72.

Redhorse, J. (1983). Indian family values and experiences. In *The Psychosocial Development of Minority Children*. New York: Brunner and Mazel.

McKenzie, B., Seidl, E., and Bone, N. (1995). Child and family service standards in First Nations: An action research project. *Child Welfare League of America* 74 (3): 633–651.

Sue, D.W., and Sue, D. (1990). *Cross-Cultural Family Counselling*. Toronto: John Wiley and Sons.

Chapter 21

Addiction and the Family

RICHARD J. BOUDREAU

WHY INVOLVE THE FAMILY?

There is still a widespread view of addiction, even among counsellors, as a problem that primarily afflicts the individual. There may be some recognition that others around the person are affected, but not necessarily in the sense that they may be playing a role in maintaining the addiction or, more importantly, could be a vital asset in its resolution.

Such views persist despite growing evidence that family and other social supports are key factors in addictions intervention. Although the role of other family members will vary in each given situation, it remains true that addiction problems generally develop within a family context. And research findings suggest that involving the family to some extent in treatment contributes to a better outcome.

A basic tenet of family counselling is that whatever happens to one member of the family affects all the other members, and similarly, the response of the other members in turn affects the original member in question. This fundamental principle of family work holds true not only in terms of a family's weaknesses and deficits, but more importantly, in relation to its strengths. It is an implicit assumption of this brief chapter that any work involving the family at any level should address and build on family strengths — despite the recognition in many cases of notable deficits.

Clearly then, the family represents a primary setting where issues of addiction are manifested. It is also a context where problems related to addiction are either successfully dealt with or inadvertently reinforced and perpetuated. For this reason, any treatment intervention that neglects this important dimension may, at the very least, miss out on potent treatment strategies, or at worst, work against itself by ignoring factors that often contribute to relapse. Most addictions counsellors can likely recall having successfully intervened with an individual only to have the client relapse upon return to an unchanged family environment.

WHAT IT MEANS TO INVOLVE FAMILIES

Many mental health and social services, in promoting their work, advertise that they "see families," "work with families" or "counsel families." What does it mean?

Work with families can involve an array of services ranging from basic orientation to long-term, in-depth family therapy. The family might merely be oriented to the program in which an addicted family member is enrolled, or might embark on a carefully developed regimen of family therapy, or something in between. This would be determined on the basis of the assessed family needs and resources available to meet them. Table 1 below outlines four categories of family involvement with suggested levels of interventions and related objectives. It should be noted that these are broad categories with numerous possible varieties within each.

TABLE 1

Types of Family Involvement	Level of Intervention	Objectives
Family orientation	Orienting the family to the philosophy and approaches of the service.	To inform the family about the program that the identified patient is embarking upon, and to enlist family support.
Parenting/family education group	Involving parents and/or families in family life education with special reference to substance abuse issues.	To inform family members about family relations issues and how they may be relevant to substance abuse.
Family counselling	Contracting with the family for interventions aimed at resolving specifically identified problems.	To bring about the resolution of problems identified by family members and related to the substance abuse.
Family therapy	Contracting with the family for interventions aimed at chronic and systemic family dysfunction.	To bring about change to elusive and intractable areas of systemic family dysfunction related to the substance abuse.

In addition to the services outlined above, which would typically be offered in family and social service agencies, family issues are also addressed by a growing array of mutual help groups such as Al-Anon, Children of Alcoholics Groups (COA), Parents Against Drugs (PAD), etc. Many agencies that work primarily from an individual perspective collaborate with such groups in having family issues addressed during therapy. It would be a mistake to assume that because a service is not set up to do formal family counselling or family therapy, it should therefore not undertake any family work. The evidence would indicate that important and effective changes can be brought about through simple but well-developed educational programs, especially with families presenting early-stage addictions problems.

An important distinction needs to be made in working with families with an addiction problem. That is whether the problem with addiction lies with the parent(s) or in one (or more) of the children. A growing number of families are presenting with addictions issues in both generations. Whether the problem is in the parenting or offspring generation will have important bearing on issues such as the following:

• Should the focus of the family work be primarily on marital or parental matters?
• Which family members most significantly need to be involved in the family sessions?
• If there are substance abuse issues in both generations, will they be addressed separately or together?

Decision-making around such matters will vary greatly from family to family. Where there is substance abuse in both generations, important factors to consider would be: the worker's experience and ability to deal with both generations; the advantages and disadvantages of dealing with each generation conjointly or concurrently; or of each generation being seen by separate workers collaboratively. The unique circumstances of each case will help determine the best approach.

Everything said to this point should make clear the importance of a comprehensive assessment in determining precisely what will be required in terms of family work for a given family. This will vary considerably from situation to situation depending on factors such as the following:

• What is the history and extent of the substance abuse? Is it early stage or long-standing? Is there evidence that the family, to a great extent, organizes around addiction?
• Does a comprehensive assessment suggest that the substance abuse is inextricably tied in with other couple/family dysfunction? Are other possibly more serious family problems being displaced upon the identified substance abuser?
• If family work is indicated, should it take place concurrently and conjointly? Should the substance abuse be brought under control before couple/family work is initiated? Which family members should make up the sessions?

• Will all the work be done in the one facility, or will the family work be referred to another service?

These are some of the essential questions that need to be addressed in determining the nature and extent of family work that may be required in conjunction with or in addition to specific addictions management interventions.

WHO SHOULD WORK WITH FAMILIES?

Once a comprehensive assessment has established that family work will be required and what the nature and level of that work might be, then it must be determined who will do the work. A major consideration in determining this is the mandate of the service of initial contact. Does its range of services include family counselling? Or is its mandate restricted to assessment/referral, primary care, detoxification, individual treatment modalities, etc.?

Given that family work is within the general mandate of the service, another important consideration would be the range of skills available within the staff to carry out the level of family intervention required. The skills of individual staff need to be clearly assessed. In addition, the combined resources of the agency to carry out family work need to be considered. These would include factors such as service hours to accommodate the school and work schedules of family members; agency attitudes and philosophies regarding family influence on addiction; and the opportunities for collaborative work among staff, which can be critical in family work. Such factors are important not only in terms of client service, but also in the ongoing assessment of staff and agency development needs in this important area of addictions intervention.

If a referral outside the agency of initial contact is indicated, the referring agency should have a thorough knowledge of family resources available in the community. This represents a key juncture in the treatment process for a number of reasons. It is at this point that some worker or agency must assume primary care responsibilities for the client and his or her family, so that continuity of care and linkages between agencies can be co-ordinated and maintained. Also at this point, decisions must be made about division of roles and responsibilities. Will the addictions management and family work be done concurrently or successively? Will it be done within the same or different agencies? By one or more workers? How these co-ordinating and referring (and follow-up) functions are carried out determines to a great extent whether the clients and their families will remain and progress in treatment. Without effective co-ordination, usually assumed by a primary care worker, clients can easily become entangled and lost within even fairly simple treatment systems.

It should be noted that there is still a great deal of debate in the field about the optimum timing of family work in the treatment of addiction. Whether it can go on while the substance abuse is being addressed, or whether it can only begin once the substance abuse is well under control continues to be argued. Many factors enter into this debate, including:

- the extent and duration of the substance abuse
- the level of deterioration in the couple/family relationships due to the substance abuse
- the possible presence of family violence associated with the substance abuse
- the willingness of the partner or other family members to be involved before the substance abuse has been brought under control.

Again, these issues need to be clarified by a comprehensive assessment. Beyond that, and for our purposes here, suffice it to say that it is crucial that there be clarity between collaborating agencies about philosophies and policies regarding this whole area of timing of family work, so that the family seeking service is not encumbered by this ongoing debate.

HOW TO WORK WITH THE FAMILY

It is well beyond the scope of this chapter to present in detail all the various schools and approaches to family counselling and family therapy in the treatment of addiction. This information is readily available in many related resources (see References section). It is important, however, for addictions counsellors to have some working knowledge of the major approaches broadly identified as structural, strategic, behavioral, solution-focused and multigenerational models of family treatment. Such knowledge allows the worker to make more informed decisions in matching clients and their families, not only in terms of the level of family work required, but also in regard to the model or approach that may be most compatible with a given family. For example (without invoking a hard and fast stance in these matters), one could expect that a family that appears to respond well to concrete contractual assignments would perhaps do better with a behavioral model of family therapy. A more multigenerational/Bowenian model might seem a more appropriate choice where substance abuse in a given family has had a clear multigenerational history and influence. Table 2 highlights five major schools of family treatment with their underlying theories and major objectives.

TABLE 2

Model/Approach	Underlying Theory	Focus of Intervention
Structural	Theory of family relations in terms of proximity/ distance and designated boundaries.	Restructuring of interactions between family members.
Strategic	Problem solving theory.	Resolving presenting problem through assignment of therapeutic tasks, directives and prescriptions.
Behavioral	Social learning theory.	Modification of family behavior through contracted changes in behavior of individual members.
Solution-focused	Expectation of change theory.	Helping the family to focus on exceptions to the problem behavior.
Multigenerational/ Bowenian	Intergenerational dynamics theory.	Resolution of individual member's role within the extended family system.

Regardless of what level of family intervention is indicated, or what modality of family work is finally adopted, three fundamental elements have been found to enhance and contribute to the effectiveness of family treatment.

The first would be the importance of identifying and promoting family strengths. Most families present with a diminished sense of their abilities and strengths because of their failure to resolve the identified problem(s) on their own. No individual or family is left devoid of all strengths or skills, no matter how intense or chronic the problem at hand may be. It is incumbent upon the effective family worker to help identify these family resources, no matter how compromised they may be under the circumstances, and develop strategies and interventions that build upon them. For example, a family may retain good problem-solving skills in other areas of life such as money management or the upkeep of the home, but be unable to bring these skills to bear on the problem of substance abuse. An important dimension of family work in such a case might be to reinforce these skills, and enable the family to apply them to the area of substance abuse.

Closely related to the question of building upon family strengths is the importance of mobilizing family members to do their own problem solving. In the final analysis, the most effective family treatment is one where family members hardly recognize that the counsellor had any part in resolving the problems.

Finally, almost all the literature on family counselling and family therapy encourages a team approach to this work. Even very basic work with families can become somewhat involved and challenging to an individual therapist working in isolation. A team approach — which might be as minimal as regular consultation with colleagues, or as elaborate as direct observation using highly technical feedback equipment — provides many benefits, including a range of insights into complex family dynamics, support to the worker, rich resources to the family, ongoing monitoring of treatment effectiveness of the individual and the agency, and a continuous atmosphere of learning and development for the team members.

Checklist for Decision-making about Involving the Family

By way of summary, the following represents a line of questioning that addictions workers might follow in deciding whether or how to include the family in their work with substance abuse.

- Is the identified client in the parenting or offspring generation? Is there substance abuse in both generations?
- Is the substance abuse of recent origin or is it long-standing?
- Is there evidence that the family is organized around substance abuse? Are there indications that other family problems or dysfunctions are displaced onto the identified substance abuser?
- What level of family involvement is indicated? Will a strategy of family support and education be adequate, or will a more structured regimen of family treatment be required?
- Given the characteristics of the identified client, and other family members, what model or approach of family treatment (structured, strategic, behavioral, solution-focused or intergenerational) would seem most appropriate?
- Who will undertake the family work? Will it be done by the worker/agency of initial contact? Or will it be referred to a specialized worker/agency?
- If referred, who will assume the responsibility for ensuring that the family becomes effectively engaged, and that proper linkages are maintained between involved agencies from assessment through follow-up?
- In terms of specific strategies of family treatment, are they based on identified areas of family strengths? Are strategies planned to clearly empower the family to identify and resolve its own problem(s)? And finally, is the family work organized to make the best use of the competencies, experience and support of the entire treatment team?

CASE ILLUSTRATION

The Smith family (not their real names) consists of four members. The parents are in their mid-40s. George, until a year and a half ago, had been a successful assistant manager in the sales department of a mid-size corporation. In a restructuring process, all positions at that level were eliminated. Since then, he and a colleague have been attempting to set up a sales consulting firm with modest success and a number of stressful start-up problems. Ruth has done paid part-time secretarial/bookkeeping work off and on and some volunteering since she married George. They have two daughters. Jane is in her second year of university in another city at some distance from home. Paula is in Grade 11 at a local high school.

Until recently, Paula had been an outgoing, popular and above-average student. In the past several months, her family and teachers noticed changes. There was a sudden and considerable drop in Paula's marks. She also had unexplained absenteeism, a new peer group, and often a sullen demeanor, coupled with angry outbursts at home. Paula had begun to come home way past the time agreed upon, which wasn't typical behavior for her. Mostly, she would go directly to her room and not want to discuss why she was late. On a couple of recent occasions, she returned home behaving peculiarly — very talkative but somewhat unfocused, with evidence of slurred speech. Drug use by this time was suspected but strongly denied by Paula. At her parents' urging, Paula agreed to see their family physician. An appointment was made but not kept.

A number of phone calls related to unexplained missed classes were made between the school and the parents. In brief meetings with the guidance counsellor, Paula expressed feelings of resentment toward her father and considerable anger toward her mother. But she refused to elaborate or become further engaged about these matters. The guidance counsellor consulted with a school board social worker. It was advised that a referral be made to the local Youth Services Centre for an assessment. The parents, George and Ruth, were contacted by the guidance counsellor and agreed with the plan. Paula reluctantly agreed on condition that her parents not be involved.

What probably facilitated the referral process is that Paula had visited the Youth Services Centre about a year earlier, in connection with a social studies school project, and had been impressed with the staff she had met. Over a period of two or three sessions with the counsellor it became clear that Paula had become increasingly anxious over the past year or more with the situation at home. Her sister had left for university; her father, whom she had always felt close to, was often away for several days at a time trying to launch his new consulting business; her mother, also preoccupied and stressed about some of the same issues, was often perceived by Paula to be emotionally unavailable (attributed in one offhand reference to "mother's drinking").

With the establishment of some trust early in the counselling, Paula became more forthcoming about her fairly frequent use of drugs (primarily alcohol and marijuana) with some of her new friends. She reported that "it helps me forget and feel better." After their third or fourth meeting, Paula agreed to involve her parents.

The next appointment was done jointly with Paula's counsellor and an experienced family therapist from the same centre. That session was helpful in beginning to surface the isolation felt by each family member over the past year or more. George felt he was letting the family down as provider; Ruth was frustrated that her part-time work, which was no longer fulfilling for her, was also not adequate to help maintain the family at the financial level they had grown accustomed to; Paula felt abandoned and, in a vague way, somehow responsible for what was happening to her parents. By the end of the session, they agreed that hearing what each was feeling and thinking had helped, and they agreed to structure some time to do things together, as they used to do, around family meals and some inexpensive outings.

The treatment plan that was agreed upon at this point was that Paula and her counsellor would continue to meet for a few more sessions, focusing primarily on alternatives to drug use in dealing with issues at school and at home. The parents agreed to meet with the family counsellor on their own for one or two sessions to look at the effects of the events of the last couple years on their relationship. The two counsellors checked in with one another on developments at regular staff conferences.

The school began to report decreased absenteeism and some improvement in Paula's academic performance. The parents confirmed that they were seeing positive changes at home as well. They also observed that Paula continued to test the boundaries for greater independence, but this was coupled with continued significant family involvement.

In their sessions, the parents were able to begin to work through the implications of their new financial situation for the family and for themselves as a couple. With the help of a financial adviser, referred to by their therapist, they were able to see how, with adjustments to the family budget and re-distribution of some investments, they could manage through their present difficulties.

A breakthrough in the couples work came between two of the sessions when Ruth was able to clearly declare to herself and George what plans she would like to pursue for herself careerwise, now that the children were less dependent. She expressed her intent to become a qualified real estate agent — an undertaking she had started earlier but had discontinued because of family demands. She reported that she had come to this decision with the help of a Women and Work support group offered at a women's counselling centre. She added, "It's a measure of how isolated we've become that I was afraid George would not support me in my decision. I wasted so much gin and tonic and psychic energy worrying. And then, when we finally got around to discussing it, he was so terrifically supportive."

Ruth elaborated that, prior to beginning these sessions, she had noticed a change in her drinking pattern — from the occasional drink when out to dinner with George or friends to almost daily consumption, especially in the evening while watching television by herself. She felt that she was now returning to her previous pattern of the occasional social drink, especially now that her time was becoming more occupied with the exploration of training in real estate work. She did, however, agree to self-monitor her intake of alcohol until the next session to ascertain more accurately her current consumption and pattern of use.

Based on the positive feedback from school and parents, eventually Paula and her counsellor mutually agreed to terminate her work with the Youth Services Centre, with the open invitation to contact them again if she needed to.

There was one final family session about a month after Paula had terminated at the centre. Paula, George and Ruth came across as busy with their individual pursuits. George reported some success in securing a few small consulting contracts, but he was obviously not feeling firmly established in private enterprise. Ruth was enthusiastic about the real estate course she had recently enrolled in and was pleased with a part-time placement that held some promise in terms of future employment. In reporting on school, Paula made reference to looking into community colleges and social services programs as she prepared to graduate from high school.

Although each was occupied with separate interests of importance to them as individuals, there was a sense that they were also aware of and interested in what was happening for each other, and that the gains they had made in the last few months were being maintained. Toward the end of the session, Ruth produced the results of her self-monitoring and proudly indicated that her use of alcohol was back to occasional and limited rather than daily use.

Summary Observations

The Smith family obviously received help early in the development of problems around family interactions and substance abuse. The problems were largely situational and stress-related. They were able to benefit from relatively short-term treatment, not only because of early intervention but also because of the basic soundness of the family as well as their individual and collective strengths.

One would expect such a family to benefit from counselling approaches that included strategies borrowing primarily from the behavioral, structural and solution-focused models of intervention. They were also able to benefit from good linkages between school and the youth service, as well as collaboration between staff within the same service.

In closing, it is important to again underline that many factors will help determine the outcome of our work with a given family presenting with substance abuse issues. They include matters that relate directly to the family, such as extent and history of substance abuse, other identified problems, basic soundness of the family structure, as well as individual and collective strengths and skills. Other key factors external to the family include availability of family services and resources within the community as well as effective linkages between services. Success in couples and family work is greatly influenced by the delicate timing, balancing and interplay between these important components of familial and social systems.

REFERENCES AND RECOMMENDED READING

The following references are provided to enable further exploration of the subject. The brief notations indicate the technical level and comprehensiveness of the individual items.

Boudreau, R. (1982). Alcohol abuse and the family system. *Canada's Mental Health* 30: 17–18.
   (Brief overview of alcohol abuse from a family systems perspective.)

Journal of Marital and Family Therapy (October 1995) 21 (4).
   (This Special Issue consists of articles that review the efficacy and effectiveness of marital/family therapy.)

Kaufman, E., and Kaufman, P. (eds.) (1992). *Family Therapy of Drug and Alcohol Abuse.* Toronto: Allyn and Bacon.
   (An important collection of chapters on key topics by various leaders in the field.)

Nicols, M., and Schwartz, R. (1995). *Family Therapy: Concepts and Methods.* Toronto: Allyn and Bacon.
   (Comprehensive up-to-date review of the history, concepts, models and practice of family therapy.)

O'Farrell, T. (ed.) (1993). *Treating Alcohol Problems: Marital and Family Interventions.* New York: Guilford Press.
   (Written for practitioners, this collection of chapters by numerous clinical researchers details various marital/family interventions.)

Pearlman, S. (1988). Systems theory and alcoholism. In *Theories on Alcoholism,* eds. Chaudron, C.D., and Wilkinson, D.A. Toronto: Addiction Research Foundation.
   (A comprehensive and detailed analysis of the topic.)

Steinglass, P., et al. (1987). *The Alcoholic Family.* New York: Basic Books.
   (A detailed analysis of important research questions related to the topic.)

Todd, T., and Selekman, M. (eds.) (1991). *Family Therapy Approaches with Adolescent Substance Abusers.* Toronto: Allyn and Bacon.
   (Excellent presentation of diverse approaches by a number of prominent practitioners who work with this special population.)

Wermuth, L., and Scheidt, S. (1986). Enlisting family support in drug treatment. *Family Process* 25: 25–33.
   (Authors describe a practical application of a psychoeducational approach with families.)

Chapter 22

Effects of Parental Substance Abuse on Children's Development

JULIANNE CONRY

INTRODUCTION

Since the 1950s, it has been recognized that while adults who abuse alcohol experience medical and psychological effects, the children growing up in such families are also at risk for suffering developmental consequences when one or both parents abuse substances. Our most comprehensive information concerns the effects of alcohol use; evidence of developmental problems for parental abuse of other substances is more sparse.

Research and clinical experience have attributed a range of psychological problems to the children of alcoholics: over-dependence, low self-esteem, withdrawal and even suicide. Externalizing behaviors such as lying, stealing and delinquency have been found. School problems, learning disabilities and neuropsychological deficits have also been reported. The belief that these are inevitable outcomes has been, perhaps, reinforced through the emergence of support organizations such as Children of Alcoholics and Adult Children of Alcoholics, which began in the United States and Canada in the 1980s.

Yet, remarkable coping skills and resilience have also been documented for some children of alcoholics. In fact, some writers believe that most children of alcoholics do *not* have lifelong problems and that the research has focused too heavily on the "casualties" of parental alcoholism. If so, what makes some children resilient when faced with disrupted family life?

Most of the research has focused on the psychosocial problems of children of the father-alcoholic. This is likely because more male alcoholics than female alcoholics are in treatment, and males, therefore, are more often identified for research studies. But those in treatment may represent a group that has more severe problems, or for whom the economic consequences of abuse are more serious. Most alcoholics, however, are not in treatment.

Conclusions from these studies often do not differentiate which parent is alcoholic. That is, statements are made about "children from alcoholic homes," but not specifically about children of alcoholic mothers or children of alcoholic fathers. The absence of this distinction raises a number of questions. Which parent is alcoholic? Does the child live with both or just one parent? Is a step-parent involved? At what stage of the child's development did the parent begin to abuse alcohol? What is the pattern of abuse? From both treatment/intervention and research perspectives, these are extremely important questions.

In 1973, a landmark study published by Jones and his colleagues described a pattern of physical abnormalities, cognitive delay and behavioral abnormalities among children born to alcoholic mothers. The term "fetal alcohol syndrome" (FAS) was coined. Since then, thousands of articles have been published on the subject in the areas of basic science (animal research), human studies, and clinical and anecdotal observations. Thus the term "children of alcoholics" takes on an expanded meaning for the children of alcoholic women who were or are drinking during pregnancy, with both biological and environmental consequences to be considered.

Fetal alcohol syndrome came to wider public attention in 1989, when Michael Dorris published *The Broken Cord*. The book is the true story of a single parent raising a developmentally delayed child who struggled with learning even simple concepts, and whose father sought to understand the reasons why. Eventually, the father learned that his son had FAS. Following publication of his book, Dorris was inundated with heart-wrenching letters written by parents who realized that he had also described their children.

With the research that has accumulated since 1973, we are just now learning what happens to those with FAS in adulthood. FAS is a lifelong, neurological disability, with its adult victims prone to various psychosocial problems, including being at risk for substance abuse. Counsellors are faced with diverse challenges when working with clients who have been prenatally exposed to alcohol.

This chapter will introduce the counsellor to the life-span implications for the child whose parents currently abuse alcohol, and whose mother used alcohol during her pregnancy with that child.

CHILDREN OF ALCOHOLICS

Since the late 1970s, there has been recognition that children of alcoholics may experience certain problems as a result of growing up in a home in which one or both parents are alcoholic. Children of alcoholics (COAs) form a potentially large group. With prevalence rates of alcoholism for men at about five to nine per cent and for women at about two per cent, the number of children of alcoholics could be estimated at one in eight (MacDonald and Blume, 1986). Recent research has focused on the cognitive and personality characteristics of these children. The interest evolved as a result of finding familial patterns of alcoholism — implying the possibility of genetic predisposition. The research sought to determine whether the children share unique characteristics that might then be used to predict their alcoholism in adulthood. It has been difficult, if not impossible, to separate the effects of environmental factors from biological factors that may make the child prone to various learning and behavioral problems.

The home environments of alcoholics have been characterized by disorganization, poverty, violence, and abuse or neglect of the children (Nylander, 1960; Woodside, 1983; Lund and Landesman-Dwyer, 1979; Tarter, Hegedus, Goldstein, Shelly and Alterman, 1984). As adults, COAs remembered their childhoods as chaotic and unpredictable — with inconsistency in care, behavioral expectations and discipline (Beletis and Brown, 1981). Their situations were often complicated by poverty and its associated problems. However, additional stressors such as divorce, parental psychopathology, parental criminality and perinatal birth complications make it more difficult to attribute the child outcomes primarily to the environmental circumstances that characterize parental alcoholism (West and Prinz, 1987).

When children are selected for research on other problems, an association with alcoholism is often present. For example, among children diagnosed with "socialized aggression," there was a high prevalence of parental alcoholism (Stewart, deBlois and Cummings, 1980). The link to hyperactivity is inconclusive. In one longitudinal study of sons of alcoholic fathers, teachers rated these children significantly higher on impulsive-restless behaviors (Knop, Teasdale, Schulsinger and Goodwin, 1985). But when children are selected first on the basis of their hyperactivity, the association disappears — that is, the prevalence of alcoholism among the hyperactive group is not significantly high (Morrison, 1980). Aggression and hyperactivity are not always separated, in research definitions or in assessment of individual cases. The association is more striking between parental alcoholism and conduct problems (West and Prinz, 1987).

Children of alcoholic mothers frequently have attention deficit and hyperactivity as well as other behavioral problems, but the results are confounded by prenatal exposure to alcohol, since FAS is also known to produce these problems (Steinhausen, Nestler and Huth, 1982).

421

In a number of studies of children's intellectual functioning and achievement in school, the scores of children of alcoholics were generally lower than their counterparts from non-alcoholic families. Particularly in this area, investigation of maternal alcoholism, and the child's known (or unknown) prenatal exposure to alcohol, confounds the generalizations. Significantly lower IQ scores for children of maternal alcoholics were documented in the early Seattle studies of FAS conducted by Streissguth and her colleagues (Streissguth, 1976; Streissguth, Little, Herman and Woodell, 1979). Gabrielli and Mednick (1983) also found lower IQ scores, but this time none of the mothers had a known diagnosis of alcoholism, although "some" drinking during pregnancy may have occurred. More recent studies of children of alcoholics have been careful to consider the factor of prenatal alcohol exposure.

The environment also plays a mitigating role. Children who had an alcoholic parent — but who came from homes where the parents were well educated and held "white-collar" jobs and earned average or above-average incomes — were compared to children from non-alcoholic homes. On cognitive and personality measures, COAs achieved test results that placed them below their controls, but still within the normal range (Bennett, Wolin and Reiss, 1988). Where children had an alcoholic father, but were otherwise in positive circumstances, they were no more likely than their counterparts from non-alcoholic homes to be truant or to drop out of school. Unfortunately, alcoholism in the family is more likely to be associated with disadvantaged circumstances (Robins, West, Ratcliff and Herjanic, 1978).

The alcoholic history is also important. In one study, the children of recovered alcoholics showed no cognitive or personality scores outside of the normal range (Whipple and Nobles, 1991). Adolescent children of a recovered alcoholic father did not differ from controls on self-esteem and locus of control. It seems that having an alcoholic father affected the quality of their lives, but not how they felt about themselves. They could now rate their lives as happy compared to children whose fathers still drank. Both groups who had experienced an alcoholic father were more positive (than controls) about alcoholics — less damning of any personality fault or weakness. They were also more positive about the alcoholic's chances of recovery (Callan and Jackson, 1986). However, among the children of relapsed alcoholics, anxiety, depression and nightmares were responses to the family environment (Moos and Billings, 1982). These findings suggest that the pattern of alcoholism and recovery has important effects on the children.

In reviewing the research on COAs, West and Prinz (1987) conclude that neither all nor a major portion of the children from alcoholic homes are inevitably doomed. In particular, they note that where differences have been found between children from alcoholic versus non-alcoholic families, the overall differences are small and there is considerable overlap between the two groups. The next step is to identify factors that could explain why some children are more resilient than others in adverse circumstances.

422

In 1955, all children born on the island of Kauai, Hawaii became the subjects of a 32-year longitudinal study (Werner, 1992). A subset of that cohort ($n = 49$) were children of alcoholic parents. Most (38) had fathers who were alcoholic, six had mothers with drinking problems, and five had parents who were both problem drinkers. Their lives were complicated by chronic poverty, little educational stimulation from their homes, family discord and divorce. A few suffered moderate to severe prenatal or perinatal trauma. By age 18, in spite of the adversity, 59 per cent had not developed any learning or behavioral problems; they did well in school, at work and in their social lives. This group of resilient children were compared with the group that had developed serious coping problems by adolescence. Three-quarters of the resilient group were females; two-thirds of those with problems were male. Only one of the resilient ones had a mother who was alcoholic, while the children of the fathers were divided between the "resilient" and problem groups.

What were the child characteristics or qualities of the caregiving environment that seemed to make a difference? In the earlier analyses, it was noted that the resilient children had received a great deal of attention from their primary caretakers during the first year of life, with no prolonged separations. Furthermore, no additional births during the first two years and the absence of conflict between the parents during the first two years, distinguished the resilient group. This finding was interpreted as fewer stressful events during the first two years of life. The temperaments of the resilient group were described as "cuddly and affectionate," which tends to elicit positive attention from others. By age two, the children who later developed problems were already delayed in intellectual and social-emotional development, and this continued throughout school. Average intelligence, communication skills and achievement orientation were associated with a better outcome in the resilient group. A responsible, caring attitude, positive self-concept, a more internal locus of control and belief in self-help also characterized the resilient group (Werner, 1986).

The final follow-up occurred when the cohort reached age 32. It was apparent that, in the absence of serious damage to the central nervous system, the effects of perinatal stress diminished over time with the outcome more dependent on the caregiving environment. Four characteristics were identified that distinguished the resilient group:

1. Temperamental characteristics that helped him or her to elicit positive responses from various caring persons;
2. Skills and values that led to an efficient use of whatever abilities they had; faith that the odds could be overcome; realistic educational and vocational plans, regular household responsibilities;
3. Caregiving styles of parents that reflected competence and fostered self-esteem in the child, mother's level of education, and rules and structure in the household; and
4. Supportive adults who fostered trust and acted as gatekeepers for the future. Some of these were "surrogate" parents such as grandparents, elder mentors, youth leaders or members of church groups.

Furthermore, for those in the resilient group, there was the opening of opportunities at major life transitions — for example, from high school to workplace. This tended to deflect the sometimes pathological "trajectory" of a significant proportion of high-risk children on to the path of normal adulthood. Particularly important was the availability of adult education and vocational training, which helped to foster responsibility and self-esteem (Werner, 1992).

Werner's findings are supported by other researchers (Rutter, 1990), who have become interested in protective mechanisms in vulnerable children. She notes that her own and others' research has found that, if a parent is incapacitated or unavailable, another person in the child's life can play an enabling role. Werner stresses the urgency of putting interventions in place for these vulnerable children, but concludes her study with a message of hope because of the children who have succeeded against the odds.

FETAL ALCOHOL SYNDROME: A LIFELONG DISABILITY

What is fetal alcohol syndrome (FAS)? Since antiquity, there has been knowledge that drinking alcohol during pregnancy can have adverse effects on the developing fetus. In a biblical reference (Judges 13:3-4), an angel appeared to Samson's mother saying, "Behold, thou shalt conceive and bear a son, and now drink no wine or strong drink." During the gin epidemic in England, a Hogarth engraving from the mid-1700s entitled "Gin Lane," portrays a drunken woman with her child falling from her arms. Computerized enhancement of the child's features are suggestive of fetal alcohol syndrome! In *Pickwick Papers,* Charles Dickens noted that maternal drinking was harmful to his character, Betsy Martin, "...widow, one child and one eye, but knows her mother drank bottled stout, and shouldn't wonder if that caused it."

It wasn't until the thalidomide tragedy of the 1960s, however, that contemporary medicine recognized that drugs, toxins and infections cross the placenta and may harm the developing fetus. Articles published in France by Lamache (1967) and Lemoine (1968) and in the United States by Jones, Smith, Ulleland and Streissguth (1973) were the first documentation of what has come to be a recognizable and unique pattern of features: retarded physical growth, altered facial characteristics (dysmorphology) and brain dysfunction caused by prenatal exposure to alcohol. In the late 1970s, the first cases of FAS in Canada were reported to the Health Protection Branch, National Health and Welfare.

It is important to realize, however, that many adults being diagnosed with FAS today were born at a time when physicians were unaware that drinking alcohol during pregnancy could be harmful. Therefore, women were not warned to avoid alcohol when pregnant. Some of the most heart-breaking stories come from women who avoided prescription and other drugs to protect their unborn babies, but believed (or were told) that alcohol was not harmful.

Diagnosis of FAS is made in a case where there is known (documented) to have been significant prenatal exposure to alcohol, and where the child has characteristic features in three areas:

1. Prenatal and/or postnatal growth delay (height and/or weight below the tenth percentile);
2. Central nervous system involvement (conditions such as head circumference below the third percentile, intellectual impairment, learning disabilities, attention deficit/ hyperactivity or other neurological abnormalities); and
3. Characteristic facial features (short palpebral fissures [eye slits], flat midface, long/indistinct philtrum (the groove between the nose and upper lip) and thin upper lip.

Figure 1 depicts the "discriminating features" of FAS — those features that form the "gestalt" of FAS, and "associated features" — other characteristics that are frequently present with FAS. When not all of the criteria for FAS are present, the term fetal alcohol effects (FAE) has been used (Sokol and Clarren, 1989). Yet, FAE is not a "milder" form of FAS. The physical features are often more subtle, but the neurological deficits may be just as devastating. We now know that, as adolescents and adults, those diagnosed with FAE are often at greater risk than those with FAS for problems with adaptive functioning ("life skills"). For both FAS and FAE, there is a continuum of effects that depends on the amount of alcohol consumed, the timing of the drinking and other metabolic and genetic factors.

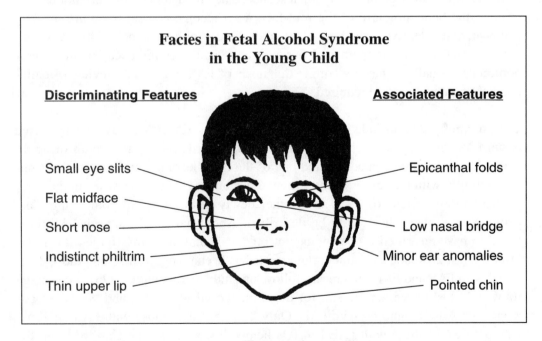

FIGURE 1

Source: Streissguth, A.P., and Little, R.E., 1994. *Project Cork Institute Medical School Curriculum,* reproduced with permission.

Recently, the U.S. Congress mandated the Institute of Medicine (IOM) to review what is known and not known about FAS. To this end, the IOM brought together a committee of American and Canadian experts on the syndrome. Among the issues debated were diagnostic criteria and terminology. One recommendation arising from the study is that the term "fetal alcohol effects" be replaced by the terms "partial FAS" (pFAS) and Alcohol-Related Neurodevelopmental Disorder (ARND), depending on which features are present (Stratton, Howe and Battaglia, 1996). For the purposes of this chapter, however, the more familiar terms, FAS and FAE, are used.

FAS/FAE is a medical diagnosis that is made by a physician trained to recognize birth defects. Other medical conditions have presentations similar to that of FAS/FAE, and these must be distinguished. These include chromosomal disorders that have similar behavioral profiles such as Fragile X and Turner's syndrome. Other conditions have a similar physical appearance such as Williams syndrome, fetal hydantoin syndrome (caused by the anti-convulsant drug Dilantin), maternal PKU and fetal toluene syndrome (caused by glue sniffing). Also, FAS/FAE may occur with other disorders; for example, FAS/FAE with autism or FAS/FAE with Tourette syndrome.

The diagnosis may be particularly difficult to make in early infancy and again in adolescence or adulthood. As with some other syndromes, the physical features change as the child grows and develops. While some individuals diagnosed with FAS/FAE remain small in stature, others grow to within the normal range of height. Girls, especially, tend to gain weight during adolescence. The characteristic facial features also change: the bone structure of the mid-face may become coarse, the philtrum may reappear, and extensive orthodontia may alter the earlier appearance of the maxillary (jaw) area. The eye slits (palpebral fissures) and head circumference remain disproportionately small. To make a correct diagnosis of FAS in an adult, review of childhood photographs is often required.

The possibility that an individual may be affected by FAS/FAE may first be raised because of learning and behavioral difficulties experienced by the youth or adult. Fetal alcohol syndrome is considered one of the three leading known causes of mental disability (with the causes of most mental disabilities being unknown). In the early published descriptions of FAS, as in other newly discovered syndromes, the most extreme cases were the first to be described. About half of those with FAS were found to have measured IQ below the cut-off for mental disability (IQ less than 70). Over the last 20 years, a continuum of effects has been recognized among those diagnosed with FAS and FAE. In a recent follow-up study (Streissguth, 1996), the average IQ was 79 ("slow learner" range) for those diagnosed with FAS, and 90 ("average" range) for those diagnosed with FAE. Only 27 per cent of those with FAS and only nine per cent of those with FAE had IQs below 70 . With IQs ranging well into the average or above range, FAS/FAE is better described as a disorder associated with learning disabilities, rather than mental disability. Scores on adaptive behavior measures are typically very low relative to IQ levels.

For school-age children, difficulties learning the basic academic subjects of reading, spelling and math are common, with math usually being the most difficult subject to master. In describing a student's learning disabilities, we can profile the underlying processes that contribute to the learning problems. Briefly, these include problems with language, memory, forming abstractions and attention (Conry, 1990 and 1996).

Young children with FAS/FAE usually show some degree of language delay. As they grow older, though, they often become adept at "cocktail chatter" — lots of words with little real meaning. At this superficial level, they appear to be more competent than they actually are. However, on closer examination, it becomes apparent that they are easily confused by the normal pace and complexity of language that occurs in day-to-day situations. Problems in processing information can occur at any of the levels of receiving the information accurately (as the speaker intends), interpreting (understanding), remembering it correctly, and then acting on that information.

Children and adults with FAS/FAE have significant problems with memory. Concepts that have been learned one day are forgotten by the following day. They may recall details from long ago, but cannot remember whether they have had lunch. They have particular difficulty recalling sequences, such as the events in a story. The information may be there, but it cannot be retrieved without prompting. They may stand accused of lying because an attempt to fill in the memory gaps results in confabulation: the weaving together of a "logical" story comprised of unrelated, separate events coming from various sources. In this regard, they are similar to those with other types of known brain dysfunction, such as traumatic brain injury or Alzheimer's disease.

The ability to think abstractly and to reason means being able to consider possibilities in the future, to make connections, to generalize from experience and to anticipate consequences. Individuals with FAS/FAE are often very concrete in their thinking; they are unable to take a perspective different from their own experience, and they can only deal with the present — often in an impulsive fashion.

In fact, attention deficit/hyperactivity disorders affect approximately 60 per cent of the FAS/FAE school-age population. Impulsive behavior gets them into trouble and distractibility causes classroom problems. Most children with FAS/FAE have disrupted school experiences, punctuated by a series of suspensions or expulsions, and many eventually drop out. Nevertheless, a significant number complete high school, usually on modified programs.

When we speak of "adaptive behavior" we are referring to the degree and efficiency with which the individual meets "the standards of personal independence and social responsibility of his age or cultural group" (Grossman, 1977). These are functional life skills and include self-care and daily living skills, "common-sense" judgment in interacting with the environment, and "appropriate" social skills. For those with an alcohol-related diagnosis, there is little correlation between adaptive skills level and IQ level, or diagnosis of FAS versus FAE. That is, a higher IQ does not necessarily improve the prognosis for successful independent living in adulthood (Streissguth, 1996).

In areas of personal care, routines of basic hygiene and wearing appropriate (and clean) clothing are often difficult to establish. Household activities such as cooking can be a problem because of failure to keep track of the food during cooking and remembering to turn off the stove. Planning ahead to purchase baby items when needed, properly preparing an infant formula, refrigerating the milk and adequately cleaning the baby bottles all have been problematic for some mothers who have FAS/FAE.

Handling money also creates a range of problems for those with FAS/FAE. This includes not understanding the value of items (giving away items of value or paying too much for items), impulsive spending, giving away ("loaning") money or squandering it on anyone they meet and being unable to account for large sums of money spent. They are frequently too trusting of those they meet. Being unable to manage money so that basic requirements for rent, utilities and food are paid has been described for over 80 per cent of adults with FAS/FAE.

By adolescence, most have learned to tell time, although this is often a late skill to develop. Having a concept of time — such as judging the difference between five minutes and five hours — is more problematic. The sequence of events — what happened when and in what order — is confusing. The person with FAS fails to recognize the importance that society places on being "on time." Such an individual is often complacent about getting to appointments, to work and to school. He or she may start out for the appointment on time, but become distracted and never arrive. Or the urgency of a "minor" need (e.g., to do the laundry) may overwhelm the "importance" of keeping a doctor's appointment. In some cases, the individual is overly literal or overly rigid concerning matters of time, so directives such as "come home right away" or "come around 11 o'clock" are too vague and are misunderstood.

Individuals with FAS often have social learning disabilities. The ability to "read" social cues, to understand others' feelings, and to respond in socially appropriate ways is immature. In this regard, the youth or young adult is "egocentric," unable to take the perspective of another. Thus, he or she is viewed by peers as strange or different and is often rejected. The youth, desperately wanting to be accepted, goes about it in the wrong way. He or she is often manipulated, set up, and easily led into situations that are likely to get him or her in trouble — or that will be dangerous. He or she lacks the ability to discriminate between friends and strangers. Both males and females are frequently victimized.

Problems getting and keeping a job were common to 79 per cent of those with FAS/FAE over age 21 (Streissguth et al., 1996). They appear to lack initiative or the ability to follow through even when job opportunities are provided. When the situations repeatedly fail to work out, those trying to help tend to give up in frustration. Often those with FAS/FAE would report losing their jobs without understanding why. The reasons include poor understanding of their job, showing poor judgment, being too easily frustrated or angered, being unreliable, not getting along with the supervisor, and other social difficulties on the job.

An additional problem of day-to-day living for the adult with FAS/FAE is not knowing how to access various social services such as disability or welfare benefits, medical or counselling services. The fact that they are told about such services does not assure the ability to utilize them.

ADULTS WITH FAS AND SUBSTANCE USE PROBLEMS

Alcohol and drug problems are common among both males and females with FAS/FAE. This may be due to a genetic predisposition and also because their life experiences put them at risk for substance abuse. In the Seattle study (Streissguth et al., 1996), among those between the ages of 12 and 20, approximately 30 per cent had alcohol problems; this rose to over 40 per cent in the 21 to 51 age group. About 20 per cent of the younger group had problems with other illicit drugs, rising to 30 per cent in the older group. Alcohol is the gateway drug: about 65 per cent who had abused alcohol later abused street drugs. For the vast majority, the age of onset of alcohol problems was young — between 12 and 20 — and 70 per cent had already had their first alcohol treatment before age 21. Problems with alcohol and drugs are more prevalent for those with a diagnosis of FAE than with a diagnosis of FAS. Not surprisingly, reasons for abstinence among those who did *not* have alcohol problems related to lack of access to alcohol or because their family did not drink. However, nearly as frequently, the experience of many alcohol problems within the family was also given as a reason for not drinking!

It is likely that the counsellor will work with clients who have FAS or FAE, but for whom the condition has not yet been diagnosed. When difficulties arise in working with the client — the usual approaches aren't working and expectations of the client are not being met — it is time to consider factors such as a medical reason for the problems: FAS/FAE.

Chapter 23 addresses the cognitive deficits that can be directly caused by excessive alcohol consumption. For the client in alcohol and drug treatment, these deficits could be interpreted as denial or a psychological defence. Reduced memory and poor ability to learn new information have been well documented during at least the first month of abstinence. The implication is that treatment modalities that rely on information processing or insight may be ineffective with clients who have a reduced ability to reason abstractly. For clients with FAS/FAE, these are the same cognitive deficits they have always had, but which are undoubtedly worsened due to the alcohol and drug problem.

When working with clients with FAS/FAE, counsellors are often frustrated by the apparent lack of carryover from session to session. When the client is asked about thoughts or feelings, the response is often "I don't know." He or she is unable to think abstractly or about present events. The client's reasoning, and the connections that are made, fail to make sense to the counsellor. The client may present with a flat or even surly affect, may make little eye contact, or walk away mid-session for no apparent reason. One day the client may be resentful, angry and even abusive, but the next day present as though nothing had happened. (The client doesn't know why people are angry with him or her; for the client, it's a brand new day and a freshly cleaned slate!) The counsellor should try not to take such circumstances personally, for the counsellor's persona has little if anything to do with the client's behavior.

The FAS/FAE group is at particular risk for additional mental health problems that the counsellor may need to address. The most frequent problem described for younger children and adolescents is attention deficit (60 per cent). By adolescence and early adulthood, serious problems with depression and suicide threats or attempts emerge in 40 to 50 per cent of those with FAS/FAE.

No single approach to alcohol and drug treatment has been found to be effective for those with FAS/FAE who have substance abuse problems. The key is recognizing the cognitive limitations and attempting to work in a concrete fashion, relying on much more repetition. Due to the underlying cause of this syndrome, those with FAS/FAE are likely to reside in environments where alcohol use is endemic. This is a very difficult barrier to successful treatment.

Is it worthwhile to seek a diagnosis of FAS/FAE? Where there is the suspicion that the adult client may have FAS/FAE, a diagnosis can help both the counsellor and the client to understand the implications. A diagnosis is not just a "label"; it can also be a blueprint for intervention planning. The diagnosis may allow the individual to access certain benefits or services. If the client is a woman who is drinking, she is at considerable risk of having children who will have second- or third-generation FAS. There is an opportunity to intervene to reduce the prevalence of alcohol-related birth defects in the next generation.

COUNSELLING WOMEN WHO DRINK DURING PREGNANCY

Early in the 1970s the prospects for eliminating more FAS children from being born seemed straightforward. Fetal alcohol syndrome is a preventable birth defect: if the pregnant woman does not drink, she will not have an affected child. However, those working in the addictions field have recognized that FAS is a complex problem surrounded by issues of the root causes of alcohol abuse, attitudes toward women drinking and, in particular, pregnant women who are drinking, and basic community education about the effects of alcohol abuse during pregnancy. The fact that FAS is a preventable birth defect is a double-edged sword. On the one hand, there is optimism that one of the leading known causes of mental and other disabilities can be eliminated by not drinking during pregnancy. But for women who, for whatever reason, do not stop drinking, the criticism levelled at them may be even more harsh. It is presumed, simply, that the woman knows better and she could stop drinking if she wanted to. This, of course, is a dubious presumption.

Chapter 12 discusses issues relevant to working with women with substance abuse problems. It highlights barriers to treatment that include their poverty, isolation, unrecognized needs, and fear of losing children as well as the broader societal attitudes toward women with substance use problems.

The reality is that, even in the 1990s, physicians may not ask a pregnant woman about her drinking habits during prenatal visits and many women have not heard the messages warning against drinking during pregnancy. In a study conducted by Armstrong (personal communication) in British Columbia, physicians agreed to include a structured set of questions about alcohol use in their usual prenatal interviews. The study identified a large proportion of women who were likely drinking enough potentially to harm their infants. Yet, at the study's conclusion, very few doctors indicated that they would continue to use the questioning in their regular practice! Researchers suggested various reasons for this. One possibility was that the physicians didn't know what to do for the pregnant woman if they did find she was drinking. Few treatment facilities were available that would accept a pregnant woman, and even in those the waiting lists were prohibitively long.

The questionnaire used in Armstrong's study is known as the T-ACE (Sokol, 1988 and Sokol et al., 1989), the structure of which is shown on the following page. To gain a more reliable result regarding quantity of alcohol consumption, the pregnant woman is asked about her drinking behavior before she knew she was pregnant. The sensitivity was such that Sokol was able to identify seven out of 10 women who drank enough to cause risk to their unborn child. In Armstrong's study, approximately 50 per cent of the women passed the criteria for Tolerance, earning a score of two points, thereby suggesting their drinking placed them at risk for causing damage to the fetus. It was thought that perhaps they somehow had an unintended interpretation of the tolerance question. However, when the cut-off score was raised to three points (Tolerance plus one other), it identified 18 per cent of the women — still a large number. As a group, they had additional risk characteristics: single parenthood, poverty and premature birth.

T-ACE Questions to Identify Risk-Drinkers

Scoring

T Tolerance	How many drinks does it take to make you feel "high" — feel the effects (tolerance)?	Three drinks or more = 2 points
A Annoyed	Have people annoyed you by criticizing your drinking?	Yes = 1 point
C Cut down	Have you felt you ought to cut down on your drinking?	Yes = 1 point
E Eye-opener	Have you ever had an "eye-opener" — a drink first thing in the morning to steady your nerves or get rid of a hangover?	Yes = 1 point

TOTAL: A total score of 2 points or more indicates a risk-drinker.

(Sokol, 1988).

Clearly, when such women are identified, priority must be given to their treatment and this requires close community co-operation among physicians, pregnancy outreach programs, and alcohol and drug counsellors.

The media present a mixed message about the dangers (or potential dangers) of drinking during pregnancy. Scare tactics such as warning that one drink will irreparably harm the baby are not only scientifically inaccurate but may also cause unwanted effects. That is, if these warnings are taken literally, they may cause undue anxiety for the woman and lead to unnecessary decisions (such as abortion). Alternatively, if women do not heed these warnings, they may be ignoring the real risks of drinking.

Alcohol has a teratogenic effect during the first three months of pregnancy, affecting the proper formation of the body organs and brain. In the latter six months of pregnancy, alcohol has a toxic effect on physical growth and brain development. FAS is more likely to occur with continuous drinking or heavy consumption of alcohol during pregnancy. But effects have also been observed after intermittent or binge drinking. Children born to mothers who have on average one to two drinks per day or who may occasionally have up to five or more drinks at a time are at increased risk for learning disabilities and other cognitive and behavioral problems (Health Canada, 1996).

Contemporary health promotion describes a continuum of risk to the unborn child and a "risk-reduction" or "harm-reduction" approach to treatment (see May, 1995 for a description of a multiple-level comprehensive approach to the prevention of FAS). For the woman who has significant problems with her drinking, any reduction — at any time during her pregnancy — will improve the outcome for her baby.

Nevertheless, there is no *known* safe level of drinking and no benefit to the baby from the mother's drinking. Health Canada's position is that the prudent choice is not to drink during pregnancy or while breastfeeding. The pregnant woman should receive such a clear, non-judgmental message from her physician, counsellor, friend or relative. At a recent conference on FAS, a panel of birth mothers with alcohol-affected children rejected the notion of the "reduce drinking/harm reduction" message. For them, any message that suggested that one or two drinks would not be harmful essentially granted women permission to drink. They stated that if one or two drinks are acceptable, what would stop women from drinking a few more? These panel members contended that women need to be informed of the need to stop drinking altogether.

Although our primary focus has been on the use of alcohol during pregnancy, women who drink during pregnancy are also likely to be "poly-drug" users — that is, they may also abuse other illicit (or non-illicit) drugs that could affect the fetus. Little is known about combined drug effects. Streissguth and her colleagues (1991) compared the drug use of women who used cocaine during pregnancy to those who did not. The results, summarized below, remind one that alcohol remains the drug about which we should be most concerned. At present, the effects of cocaine alone on the fetus are not well understood. Most importantly, cocaine users are likely to also use alcohol and they may have a pattern of binge drinking that can be harmful.

Cocaine and Other Drugs in Pregnancy

	No Cocaine *n* = 777	Cocaine *n* = 97
Any alcohol	56%	82%
Binge alcohol (>5 drinks/occasion)	8%	30%
Cigarettes	31%	89%
Marijuana	14%	68%
Other illicit drugs	4%	33%

(Streissguth et al., 1991)

DRINKING FATHERS

Finally, the issue of paternal effects must be addressed. To date, the data on fetus effects from prenatal paternal exposure to alcohol are sparse. Animal studies show some effects on organ weights, hormone secretion and immune response. In reviewing the literature, however, the Institute of Medicine clearly states that paternal consumption does not cause FAS. With great caution, they recognized that the combinations of maternal and paternal alcohol abuse are so complex that some anomalies attributed to maternal drinking may be exacerbated by paternal drinking, but clarification of this issue requires further research (Stratton et al., 1996).

Even so, fathers play an extremely important role in supporting their partners in not drinking during pregnancy. It can be difficult for the pregnant woman to withstand pressures from her partner, relatives and friends who encourage her to drink with them. On the other hand, pregnancy can be a powerful motivator. With positive support from family, friends and the professionals working with her, many women have successfully stopped drinking for the sake of the health of their fetus, sometimes in situations in which their male partners continue to drink.

CONCLUSION

Even the most effective community services can be disjointed for lack of integration. Some communities have established programs for pregnant women to improve the pregnancy outcomes through better prenatal care, nutrition and supported living arrangements. But often there is no direct link to alcohol and drug counselling, perhaps due to the long waiting lists. Pregnant women with children may fear that seeking alcohol and drug treatment will result in their children being apprehended. Or they may not have a safe place for their children to stay during alcohol and drug treatment and therefore may not seek help. Or there is no transition after the birth of the baby to community agencies that might continue the counselling and other services. Alcohol and drug counsellors play an extremely important role in integrating services to minimize the developmental consequences of parental substance abuse.

REFERENCES

Beletis, S., and Brown, S. (1981). A developmental framework for understanding the adult children of alcoholics. *Focus on Women Journal of Addictions Health* 2: 187–203.

Bennett, L.A., Wolin, S.J., and Reiss, D. (1988). Cognitive, behavioral, and emotional problems among school-age children of alcoholic parents. *American Journal of Psychiatry* 145: 185–190.

Callan, V.T., and Jackson, D. (1986). Children of alcoholic fathers and recovered alcoholic fathers: Personal and family functioning. *Journal of Studies on Alcohol* 47: 180–182.

Conry, J.L. (1990). Neuropsychologic deficits in fetal alcohol syndrome and fetal alcohol effects. *Alcoholism: Clinical and Experimental Research* 14: 650–655.

Conry, J.L. (1996). *Working with Students with Fetal Alcohol Syndrome/Effects. A Resource Guide for Teachers*. Victoria, BC: Ministry of Education.

Dorris, M. (1989). *The Broken Cord*. New York: Harper and Row.

Gabrielli, W., and Mednick, S. (1983). Intellectual performance in children of alcoholics. *Journal of Nervous and Mental Disease* 171: 444–447.

Grossman, H. (1977). *Manual and Terminology on Classification in Mental Retardation*. Washington, DC: American Association on Mental Deficiency.

Health Canada. (1996). *Joint Statement: Prevention of Fetal Alcohol Syndrome (FAS) Fetal Alcohol Effects (FAE) in Canada*. Ottawa: Government of Canada.

Jones, K.L., and Smith, D.W. (1973). Recognition of the Fetal Alcohol Syndrome in early infancy. *Lancet* 2 (836): 999–1001.

Jones, K.L., Smith, D.W., Ulleland, C.N., and Streissguth, A.P. (1973). Pattern of malformation in offspring of chronic alcoholic mothers. *Lancet* 1 (815): 1267–1271.

Knop, J., Teasdale, T., Schulsinger, F., and Goodwin, D. (1985). A prospective study of young men at high risk for alcoholism: School behavior and achievement. *Journal of Studies on Alcoholism* 46: 273–278.

Lamache, A. (1967). Réflexions sur la descendance des alcooliques. *Bulletin de l'Académie Nationale de Médecine* 151: 517–524.

Lemoine, P., Harouseau H., Borteryu, J.T., and Menuet, J.C. (1968) Les enfants des parents alcooliques: Anomalies observées à propos du 127 cas. *Ouest Médical* 21: 476–482.

Lund, C., and Landesman-Dwyer, S. (1979). Pre-delinquents and disturbed adolescents: The role of parental alcoholism. In *Currents in Alcoholism*, Vol. 5., ed. Galanter, M. New York: Grune and Stratton.

MacDonald, D.R., and Blume, S.B. (1986). Children of alcoholics. *American Journal of Diseases of Children* 140: 750–754.

May, P. (1995). A multiple-level comprehensive approach to the prevention of Fetal Alcohol Syndrome and other alcohol-related birth defects. *The International Journal of Addictions* 30 (12): 1549–1602.

Moos, R., and Billings, A. (1982). Children of alcoholics during the recovery process: Alcoholic and matched control families. *Addictive Behaviors* 7: 155–163.

Morrison, J. (1980). Adult psychiatric disorders in parents of hyperactive children. *American Journal of Psychiatry* 137: 825–827.

National Institutes of Health. (1994). *Alcohol Health and Research World* 18 (1): 1–92.

Nylander, I. (1960). Children of alcoholic fathers. *Acta Paediatrica Scandinavica*, 49: Suppl. 121.

Robins, L., West, P., Ratcliff, K., and Herjanic, B. (1978). Father's alcoholism and children's outcomes. In *Current in Alcoholism,* Vol. 4, ed. Seixas, F.A. New York: Grune and Stratton.

Rutter, M. (1990). Psychosocial resilience and protective mechanisms. In *Risk and Protective Factors in the Development of Psychopathology*, eds. Rolf, J., Masten, A.S., Cicchetti, D., Nuechterlein, K.H., and Weintraub, S. New York: Cambridge University Press.

Sokol, R.J. (1988). Finding the risk drinker in your clinical practice. In *Alcohol and Child/Family Health*, eds. Robinson, G.C., and Armstrong, R.M. Vancouver: FAS Resource Group.

Sokol, R.J., and Clarren, S.K. (1989). Guidelines for use of terminology describing the impact of prenatal alcohol on the offspring. *Alcoholism: Clinical and Experimental Research* 13: 597–598.

Sokol, R.J., Martier, S.S., and Ager, J.W. (1989). The T-ACE questions: Practical prenatal detection of risk-drinking. *American Journal of Obstetrics and Gynecology* 160: 863–868.

Steinhausen, H., Nestler, V., and Huth, H. (1982). Psychopathology and mental functions in the offspring of alcoholic and epileptic mothers. *Journal of the American Academy of Child Psychiatry* 21: 268–273.

Stewart, M., deBlois, S., and Cummings, C. (1980). Psychiatric disorder in the parents of hyper-active boys and those with conduct disorder. *Journal of Child Psychology and Psychiatry* 21: 283–292.

Stratton, K., Howe, C., and Battaglia, F. (eds.). (1996). *Fetal Alcohol Syndrome: Diagnosis, Epidemiology, Prevention, and Treatment.* Washington, DC: National Academy Press.

Streissguth, A.P. (1976). Psychologic handicaps in children with fetal alcohol syndrome. *Annals of the New York Academy of Sciences* 273: 140–145.

Streissguth, A.P., Little, R.E., Herman, C., and Woodell, S. (1979). IQ in children of recovered alcoholic mothers compared to matched controls. *Alcoholism: Clinical and Experimental Research* 3: 197.

Streissguth, A.P., Barr, H.M., Kogan, J., and Bookstein, F.L. (1996). *Understanding the Occurrence of Secondary Disabilities in Clients with Fetal Alcohol Syndrome (FAS) and Fetal Alcohol Effects (FAE). Final Report.* Centers for Disease Control and Prevention Grant No. R04/CCR008515. Seattle: University of Washington.

Streissguth, A.P., Grant, T.M., Barr, H.M., Brown, Z.A., Mayock, D.E., Ramey, S.L., et al. (1991). Cocaine and the use of alcohol and other drugs during pregnancy. *American Journal of Obstetrics and Gynecology* 164: 1239–1243.

Streissguth, A.P., and Little, R.E. (1994). *Project Cork Institute Medical School Curriculum, Unit 5.* Milner Fenwick.

Tarter, R., Hegedus, A., Goldstein, G., Shelly, C., and Alterman, A. (1984). Adolescent sons of alcoholics: Neuropsychological and personality characteristics. *Alcoholism: Clinical and Experimental Research* 8: 216–222.

Von Knorring, A.L. (1991). Annotation: Children of alcoholics. *Journal of Child Psychology and Psychiatry* 32 (3): 411–421.

Werner, E.E. (1986). Resilient offspring of alcoholics: A longitudinal study from birth to age 18. *Journal of Studies on Alcohol* 47: 34–40.

Werner, E.E. (1992). The children of Kauai: Resiliency and recovery in adolescence and adulthood. *Journal of Adolescent Health* 12: 262–268.

West, W.O., and Prinz, R.J. (1987). Parental alcoholism and childhood psychopathology. *Psychological Bulletin* 102: 204–218.

Whipple, S.C., and Noble, E.P. (1991). Personality characteristics of alcoholic fathers and their sons. *Journal of Studies on Alcohol* 52: 331–337.

Woodside, M. (1983). Children of alcoholic parents: Inherited and psychosocial influences. *Journal of Psychiatric Treatment and Evaluation* 5: 51–537.

Chapter 23

Alcohol-Produced Cognitive Deficits: Treatment Implications

TONY TONEATTO

There is no doubt that severely dependent or chronic alcohol abusers suffer significant neuropsychological impairment. In fact, 45 to 70 per cent of alcohol-dependent individuals will have deficits in memory, attention, new learning, visual-spatial skills, concept formation, cognitive flexibility, set shifting, problem solving and ability to follow complex demands as a result of excessive alcohol use (Parsons, 1987). Such cognitive deficits can be observed in the mental status assessment of recently detoxified alcoholics (e.g., impaired memory, confusion) and on neuropsychological tests. However, the most common cognitive effects of alcohol are sub-syndromal, since they are not indicative of a permanent or well-defined diagnostic syndrome such as Korsakoff's or dementia. It is important to know whether an alcoholic has experienced irreversible cognitive deficits that may affect his or her ability to adjust to an abstinent lifestyle and to cope with life stresses, as well as his or her likelihood of benefiting from traditional alcohol treatments.

Tarter and Edwards (1986) have categorized chronic alcoholics into four groups. The first group consists of young, early-stage alcoholics who do not show any disturbances on neuropsychological measures. The second group shows some abnormalities when assessed on neuropsychological tests but are generally not clinically impaired. This group is the primary focus of this chapter. The third group exhibits serious memory disturbances but may otherwise show normal intellectual abilities. Patients with Korsakoff's syndrome are included in this group. This condition is usually preceded by Wernicke's encephalopathy, which is characterized by confusion, ataxia (i.e., involuntary muscle movements) and eye-muscle paralysis. Alcoholics who demonstrate residual alcohol-related amnesia (accompanied by lack of spontaneity and indifference towards their condition) are usually diagnosed with Korsakoff's syndrome only when other cognitive functions (e.g., orientation to time, place and people) are relatively intact. Confabulation, or "making up" experiences, is a common way of coping with severely impaired short-term memory. These individuals remain alert, and maintain social behaviors, self-care and grooming. The fourth group includes individuals whose intellect is also impaired and for whom alcohol dementia is a more appropriate diagnosis. These clients may show difficulty in maintaining self-care behaviors. Ten per cent of alcoholics have full-fledged alcohol amnestic syndromes such as Korsakoff's and dementia.

The Wechsler Intelligence Scale has been one of the most common measures of the effects of severe alcohol use on cognitive abilities. However, there is inconsistent evidence on the effects of chronic alcohol use on this measure of intelligence. Some studies have found significant deterioration in alcoholics versus the general population (Franceschi et al., 1984), while others have failed to find reliable differences (Grant, Adams and Reed, 1979). Verbal IQ scores tend to fall in the normal range (Tarter and Edwards, 1976) while performance IQ tends to be decreased, reflecting the damaging effect of alcohol on perceptual-motor abstraction and co-ordination skills. Less complex sensory or motor functions such as vocabulary, which depend on long-term memory, are less affected by alcohol. Four WAIS-R subtests (i.e., Picture Arrangement, Digit Symbol, Block Design and Object Assembly) seem to consistently yield differences between alcoholics and controls, indicating significant sequential organization and visuospatial deficits (Knight and Longmore, 1994).

The Halstead-Reitan Battery (HRB) has also been widely used to investigate cognitive impairment in alcoholics. The Category Test, a subtest of the HRB that assesses conceptual learning and problem solving, is the most sensitive HRB test for measuring the effects of alcohol. The Tactual Performance Test (which assesses spatial identification and memory) and Trails B (which assesses motor skills) are also sensitive to the effects of alcohol (Parsons and Farr, 1981). However, not all alcoholics will show evidence of brain damage on the HRB. Age, education level and the WAIS Verbal IQ have all been shown to be significantly correlated with the HRB Impairment Index. Results with the Luria-Nebraska neuropsychological battery show similar results. These tests show that the most reliable effect of chronic alcoholism is a deterioration in abstract cognitive functioning as indicated by a difficulty in forming hypotheses (necessary for effective problem-solving), perseveration and difficulty in shifting problem-solving strategies (e.g., failing to try new strategies when initial ones are unsuccessful; Parsons, 1987). Research to date does not indicate deficits in basic perceptual processes but does reveal disturbances in spatial tasks requiring perceptual analysis, synthesis, orientation and sequencing. These deficits are typical of alcoholics in the intermediate stage of the disorder, which includes individuals without a diagnosable organic brain syndrome but who nevertheless show cognitive and behavioral difficulties due to alcohol.

Memory is a cognitive function that is highly sensitive to damage to the central nervous system and, as a result, is frequently used to assess the presence of neurological damage in alcoholics. The Wechsler Memory Scales (WMS) have been widely used in this regard. However, early studies consistently failed to demonstrate that memory impairment was a feature of chronic alcohol use (Parsons and Prigatano, 1977; Butters et al., 1977). This finding may demonstrate that many subtests are insensitive to even profound memory damage. However, in a modified version of the WMS, in which a second assessment occurs 30 minutes after the initial testing (Russell, 1988), there is strong evidence of memory deficits (Nixon et al., 1987), especially weak or poor encoding strategies. Similarly, tests assessing memory for geometric designs after a brief delay, such as the Benton Visual Retention Test, have also been found to show deficits for some alcoholics. Short-term memory, where material is recalled after delays up to 60 seconds, also seems to be impaired in alcoholics (Brandt et al., 1983).

PREDICTING ALCOHOL-RELATED COGNITIVE DEFICITS

Yet, not all alcoholics will show cognitive deficits. In fact, age at which alcohol consumption begins appears to be the most important variable in determining whether alcohol leads to cognitive impairment. Alcoholics who began to drink by age 14 showed more impairment on measures of abstraction, visuospatial sequencing and verbal memory than those who began to drink at a later age. Frequency, quantity and duration of drinking do not appear to be related to neuropsychological deficits in any simple fashion (Parsons and Leber, 1981). This relationship is independent of the chronicity of alcohol consumption (Hesselbrock, Weidenman and Reed, 1985). Family history of alcoholism has also been inconsistently shown to be related to cognitive deficits (Schaeffer et al., 1991). While children of alcoholics may show dysfunctional personal behavior and have disturbed family backgrounds, this is not necessarily accompanied by cognitive deficits. Such deficits seem to be related to the maximal quantity and frequency of drinking and the toxic effects that such drinking has on brain functioning (Parsons, 1987). Evidence also shows that "primary alcoholics" showed a greater degree of cognitive impairment than did "secondary alcoholics." Primary alcoholics are those whose drinking pattern is independent of stress and characterized by six of the following features: withdrawal, tolerance, euphoria following first drink, euphoria following first drink after period of abstinence, loss of control, no history of social drinking, onset of heavy drinking prior to 40 years of age, with associated intrapersonal and interpersonal problems (Tarter and Edwards, 1986), while secondary alcoholics suffer from stress-related alcoholism.

However, the cognitive impairment observed in alcoholics is not unique to this group; profiles of impairment on the measures discussed above tend to be similar regardless of the source (such as alcohol abuse, brain injury, multiple sclerosis). As Knight and Longmore (1994) note, "it must be acknowledged that there is little of exceptional interest in the neuropsychological performance of chronic alcoholics." However, one potential confound to this literature showing evidence of cognitive impairment in alcoholics is the role of motivation and attention, which may diminish

441

performance independent of the effects of alcohol on the central nervous system. Lack of motivation to perform well or lack of persistence may produce sub-optimal performance compared to the healthier control groups (Cynn, 1992). Educational attainment and IQ have been shown to be related to cognitive deficits with individuals who are better educated (and younger) performing better than poorly educated and older alcoholics.

ALCOHOL-RELATED COGNITIVE DEFICITS AND TREATMENT OUTCOME

Evidence suggests that cognitive performance accounts for only a small portion of the variance in outcome of treatments for alcohol dependence. Work by Donovan, Walker and Kivlahan (1987) found some evidence that neuropsychological impairment may predict occupational status but not relapse rates or drinking patterns. Of course, cognitive deficits are only one of a wide range of variables, both external (e.g., psychosocial stability) and internal (e.g., psychopathology) to the individual, that will influence treatment outcome. In any case, these studies suggest that, to obtain maximum benefit, treatment must accommodate the cognitively impaired alcoholic's cognitive deficits. Despite the presence of such deficits, the cognitively impaired alcoholic can participate effectively in treatment.

Although neuropsychological status does not appear to significantly affect treatment outcome, this tends to apply mainly for younger, more mildly impaired individuals. Traditional treatments may need to be adapted for older, more severely affected alcoholics. These individuals may have severe memory impairments and disorientation (e.g., Korsakoff's syndrome, alcohol dementia). There may also be individuals who do not show obvious clinical signs of impairment such as impaired memory, but have impaired abstraction, problem-solving and perceptual-motor functioning. It may appear that their cognition is intact as their conversational skills may be normal. Yet, they may experience great difficulty in traditional treatments, which may be attributed to poor motivation or denial on the part of the client. Nevertheless, the cognitive effects of alcohol may interfere with the therapeutic tasks that occur in treatment programs, which require intact memory, learning and problem-solving skills. In addition, cognitive impairments may affect client motivation to use the skills that they possess or have been taught.

Due to the deficits observed early in abstinence, therapeutic interventions during this period may need to be repeated. In fact, repetition of treatment components is essential for older alcoholics, who have more severe cognitive deficits and require longer to recover. As suggested by Goldman (1983), complex therapy should be delayed until cognitive function has recovered. Treatment may need to be structured for those with impairments in memory, concentration and retention to avoid premature exposure to treatment demands for which the individual is unprepared. Clients may also need help to re-integrate into everyday functioning, since they may have difficulty coping with alcohol-induced residual deficits. Since alcoholics with cognitive impairment may comprise a fairly large proportion of clients in residential programs, the intensity of therapeutic interventions may need to be reduced in the initial phase to allow individuals maximal cognitive recovery (McKenna, 1997).

RECOVERY FROM ALCOHOL-RELATED COGNITIVE DEFICITS

Neuropsychological function can improve within weeks following abstinence (Goldstein, 1987). This recovery can follow at least two paths: neurobiological recovery from the direct or indirect CNS effects of alcohol, and experience-dependent recovery in which practice, stimulation and activity enhance the rate of recovery (Stringer and Goldman, 1988). Verbal ability deficits (e.g., verbal paired-associate learning) appear to remit very quickly, within a month (Goldman, 1983), while some deficits (e.g., abstraction deficits) may persist for years. Similarly, new learning, visual-spatial abstraction, problem solving and short-term memory may show persistent impairment, especially in older alcoholics. In a series of studies, Goldman (1987) and his colleagues (Ellenberg et al., 1980) showed that verbal functioning (as assessed by the WAIS Verbal scales) and visuospatial learning ability reach normal levels within two weeks of abstinence. Similarly, problem solving and new learning were also impaired for one to two weeks following abstinence. However, tests requiring complex skills, using novel stimuli or requiring adaptation tended to show persistent deficits. Goldman (1983) summarized the recovery process as follows:

> existing verbal abilities (vocabulary) are not impaired following drinking cessation. Most other abilities, especially when any new learning is involved, are impaired during the first week or two of abstinence. New verbal learning then recovers. Visual-spatial abilities, abstraction and problem-solving, short-term memory, and perhaps simple sensory reception show persistent impairment, particularly in older alcoholics. It is possible that with prolonged abstinence, some of these abilities will also recover. In general, the more novel, complex and rapid the information processing that a task requires, the longer it takes to recover.

Age also influences the rate of recovery. Alcoholics under age 40 frequently show no functional impairment two to three weeks following abstinence. Older subjects required three or more months to reach comparable recovery (Goldman, Williams and Klisz, 1983). Volume of alcohol consumed or chronicity appear to be insignificant predictors. In addition, alcoholics who resume drinking after prolonged abstinence, even at much lower rates, show significantly less improvement than individuals who remain abstinent (Yohman, Parsons and Leber, 1985).

443

Rate of recovery can also be affected by repeated assessments, indicating that experience with a test can improve functioning. Ellenberg et al. (1980) showed that repetition of the testing materials resulted in improvement, suggesting that neuropsychological deficits were amenable to environmental modification. For example, Forsberg and Goldman (1987) showed that repeated testing with a measure of verbal and visuospatial functions yielded a decreasing number of errors until they were within the normal range. These authors also showed that learning with one task generalized to different tasks assessing the same function. This suggested that neuropsychologically impaired alcoholics could benefit from experience-dependent learning to reduce such deficits and that such benefits were not task-specific. Parsons (1987) has found that clients receiving memory training (i.e., sessions on attention, chunking, visual memory, list learning paired-associates, digit symbol, use of mnemonics) or problem-solving training (i.e., sessions on identifying goals, brainstorming) performed better than no treatment controls on measures of memory and problem-solving.

Goldman (1983) used the following types of training in the rehabilitation of alcohol-related cognitive deficits: (i) general activation increases overall cognitive activity and appears to aid recovery by improving the alcoholic's efficiency at developing compensatory behaviors, integrating remaining functions more efficiently, overcoming mental apathy, and learning through trial and error; (ii) practice and guided rehearsal teaches the individual specific behaviors required to overcome a deficit (e.g., visuospatial deficit recovery enhanced through training on visuospatial tasks); and (iii) behavioral compensation trains the individual in alternative strategies to accomplish cognitive tasks, especially where there has been neurological damage (e.g., visual-spatial performance may be enhanced through the use of verbal mediators). Goldman (1987) has also stressed the importance of repetition of material to ensure adequate processing has occurred. Since the first few weeks of abstinence are characterized by cognitive "haziness," much of what is learned during this period may be forgotten. Thus, treatment should be delayed until the individual recovers his or her cognitive capacities.

Goldstein (1987) has suggested placing less emphasis on training cognitively impaired alcoholics on remediating memory impairments, which may often be subtle (excluding Korsakoff-afflicted individuals), and focusing on teaching problem-solving skills, abstraction skills, and how to learn and recall what is learned. Goldstein (1987) suggests that since the brain has a reduced ability to process information (which affects several cognitive domains, including memory), efforts to improve the processing of information will be a useful approach to rehabilitation.

Staff may need to modify their attitudes towards this population to respond to the particular characteristics of neuropsychologically impaired individuals. The interpretation of behaviors and attitudes in cognitively intact populations may not apply to cognitively impaired drinkers. For example, what appears to be denial or resistance to treatment may indicate difficulty in comprehension or memory; what appears to be a motivational problem may in fact be a memory problem. For example, the cognitively impaired alcoholic may initially have difficulty applying abstract principles to his or her life problems, reasoning by analogy or recalling material taught earlier in the program. Thus, he or she may give the impression that he or she is not making sufficient effort. These difficulties may be accompanied by emotional reactions such as anger, frustration and depression. Consequently, counsellors must be aware of the client's neuropsychological status and adjust their clinical interventions accordingly.

PRACTICAL IMPLICATIONS

There is a considerable body of research on the means of improving memory in individuals who have experienced memory loss or damage due to substance use, disease or injury. Of particular relevance to interventions with cognitively impaired alcoholics are the following recommendations:

(i)   It is important to structure therapeutic tasks to increase the client's ability to engage in effortful processing (Hertel, 1992). Unstructured, unfocused therapeutic tasks will confuse and inhibit learning in cognitively impaired alcoholics. It is important to maintain a clear focus and structure in both the process and content of therapeutic interventions. Presenting information in modules may also be helpful.

(ii)   "Deeper" encoding of information can be encouraged through elaborative interrogation. In this process, the individual is queried with "why" questions about the "to be remembered material" (Pressley and El-Dinary, 1992), encouraging self-referential processing whereby the material is made personally relevant (Rogers, Kuiper and Kirker, 1977), and the activation of episodic memory processes in the encoding of material to enhance retrievability (vs. semantic learning; Tulving, 1972).

(iii)   Systematic and planned repetition, especially if it is elaborated with imagery, can help to enhance the recall of information; this can be encouraged, for example, through the taking of notes, which are then regularly reviewed.

(iv)   Enhancing cognitive knowledge and skills that instruct the individual when to use what he or she has learned, how to apply new learning, and in what situations (Pressley and El-Dinary, 1992) is important in helping the cognitively impaired individual know the limits of his or her memory and remedial steps to take.

(v)   Spaced (i.e., daily and regular sessions) rather than massed (i.e., intensive learning sessions or "cramming") practice of important therapeutic information will lead to better encoding and retrievability (Payne and Wenger, 1992).

(vi)   Teaching how to focus attention, screen out distractions and maintain concentration can help the individual devote the attentional resources necessary for the encoding and recall of information.

(vii)   Build in external retrieval cues (i.e., cue cards, making notes) to enhance recall (Zacks and Hasher, 1992) as a practical means of improving daily functioning when deficits do not fully recover.

(viii)   Improve metamemory through mindfulness of the information to be remembered (i.e., knowing that you know; Plude, 1992).

(ix)   The use of mental imagery and imagination helps encode important therapeutic material and learning.

(x)   Training in problem-solving strategies in which the individual is guided in a step-by-step process defining the problem, and selecting and executing reasonable solutions may be useful. Training in monitoring the effectiveness of problem-solving efforts is critical in helping the individual shift strategies (i.e., metacognitive strategies) from ones that will not succeed to ones that may (e.g., lose, shift, win).

SUMMARY

This chapter has surveyed some of the literature on the chronic effects of alcohol on cognition and their relationship with treatment outcomes. A discussion of some practical techniques to enhance cognitive processing indicates that treatment programs that include a significant proportion of alcohol-impaired individuals may need to focus on the timing of interventions (i.e., to allow maximal recovery and to minimize forgetting due to residual cognitive deficits), encouragement of creative solutions by staff and client, and education of treatment staff on the cognitive limitations of this sample.

REFERENCES

Brandt, J., Butters, N., Ryan, C., and Bayog, R. (1983). Cognitive loss and recovery in long-term alcohol abusers. *Archives of General Psychiatry* 40: 435–442.

Butters, N., Cermak, L.S., Montgomery, K., and Adinolfi, A. (1977). Some comparisons of the memory and visuoperceptive deficits of chronic alcoholics and patients with Korsakoff's disease. *Alcoholism: Clinical and Experimental Research* 1: 73–80.

Cynn, V.E.H. (1992). Persistence and problem-solving skills in young male alcoholics. *Journal of Studies on Alcohol* 53: 57–62.

Donovan, D.M., Walker, R.D., and Kivlahan, D.R. (1987). Recovery and remediation of neuro-psychological functions, implications for alcoholism rehabilitation process and outcome. In *Neuropsychology of Alcoholism: Implications for Diagnosis and Treatment,* eds. Parsons, O.A., Butters, N., and Nathan, P.E. New York: Guilford Press.

Ellenberg, L., Rosenbaum, G., Goldman, M.S., and Whitman, R.D. (1980). Recoverability of psychological functions following alcohol abuse: Lateralization effects. *Journal of Consulting and Clinical Psychology* 481: 503–510.

Forsberg, L.K., and Goldman, M.S. (1987). Experience-dependent recovery of cognitive deficits in alcoholics: Extended transfer of training. *Journal of Abnormal Psychology* 96: 345–353.

Franceschi, M., Truci, G., Comi, G., Lozza, L., Marchinettini, P., Galardi, G., and Smirne, S. (1984). Cognitive deficits and their relationship to other neurological complications in chronic alcoholic patients. *Journal of Neurology, Neurosurgery, and Psychiatry* 47: 1134–1137.

Goldman, M.S. (1987). The role of time and practice in recovery of function in alcoholics. In *Neuropsychology of Alcoholism: Implications for Diagnosis and Treatment,* eds. Parsons, O.A., Butters, N., and Nathan, P.E. New York: Guilford Press.

Goldman, M.S., Williams, D.L. and Klisz, D.K. (1983). Recoverability of psychological function-ing following alcohol abuse: Prolonged visual-spatial dysfunction in older alcoholics. *Journal of Consulting and Clinical Psychology* 51: 370–378.

Goldman, M.S. (1983). Cognitive impairment in chronic alcoholics: Endogenous and exogenous processes. *Alcoholism: Clinical and Experimental Research* 38: 1045–1054.

Goldstein, G. (1987). Recovery, treatment and rehabilitation in chronic alcoholics. In *Neuro-psychology of Alcoholism: Implications for Diagnosis and Treatment,* eds. Parsons, O.A., Butters, N., and Nathan, P.E. New York: Guilford Press.

Grant, I., Adams, K., and Reed, R. (1979) Normal neuropsychological abilities of alcoholic men in their late thirties. *American Journal of Psychiatry* 136: 1263–1269.

Hertel, P.T. (1992). Improving memory and mood through automatic and controlled procedures of mind. In *Memory Improvement: Implications for Memory Theory,* eds. Herrmann, D.J., Weingartner, H., Searleman, A., and McEvoy, C. New York: Springer-Verlag.

Hesselbrock, M.N., Weidenman, M.A., and Reed, H.B. (1985). Effects of age, sex, drinking history and antisocial personality on neuropsychology of alcoholics. *Journal of Studies on Alcohol* 46: 313–320.

Knight, R.G., and Longmore, B.E. (1994). *Clinical Neuropsychology of Alcoholism.* Hove, UK: Lawrence Erlbaum Associates.

McKenna, C. (1997). Neurocognitive syndromes and neuroimaging in addictions. In *The Principles and Practice of Addictions in Psychiatry,* ed. Miller, N. Philadelphia: W.B. Saunders Company.

Nixon, S.J., Kujawski, A., Parsons, O.A., and Yohman, J.R. (1987). Semantic (verbal) and figural memory impairments in alcoholics. *Journal of Clinical and Experimental Neuropsychology* 9: 311–322.

Parsons, O.A., and Farr, S.P. (1981). The neuropsychology of drug and alcohol abuse. In *Handbook of Clinical Neuropsychology,* eds. Filskov, S.B., and Boll, T.J. New York: Wiley Interscience.

Parsons, O.A. (1987). Do neuropsychological deficits predict alcoholics treatment course and post-treatment recovery? In *Neuropsychology of Alcoholism: Implications for Diagnosis and Treatment,* eds. Parsons, O.A., Butters, N., and Nathan, P.E. New York: Guilford Press.

Parsons, O.A., and Leber, W.R. (1981). The relationship between cognitive dysfunction and brain damage in alcoholics: Causal interactive or epiphenomenal? *Alcoholism: Clinical and Experimental Research* 14: 746–755.

Parsons, O.A., and Prigatano, G.P. (1977). Memory functioning in alcoholics. In *Alcohol and Memory,* eds. Birnbaum, I.M., and Parker, E.S. Hillsdale, NJ: Lawrence Erlbaum Associates Inc.

Payne, D.G., and Wenger, M.J. (1992). Improving memory through practice. In *Memory Improvement: Implications for Memory Theory,* eds. Herrmann, D. J., Weingartner, H., Searleman, A., and McEvoy, C. New York: Springer-Verlag.

Plude, D.J. (1992). Attention and memory improvement. In *Memory Improvement: Implications for Memory Theory,* eds. Herrmann, D.J., Weingartner, H., Searleman, A., and McEvoy, C. New York: Springer-Verlag.

Pressley, M., and El-Dinary, P.B. (1992). Memory strategy instruction that promotes good information processing. In *Memory Improvement: Implications for Memory Theory,* eds. Herrmann, D.J., Weingartner, H., Searleman, A., and McEvoy, C. New York: Springer-Verlag.

Rogers, T.B., Kuiper, N.A., and Kirker, W.S. (1977). Self-reference and the encoding of personal information. *Journal of Personality and Social Psychology* 35: 677–688.

Russell, E.W. (1988). Renorming Russell's version of the Wechsler Memory Scale. *Journal of Clinical and Experimental Neuropsychology* 10: 235–239.

Schafer, K., Butters, N., Smith, T., Irwin, M., Brown, S., Hanger, P., Grant, I., and Schuckit, M. (1991). Cognitive performance of alcoholics: Longitudinal evaluation of the role of drinking history, depression, liver function nutrition, and family history. *Alcoholism: Clinical and Experimental Research* 15: 653–660.

Stringer, A.Y., and Goldman, M.S. (1986). Experience-dependent recovery of block design performance in male alcoholics: Strategy training versus unstructured practice. *Journal of Studies on Alcohol* 49: 406–411.

Tarter, R.E., and Edwards, K.L. (1986). Multifactorial etiology of neuropsychological impairment in alcoholics. *Alcoholism: Clinical and Experimental Research* 10: 128–135.

Tulving, E. (1972). Episodic and semantic memory. In *Organization of Memory,* eds. Tulving, E., and Donaldson, W. New York: Academic Press.

Yohman, J.R., Parsons, O.A., and Leber, W.R. (1985). Lack of recovery in male alcoholics' neuropsychological performance one year after treatment. *Alcoholism: Clinical and Experimental Research* 9: 114–117.

Zacks, R.T., and Hasher, L. (1992). Memory in life, lab, and clinic: Implications for memory theory. In *Memory Improvement: Implications for Memory Theory,* eds. Herrmann, D.J., Weingartner, H., Searleman, A., and McEvoy, C. New York: Springer-Verlag.

Chapter 24

Sexuality, Sexual Problems, and Sexual and Physical Assault

BETTY-ANNE M. HOWARD AND DEBORAH HUDSON

INTRODUCTION

A holistic approach to addictions assessment includes sexuality. Feeling joy and connection sexually is a right of all. This sensitive and most often private area of our lives is affected physically, emotionally and relationally by substance use. In order to be sexually healthy, we must be able to feel comfortable with our bodies, protect ourselves from unwanted touch, and be able to discern what feels good and okay and what doesn't. An addiction can dull one's awareness of all these aspects of oneself. Being sexual under such circumstances could prove more than unrewarding; it could be psychologically and emotionally damaging — even abusive.

This chapter presents an overview of a wide number of issues related to sexuality. The hope is to give the reader tools to assess problems within the area of sexuality, to determine the need for referral to more specialized care, and to outline the wide range of issues that influence or interfere with one's sexual experience.

ADDRESSING THE ISSUES

Attitudes

We have all been affected in a variety of ways by our own personal experiences, by the messages we receive through the media, by the lessons we learned from our parents, peers, schools and other people around us. No one is exempt from these influences.

For instance, what are your stereotypes for gays and lesbians? What are your feelings and knowledge about gay and lesbian sex? Do you believe that making love without intercourse is less than the ideal, or not really sex at all? Is it all right to stop lovemaking at any time if you feel uncomfortable? Is it all right for someone to choose celibacy?

It is important to notice our feelings in a counselling situation. Is the tone judgmental? Is there any sense of feeling shocked, scared, angry or grief stricken? These reactions may be clues about our own traumatic sexual experiences that need attention, or our attitudes and beliefs that need examination. For example, if you believe that sexual experience outside of marriage is wrong — even somewhat unacceptable — then when a single 24-year-old woman discusses her sexual experiences with you, you could pass judgment on her in many ways. Needless to say, this could have a negative impact on your ability to help this client. If you were assaulted at age 17 and have blocked these feelings, a young woman talking about a rape may evoke a lot of your feelings. If you assume a client is sexually active, or knows the facts of life, or is orgasmic, or is heterosexual, you may miss an accurate description of his or her sexual experience.

It is important to acknowledge male and female differences in sexual needs and experiences, and society's sex-specific pressures, attitudes and judgments. For example, female alcoholics are often viewed as promiscuous. Be aware that you are probably working with a survivor of sexual abuse and that her sexual behavior is closely linked to her history. Also, female alcoholics are very vulnerable to continued sexual abuse within a culture that still believes women ask for abuse by their behavior, dress and where they go. There seems to be more cultural tolerance for men being sexual and inebriated. Men, on the other hand, are pressured by expectations to perform. For example, men often believe that if they are unable to obtain and maintain an erection during sex, then they are somehow inadequate. Even the word impotence — which means "lack of power" — reflects the underlying attitude that exists. This definition immediately puts a man on the defensive. His self-image demands he do anything not to seem powerless.

Our sexually oriented culture puts pressure on relationships. Sex has been elevated to such a level of importance it is often the test of the significance of a relationship. Thus, natural differences and desires may be interpreted as signs of something fundamentally wrong with the relationship. An underlying assumption seems to be that a man, by his nature, needs sex, and a partnership will fail if a woman cannot satisfy his appetite. Relationship difficulties are sometimes labelled as sexual difficulties. As a counsellor, it is important to be aware of this possibility. Rather than a "sexual problem," you may be dealing with a communication problem, or a scarcity of any physical contact, or a feeling that one partner does not have enough time for the relationship. It could be a relationship phase where emotional energy is going elsewhere such as to children, to work, or to healing from a sexual abuse history and a related addiction to alcohol or other drugs.

Finally, dealing with sexuality issues can cause anxiety. Most of us were taught that sex is not something you discuss in public — that what goes on in the privacy of someone's bedroom is his or her own business. When you consider the discomfort a client may already be experiencing in discussing his or her alcohol/drug problem, and add to that an increased dose of anxiety that both the client and the counsellor may experience when discussing sexual issues, what you get at the very least are some foreseeable difficulties. One way to reduce these difficulties is for the counsellor to begin doing some personal work in this area. Initially, the goal would be to begin getting comfortable discussing and addressing sexual issues. A good start would be going to workshops on sexuality, talking to other staff and reading some of the material cited in the Resources section at the end of this chapter. Many clinicians who have not been trained in the area of sexuality and sexual functioning tend to gloss over this topic with their clients, hoping that nothing that needs to be addressed will surface. Still others may revel in the thought of delving into someone else's sex life. Neither of these approaches is helpful or respectful towards the client.

Consultation Needs

There may be times you need to consult with others about what your client has shared with you, while of course respecting the rules of confidentiality. An exception is child sexual abuse: those who know of or suspect abuse are legally obliged to report it to the appropriate authorities. Issues you may want to discuss with a colleague are your feelings about homosexuality, sado-masochism, bisexuality, celibacy, etc. These are some of the issues you might face. An unwillingness to examine your own attitudes or any resistance to changing them can prove detrimental to the people you are trying to help.

It is not uncommon to become sexually aroused while discussing sexuality issues with clients. What is most important is that you be aware that this is happening and to tell yourself to stop. There are absolutely no situations or circumstances where it is okay to engage in any form of sexual behavior with your client. This is a violation of professional ethics and could do serious damage to your client. It is important to be clear about your own boundaries.

Boundaries protect both you and your client, and enable you to work together. By boundaries, we mean the respectful lines you draw between yourself and your client. It is important to acknowledge that you are a counsellor functioning in a professional role. You are not a friend, a potential date, a surrogate parent/protector or rescuer. It is important for you to be a counsellor and stay a counsellor. You are there for the client in a therapeutic role. It is not a friendship with a 50-50 exchange of energy. Acknowledge the power differential and do not abuse it. Given the sensitive and difficult nature of dealing with these types of problems, ensure that appropriate supervision is available — and used.

Action

The first step, after understanding and addressing your own attitudes and assumptions, is to assess the problem. Given what you will come to know about the types of sexual problems that can occur and how alcohol and other drugs affect sexual response, you can begin to put this information together by asking appropriate questions to determine whether a problem exists, its nature, and the best course of action for the client. Providing a safe, nonjudgmental environment where you are able to display a certain comfort level in discussing these issues can be very effective.

Basic education may be all that is needed to solve a sexual problem. In this society we tend to shy away from teaching our children how to be loving towards their own bodies and towards a partner. As a result, the learning process is often trial and error. For instance, children are often discouraged from what is perceived as inappropriate sexual self-exploration and, therefore, as adults may need encouragement to explore their own sexuality. The counsellor can guide this process with written or audiovisual information, discussion and suggestions.

It is important to stress with clients that they need to say "no" to unwanted sex. It is all right to begin having sex and to change your mind and stop. To begin healing, your body needs to know you will respect its signals.

SEXUAL RESPONSE

Physiological, cognitive and cultural/social factors affect sexual response. This section will discuss the research on the physical effects of drugs and alcohol on sexual functioning. The cognitive factors include the beliefs that become part of a brain's functioning, which directs sexual response. Cultural and social factors are the sexual expectations placed on an individual because of his or her gender, race, sexual orientation, age and physical disability.

To aid in understanding the effects of alcohol and drug abuse on sexuality, these factors will be discussed individually.

Alcohol and Drug Use and Physiological Response

Much of the research in this area has been conducted on animals (Wilson, 1977). It is difficult to generalize from these findings to the human population, especially since cognitive and social factors play such an important role in how we respond sexually. However, a small body of literature has examined the impact of specific chemicals on sexual performance. Doweiko (1990) provides a brief summary of this literature according to drug type (i.e., alcohol, narcotics, amphetamines and cocaine, marijuana, hallucinogens, central nervous system depressants and other drugs). Doweiko points out that we are dealing in many instances here with a "chicken and egg" situation. It is difficult to determine whether using drugs created a sexual problem or whether the sexual problem existed first and then led to the use of drugs. There is some evidence that drug use may occur as a way of dealing with a lack of adequate intimacy skills and/or other sexual problems that already exist. These observations are important to consider when working with clients.

You may be counselling on the premise that alcohol has negatively affected your client's sexual performance, but if problems continue following a period of sobriety, more intensive sex therapy may be required.

Alcohol use can lead to a decrease in a man's ability to achieve and maintain an erection (Kolodny, Masters and Johnson, 1979; Gold, 1988) and a decrease in sexual pleasure for women (Gold, 1988; Kolodny et al., 1979). The probable basis for this is alcohol acting as a depressant on the central nervous system, thus interfering with pathways of reflex transmission of sexual arousal. According to Doweiko (1990), Masters and Johnson (1966) concluded that "the excessive use of alcohol was the most frequently encountered cause of impotence in middle-aged men" (p. 298).

Other central nervous system depressants (tranquillizers, sedatives and hypnotics) affect people in a similar fashion, that is by decreasing sexual responsiveness. Kolodny et al. (1979) noted that barbiturate users describe depressed libido, impotence or loss of orgasmic responsiveness associated with drug use.

The analysis of the effects of marijuana on sexual response and behavior is quite interesting. Cognitive factors seem to play an important role when determining the effects of this drug on sexual functioning. Although it has been reported that some men have been found to be impotent after chronic use of the drug (Kolodny et al., 1979), and that 20 per cent of men using this drug on a daily basis will experience erectile problems (Masters et al., 1966), many users report an increase in sexual desire and pleasure.

Narcotic use impairs sexual desire, performance and satisfaction (Gold, 1988). Amphetamines and cocaine may inhibit orgasm, especially in women (Kaplan, 1979).

In summary, though there is some evidence regarding the impact of alcohol and drugs on sexual functioning, most researchers forewarn the reader that the evidence is inconclusive.

Cognitive Factors

The circumstances under which alcohol and other drugs are used may be more important than the effects of the drugs themselves on male or female sexual arousal

(Wilson, 1977). For example, studies conducted with women have found an increase in reported sexual arousal with increased alcohol consumption, but, at the same time, women's physiological responses do not correspond with this perception. That is, there is a decrease in vaginal responsiveness (Wilson and Lawson, 1978). In addition, Wilson (1977) notes that the presence of alcohol may create a certain environment where attitudes toward sexual behavior may become more permissive. Another point to consider is that, in using alcohol, the initial physiological response mirrors that of sexual arousal (i.e., an increased heart rate, and increased warmth as blood vessels dilate). It is no wonder then that there are many different issues to consider when assessing sexual functioning among people experiencing an alcohol or drug problem.

Kolodny et al. (1979) offer a similar perspective on issues pertaining to women's sexual functioning and heroin use, illustrating the confounding variables that may exist. They suggest that, because many women resort to prostitution as a means of supporting their drug habit, they may have negative feelings toward sex that reflect guilt, low self-esteem or hostility toward men. In addition, given that many (60 to 90 per cent) women in treatment programs for substance abuse are survivors of childhood and adult sexual abuse (Covington, 1983; Benward and Densen-Gerber, 1975; Wachtel and Lawton-Speert, 1983), one can assume that sexual difficulties will be present.

Cognitive factors in marijuana use are also quite evident. Although most users report an increase in sexual responsiveness, Doweiko (1990) notes that research has shown that "marijuana either has no impact on tactile perception, or that it actually lessens touch perception" (p. 301). However, Kolodny et al. (1979) report that, although both men and women report an increased sense of touch, a greater degree of relaxation and being in tune with one's partner, they are also very quick to point out that both people needed to be "high" *at the same time* for the sexual experience to be enhanced.

Finally, for the drugs that lower anxiety (i.e., tranquillizers, sedatives and hypnotics), it is anticipated that a reduction in anxiety means enhanced sexual performance. According to Kolodny et al. (1979, p. 331), "barbiturates may sometimes lower sexual inhibitions and in this sense may enhance sexual function, but more commonly barbiturate users describe depressed libido, impotence, or loss of orgasmic responsiveness associated with drug use." This is usually associated with high dosage levels and infrequently reported.

Cultural/Social Factors

Alcohol, within the majority of North American and other cultures, is associated with friends and good times, romance, courtship and special events. These activities often include sexual experiences. As stated earlier, alcohol can sometimes set the wheels in motion for sex to occur by creating a more permissive atmosphere. Indeed, the saying "to wine and dine someone" certainly implies a potential sexual encounter. These types of societal expectations and pressures to perform certainly affect people's attitudes and experiences.

ASSESSING SEXUAL DIFFICULTIES

Asking questions about sex can be uncomfortable at first. Remember that people generally feel very alone in learning about sex and in wondering about their sexual experiences, and rarely talk openly about their concerns, fears and pleasures. Thus it is important that the counsellor provide an environment in which asking questions about sexual issues is as natural as asking about diet, work habits and recreation.

An opening statement could be: "Problems with addictions are often related to sexual problems, so this is part of our assessment today." At this point, the client may indicate that this is okay or definitely not okay. Respect that choice and let the client know that this is a place where he or she can discuss any sexual concerns when ready.

There are several situations where it seems appropriate for a counsellor to directly ask questions about sexual issues. First, it would be appropriate if a person raises the issue, suggesting that a problem exists. The person may say: "I'm having some problems with sex" or may allude to a problem in a joking fashion. At that point, it would be good to ask directly: "Are you having some problems related to your sexual experiences?"

The second situation would be where the person seeking help has acknowledged that he or she was sexually victimized in some way. It might be useful to ask such clients if they have any issues regarding sex in their lives, or if they have what they feel is a sexually satisfying relationship. In addition, if such clients express general relationship concerns, it might be helpful to ask specifically about the sexual aspects of their relationships. This could be explored by asking questions about sexual boundaries (i.e., how they take care of themselves sexually).

A third situation could be with a young lesbian or gay person who is sexually inexperienced and is wondering what is "normal" sexual behavior. You may want to ask if the client is comfortable with what he or she has been doing sexually, since the client may not realize that only the individual can define what is "normal" — and that trusting oneself and knowing what an individual is comfortable doing or not doing is important.

Another situation in which it may be appropriate to ask questions about sexual issues involves the person who had a history of daily or chronic drug use but who has quit using. Given that the person's past sexual behavior was accompanied by drug use, it would be helpful to know how that person is handling sexual issues without the involvement of drugs.

Talking about sex can feel degrading or unsafe to a survivor of sexual abuse, so it is important to be aware of your client's history and to let her or him know that you are aware of the impact it can have. Because substances may have been used to block out memories of assault, the counsellor needs to also be knowledgeable about the effect that recall may have on the client and allow the client to set the pace. "Remembering" is terrifying, so do not push this. As the client reduces or stops substance use, memories often surface rapidly. Be sure that the necessary supports are in place for the client before you begin to explore this sensitive subject.

In exploring sexual abuse, it may be useful to start with a neutral statement such as: "Using alcohol or drugs can be a way of helping us block out frightening or unpleasant experiences we may have had as children. Do you remember any experiences as a child where you felt afraid or were touched in a way that you didn't like or that felt uncomfortable?" Remember, this is simply a way for you to get a sense of whether a sexual abuse history is an issue and to help your client acknowledge this possibility.

Fears that are common among survivors include being afraid of the dark, of putting their face under water, or of falling asleep. Be aware, however, that many other people also have these fears. Many survivors may also repeat their childhood experiences in adult relationships. That is, they may have repeated relationships in which they are physically or sexually abused. For a checklist of possible survivor behaviors, an excellent resource is *Secret Survivors* (Blume, 1990).

If clients disclose sexual abuse, they need to hear that you believe them, that it was not their fault, and that help with healing can be found. Most communities have sexual assault crisis services that can help survivors. This would be a very good place to find information, crisis support for survivors, support groups and counselling. It is also important to note the comments of Harrison et al. (1990), who stress the need for agencies to develop policies and procedures to help identify and aid victims of abuse. Otherwise, the addictions intervention may prove ineffective, and, in the case of adolescents, you may be returning the client to an abusive situation that could be extremely harmful.

If disclosure has occurred, it is probably wise not to extend the assessment, but take some time to ensure that the client is not disoriented — that he or she is in the present, able to leave your office and cope with the aftermath of disclosure. If you are inexperienced in sexual assault assessment and counselling, it would be helpful to consult someone on how to proceed before meeting the client again.

As you proceed with an assessment, it is important to acknowledge sexual orientation early on, or you might ask some irrelevant questions and the lesbian or gay client will feel discounted. A simple question such as "Is your sexual preference currently for women, men or both?" will suffice. Use language that will include everyone, such as "Is your partner (rather than "boyfriend" or "wife") aware of this?"

You may want to do a specific assessment of possible sexual difficulties in order to determine the need for referral. The nature of the referral will depend on the type of sexual problem or the phase of the sexual response that is problematic.

SEXUAL RESPONSE

Sexual response has been divided into three phases: the desire phase, the excitement phase and the orgasm phase. Loulan (1984) adds willingness (to have sex) to the cycle, suggesting this can lead to desire. These phases are interconnected but governed by separate narrow physiological systems — there is therefore the possibility of separate inhibitions of the phases. Certain traumas, if sufficiently intense, disturb the entire system, but often only one component is disturbed. For example, a woman may have no sexual desire but be able to lubricate and have orgasms.

Understanding the nature of sexual response allows a specialized counsellor to intervene at certain points with specific therapeutic tools. However, in an addictions assessment, it would be sufficient to get a definition of the problem, assess whether it is a priority concern at this time, and if so, offer some self-help literature and/or a referral to a sex therapist. The context of a relationship makes working on sexuality far more complex, as sex works best in a healthy relationship. Allow room for self-sexuality and celibacy as healthy choices for some people. Only the client knows what he or she wants and needs.

SEXUAL PROBLEMS IN WOMEN

Desire-Phase Problems
Asking simply "Do you feel desire for sex?" is a good start.

Desire-phase problems can be classified as primary or secondary. Primary problems are rare and represent a life-long history of asexuality. Secondary problems represent a loss of sex drive, which may be the result of physical illness, psychological traumas — such as incest, rape or receiving oppressive sexual messages — and major life changes such as the birth of a child.

Desire-phase problems can be global or situational. With global problems a woman ceases to be interested in sex at all; this is associated with depressive states, severe anxiety and physical causes. With situational problems a woman feels desire in only certain situations and often not with the most appropriate and desirable partner. As noted earlier, it is common for survivors of sexual abuse to find themselves in sexually abusive relationships in adulthood. It generally takes a great deal of personal work for survivors to feel worthy of a respectful relationship, to understand what it may be like, to learn to protect themselves and to feel desire for gentle loving sex. Generally this experience is quite foreign to them. If they did feel some pleasure with the abuse as children, which would be a normal reflexive body response to stimulation, they may feel shame with desire as adults. It is important to validate that the assault should never have happened and their bodies were just responding normally — as their taste-buds would respond to food they liked.

In general, a desire-phase problem is characterized by asexual behavior; it is as if a woman's sexual circuits have been shut down. She will not pursue sexual gratification, and loses interest in sex. She may be able to experience lubrication and orgasm, but in a mechanical manner without much pleasure. Anxiety is evoked early, often when sex is anticipated or as soon as the initial sensations or erotic desire are experienced. These early stirrings are threatening, and the individual defends herself by suppressing desire rapidly and involuntarily, often before it can develop fully and emerge into conscious awareness. This may be accomplished by focusing on negatives — the opposite of conjuring up fantasies to liberate sexual desire. Characteristically the individual has no insight into the mechanism of active suppressions.

The reasons for suppressing desire may be quite realistic: a woman may be reacting to a dangerous situation, or sexual activity may always have disappointed her.

Kaplan (1979) has found that, generally, a woman's anger toward her partner will inhibit her sexual desire, while men can feel intense desire for a partner even when angry. This is an example of emotional differences between men and women that may impinge upon sexual desire and experience.

Kitzinger (1983) has found from women's experiences that when a couple communicates well about their feelings and all other things happening in their lives, there are likely to be fewer sexual problems. When sex is approached out of context, seen as an isolated activity separate from all else, there are more likely to be obvious differences in desire.

Excitement-Phase Problems

Asking "Do you experience pain during sex?" and "Do you have trouble lubricating?" defines these problems.

The excitement phase in women is characterized by the vascular engorgement of the genital organs, the swelling and coloration of the vaginal walls, formation of the orgastic platform, and lubrication. Excitement-phase disorders are marked by difficulty with lubricating during lovemaking. Inhibition of lubrication may become more common following menopause because of lower estrogen levels. The painful and uncomfortable experience of intercourse with a dry vagina that is not distended can cause a secondary inhibition of desire and/or avoidance of sex. A referral to a sensitive family doctor knowledgeable in this area would be appropriate.

Orgasmic Problems
Asking "Do you experience orgasm?" will define this problem.

Problems with orgasm can range on a spectrum of severity from total anorgasmia (inability to experience orgasm) to mild situational difficulties. Orgasm is a genital reflex that can be under the individual's voluntary control. All reflexes subject to voluntary control can be inhibited when conscious attention is focused on the process. For example, the knee-jerk reflex cannot be elicited when an individual is staring at his or her knee. Self-consciousness makes us awkward, as when we attend to swallowing or dancing. The causes of anorgasmia vary. Studies have revealed fears of losing control of aggressive as well as sexual impulses, fear of urinating, unrealistic fantasies about dangers and pleasures of orgasm, performance anxieties related to fear of failure, taking too long, and so on. The specific inhibition of the orgasmic reflex may be accompanied by secondary inhibition of arousal, but as a general rule women who have problems achieving orgasm are responsive sexually, experience erotic feelings and lubricate.

Often women are not orgasmic because they have never been taught how to do it. Learning to become orgasmic can be a fairly straightforward process. Self-help groups and self-help books such as Lonnie Barbach's (1975) *For Yourself: The Fulfilment of Female Sexuality* are excellent starting places and may be sufficient to solve the problem. It is important for a woman to have the time she needs to learn to become orgasmic herself without being pressured in any way to be sexual with a partner.

FEMALE SEXUAL PROBLEMS NOT RELATED TO A SPECIFIC SEXUAL PHASE

Vaginismus
Asking "Does your vagina sometimes close up tight without your control?" can define vaginismus.

Women with vaginismus often feel a lot of shame and hopelessness and are under a great deal of pressure in their relationships. If the client feels ready, a referral to a therapist *knowledgeable in this area* could be offered. Vaginismus is a conditioned reflex spasm of the vaginal entrance that occurs whenever entry is attempted. In milder forms, this genital spasm causes dyspareunia, where entry is possible but intercourse is painful. Otherwise, women with vaginismus tend to be sexually responsive.

Kitzinger (1983) reframes vaginismus, describing it as the natural protection of women against penetration. She suggests: "Why not respect this and look for options?" Kitzinger describes an approach to dealing with vaginismus focusing primarily on the couple's communication, with women in complete control of vaginal penetration, and the understanding that they may (or may not) move to partner penetration. For example, in heterosexual situations she teaches other ways for an erection to be contained, such as between the thighs, under an arm or between breasts. Kitzinger views vaginismus as occurring in women who do not enjoy penetration or like it only occasionally and usually prefer other ways of lovemaking. She questions the focus of our society on penetration as the normal necessary routine and challenges sex therapists to be creative in encouraging their couples to find solutions to their sexual difficulties and to question their own belief systems about the necessity of penetration.

Sexual Phobias
Asking "Do you have some specific fears about sex?" should open this discussion.

Sexual phobias are an avoidance of erotic feelings and/or certain sexual activities. For example, a woman may have a phobic avoidance of penetration, oral sex, anal sex, masturbation, semen, pubic hair, or getting undressed in front of a partner. Sexual phobias are common in adult survivors of sexual abuse. Psychotherapy instead of or in addition to sex therapy is called for.

MALE SEXUAL PROBLEMS

Problems with Erection
Asking "Do you have problems getting or keeping an erection?" should open this discussion.

Secondary impotence is the development of impotence in men who have previously not had problems with erection. Men with primary impotence, which is rarer and far less amenable to treatment, have never functioned well in terms of erection. As noted previously, erectile problems can be due to physical, cognitive or social factors. Although the man may be aroused and want to make love, his penis will not co-operate. The erectile and ejaculate reflexes are dissociable and some men are able to ejaculate despite their flaccid penis. Generally, a man has trouble with his erection the moment he becomes anxious. Some men cannot achieve an erection before intercourse, others attain an erection easily but lose it upon entry or during intercourse. Some men can achieve an erection only if their partner dominates, others lose their erection if a partner tries to assume control.

In talking with men about erectile problems, it is important to take a detailed account of what happens, the first time they remember the situation arising and how they felt. Be aware that the cure may be in the present: it may be a statement about whether he wants to have intercourse. Ironic as it may seem, most men would rather feel they have a medical problem than say very simply to their partner, "I don't want to have sex with you." Of course the possibility of a physiological basis for erectile problems cannot be ignored, but generally it is more constructive to begin by looking at other possibilities.

In addressing erectile problems, it is important to remove the expectation to perform, asking the couple to refrain from attempting intercourse, and to take time to explore the total sensuality of each other's bodies. The ban on intercourse can be for an extended time. It is important to know that just because a man gets an erection doesn't mean he has to use it; he will get another. In other words, change the focus of lovemaking to more total sensual experience. Although as an addictions counsellor you are not expected to do sex therapy, this simple advice may suffice.

Premature Ejaculation

This is a condition where a man is unable to control his ejaculatory reflex voluntarily. It is important again to assess feelings. Does this problem translate into "I want to get this over with as fast as possible?" It is possible to become increasingly aware of the point of ejaculatory inevitability by stopping stimulation well before ejaculation, letting the excitement subside and then starting again. This way awareness increases and the ability to control improves.

To summarize this section, in looking back on the sexual response cycle, it is important to determine whether a client's problem is one of willingness, desire, excitement or orgasm. In the area of willingness and desire you would need to determine whether clients are really interested in experiencing sex at this point in their lives. Perhaps they are not ready and need to be reassured that their own timing is important. Were they sexually abused as children? This could affect their desire for sex. Are they sexually attracted to the opposite sex? Perhaps they are homosexual and forcing themselves to engage in sexual activity with the opposite sex for fear of being rejected or taunted by peers. These are but a few examples of the types of questions that can be pursued in this situation. From there, in looking at the excitement and orgasm phase, it would be important to isolate a specific problem if possible (i.e., getting and maintaining an erection, lubricating or experiencing an orgasm). Each area may be affected by alcohol and drug use and could be explored in more detail.

SEXUAL AND PHYSICAL ASSAULT

One cannot consider sexuality and addiction without a keen awareness of the role that sexual and physical abuse play in the histories of many with alcohol and drug addictions. Given that the pioneering work in the area of sexual assault has been done by the grassroots feminist movement, most of the information has focused on women's experience. Consequently the female pronoun is used in most of this section of the chapter. With increasing awareness and attention to sexual assault of boys, one can anticipate that the literature will address the male perspective in more detail.

This section includes some definitions of terms that will be used throughout the rest of this chapter.

Sexual Assault
The Criminal Code of Canada does not include a specific definition of sexual assault, only a definition of assault, which occurs when someone applies physical force to another person without that person's consent. So, sexual assault is seen as an assault committed in circumstances that are sexual in nature. A non-legal definition would include a wide spectrum of acts, ranging from unwanted sexual touching to life-threatening assaults. The keys are lack of consent on the part of the victim and the victim's experience of it being sexual in nature.

Rape
The term "rape" no longer exists in the legal sense. Rape is one form of sexual assault that involves penetration of the vagina or rectum by a penis or other object.

Sexual Abuse
This is any unwanted sexual interaction and can include physical contact or verbal contact such as obscene phone calls, and visual contact such as "Peeping Toms" or flashers. Regardless of the type of contact, the victim has not consented and the abuser is using his or her power to violate the victim.

Incest
Generally, incest is any form of sexual abuse that takes place with a blood relation.

Incidence: General Statistics

One-half (51 per cent) of Canadian women have experienced at least one incident of physical or sexual violence since the age of 16. Twenty-five per cent of all women have experienced physical or sexual violence at the hands of a marital partner (marital partners include common-law relationships throughout this report). One in five violent incidents reported to this survey were serious enough to result in physical injury (Statistics Canada, 1993).

Connection between Assault and Alcohol and Drug Abuse

THE PERPETRATORS

Alcohol was a prominent factor in women's experiences of violence: perpetrators had been drinking in more than 40 per cent of violent incidents. Victims were more likely to report that perpetrators had been drinking in cases involving intimates (dates, boyfriends and marital partners) than in cases involving other known men or strangers. The rate of wife assault for women currently living with men who drank regularly (at least four times per week) was triple the rate of those whose partners didn't drink at all. Rates were six times as high for women living with men who drank heavily (those who frequently consume five or more drinks at one time) (Statistics Canada, 1993).

According to Claudia Black, as cited in the *Double Jeopardy: Alcohol and Domestic Violence*[1] training package, adults who grew up in alcoholic families experienced, or witnessed, a significantly greater amount of violence than did individuals from non-alcoholic homes. Sixty-nine per cent of children of alcoholics reported violence on the part of fathers, and 26.5 per cent reported violence on the part of mothers, as opposed to 6.8 per cent and 6.7 per cent respectively reported by people from non-alcoholic backgrounds.

THE SURVIVORS

The estimates of the number of women in substance abuse programs who are survivors of some form of either adult or child sexual abuse range from 30 to 70 per cent (Covington, 1983; Benward and Densen-Gerber, 1975; Wachtel and Lawton-Speert, 1983). At a conference of 45 federally funded programs in the United States, it was reported that 45 to 70 per cent of their clients had been victims of incest or rape (Hamilton and Volpe, 1983). According to the Alcoholism Centre for Women (Los Angeles) in the *Double Jeopardy Fact Sheet,* the incidence of alcohol problems in families experiencing violence is estimated to be as high as 80 per cent.

Two recent studies conducted in the United States with adolescents in substance abuse treatment programs found the following:

Harrison and Hoffman (1989) found that among the adolescent girls, 35.2 per cent identified as being victims of sexual abuse. Victims of abuse reported earlier onset of alcohol and drug use and more use of medication — with use of sedatives, minor tranquillizers, painkillers and opiates higher than among non-victims. In terms of the function of the drugs, all sexual abuse victims were significantly more likely to acknowledge that the substance was being used to "get away from family problems," which one would assume includes the sexual abuse.

Harrison, Edwall and Worthen (1990) found a small proportion (6.6 per cent) of males in treatment for alcohol and other drug problems who disclosed a history of sexual abuse. Certain behaviors distinguished them from the non-victims in treatment. The victims experienced more family violence (they were twice as likely as the other boys to have been physically abused by a family member or by someone outside the family); they reported more substance abuse (i.e., the frequency of use was higher, they were twice as likely to be drinking daily; more likely to report regular use of stimulants, sedatives, tranquillizers, opioids, hallucinogens, inhalants, painkillers and over-the-counter drugs); more agitation (i.e., nervousness, tension, insomnia and sexual problems); more suicidal behavior; and earlier legal troubles. Similar to the findings cited earlier regarding adolescent girls, the boys who were victims started drinking and drug use earlier than non-victims. Half the victims were drinking at age 10, compared with one-third of the non-victims, and one-third of the victims were using drugs other than alcohol or marijuana by age 12 compared with 14 per cent of non-victims. The incidence of sexual abuse in boys is probably grossly under-reported. We are just beginning to focus on this issue and the aftermath of abuse for boys.

A recent series of studies in Ontario by Addiction Research Foundation researchers Groeneveld and Shain (1989) found that women who were sexually assaulted either as adults or as children are at least twice as likely as non-abused women to use medication to calm them down or to help them to sleep. They also noted that women who were physically abused by their current partners were 74 per cent more likely to use such medication than were non-abused women.

This evidence demonstrates the importance of examining the role of alcohol and drug use as a method of coping and surviving. As mentioned earlier, once the drugs are no longer being used, memories of the abuse may well surface. Working on other means of coping with this trauma is an essential component of working with survivors of child or adult sexual or physical abuse who also have alcohol or other drug problems.

General Issues Related to Abuse

We will now provide a brief look at some of the issues present in the sexual abuse literature. Issues pertaining to boundaries, flashbacks, abuse of power, loss of control, multiple personalities and self-injurious behavior will be discussed.

When a person is sexually abused, her boundaries are violated in the most terrifying way. She may have no sense of how far to let people go. Even if she is feeling horrible, she has little or no sense of how to limit what is asked or demanded of her (Utain and Oliver, 1989; Bass and Davis, 1988). In many instances she has no real sense of her own thoughts and feelings apart from what other people think and feel. The ability to know who you are as a separate, fully functioning human being is not something

466

that comes easily for a survivor of childhood sexual abuse. It is extremely important therefore for the counsellor to do everything possible not to violate the boundaries of the client. For example, pushing or forcing clients to discuss sexual abuse experiences when they don't want to is a violation of their right to say "no." Learning to say no should be supported and celebrated. The client should be entitled to share this painful experience with you only when he or she feels ready and feels you can be trusted. It is important to reinforce with a client that trust is something to be earned, and to take the time he or she needs to do this. It is important to ask survivors which gender of counsellor they prefer.

ABUSE OF POWER AND LOSS OF CONTROL

Sexual abuse is not sex — it is an act of violence, with one person wanting to exert power and control over someone else less powerful (like a child).

In a *Report on Sexual Assault in Canada* (Kinnon, 1981) the author notes that researchers have suggested that sexual assault is perceived as the most serious violation of the self, short of murder. Kinnon (1981, p. 20) goes on to say that, "the experience of sexual assault is the total loss of power over one's destiny. The victim is totally under the control of the assailant and has no knowledge of the outcome of the attack."

MEMORIES/REMEMBERING

It is possible that a survivor may begin to experience her first memories of abuse once she is no longer using alcohol or other drugs. It is quite common for survivors of childhood sexual abuse to suppress the memories of the abuse as a method of coping with their trauma. Remembering the abuse and the feelings associated with it can be very frightening. It is important that the client receive the counselling she needs to deal with the abuse. You will hear, "I never had any problems with sex until I gave up alcohol." It may be that she didn't really let herself feel before she gave up alcohol, which gave the misconception that sex was easy. Reassure the client that with healing from the abuse, she will be able to be sexual in the way she wants to be, and to feel pleasure.

Because drugs and alcohol were used to cope and suppress memories, the positive effects of remaining abstinent will not be readily and quickly experienced. It is important to be nonjudgmental and to work closely with the sexual abuse counsellor to be able to pace your work and to set realistic expectations.

FLASHBACKS AND REPRESSED MEMORIES

Flashbacks are images that are reminders of the abuse. Clients may feel, see, hear or smell something in the present that was part of the past abuse experience. This can happen anytime and many women report experiencing flashbacks during sexual activities (Bass et al., 1988). It is important to reassure the survivor that she is not crazy and that flashbacks are quite common. If a client feels comfortable, often the best way to deal with these experiences is to talk about them. However, some women prefer to be alone, to stay with the flashback and open it up to gain information about the past (Bass et al., 1988). If a woman is with a supportive lover, it would be important to discuss what would help if she has a flashback. Perhaps being held and rocked and being told "she is safe now" would reassure her and allow her to release some of her suppressed fear, hurt and anger.

MULTIPLE PERSONALITIES

According to Bass and Davis (1988), one result of repressing the memories of abuse is a feeling of being divided into more than one person. In cases of extreme abuse, this kind of splitting can result in the development of multiple personalities. It is important to be alert to the possibility that you may experience this in your clinical practice and be prepared to identify it and make a necessary referral.

SELF-INJURIOUS BEHAVIOR

Injuring oneself physically, by "slashing" or "cutting" is one way survivors control their experience of the pain associated with remembering and working through the abuse (Bass et al., 1988). It is quite natural that survivors struggle with self-abuse, and again it is important that you treat the survivor respectfully and help her get the help she needs. These are all methods of coping that the woman has created in order to keep surviving — they should be acknowledged as such while helping her find alternative ways to cope that are not self-abusive.

ROLE OF THE COUNSELLOR

Many survivors of physical or sexual abuse also have problems related to substance use. In addressing substance use problems with your client, it is very important that you work closely with those who are addressing the abuse issues so that the client and her counsellors can have a common understanding of her goals and progress towards them. This is particularly important when dealing with issues like relapse prevention, since clients are at increased risk of relapse when processing their abuse issues.

CONCLUSION

Substance abusers often wonder whether their drug use has in any way affected their sexual functioning. It is difficult to answer this conclusively considering the impact that cultural, social and physiological factors have on sexual response. However, you can begin to explore how these factors affect the client's sexual experience.

In this chapter you have been exposed to a fairly detailed description of the sexual response cycle and sexual difficulties. The purpose was to provide you with a broad range of background information from which you can form assessment questions. However, the role of a substance abuse counsellor is not to be a sex therapist, which requires extensive training. If you are interested in more extensive work with clients, seek a training program and the supervision of an experienced sex therapist.

We encourage you to refer to the Resource section at the end of this chapter to broaden your understanding of sexual assault issues, as this is critical in helping clients who have a substance abuse problem and a history of sexual assault.

In conclusion, the connections to be made between addictions and sexuality are many. As the addictions counsellor you will often be the central person defining the problems and forming the team of helpers. Your contribution will be invaluable in this process.

NOTE

[1] This information was gathered from the Fact Sheet on Alcohol and Domestic Violence compiled by the Alcoholism Center for Women and Haven House Inc. and is a part of the *Double Jeopardy Training Package.*

REFERENCES

Alcoholism Centre for Women. (1987). *Double Jeopardy: Alcohol and Domestic Violence.* Cross Training Manual. Los Angeles: Authors.

Barbach, L. (1975). *For Yourself: The Fulfilment of Female Sexuality.* New York: Doubleday.

Bass, E., and Davis, L. (1988). *The Courage to Heal: A Guide for Women Survivors of Child Sexual Abuse.* New York: Harper and Row Publishers.

Benward, J., and Densen-Gerber, J. (1975). Incest as a causative factor in anti-social behavior: An exploratory study. *Contemporary Drug Problems* 4: 323–340.

Blume, E.S. (1990). *Secret Survivors.* New York: John Wiley and Sons.

Covington, S. (1983). Alcoholism and family violence. Paper presented at the 29th International Institute on the Prevention and Treatment of Alcoholism. Zagreb, 1983.

Doweiko, H. (1990). *Concepts of Chemical Dependency.* Pacific Grove, CA: Brooks/Cole Publishing Company.

Findelstein, N., Duncan, S.A., Derman, L., and Smeltz, J. (1990). *Getting Sober, Getting Well: A Treatment Guide for Caregivers Who Work with Women.* Cambridge, MA: The Women's Alcoholism Program of CASPAR, Inc.

Gold, M. (1987). Sexual dysfunction challenges today's addiction clinicians. *Alcoholism and Addiction* 7 (6) (July-August): 11.

Gold, M. (1988). Alcohol, drugs and sexual dysfunction. *Alcoholism and Addiction* 9 (2) (December): 13.

Groeneveld, J., and Shain, M. (1989). *Drug Use among Victims of Physical and Sexual Abuse: A Preliminary Report.* Addiction Research Foundation.

Hamilton, G., and Volpe, J. (1982/83). How women recover: Experience and research observations. *Alcohol Health and Research World* 7 (2) (Winter): 28–40.

Harrison, P.A., Edwall, G.E., Hoffman N.G., and Worthen, M.D. (1990). Correlates of sexual abuse among boys in treatment for chemical dependency. *Journal of Adolescent Chemical Dependency* 1 (1): 53–67.

Harrison, P.A., and Hoffman, N. (1989). Differential drug use patterns among sexually abused adolescent girls in treatment for chemical dependency. *The International Journal of the Addictions* 24 (6): 499–514.

Kaplan, H.S. (1979). *Disorders of Sexual Desire*. New York: Brunner/Mazel.

Kaplan, H.S. (1974). *The New Sex Therapy*. New York: Brunner/Mazel.

Kinnon, D. (1981). *Report on Sexual Assault in Canada*. Ottawa: Canadian Advisory Council on the Status of Women.

Kitzinger, S. (1983). *Women's Experience of Sex*. New York: G.P. Putnam's Sons.

Kolodny, R.C., Masters, W.H., and Johnson, V.E. (1979). *Textbook of Sexual Medicine*. Boston: Brown and Co.

Loulan, J. (1984). *Lesbian Sex*. San Francisco: Spinsters/Aunt Lute Book Company.

Masters, W.H., Johnson, V.G., and Kolodny, R.C. (1966). *Sex and Human Loving*. Boston: Little, Brown and Co.

Murphy, W.D., Coleman, E., Hoon, E., and Scott, C. (1980). Sexual dysfunction and treatment in alcoholic women. *Sexuality and Disability* 3 (4) (Winter).

Statistics Canada. (1993). *The Violence Against Women Survey*. Highlights. Ottawa: Author.

Utain, M., and Oliver, B. (1989). *Scream Louder: Through Hell and Healing with an Incest Survivor and Her Therapist*. Dearfield Beach, FL: Health Communications Inc.

Wachtel, A., and Lawton-Speert, S. (1983). Child sexual abuse: Descriptions of nine program approaches to treatment. Incest and Childhood Sexual Abuse Program, Child Sexual Abuse Project. Working Paper 3, Vancouver, BC. Social Planning and Research.

Wilsnack, S. (1983). Drinking, sexuality and sexual dysfunctions in women. In *Alcohol Problems in Women*, eds. Wilsnack, S., and Beckman, L. New York: Guilford Press.

Wilson, G.T., and Lawson, D.M. (1978). Expectancies, alcohol and sexual arousal in women. *Journal of Abnormal Psychology* 37 (3): 358–367.

Wilson, G.T. (1977). Alcohol and human sexual behavior. *Behaviour, Research and Therapy* 15: 239–252.

RESOURCES

Sexual Assault

SERVICES

Most communities have services that provide assistance, support and counselling to sexual assault survivors. Try looking in your phone book under Rape Crisis Centre or Sexual Assault Crisis Centre.

BOOKS

Blume, E. S. (1990). *Secret Survivors*. New York: John Wiley and Sons.
This is an excellent resource book on the after-effects of childhood sexual abuse and the healing process.

Bass, E., and Davis, L. (1988). *The Courage to Heal: A Guide for Women Survivors of Child Sexual Abuse*. New York: Harper and Row Publishers.
This ground-breaking book is a comprehensive guide that offers hope and encouragement to every woman who was sexually abused as a child, and to those who care about her. The authors provide clear explanations, practical suggestions, a map of the healing journey and many moving first-person examples of the recovery process drawn from interviews with hundreds of survivors.

Sexuality

BOOKS

Barbach, L. (1975). *For Yourself: The Fulfilment of Female Sexuality*. New York: Doubleday.
This is a concise self-help manual for women on becoming orgasmic.

Kitzinger, S. (1983). *Women's Experience of Sex*. New York: G.P. Putnam's Sons.
This book places techniques and methods of lovemaking in the context of who women are as people, their values, their relationships with others and the emotions that their experiences arouse in them. Sexuality in the midst of the crises some women face, including childbirth, menopause, mastectomy and hysterectomy, is also addressed.

Chapter 25

Eating Disorders
and Substance Abuse

FRED J. BOLAND

The eating disorders of concern to addictions counsellors are anorexia nervosa and bulimia nervosa. This chapter is largely devoted to a consideration of bulimia nervosa as it is more likely to be encountered by addiction counsellors. Nevertheless, a great deal of the material on bulimia is directly relevant to both disorders.

ANOREXIA NERVOSA

According to DSM-IV (1994), the essential diagnostic criteria for anorexia nervosa are:
(a) refusal to maintain body weight at or above 85 per cent of normal for age and height;
(b) intense fear of gaining weight or becoming fat;
(c) disturbances in the experience of body shape, weight and/or size;
(d) in females, absence of at least three consecutive menstrual cycles.
DSM-IV distinguishes between restricting subtype and binge-eating/purging subtype of anorexia nervosa.

The incidence of the disorder among substance abusers is unknown but is about one in 100 among women under 30 and about one in 1,000 for males.

An enquiry relevant to the diagnostic criteria, together with the person's emaciated appearance, give a good indication of the presence of anorexia nervosa. However, a structural interview format is useful in gaining a broader understanding (Johnson, 1985). Often, a family member or friend will directly express concern about the person's weight or eating behavior. Be aware, however, that the disorder is associated with denial and resistance. To the anorectic, treatment threatens weight gain and lack of control. These are her most central fears.

The disorder is definitely life-threatening, with many associated medical complications. Hospitalization is commonly needed to raise weight to a safer level. Treatment
tends to be a long and difficult process. The addictions counsellor is strongly advised
to refer any suspected cases of anorexia nervosa to professionals who are familiar
with the disorder. The counsellor can work concurrently to resolve the substance
abuse problem. However, consultation between the addictions counsellor and the
therapist treating the eating disorder is highly recommended, as a decision may be
made to treat the disorders sequentially. Clients with full-blown anorexia nervosa
may be so wrapped up in their disorder that it is extremely difficult to involve them in
treatment for substance abuse, or vice versa.

BULIMIA NERVOSA

The DSM-IV essential criteria for bulimia nervosa are:
(a) recurrent episodes of binge eating, defined as eating more than a normal person
    would in a discrete period of time (e.g., within two hours) and feeling of lack of
    control over eating behavior during a binge;
(b) regular engagement in some form of purging (vomiting, laxatives, diuretics, strict
    dieting, fasting or compulsive exercise) in order to prevent weight gain;
(c) minimum average of two binge-eating and purging episodes a week for at least
    three months;
(d) persistent overconcern with body shape and weight; the disturbance is not associ-
    ated with anorexia nervosa.
DSM-IV distinguishes between purging type and nonpurging type bulimia nervosa.
In the latter case, fasting and excessive exercise are used as inappropriate compensatory mechanisms.

Prevalence rates in the general population range between one per cent and three per
cent for women. Rates among males have increased, but the disorder is still far more
prevalent in women. However, many people seek help who do not completely satisfy
these criteria. Most bulimics are in the normal weight range, with a minority being
either overweight or underweight (Fairburn, 1984). At least one-third of anorexia nervosa patients are also bulimic.

NOTE: DSM-IV also lists binge-eating disorder as a third major category of eating
disorders. Binge-eating disorder is essentially bingeing without purging, and it mainly occurs in obese individuals (about 20 per cent of the population). Treatment would
not be much different from treatment of bulimia nervosa and it will not be covered
further in this chapter.

THE CONNECTION TO SUBSTANCE ABUSE

An association between substance abuse and bulimia is not hard to document. Surveys of bulimics suggest that 30 per cent or more have a history of alcohol abuse (e.g., Mitchell, Hatsukami, Eckert and Pyle, 1985). A survey of female alcoholics found three times as many bulimics as in a matched sample of nonalcoholic women (Boland and Butt, 1989). A survey of patients in treatment for problems with alcohol or other drugs also reported that up to three per cent of the males satisfied DSM-III criteria for bulimia (Perlman and McKenna, 1988). The association between the two may be somewhat inflated because much of the survey data is from clients seeking treatment, and it is probable that patients with both disorders are more likely to seek treatment (Wilson, 1993).

Both alcoholic and bulimic women share an increased association with depression (e.g., Hatsukami, Eckert, Mitchell and Pyle, 1984), and similar MMPI profiles with elevations on depression, impulsiveness, anxiety and social withdrawal (Hatsukami, Owen, Pyle and Mitchell, 1982). Increased incidence of disturbed childhoods and sexual abuse is also associated with both populations (Walker, Bonner and Kaufman, 1988). Clinical experience suggests that both groups tend to be poor at coping with stress, and to have very low self-esteem.

Patients with dual problems are likely to present with more depression, anxiety, obsessiveness and somatic concerns than their nonbulimic, substance-abusing counterparts (Boland and Butt, 1989). The Hazelden survey reports that they are more likely to be polydrug abusers, have experienced more adolescent antisocial behavior problems, more self-reported suicidal thoughts and attempts, and more previous treatment for mental health problems (Perlman and McKenna, 1988). They are more likely to have been hospitalized for psychiatric problems, to have a history of stealing, abuse of diuretics and social impairment (Hatsukami, Mitchell, Eckert and Pyle, 1986). Women who have both disorders report great overlap in the emotions and situations prompting both abuses (Rand, Lawlor and Duldau, 1986). For further consideration of possible mechanisms linking the two disorders, see Krahn (1991).

We could find no association between the severity of dependence on alcohol and the severity of the bulimic problem, nor was there any relationship between the frequency of bulimic episodes and whether the person was drinking or abstinent (Boland and Butt, 1989). Some were worse when drinking; some after they stopped. One exception to this may be women who abused cocaine or amphetamines. It would appear that the voracious appetite experienced coming off stimulant abuse can trigger severe bingeing with associated purging.

475

REFER, CONSULT OR TREAT

If bulimia nervosa is suspected or confirmed, it is wise, if possible, to refer the person to a therapist familiar with eating disorders as well as substance abuse. If that is not possible, some liaison should be maintained between the therapist responsible for the assessment and treatment of the eating disorder and the therapist responsible for treatment of the alcohol or other drug problem. At the Hazelden inpatient program, psychologists assess patients for eating disorders and make a judgment as to whether they can be managed in a substance abuse treatment unit. If patients are so preoccupied with bingeing, purging and related behaviors that they miss groups and are otherwise not available to treatment efforts aimed at their substance abuse, they are referred to more suitable treatment for their eating disorder.

If the addictions counsellor turns out to be the only source of help for the patient with dual disorders, there is an obligation to become more familiar with factors known to trigger and maintain the binge-purge behavior, with variables potentially involved in the origin of the disorder, and with appropriate treatment strategies. The remainder of this chapter is meant to serve as an introduction to these topics. Recommended readings are provided for a more comprehensive understanding.

TRIGGERS ASSOCIATED WITH BINGE-PURGING

Severe bingeing seldom occurs "out of the blue." At the time, the person is typically experiencing some negative mood state (e.g., he or she is anxious, angry, bored, depressed, frustrated, lonely, rejected). Such negative mood states are associated with relapses into substance abuse as well (Marlatt and Gordon, 1985).

Dieting is strongly related to bingeing; the stricter the diet, the more severe the bingeing (Vanderheyden and Boland, 1987). Bulimics diet chronically, often skipping meals early in the day only to binge in the evening. At the time they binge they are usually obsessing about food — often their favorite binge food. In general, chronic dieters and those with bulimia nervosa have many foods they label as forbidden when dieting. Paradoxically, these "taboo" foods take on the power to trigger binges, since consumption of even small amounts symbolizes the breaking of the diet (Knight and Boland, 1989). It is of more than passing interest for addictions counsellors that alcohol consumption has been shown to disinhibit eating in dieters in much the same way as consumption of "taboo" foods (Polivy and Herman, 1976).

Increases in stress level or relatively sudden increases in concern over appearance are also observed to be associated with bingeing and purging. There may be other triggers uniquely associated with an individual's bingeing (e.g., a need to be impulsive, a need to punish one's self), but the above elements, either alone or in combination, are commonly observed.

PAYOFFS THAT HELP MAINTAIN BINGE-PURGING

As with alcohol or drug taking, consequences or payoffs from bingeing and/or purging help maintain the behavior. As with substance abuse, the positive consequences tend to be immediate, the negative consequences delayed. Initially, there is the anticipation, tasting and eating of the rich "taboo" foods that the person craves, and normally excludes from the diet. There is at least a temporary satisfaction of hunger. Psychologically, there is usually a temporary relief from the tension and negative mood that helped trigger the binge. If the person was bored, eating is entertaining; if lonely and depressed, it becomes a source of comfort and pleasure. In effect the person is using a food binge much like alcohol or drugs — to serve some function, to achieve some effect.

As the binge progresses (the typical binge lasts 30 to 60 minutes), the negative consequences appear. There is a return of negative mood states and the aversive feeling of being out of control. Many bulimics go to bed disgusted and full of self-hatred. There is the fear of weight gain, and the pain, nausea and bloating that eventually help stop the binge.

The negative consequences lead to attempts to undo the binge by purging, usually by vomiting within 30 minutes. This tends to "lock in" the binge-purge cycle, as the purging is powerfully rewarded by physical relief of nausea and bloating, and psychologically, by reduction in anxiety over weight gain. Eventually, the purging comes to play a large part in controlling the bingeing, as the bulimic will often not binge unless there is an opportunity to purge shortly thereafter. Many purge even after "normal" meals. Even when they don't vomit, there is still the commitment to undo the binge by such methods as fasting ("I'm not going to eat anything tomorrow!"), strict dieting ("I'm going to stick to 600 calories a day for the next week"), or laxative abuse.

In a way, the person is setting herself up for the next binge. The negative feelings have returned, and the purging, in whatever form, recreates the state of hunger and the obsession with food. Given the ability of humans to rationalize, coming into contact again with "taboo" foods is probably the easiest trigger to reinstate.

It is possible that in some cases a physiological response to a binge on refined carbohydrates can contribute to maintaining the binge-purge cycle. Refined sugars are absorbed directly into the blood, causing an acute rise in blood glucose levels. In response, the body releases large amounts of insulin to bring down the blood sugar level by transporting it into cells. In binge-purgers who chronically diet, this process can serve as a stimulus to eat (Spitzer and Rodin, 1987). Also, since most of the calories consumed during bingeing are soon purged, there is a possibility of insulin overshoot, resulting in an acute hypoglycemic state that may contribute to instability of mood, and craving for more sugar.

477

Helping the person understand the triggers and consequences that help maintain her particular binge-purge cycle is very important for interrupting the cycle in the early stages of treatment.

CAUSES OF EATING DISORDERS

There are many things we don't know about the etiology of eating disorders. So far, research suggests that multiple factors are involved, and that not all factors need be present in every case. The repetitive pattern of bingeing and purging described above has some similarities to addictive use of alcohol and drugs. However, the reasons why this pattern develops in the first place are different in many respects.

The gender difference in the incidence of eating disorders suggests a strong socio-cultural component (Striegel-Moore, Silberstein and Rodin, 1986). Our culture has strong expectations of women from many sources (e.g., magazines, television, fashion) to be thin. Thinness is associated with success, femininity, attractiveness, self-control and many other desirable characteristics; fatness with negative characteristics (e.g., laziness, lack of discipline, lack of femininity and ugliness). Since females are generally socialized more than males to value appearance concerns, they are more likely to internalize this ideal of thinness, and to fear the anti-ideal of fatness. Perceived deviations from this unrealistic ideal are associated with body dissatisfaction and low self-esteem. Indeed, the perceived rewards for thinness are so great that, no matter what the source of their low self-esteem (e.g., sexual abuse) or body dissatisfaction, losing weight is often seen as a solution.

Paradoxically, while women experience excessive cultural pressure to be thin, they are also more socialized to interact with food than are men, and to form functional relationships with food — i.e., to use it as a coping mechanism or for pleasure. Clients have often pointed out to me that cartoon characters such as Cathy and characters on many television shows display a typical pattern. Something doesn't turn out right, or some problem arises. Solution: go for the chocolate ice cream or the cheesecake! This is compounded by the fact that most food advertising is aimed at women — often in the same magazines that suggest ways to diet and avoid these very foods.

It is in this cultural context that many women start to diet. Their strong desire for thinness is motivated by all the perceived rewards associated with achieving their desired weight, and by avoiding all the perceived punishments associated with fatness. Unfortunately this sets up a serious conflict with forces seeking to maintain the "status quo." First, the individual typically deprives herself of the very foods from which she derives most pleasure — high-calorie, rich foods. It is no wonder that their absence engenders the "poor me's," "the blues," and obsessive thinking concerning these foods.

Second, many use pleasurable foods as a coping mechanism, much like they might use alcohol or drugs. The mechanism is missed when dieting, especially in stressful situations that normally provoke eating (Knight and Boland, 1989).

Third, the induced weight loss often puts the person below a comfortable biological weight — the weight (whether lean or fat) that we can comfortably maintain without undereating or overeating. This weight is likely determined by a physiologically based "set point" mechanism that is influenced a great deal by genetics (Bennett and Gurin, 1982; Keesey and Powley, 1986). The body's "set point" response to weight loss is to seek to maintain its fat stores by slowing down metabolic rate. Bennet and Gurin (1982) and others maintain that the overwhelming failure of treatment for obesity — 95 per cent eventually gain back the weight they lose — supports a "set point" explanation. Indeed, some prominent researchers and therapists are seriously questioning the rationale for the treatment of most obesity problems (Garner and Wolley, 1991). The main point is that the chronic, strict dieting seen in bulimic and anorectic individuals places them so far below their comfortable biological weight that their bodies react as if they were starving.

A study by Keys, Biozek, Henschel, Mickelsen and Taylor (1950) is enlightening in showing the extent to which semistarvation in and of itself generates symptoms of eating disorders. The authors deprived 36 young, mentally healthy male volunteers of half their normal calorie intake for a period of about six months, until they lost about 25 per cent of their original body weight. These subjects were objectors to military service who had none of the motivations for losing weight seen in women with eating disorders. Nevertheless, as the dieting continued, these men became obsessed with food, (e.g., read cookbooks, collected recipes, fantasized about food, etc.). Their concentration suffered, their work capacity dropped, and there was an increase in depression, anxiety, irritability and hypochondria. Their self-esteem grew more negative, they reported feelings of social inadequacy, and became more isolated and withdrawn.

In people with eating disorders, these same negative experiences are accompanied by illusory beliefs such as: "If I diet even harder, these feelings will go away; when I reach 100 pounds, all will be wonderful." These and other irrational beliefs feed into the disorder (Garfinkel and Garner, 1982). Also, like those with eating disorders, many subjects in the starvation study showed body image disturbance, and developed a bingeing pattern, especially during the refeeding period. Some reported guilt over eating, complained of feeling fat, and vomited. Some of the disordered-eating symptoms persisted even after the individuals had gained back their weight. In summary, no matter what the motivation for strict dieting, the resulting conflict with normal biological and psychological patterns can generate major symptoms seen in individuals with eating disorders, and contribute to the maintenance of the binge-purge cycle described earlier.

479

Many factors known to be associated with bulimia and anorexia nervosa feed into the above process, and contribute to the development of abnormal attitudes towards food, weight, shape and a pathological drive for thinness. For example, a career choice of ballet dancer or model is associated with increased risk of eating disorders, presumable because of the thin body shape they must achieve (Garner and Garfinkel, 1980).

Obesity is another risk factor. A high proportion of bulimics have a prior history of obesity. Such individuals would likely experience more punishment (ridicule, embarrassment, etc.) for fatness, and have more reason to believe that dieting would answer their problems (Loro and Orleans, 1981).

Some evidence suggests that family dysfunctions that discourage autonomy and a sense of personal control over life can contribute to eating disorders as well. For individuals in these families, weight and shape may be one of the few areas of their lives that they can control. Refusing to follow directives to eat can be a way of expressing autonomy. Unfortunately, this narrow attempt at control and autonomy becomes an anxious obsession with no general alleviation of feelings of ineffectiveness and low self-esteem (Bruch, 1977).

Juvenile diabetics have an increased incidence of eating disorders (Rodin, Daneman, Johnson, Kenshole and Garfinkel, 1986). In part, this may be due to their having to chronically restrict the rich high-calorie food that their peers enjoy.

Recent research suggests that individuals with a personality disorder are also at higher risk for bulimia, possibly because of poor impulse control (Piran, Lerner, Garfinkel, Kennedy and Brouilette, 1988). A similar case has often been made for an association between personality disorders and alcohol and drug problems.

Various other variables, including those related to personality (Vitousek and Monke, 1994), genetics (Strober, 1991) and family (Vandereycken, Kog and Vanderlinden, 1989) have been put forth as playing a causal role in the development of eating disorders. However, it is difficult to determine whether they are causes or consequences of the disorder. For example, although depression is strongly associated with bulimia nervosa (and for that matter, alcohol problems), it is likely that most depression is secondary to the bulimia, and is alleviated as the bulimic behavior decreases (Cooper and Fairburn, 1983). Similarly, although neurochemical abnormalities, especially those involving serotonin, can be associated with eating disorders (Fava, Copland, Schiveiger and Herzog, 1989), it is impossible at this time to distinguish whether they are a consequence or cause of the disorder.

In summary, a number of factors are known to be associated with an increased risk of developing bulimia. These factors may vary from individual to individual, and it is important for the counsellor to determine and deal with the particular factors that make their clients vulnerable.

TREATMENT CONSIDERATIONS

Only a small minority of bulimics require hospitalization, usually because of medical consequences (e.g., electrolyte imbalance), suicide risk, or because a severe binge-purge pattern cannot be brought under control with good outpatient treatment.

Addictions counsellors in an inpatient facility who work with clients who have been identified as having an eating disorder should be encouraged by Hazelden's report that in most cases, the course of treatment was similar for bulimic and nonbulimic clients who have problems with alcohol or other drugs. Throughout treatment, the focus at Hazelden remained on alcohol/drug problems with no insistence on total abstinence from disordered eating behavior. It would appear that counsellors arranged some education about eating disorders, helped patients identify factors associated with their bulimic behavior, supplied them with a food plan and helped them relax before meals. As part of their aftercare plan, bulimic patients were referred to a relevant support group or eating disorder treatment program. No information on treatment outcome was supplied.

Some outcome information is available on dual-problem women treated for their bulimia in a cognitive-behavioral program (Mitchell, Pyle, Eckert and Hatsukami, 1990). These authors found that the outcome of bulimia treatment in women with substance abuse problems was comparable to the outcome with bulimics without substance abuse problems (over 60 per cent free of bulimic symptoms and another 15 per cent improved at two- to five-year followup). In this program, individuals with an alcohol or drug problem who are being treated for bulimia must first undergo treatment for their alcohol or other drug problem.

Pharmacological treatments have been explored with bulimics and anorectics. Tricyclic antidepressants (e.g., imipramine, desipramine) have proven most beneficial, at least in the short term (less than eight weeks). In the long run (one to two years), it is difficult to keep patients on medication, with frequent changes of drugs required, a high dropout rate, and a high relapse rate occurring when medication is withdrawn (Mitchell, P.B., 1988). When cognitive-behavioral therapy has been compared to pharmacologic therapy, the former has proved more effective, but a combination of the two may be beneficial in some circumstances (Agras et al., 1992).

A variety of psychological treatments have been explored with bulimic patients either on an individual or group basis, in either an outpatient, inpatient or day hospital program. Family therapy is also often useful, especially with young patients living at home. Excellent outlines of a wide variety of treatment approaches are presented by Garner and Garfinkel (1985), Brownell and Foreyt (1986), and Schlundt and Johnson (1990). Many therapists use an eclectic approach, borrowing a variety of techniques from different theoretical orientations.

Cognitive-behavioral approaches have received the most research attention and are associated with probably the best outcome (Fairburn, 1988; Mitchell, 1988). A good "how-to manual" was published in 1993 (Fairburn, Marcus and Wilson, 1993), and a more readable version can be used by therapists or clients for self-help (Fairburn, 1995). The approach concentrates on instilling self-control by changing maladaptive attitudes, beliefs and behaviors to more adaptive patterns, and by increasing the person's problem-solving and other coping skills. Various combinations of cognitive and behavioral skills training have also been used successfully in the treatment of alcoholism (Hester and Miller, 1989), and the approach could serve as the basis of integrating treatment of both disorders.

SEQUENCE OF TREATMENT

The first one or two sessions are usually devoted to a general assessment of the client along with answering the client's questions about eating disorders. The Diagnostic Survey of Eating Disorders (Johnson, 1985) is a useful structured interview for gaining information on such matters as weight, dieting, menstrual history, negative consequences experienced, attitudes towards body, sexual abuse, drug abuse, etc. In these initial sessions the therapist might outline for the client the general strategy for treatment, emphasizing that it involves gradually increasing self-control and that change is the client's responsibility.

A thorough medical checkup complements a psychological assessment of eating disorders. Medical complications result not only from binge-purging, but also from the state of starvation or semistarvation that individuals with eating disorders endure. Kaplan and Woodside (1987) give an excellent overview of these symptoms. Among the more common are tiredness, headaches and poor concentration. Dry skin and hair often result from dehydration. Dental cavities, bursting of veins around the eyes, puffy cheeks related to salivary gland enlargement, and cracks at the corners of the mouth are largely due to chronic vomiting. Purging also eliminates sodium and potassium, which could cause an electrolyte imbalance that could result in hospitalization. Deficits in potassium can produce symptoms such as apathy, delirium, irritability and mood swings. Electrolyte deficiencies affect nerves and muscles, sometimes resulting in abnormal brainwaves and serious heart irregularities. Low potassium levels, especially when aggravated by laxative abuse, can cause interference in the wave-like contractions of the gut and intestine that pass food through the body. This can result in stomach cramps and chronic constipation.

Amenorrhea is a diagnostic symptom of anorexia nervosa. Possibly 20 per cent or more of bulimics also experience this problem, while at least half experience some degree of menstrual irregularity. Eating disorders tend to interfere with normal hormonal functions, especially when the person is below her comfortable biological weight. The evolutionary message is: if you're starving, this is not a good time to have children. Sexual desire usually drops with chronic dieting. As a result of purging, low intake and the stress of dieting, calcium levels can become abnormally low, encouraging osteoporosis. Alerting clients to these and other potentially negative consequences of eating disorders (Schlundt and Johnson, 1990) can help them to change and better understand their disorder.

The general strategy for cognitive-behavioral treatment can be described in terms of a direct and indirect attack on the disordered eating. Early treatment directly focuses on the bingeing and purging. As these problems become reduced, the focus shifts to factors that indirectly contribute to the bingeing (e.g., poor coping skills, body dissatisfaction).

The direct attack has a number of components. Typically, between the first and second session, the client is asked to self-monitor her eating, purging, weighing, exercise and other relevant patterns without attempting change. When does the bingeing take place? What is going on at the time? What kinds of thoughts and feeling accompany the binge? What is consumed? Which meals are eaten or skipped? When and how frequently does purging occur? In which situations are urges to binge or purge most likely to occur? Which situations appear safe? Answers to these and other questions supply useful information on current maintaining factors, and offer a baseline from which to judge the progress of treatment. In this context, some self-monitoring should be maintained (e.g., binges, purges). It is wise to encourage clients to keep a diary of their relevant thoughts, feelings and behaviors throughout treatment. This will prove a continuous learning experience for both patient and therapist. Where normal self-monitoring is impossible because the patient has been placed in an inpatient setting, self-reports concerning the same material should be carefully gathered in as much detail as possible. As women with dual disorders report high similarity in factors precipitating both bingeing and drinking, it should be possible to integrate a functional analysis of dangerous situations associated with both disorders.

When clients first see you, they invariably believe, and fervently hope, that you can eliminate their bingeing, purging and associated problems while they continue to diet and maintain unhealthy weight levels. However, given the strong relationship between dieting and bingeing, one of the first components of the direct phase is to normalize the client's eating — three planned meals and one or two snacks per day. Many bulimics do not know what it is like to eat normally, and have lost touch with cues of hunger and satiety. Stimulus control is useful at this stage (e.g., eating planned meals at the same time and place each day, limiting availability of forbidden foods, etc.). Of course, eating normally usually makes them anxious about weight gain, and it's important for the therapists to deal with this in a supportive manner. I start clients at approximately 1,800 calories and eventually work up, if need be, to a sensible caloric intake for that person (about 2,200 calories for the average woman). Some do gain weight because they must reach a comfortable biological weight that they can maintain without dieting or overeating. Some bulimics maintain their approximate weight throughout treatment, possibly due to eliminating bingeing. Certainly, in severe bingers who do not purge by vomiting, eliminating the bingeing is commonly associated with weight loss. One sensible guideline is a goal weight not less than 90 per cent of the highest adult weight ever attained by the client (Garner, Rockert, Olmsted, Johnson and Coscina, 1985). The key is to find a comfortable weight that clients can maintain without dieting or bingeing.

Goal setting for bingeing, purging, weighing and exercise is very important. An agreement is struck between the client and therapist for the general reduction of bingeing and purging. For example, a client who binges every day might attempt to reduce bingeing to four days per week. Once this goal is accomplished she might reduce it to two days per week, and so on. I actually encourage clients to binge without guilt on binge days. This sometimes has the paradoxical effect of reducing bingeing on those days as well. As one client said: "It's just not the same when you tell me it's okay to do it." Reducing weighing to once a week tends to reduce the obsession with weight. If this is done in the presence of the therapists, any anxiety caused can be used productively as a treatment topic. Eventually, weighing can be dropped completely. A common saying in self-help groups is: "Scales are for fish."

If a patient is not exercising, I encourage moderate activity as it seems to help self-control. If the client is exercising obsessively, attempt to reduce it to less obsessive levels, and encourage fun activities rather than activities aimed at pure calorie reduction. Laxative and diuretic abuse are very inefficient means of eliminating food from the body (Bo-Lynn, Santa-Ana, Morawski and Fordtran, 1983). They essentially eliminate fluids and are associated with many dangerous side effects. Most clients respond well to therapeutic attempts to give up these substances.

Friends and family can be helpful during this first phase of treatment. Eating with others, having them around at dangerous times (e.g., after meals, evenings), being able to call on them for support when urges to binge or purge are present, are all very valuable. This presupposes that the friends or family members will be supportive. In some cases it is necessary to involve a friend or family member in treatment, not only to specify how they can be supportive, but to resolve conflict and prevent sabotage of the client's efforts. When clients live at home with parents, this is very important and often needs special attention.

The therapist should help clients generate alternative behaviors, preferably pleasurable ones (e.g., a walk, a movie, talking to a friend, rewarding themselves with non-food purchases, etc.), which can distract them or help them cope with difficult periods. In the early phase of treatment it also helps to avoid some situations (e.g., staying home alone to bake double chocolate-chip cookies when they are feeling lonely and anxious).

A client with a severe bulimic pattern will often claim that she has no control over her bingeing urges, that the urge and the binge are one. Some form of systematic urge control training is useful here, and would have direct relevance to drinking or drug-taking urges as well. Clients can be educated about urges. An urge is only the first link in the chain that leads to the bingeing or substance use. It is a lot easier to control the urge than it is to control the bingeing or drug taking. If not satisfied, urges will eventually decline in frequency, but not necessarily in intensity. Urges are a normal part of breaking a habit. The worst strategy for dealing with urges is to remain passive or to think negatively. An urge should be a signal to go into action, go on the attack (engage in distraction activities, call a friend, go to an AA meeting, etc.). I find it helps to have clients write down thoughts or ideas that they find helpful and to rehearse them when experiencing an urge. ("The more urges I extinguish, the less frequent they will get, the more control I will have. I will not be passive. I'll outsmart this urge by doing the following. I will call a friend," etc.)

Some clients find imagery techniques helpful (e.g., imagining an on/off switch that controls the urge and picturing themselves turning the switch slowly to off, feeling in control and coping effectively). It's useful here to introduce clients to cognitive therapy techniques for combatting discouragement, catastrophic thinking, perfectionism, and other self-defeating cognitive patterns (Garfinkel and Garner, 1982).

The net effect of all the strategies and techniques used during the direct attack phase is to greatly reduce or eliminate the bingeing and purging, and normalize eating.

As the person grows more confident in her ability to control the bingeing and purging, the therapist increases the time spent indirectly attacking the disordered eating. If the person uses bingeing to cope with anxiety and stress, then the therapist can teach anxiety and stress management skills. If the person binges in response to boredom, skills at structuring time may be required. If they are lonely and depressed, then social skills and mood control may need to be developed. I find it most useful to teach skills in a general problem-solving format (i.e., identify problem, generate solutions, choose solution, implement and evaluate solution, etc.).

Along with an increase in coping skills, and the increase in confidence that usually accompanies effective coping, clients should be gradually reintroduced to coping with "taboo" foods. As long as these foods are avoided they tend to have the power to elicit bingeing. The approach I like best is a graded exposure from least-avoided to most-avoided "taboo" foods, but some programs require patients to eat all food right from the beginning of treatment. This may be particularly suitable in an inpatient or day treatment program where monitoring and access to therapists are readily available. Careful planning and initial exposure to "taboo" foods in the presence of the therapist or a trusted friend is helpful. Remember, consumption of these foods generates anxiety, and in the past was almost invariably followed by purging. It is therefore especially important to avoid purging, and deal with any anxiety generated. Indeed, Rosen and Leitenberg (1982) make this exposure-plus-response-prevention strategy the central basis of their promising treatment of bulimia nervosa. If the avoidance behavior (purging) is blocked, then the anxiety response to the "taboo" foods should eventually subside, enhancing the client's sense of control.

During the indirect phase of treatment, the therapist continues cognitive therapy to correct any myths or irrational thoughts the client has concerning food, weight or shape (e.g., "I have to be 105 lbs. to feel good. I can't be attractive unless I'm thin. It would be terrible if I gained any weight. I can't be happy unless I'm thin"). This emphasis blends nicely into general consciousness-raising over how society shapes women's attitudes and behavior in destructive ways. Exercises such as critically evaluating women's fashion magazines, and contacting organizations such as HERSIZE, are useful. The National Eating Disorder Information Centre in Toronto can supply excellent handouts relevant to consciousness raising. A healthy dose of feminist-oriented literature, such as *Fat Is a Feminist Issue* by Orbach, or *Making Peace With Food* by Kano, is highly recommended.

As the person gains control over bingeing and purging, therapists also work to increase the client's self-esteem and body esteem. The general strategy is to broaden self-esteem beyond appearance and weight to other aspects of one's personality and behavior, and to encourage less judgmental, more accepting and more positive attitudes toward the self. Often, the therapist and client together must work through negative attitudes towards body and self that stem from past sexual abuse or chronic criticism. Problems concerning sexuality and intimacy are commonly encountered. In clients with dual disorders, shame and embarrassment over events associated with an alcohol- or drug-abusing lifestyle also require a therapist's attention.

There are numerous exercises and homework assignments for improving body image (e.g., Butters and Cash, 1985; Wooley and Kearney-Cooke, 1986). The person is encouraged to get rid of clothes that don't fit, stop judging her body, make friends with it and discard beliefs such as "A flatter stomach and thinner thighs are the answer to school, job, family and relationship problems." The person can be encouraged to do now all the things she had planned to do on reaching her magical ideal weight.

The final stage of treatment concerns planning for the future, and relapse prevention training (Marlatt and Gordon, 1985). In an ideal world there would be no lapses after the end of treatment. Unfortunately, data from many areas of addictive behavior suggest that occasional lapses are the norm. The therapist is then wise to help the client not only to avoid lapses, but also to prevent them from turning into full-scale relapses. Here, relapse prevention training for substance abuse can easily be integrated with relapse prevention considerations for bulimia nervosa. The latter involves teaching the client to recognize potentially dangerous situations (e.g., going home for Christmas), and to have a good coping plan for dealing with them.

486

The problem-solving strategies used earlier are obviously relevant here. If a binge occurs, the client should have the attitude of learning from the mistake, reintroducing self-control strategies, enlisting the help of friends, etc. Going back to dieting will only encourage more bingeing, which in turn makes purging more likely.

Recently, Wilson (1996) evaluated a case where cognitive-behavioral therapy fails. There is little doubt that having a concurrent disorder such as a substance abuse problem and an eating disorder would complicate treatment and, possibly, result in a poor general outcome. In these cases, Wilson recommends a more intense and expanded version of cognitive-behavioral treatment, possibly on an inpatient basis.

It should also be noted that interpersonal therapy, which concentrates on relationship problems, has also had a good outcome in the treatment of bulimia nervosa (Fairburn, Jones, Reveler, Hope and O'Connor, 1993).

If appropriate self-help groups for eating disorders are available in the community, therapists might consider suggesting that the client join. The best groups are those that concentrate on problem solving and social support. I have now seen a number of dual-problem clients who also attend meetings of AA or Women for Sobriety. In general, while these self-help groups deal primarily with substance abuse, they have been rather helpful as they deal with many issues that are also relevant to recovery from eating disorders.

However, the philosophy of abstinence as the only goal just does not apply to eating disorders. For example, to think that one can treat bingeing by helping patients avoid rich foods associated with bingeing will leave the person wide open to a later relapse. The best approach is to help the client control the eating of all types of food.

ACKNOWLEDGMENT

The author thanks Joanne Trousdale for typing this chapter and for her expert editorial assistance.

REFERENCES

Agras, W.S., Rossiter, E.M., Arnow, B., Schneider, J.A., Telch, C.F., Raeburn, S.D., Bruce, B., Perl, M., and Koran, L.M. (1992). Pharmacologic and cognitive-behavioral treatment for bulimia nervosa: A controlled comparison. *American Journal of Psychiatry* 49: 82–87.

American Psychiatric Association. (1994). *Diagnostic and Statistical Manual of Mental Disorders,* 4th ed. Washington, DC: Author.

Bennett, W., and Gurin, J. (1982). *The Dieter's Dilemma.* New York: Basic Books, Inc.

Boland, F.J., and Butt, J. (1989). Increased signs of eating disorders in women with alcohol problems. Paper presented to Canadian Psychological Association. Halifax, 1989.

Bo-Lynn, G., Santa-Ana, C.A., Morawski, S.G., and Fordtran, J.S. (1983). Purging and calorie absorption in bulimic patients and normal women. *Annals of Internal Medicine* 99: 14–17.

Butters, J.W., and Cash, T.F. (1987). Cognitive behavioral treatment of women's body image dissatisfaction. *Journal of Consulting and Clinical Psychology* 55: 889–897.

Bruch, H. (1977). Psychological antecedents of anorexia nervosa. In *Anorexia Nervosa,* ed. Vigersky, R.A. New York: Raven Press.

Cooper, P.J., and Fairburn, C.G. (1983). Binge-eating and self-induced vomiting in the community: A preliminary study. *British Journal of Psychiatry* 142: 139–144.

Fairburn, C.G. (1995). *Overcoming Binge Eating.* New York: The Guilford Press.

Fairburn, C.G. (1988). The current status of the psychological treatment of bulimia nervosa. *Journal of Psychosomatic Research* 32: 635–645.

Fairburn, C.G. (1984). Bulimia: Its epidemiology and management. In *Eating and Its Disorders,* eds. Stunkard, A.J., and Stellar, E. New York: Raven Press.

Fairburn, C.G., Jones, R., Reveler, R.C., Hope, R.A., and O'Connor, M. (1993). Psychotherapy and bulimia nervosa: The longer-term effects of interpersonal psychotherapy, behavior therapy and cognitive behavior therapy. *Archives of General Psychiatry* 50: 419–428.

Fava, M., Copland, P.M., Schiveiger, U., and Herzog, D.B. (1989). Neurochemical abnormalities of anorexia nervosa and bulimia nervosa. *American Journal of Psychiatry* 146: 963–971.

Garner, D.M., and Garfinkel, P.E. (1980). Socio-cultural factors in the development of anorexia nervosa. *Psychological Medicine* 10: 647–656.

Garfinkel, P.E., and Garner, D.M. (1982). *Anorexia Nervosa: A Multidimensional Perspective.* New York: Brunner/Mazel.

Garner, D.M., and Wooley, S.C. (1991). Confronting the failure of behavioral and dietary treatments for obesity. *Clinical Psychology Review* 11: 729–780.

Hatsukami, D., Mitchell, J.E., Eckert, E.D., and Pyle, R.L. (1986). Characteristics of patients with bulimia only, bulimia with affective disorder, and bulimia with substance abuse problems. *Addictive Behaviors* 11: 399–406.

Hatsukami, D., Owen, P., Pyle, R.L., and Mitchell, J.E. (1982). Similarities and differences on the MMPI between women with bulimia and women with alcohol abuse problems. *Addictive Disorders* 7: 435–439.

Hatsukami, D., Eckert, E.D., Mitchell, J.E., and Pyle R.L. (1984). Affective disorder and substance abuse in women with bulimia. *Psychological Medicine* 14: 701–704.

Hester, R.K., and Miller, W.R. (1989). *Handbook of Alcoholism Treatment Approaches*. New York: Pergamon Press.

Johnson, C. (1985). Initial consultation for patients with bulimia and anorexia nervosa. *Handbook of Psychotherapy for Anorexia Nervosa and Bulimia,* eds. Garner, D.M., and Garfinkel, P.E. New York: The Guilford Press.

Kaplan, A.S., and Woodside, D.B. (1987). Biological aspects of anorexia nervosa and bulimia nervosa. *Journal of Consulting and Clinical Psychology* 55: 645–653.

Keesey, R.E., and Powley, T.L. (1986). The regulation of body weight. *Annual Review of Psychology* 37: 109–133.

Keys, A., Biozek, J., Henschel, A., Mickelsen, O., and Taylor, H.L. (1950). *The Biology of Human Starvation*. Minneapolis: University of Minnesota Press.

Knight, L.J., and Boland, F.J. (1989). Restrained eating: An experimental disentanglement of the disinhibiting variables of perceived calories and food type. *Journal of Abnormal Psychology* 98: 412–420.

Krahn, D.D. (1991). The relationship of eating disorders and substance abuse. *Journal of Substance Abuse* 3: 230–254.

Loro, A.D., and Orlens, C.S. (1981). Binge-eating in obesity: Preliminary findings and guidelines for behavioral analysis and treatment. *Addictive Behaviors* 6: 155–166.

Marlatt, G.A., and Gordon, J.R. (1985). *Relapse Prevention*. New York: The Guilford Press.

Mitchell, J.E., Hatsukami, D., Eckert, E.D., and Pyle, R.L. (1985). Characteristics of 275 patients with bulimia. *American Journal of Psychiatry* 142: 482–485.

Mitchell, J.E., Pyle, R.L., Eckert, E.D., and Hatsukami, D. (1990). The influence of prior alcohol and drug abuse problems on bulimia nervosa treatment outcome. *Addictive Behaviors* 15: 169–173.

Mitchell, P.B. (1988). The pharmacological management of bulimia nervosa: A critical review. *International Journal of Eating Disorders* 7: 29–41.

Perlman, A., and McKenna, T. (1988). A comparison of bulimic and non-bulimic chemical dependency patients. *Hazelden Professional Update* 7: 1–6.

Piran, N., Lerner, P., Garfinkel, P.E., Kennedy, S., and Brouilette, C. (1988). Personality disorders in restricting and bulimic forms of anorexia nervosa. *International Journal of Obesity* 1: 589–600.

Polivy, J., and Herman, C.P. (1976). The effect of alcohol on eating behavior: Disinhibition or sedation? *Addictive Behaviors* 1: 121–125.

Rand, C.S.W., Lawlor, B.A., and Duldau, J.M. (1986). Patterns of food and alcohol consumption in a group of bulimic women. Bulletin of Society of Psychologists in *Addictive Behaviors* 5: 95–104.

Rodin, G., Daneman, D., Johnson, L., Kenshole, A., and Garfinkel, P.E. (1986) Anorexia nervosa and bulimia in insulin-dependent diabetes melitis. *International Journal of Psychiatric Medicine* 16: 49–57.

Rosen, J.C., and Leitenberg, H. (1982). Bulimia nervosa: Treatment with exposure and response prevention. *Behavior Therapy* 13: 117–124.

Spitzer, L., and Rodin, J., (1987). Effects of fructose and glucose preloads on subsequent food intake. *Appetite* 8: 135–145.

Striegel-Moore, R.H., Silberstein, L.R., and Rodin, J. (1986). Towards an understanding of risk factors for bulimia. *American Psychologist* 41: 246–263.

Strober, M. (1991). Family-genetic studies of eating disorders. *Journal of Clinical Psychiatry* 52: 9–12.

Vandereycken, W., Kog, E., and Vanderlinden, J. (1989). *The Family Approach to Eating Disorders: Assessment and Treatment of Anorexia Nervosa and Bulimia.* New York and London: PMA Publishing.

Vanderheyden, D.A., and Boland, F.J. (1987). A comparison of normals, mild, moderate and severe binge-eaters, and binge-vomiters using discriminant function analysis. *International Journal of Eating Disorders* 6: 331–337.

Vitousek, K., and Monke, F. (1994). Personality variables and diagnoses in anorexia nervosa and bulimia nervosa. *Journal of Abnormal Psychology* 103: 137–148.

Walker, C.E., Bonner, B.L., and Kaufman, K.L (1988). *The Physically and Sexually Abused Child: Evaluation and Treatment.* Toronto: Pergamon Press.

Wilson, G.T. (1993). Binge eating and addictive disorders. In *Binge Eating: Nature, Assessment and Treatment,* eds. Fairburn, C.G., and Wilson, G.T. New York: Guilford Press.

Wilson, G.T. (1996). Treatment of bulimia nervosa: When CBT fails. *Behavior Research and Therapy* 34: 197–212.

Wooley, S.C., and Kearney-Cooke, A. (1986). Intensive treatment of bulimia and body-image disturbance. In *Handbook of Eating Disorders,* eds. Brownell, K.D., and Foreyt, J.B. New York: Basic Books, Inc.

RECOMMENDED READINGS

Any of the following three books would serve as an excellent general reference to all aspects of eating disorders and their treatment:

Brownell, K.D., and Foreyt, J.P. (1986). *Handbook of Eating Disorders.* New York: Basic Books.

Garner, D.M., and Garfinkel, P.E. (1985). *Handbook of Psychotherapy for Anorexia Nervosa and Bulimia.* New York: The Guilford Press.

Schlundt, D.G., and Johnson, W.G. (1990). *Eating Disorders: Assessment and Treatment.* Boston: Allyn and Bacon.

For a very readable and comprehensive summary of information related to eating disorders see:

Garner, D.M., Rocket, W., Olmasted, M.P., Johnson, C., and Coscina, D.V. (1985). Psycho-educational principles in the treatment of bulimia and anorexia nervosa. In *Handbook of Psychotherapy for Anorexia Nervosa and Bulimia,* eds. Garner, D.M., and Garfinkel P.E. New York: The Guilford Press.

Popular nontechnical books that are useful in therapy by both client and therapist:

Chernin, K. (1981). *The Obsession: Reflections on the Tyranny of Slenderness.* New York: Harper and Row.

Fairburn, C. (1985). *Overcoming Binge Eating.* New York: The Guilford Press.

Hutchinson, M. (1985). *Transforming Body Image.* New York: Crossing Press.

Kano, S. (1989). *Making Peace with Food.* New York: Harper and Row.

Orbach, S. (1982). *Fat Is a Feminist Issue II.* New York: Berkeley Books.

Polivy, J., and Herman, C.P. (1983). *Breaking the Diet Habit: The Natural Weight Alternative.* New York: Basic Books.

For family and friends of a person with an eating disorder, the following is a particularly good book that deals with identifying an eating disorder and getting a person to treatment:

Seigel, M., Brisman, J., and Wienshel, M. (1988). *Surviving an Eating Disorder: New Perspectives for Families and Friends*. New York: Harper and Row.

The following organizations can help by sending newsletters, and informing about therapists, self-help groups, workshops and conferences on eating disorders.

The National Eating Disorder Information Centre
Toronto General Hospital, 200 Elizabeth Street 2-332
Toronto, ON M5G 2C4.

Anorexia Nervosa and Bulimia Foundation of Canada
P.O. Box 3074
Winnipeg, MN R3C 4E5

Bulimia Anorexia Nervosa Association
c/o Psychological Services, University of Windsor
Windsor, ON N9B 3P4.

HERSIZE
223 Concord Avenue
Toronto, ON M6H 2P4.

BASH (Bulimia, Anorexia, Self-Help) Magazine
6125 Clayton Avenue, Suite 215
St. Louis, MS 63139, USA

Radiance Magazine
P.O. Box 31703
Oakland, CA 94604–9937, USA

Chapter 26

Helping Clients
with Concurrent Disorders

GERRY COOPER AND CARL KENT

INTRODUCTION

Concurrent psychiatric and substance abuse disorders within individual clients are not new, but the condition has only recently become the focus of a growing body of scientific literature.

Freed's 1975 article "Alcoholism and Schizophrenia" listed almost 200 references, including some works that were published in the 1930s. Indeed, the association between psychiatric syndromes and substance abuse dates back about 200 years to Rush (Glass, 1989).

Several factors may account for the increased attention to concurrent disorders. First, improvements to diagnostic instruments and procedures, in both the psychiatric and substance abuse fields, have assisted clinicians in their ability to identify clients and their problems (e.g., the American Psychiatric Association's *DSM-IV* [APA, 1994] classification system).

The second factor concerns deinstitutionalization, which has resulted in many psychiatric patients living in the broader community (Brown et al., 1989). This development created a new group of clients who encountered community-based problems previously unknown to many of them: homelessness, unemployment, and easy access to psychoactive substances, to name a few.

Not surprisingly, the system of care has been overwhelmed by such deinstitutionalized patients. As a result, at least in the U.S., "psychiatric chemical dependency and rehabilitative hospital care [programs] ... are now booming" (Peele, 1990, p. 181).

Finally, several large federal funding agencies in the United States have co-ordinated their efforts regarding concurrent disorders. American mental health and substance abuse treatment systems have traditionally been separate. But, with concurrent disorders, these bodies are attempting to bridge the knowledge gaps by funding cross-over demonstration treatment programs and associated research projects (Brown et al., 1989). These developments are paralleled in Canada.

From the foregoing, two conclusions can be drawn:
(1) Concurrent disorders are extremely prevalent among both psychiatric and substance abuse treatment system populations.
(2) The level of care provided to such persons has frequently failed to respond to their unique treatment needs.

Gottheil and colleagues (1980) aptly summarize this last point: "Often these patients are shuttled back and forth, or they fall through the cracks of the system and are lost to treatment, or they are treated in both [psychiatric and substance abuse] clinics with conflicting methods and confusing effects" (p. xii).

The remainder of this chapter addresses the issues of definitions and diagnoses; prevalence; etiology; and obstacles to effective treatment. It also summarizes the literature and lists a series of recommendations for providing treatment that will best meet the special needs of clients with concurrent disorders.

PROBLEMS WITH DEFINITIONS AND DIAGNOSES

The term "concurrent disorders" is sometimes used in several ways and therefore requires further definition. For example, Fisher et al. (1989) use "dual diagnoses" to refer to persons with mental retardation and psychiatric comorbidity. In many instances, the use of the word "dual" may be a misnomer, because individuals often suffer from more than two (dual) disorders. As a result, the term "concurrent" has recently been introduced and its acceptance seems to be growing.

Still, terms like these are generic. They are often used to describe the co-existence of any number of medical, psychological and/or social problems.

With reference to psychiatric and substance abuse problems, it is important to establish that there are many kinds of complex psychiatric disorders, the most frequent of which include the general classifications of schizophrenia, mood disorders, anxiety disorders, and personality disorders (each of these categories can be further subdivided).

In addition, a wide variety of psychoactive substances, which can be abused alone or in combination, exist. These include stimulants (e.g., amphetamines, caffeine, cocaine, nicotine), sedatives (e.g., alcohol, barbiturates, benzodiazepines, inhalants), narcotics (e.g., heroin, morphine) and hallucinogens (e.g., cannabis, LSD, PCP).

The possible combinations of certain kinds of psychiatric problems with certain kinds of substance abuse problems are virtually endless. In addition, some individuals' abuse of substances predates their mental disorders, while in others the reverse is true. By way of illustration, is a given client's drinking motivated by (1) relatively recent feelings of sadness, or (2) an attempt to help cope with a long-standing serious problem with depression, or (3) is the person's depression a direct result of heavy and chronic alcohol use? The answers to this puzzle are critical in terms of knowing what kinds of treatment will have the greatest likelihood of success.

For these reasons, it is essential that health care providers approach the care of individuals based on each person's unique characteristics. As a group, persons with concurrent disorders are made up of different clinical presentations. For example, the following "clients" have symptoms and complaints that are quite diverse, although these people are all said to have "concurrent disorders":

- Jim, 45, has Antisocial Personality Disorder and abuses cocaine regularly.
- Mary, 30, experiences bouts of severe anxiety and uses alcohol to cope with her nerves.
- Tom, 22, suffers from schizophrenia, and his cannabis use exacerbates his symptoms.
- Susan, 67, has a long history of depression and has been increasing her use of benzodiazepines for some time.

Due to the persistence of symptoms that often closely resemble those from another disorder, it is clear that proper assessment needs to be conducted on an ongoing basis. A provisional diagnosis, usually made once a person has been safely detoxicated and at the outset of treatment, must be adjusted accordingly as new and clinically significant information becomes apparent (Ananth et al., 1989). Universally accepted diagnostic classification systems, such as *DSM-IV,* should be used consistently when addressing a client's problems, as they outline standard criteria for rendering diagnoses based on observable symptoms.

The diagnostic picture is further complicated by smaller subgroups within the concurrent disorder population. For example, young, chronically mentally ill people have been described as "hypervulnerable — chemically, psychologically and socially — to the effects of even mild or recreational use of drugs and alcohol" (Brown et al., 1989, p. 567). These individuals' psychiatric treatment often includes pharmacotherapy, but even modest amounts of alcohol could interact with medication to produce a compounded effect. Substance use, and not necessarily full-fledged dependence, may provoke psychiatric problems in this particular subgroup (Schmidt, 1989). Therefore, to make accurate diagnoses, clinicians may need to examine their beliefs and values about what it means to be a substance abuser.

PREVALENCE

Substance abuse among psychiatric patients and psychological problems among substance abusers seem quite common, but many prevalence studies have limitations. It is therefore difficult to establish just how common these phenomena really are.

Estimates of the prevalence of concurrent disorders vary according to the kind of diagnosis, the location and type of treatment program being studied, and the procedures used in the research study. It is generally believed that about one-half of all people receiving psychiatric treatment also experience a substance abuse problem — or problems — while about the same percentage of all substance abusers in treatment experience some form of co-existing psychiatric problem(s). For the most part, a person's risk of experiencing a concurrent psychiatric problem increases with the number of substances abused.

In general, however, studies have found that the percentages of concurrently disordered clients in both the psychiatric and substance abuse systems are indeed cause for concern by all who staff such programs.

The extent to which the statistics obtained from these studies reflect the concurrent disorder problem in the general population is not known, although several studies have tried to evaluate the situation using U.S. data. (Weissman and Meyers, 1980; Helzer and Pryzbeck, 1988; and Schmidt, 1989). Due to the seriousness of their symptoms, those with concurrent problems may be more likely to eventually find their way into treatment than are people with uncomplicated disorders (Woody et al., 1990). In this way, people with concurrent disorders would comprise a greater proportion of the client population, as compared to persons with uncomplicated substance abuse or psychiatric problems. People with uncomplicated, or single, disorders may be more likely to recover on their own.

What is not known are the characteristics of those who fall between the cracks and, as a result, are left out of study samples (Cooper et al., 1990). However, even for those included in study samples, the usefulness of the research findings must be viewed with caution. These study clientele are usually quite distinct, and it has already been noted that "dual disorders" is a catch-all term for many different conditions. In short, it is difficult to draw many conclusions about a population as heterogeneous as the dually disordered.

Schmidt (1989), however, suggests that, while her prevalence data indicate that the burden of comorbidity is not as great as that implied by other studies, such cases pose special problems to service providers.

One possible explanation for the potentially inflated prevalence ratios arising from some studies concerns "the validity of such diagnoses when they are made at the point of entry into treatment, at a time when intoxication or withdrawal symptoms may mimic other psychiatric disorders" (Ross et al., 1988b, p. 1191). Some studies of the past two decades interviewed only post-detoxification clients, while others did not. Ross and her colleagues (1988a) interviewed three-fifths of their research subjects within three days of registration to an addictions treatment facility, at a time when one might expect to find at least some clients still in a state of withdrawal. This could elevate the prevalence of current psychiatric symptoms, which might simply disappear with abstinence (Attia, 1988).

Nevertheless, any question about over-inflated prevalence statistics must be tempered by the number of dually disordered individuals who are served poorly or not at all, due to the inflexible status quo of many of the treatment systems' structures (Carey, 1989). Such clients are often denied treatment at substance abuse programs because of their psychiatric condition, and/or at psychiatric facilities because of their substance abuse problems.

These people often receive less than optimal care, which results in their attrition from the helping system — hence the term "falling through the cracks." This rather bleak scenario has spawned some unflattering jargon such as "the patient shuffle," "system misfits," "ping-ponged" and "pigeonholed." Published accounts of comprehensive information about these people are rare, but anecdotal-type data suggest that these individuals abound (Willauer et al., 1990). It is hoped that preliminary work in this area will provide some clues as to how their care might be improved in future.

ETIOLOGY

With respect to the cause of concurrent disorders, it appears that the jury is still out. Some claim that two-thirds of all such cases are a direct result of prior alcohol abuse (McEvoy, 1989). Others contend that substance abuse often results from psychiatric illness as individuals attempt to self-medicate. For example, Hall et al. (1979) found as many as 50 per cent in one study where self-medication was the case.

The self-medication hypothesis has received considerable support from other researchers. Reich et al. (1974) found that, contrary to the assumption that alcohol is used to counteract depressive symptoms, their subjects drank excessively primarily during the manic phase of bipolar affective disorder, and did so to reduce their manic symptoms. Ross and colleagues (1988a) reported a predictive relationship between the severity of substance abuse and the likelihood of psychiatric problems, while others have reported a causal relationship.

Some interesting gender differences have also been observed, which may contribute to the etiologic picture. Generally, women have been found to have a later age of onset of alcoholism than do men (Winokur et al., 1970) and, correspondingly, psychiatric problems frequently predate substance abuse in women (Fine, 1980). The reverse is true for men (Hesselbrock et al., 1985).

Clearly, age of onset of substance abuse and/or psychiatric problems is an important factor. It has been demonstrated that early onset of alcoholism and additional psychiatric syndromes are significantly related to a family history of alcoholism (Powell et al., 1982).

Other factors that should be considered include the absence of social support mechanisms (Lin et al., 1979) and stressors such as homelessness (Koegel et al., 1988). Each of these issues has influenced illness symptoms and their prevalence.

OBSTACLES TO EFFECTIVE TREATMENT

It is not surprising that treatment services often fail to help the individual with concurrent disorders. Many researchers have found, unfortunately, that these persons often go undetected, are misdiagnosed, or otherwise improperly treated due to inappropriate staff attitudes and/or lack of skills.

This latter point has been directly related to the limited availability of appropriate training in medical and other professional schools. Few programs attempt to identify and fully assess a client's psychiatric and substance abuse status, and even fewer complement their findings with corroborative data from significant others and/or biochemical laboratory tests.

For those few who are correctly identified, sadly, there are few specialized programs to which they can be referred. Programs that do provide these services are usually not well known to most potential referral agents. Program directors who want to expand their service delivery base to better help people with concurrent disorders will find little treatment outcome research to help with their task. Furthermore, the absence of any large-scale advocacy group for people with concurrent disorders — a group that could influence policy-makers, practitioners and administrators — may also have contributed to this state of affairs (Kopolow, 1981). Until recently, the necessary political will to alter this unfortunate course did not seem to exist.

Fortunately, this scenario is undergoing rapid change. Concurrent disorder mutual help groups are being formed in many communities, clinicians are very predisposed to specialized training, and governmental position documents herald a commitment to change.

RECOMMENDATIONS FOR TREATMENT EFFICACY

Much work still needs to be done towards understanding concurrent disorders and empirically demonstrating the effectiveness of various therapeutic approaches. However, some consensus regarding relevant treatment principles seems to be emerging. What follows is a synthesis of this consensus, which is based on 24 published program descriptions, case studies and best advice models.

The reader may want to look at the following list as a recipe for success in planning for dual disorder interventions. Naturally, the degree to which these principles are implemented will affect the probability for consistently positive outcomes. However, it may not be within the mandate of any one person or program to enact each of these principles and hence, a systems approach appears to be necessary.

Recommendations

1. Complete detoxification, ideally from all psychoactive substances, should occur prior to assessment and treatment planning.
2. A comprehensive assessment of the client's presenting problems (both mental and substance abuse) and strengths (i.e., support systems), should occur as soon as the client is free of intoxication and/or withdrawal.
3. The assessment should incorporate laboratory measures, such as urinalysis, and solicit corroborative input from significant others whenever possible.
4. A provisional diagnosis of the client's problems and an individualized treatment plan should accompany this process. Both the client and significant others should be involved as much as possible.
5. The provisional diagnosis should be reviewed periodically throughout the course of treatment, and interventions should be adjusted accordingly.
6. When attempting to match interventions to the client's needs, it is crucial to adhere to several principles:
   - Approaches need to be flexible.
   - Abstinence should usually be understood to be the most desirable treatment goal.
   - Prior abstinence is not necessarily a requirement for treatment to begin.
   - Mental health and substance abuse interventions are employed as indicated.
   - A holistic orientation is required.
   - Confrontational interventions may actually hinder the recovery process for many clients (especially people with schizophrenia).
   - A range of residential and outpatient options should be available.
   - Special attention may need to be focused on safe and supportive housing needs of the client.
   - Treatment outcomes will likely be a function of the type and severity of a client's disorder, but appropriate matching of treatment to each client's needs will improve the chances of good outcomes.

7. Treatment should simultaneously address psychiatric and substance abuse problems under "one program roof." Failing that, extensive communication between the various treatment components by one case manager (who has major responsibility for the case) is recommended.

8. The unified clinical team should ideally be comprised of professionally trained mental health and substance abuse staff (including physicians to administer and monitor pharmacotherapy) and supplemented, as required, by persons stabilized in their own recovery (i.e., members of mutual help groups).

9. Treatment should be open-ended. Emphasis should be placed on ongoing care (aftercare), with extensive use of case management workers and rigorous outreach efforts.

10. Clients should be encouraged to use mutual help programs, but should be carefully assisted by a member of the clinical team in "shopping" for a group where they are comfortable. In some cases, new groups with a special orientation to concurrent disorders may need to be established.

11. Priority should be given to ongoing in-service education, where mental health and substance abuse staff train each other in their respective specialties. Staff may also need to advocate additional training from within their organizations and/or from accredited academic institutions.

12. Input by clients and significant others at a program advisory level is essential.

CONCLUSION

The "concurrent disorder" population is complex, heterogeneous and often demanding of counsellor time, effort and creativity. It is hoped that a greater awareness of these clients and their special needs will lead to more regular identification, accurate diagnoses and better treatment in the future.

As alluded to earlier, when outlining a systems approach to treatment, the notion of a case manager who follows and co-ordinates the many treatment facets, through crises and over time, is crucial. After all, the problems of people with concurrent disorders are often chronic in nature and subject to setbacks. Change is likely to occur slowly and incrementally. Consequently, being the case manager for a dually disordered client may represent a large commitment. Counsellors who are not working out of a specialized treatment setting for the dually disordered might be advised to seek administrative backing for this time- and energy-consuming task.

Clearly, these clients demand and deserve more than the predominant short-term approach to counselling. The argument must be made that, in the long run, only a long-term commitment to this client population will save money, effort and staff time. It will also alleviate considerable suffering by clients and their significant others.

ACKNOWLEDGMENT

The authors wish to thank Egle Wennerstrom for the preparation of this manuscript.

REFERENCES

American Psychiatric Association. (1994). *Diagnostic and Statistical Manual of Mental Disorders,* 4th ed. Washington, DC: Author.

Ananth, J., Vandewater, S., Kamal, M., Brodsky, A., Gamal, R., and Miller, M. (1989). Missed diagnosis of substance abuse in psychiatric patients. *Hospital and Community Psychiatry* 40 (3): 297–299.

Attia, P.R. (1988). Dual diagnosis: Definition and treatment. *Alcoholism Treatment Quarterly* 5 (3/4): 53–63.

Brown, V.B., Ridgely, M.S., Pepper, B., Levine, I.S., and Ryglewicz, H. (1989). The dual crisis: Mental illness and substance abuse. *American Psychologist* (March): 565–569.

Carey, K.B. (1989). Emerging treatment guidelines for mentally ill chemical abusers. *Hospital and Community Psychiatry* 40 (4): 341–349.

Cooper, G., Graham, D., Hill, J.M., and Huneault, N. (1990). Chronic mental illness and substance abuse: A needs assessment. *Rural Community Mental Health Newsletter* 17 (1): 5.

Fine, E.W. (1980). The syndrome of alcohol dependency and depression. In *Substance Abuse and Psychiatric Illness,* eds. Gottheil, E., McLellan, A.T., and Druley, K.A. New York: Pergamon Press.

Fisher, W., Piazza, C., and Page, T.J. (1989). Assessing independent and interactive effects of behavioral and pharmacologic interventions for a client with dual diagnoses. *Journal of Behavioral Therapy and Experimental Psychiatry* 20 (3): 241–250.

Freed, E.X. (1975). Alcoholism and schizophrenia: The search for perspectives; A review. *Journal of Studies on Alcohol* 36 (7): 853–881.

Glass, I.B. (1989). Psychiatric education and substance problems: A slow response to neglect. *International Review of Psychiatry* 1: 17–19.

Gottheil, E., McLellan, A.T., and Druley, K.A. (1980). *Substance Abuse and Psychiatric Illness.* New York: Pergamon Press.

Hall, R.C.W., Stickney, S.K., Gardner, E.R., Perl, M., and LeCann, A.F. (1979). Relationship of psychiatric illness to drug abuse. *Journal of Psychedelic Drugs* 11 (4): 337–342.

Helzer, J.E., and Pryzbeck, T.R. (1988). The co-occurrence of alcoholism with other psychiatric disorders in the general population and its impact on treatment. *Journal of Studies on Alcohol* 49 (3): 219–224.

Hesselbrock, M.N., Meyer, R.E., and Keener, J.J. (1985). Psychopathology in hospitalized alcoholics. *Archives of General Psychiatry* 42 (Nov.): 1050–1055.

Koegel, P., Burman, M.A., and Farr, R.K. (1988). The prevalence of specific psychiatric disorders among homeless individuals in the inner city of Los Angeles. *Archives of General Psychiatry* 45: 1085–1092.

Kopolow, L.E. (1981). Client participation in mental health service delivery. *Community Mental Health Journal* 17 (1): 46–53.

Lin, N., Ensel, W.M., Simeone, R.S., and Kuo, W. (1979). Social support, stressful life events, and illness: A model and an empirical test. *Journal of Health and Social Behaviour* 20 (June): 108–119.

McEvoy, L. (1989). Alcoholism often goes undetected in psychiatric patients. *The Medical Post* (June 20): 40.

Peele, S. (1990). Research issues in assessing addiction treatment efficacy: How cost effective are Alcoholics Anonymous and private treatment centres? *Drug and Alcohol Dependence* 25: 179–182.

Powell, B.J., Penick, E.C., Othmer, E., Bingham, S.F., and Rice, A.S. (1982). Prevalence of additional psychiatric syndromes among male alcoholics. *Journal of Clinical Psychiatry* (10): 404–407.

Reich, L.H., Davies, R.K., and Himmelhoch, J.M. (1974). Excessive alcohol use in manic-depressive illness. *American Journal of Psychiatry* 131 (1): 83–86.

Ross, H.E., Glaser, F.B., and Germanson, T. (1988a). The prevalence of psychiatric disorders in patients with alcohol and other drug problems. *Archives of General Psychiatry* 45 (Nov.): 1023–1031.

Ross, H.E., Glaser, F.B., and Strasny, S. (1988b). Sex differences in the prevalence of psychiatric disorders in patients with alcohol and drug problems. *British Journal of Addiction* 83: 1179–1192.

Schmidt, L.A. (1989). Prevalence and correlates of problem drinking in a psychiatrically treated population. Paper presented at the Annual Meeting of the American Public Health Association, October 23, 1989.

Weissman, M.M., and Meyers, J.K. (1980). Clinical depression in alcoholics. *American Journal of Psychiatry* 137: 372–373.

Willauer, S., Cooper, G., Graham, D., Todd, L., and Mainer, B. (1990). Dual disorders needs assessment: Phase I interim report. Unpublished manuscript available from the second author.

Winokur, G., Reich, T., Rimmer, J., and Pitts, F.N. (1970). Alcoholism: III. Diagnosis and familial psychiatric illness in 259 alcoholic probands. *Archives of General Psychiatry* 23: 104–111.

Woody, G.E., McLellan, A.T., and O'Brien, C.P. (1990). Research on psychopathology and addiction: Treatment implications. *Drug and Alcohol Dependence* 25: 121–123.

Chapter 27

AIDS and Substance Abuse

PETER M. FORD AND HANNAH KAUFMAN

INTRODUCTION

AIDS is a disease caused by the human immunodeficiency virus (HIV). The virus is transmitted primarily by exchange of body fluids from infected to uninfected individuals. The body fluids most likely to transmit HIV are blood and semen. Maternal milk has also been implicated in mother-child transmission. Other body fluids such as sweat, saliva and urine are relatively non-infectious. Thus the major modes of transmission are:

(1) Injection with blood-contaminated syringes, infected blood transfusions or infected blood products as in Factor VIII preparations for hemophiliacs.

(2) Sexual/anal intercourse, because of the trauma to mucous membranes lining the anus and rectum, is the most frequent sexual mode of transmission, but oral sex with ingestion of semen and vaginal sex are also capable of transmission. In the Third World, vaginal intercourse is the predominant mode of transmission, although, at least in Africa, genital ulceration due to other sexually transmitted diseases seems to facilitate spread by this route.

(3) Maternal-fetal transmission may occur in the womb, but probably most commonly occurs at birth. Infants may also be infected by breastfeeding, since breast milk of infected mothers may contain HIV-infected lymphocytes.

HIV infects a number of cells, the most significant of which are lymphocytes, macrophages and cells of the central nervous system. Until recently it was thought that once the virus entered a cell, it translated the viral RNA into DNA, inserted itself into the cell nucleus and remained dormant for years until triggered to reactivate. It is now known that the virus actively replicates from the time of infection, and every day billions of viral particles are produced and millions of lymphocytes are destroyed. At some point, usually several years from the time of infection, the immune system starts to fail, either because the virus has mutated into a new, more malignant form or additional factors, such as other infections, tip the balance against the struggling immune system. This phase where the patient appears well may last from two years to more than 10 years. Indeed, 10 years after infection only about 50 per cent of infected individuals will be showing signs of disease. The remainder will be well, but are capable of spreading the disease to others. Once infected, an individual remains capable of transmitting the infection for the rest of his or her life.

TESTING

A number of laboratory tests can detect whether an individual has been infected with HIV. The commonly used ones depend on the production of antibodies to the virus. These antibodies may take up to six weeks after infection to appear (in a few cases, it may be as long as three to four months). During this time, HIV screening tests will be negative, but the patient is capable of transmitting the infection — this is the so-called "window period." The main screening test is called the ELISA test. While this test will be positive when antibodies to HIV are present, it may occasionally produce false positive results. Thus, if the ELISA is positive, a confirmatory test called the Western Blot Test (the name refers to the laboratory procedure) is usually carried out. The Western Blot is regarded as the gold standard. All positive tests should be repeated for confirmation.

When counselling either before or after testing for HIV, it is important to remember that, if an individual has been exposed to risk within the previous three to four months, he or she may be in the "window period." This means that he or she may have been infected, but has not yet developed antibodies that would show up on test-ing. The individual needs to be tested again within six months. Many injection drug users continue to expose themselves to potential infection and a single negative test will be meaningless; repeated testing will be required until risk behavior has ceased.

NOTE: The viral levels in the blood of an infected individual during the window peri-od will be extremely high and the individual is thus *highly infectious*. Individuals who are thought to be in the window period must be counselled to practise safe sex and to avoid risk behavior that might put others at risk.

There is often confusion about the difference between being infected with HIV and having AIDS. Someone with a positive confirmatory or Western Blot test is infected with HIV, but that person does not have AIDS until he or she actually becomes physi-cally ill with some of the disease manifestations described below.

PROGRESSION TO AIDS

As the infection progresses, the virus destroys the macrophages and the immune system's "helper" lymphocytes. Both of these cells are involved in protecting the body against infection and the damage to them results in loss of immunity to a whole range of micro-organisms, many of which never trouble people with intact immune systems. The decline in immune function occurs over several years and may be slowed by a number of drugs that inhibit viral growth but, unfortunately, do not kill the virus. It has recently become possible to measure the amount of virus in the bloodstream — the "viral load" — and this can be used as a guide to treatment. A high viral load indicates that the current therapy is not working and a reduction in viral load after starting a new treatment indicates that the drug is effective.

Some recent treatment advances, in the short time that they have been available, have resulted in significant improvement in quality of life and are showing evidence of the ability to extend life. The first generation of anti-HIV drugs acted by blocking the conversion of viral RNA to DNA when the virus entered the cell. These drugs included Zidovudine (AZT), DDI, 3TC and DDC. The second generation of drugs, the protease inhibitors, act at the point where the newly generated viral particles are about to leave the cell. These drugs include Saquinavir, Ritonavir and Indinavir. The current standard of care is to use two of the first-generation drugs in combination with a protease inhibitor, and to follow the viral load and change medication to a different combination if the viral levels fail to fall or rise after an initial fall. These drug combinations are not free from side effects and are very expensive. The cost per year for three-drug therapy is about $14,000 to $16,000 (Canadian). The availability of these drugs varies from province to province, with some being provided free (e.g., AZT) and many others being funded through a variety of public and private drug plans. Payment for these expensive drugs has become a major problem for AIDS health care providers.

As the immune system declines in activity and the risk of infection increases, it is possible to provide prophylactic therapy to prevent a number of the more common infections such as candida (thrush), herpes and pneumocystis (which causes a severe pneumonia). Ongoing care and monitoring are usually provided either by regional AIDS clinics — which, in Canada, have been established in most major cities with provincial funding — or by interested family physicians. With close supervision, both the duration and quality of life can be improved. There is thus a positive incentive for HIV-positive individuals to seek appropriate medical care.

In addition to attacking the immune system, the virus also attacks the central nervous system and may cause dementia. This is usually only pronounced in the late stages of the disease and its incidence has been much diminished with the use of antiviral drugs. Dementia in the terminal stages of the disease may not only complicate management, but can also cause considerable strain and distress to care-givers and patients alike.

An additional problem in AIDS patients has been the occurrence of certain tumors. These include Kaposi's Sarcoma, a tumor rarely seen other than in AIDS patients, intracranial lymphoma, and in females, cervical cancer.

AIDS AND WOMEN

The incidence of HIV infection has recently taken a sharp upturn in women. In the northeastern United States, women are now the fastest-growing group testing HIV-positive. In Canada, this trend is clearly present and growing, but women have not yet surpassed the other two major groups of HIV-infected people.

Women and men with HIV show some differences in presentation and complications, although the survival times are probably much the same in similar socio-economic groups. Women may present with recurrent and persistent vaginal candidiasis and may also have recurrent problems with pelvic inflammatory disease. In addition, as noted above, there appears to be an increased risk of cervical cancer. Because it is less familiar to physicians in Canada, HIV disease in women is often missed in the early phase, particularly when it presents as recurrent pelvic inflammatory disease. Although there has been some suggestion that AIDS is a more rapidly fatal disease in women than in men, this only appears to be so because more of the female cases come from the lower socio-economic groups. Women do no worse than males from the same groups. Male statistics are skewed by the fact that many of the homosexuals with AIDS come from the middle class with better access to health care and money to pay for treatment.

An HIV-positive pregnant woman has a 25 to 30 per cent chance of giving birth to an infected infant. A recent study has shown that Zidovudine (AZT) given through pregnancy, starting after the third month, can reduce the transmission rate to eight per cent. There is thus good reason to counsel and test pregnant women regardless of their perception of risk, because there is a real benefit to timely treatment.

EPIDEMIOLOGY

When AIDS first appeared in North America in 1981, it was initially recognized in homosexuals. Although it was also noted to occur in other groups, such as intravenous (IV) drug users and Haitian immigrants, for several years AIDS was regarded in North America as a "gay" disease. By the late 1980s, however, it had become clear that there was a second major epidemic of HIV infection in the IV drug-using population of some, but not all, U.S. cities.

By the early 1990s three epidemics of HIV infection were recognized: in homosexuals; IV drug users; and the heterosexual population. While all three overlap to some extent, this is particularly true for the latter two groups. What is less generally appreciated is that the rates of spread will be different in all three groups. The slow rise of numbers among heterosexuals has given a false sense of security regarding this group. However, the chance of an individual becoming infected with HIV depends on how risky the behavior is, the likelihood of infection of the other partner, and the number of partners the individual has. Vaginal intercourse with an infected male, even without condom use, carries a relatively low risk of transmission in the intact vagina and, despite the impression given by the media, the average heterosexual does not have large numbers of partners. Female-to-male spread is less likely than vice versa. Thus initially, infected females were drug users or sex trade workers or both. Non-drug-using partners of IV users then began to appear in the statistics, and now heterosexual spread in the non-drug-using population is increasing and is reflected in the rising number of newly infected women — many of whom were unaware that they were at risk.

The prevalence of HIV in prison populations is generally about 10 times that in the non-prison population. A number of studies showed that the rate of HIV in prisoners two to three years ago was around one per cent and it has likely risen since then.

Once HIV entered a city's IV drug user population — in both developed and developing nations — it spread very quickly. For example, the incidence of HIV-positivity in IV drug users in Bangkok in 1988 jumped from 16 per cent in the spring to 46 per cent in the fall, and more than 75 per cent were infected before the first AIDS case appeared. The current prevalence of HIV in injection drug users varies considerably in the Western Hemisphere, being very high in cities such as New York and Edinburgh and, until recently, very low in cities such as Vancouver and Glasgow.

Glasgow and Edinburgh make a fascinating and instructive comparison: at the beginning of the HIV epidemic, Glasgow already had in place a needle exchange program because of concern about the spread of hepatitis. Edinburgh not only did not have such a program in place, but the police actually closed down the only pharmacy in the city prepared to sell clean needles and syringes to users. Thus in Edinburgh at the end of the 1980s, the prevalence of HIV in IV drug users was over 70 per cent; in Glasgow it was around five per cent. There is now mounting evidence that needle exchange and methadone treatment programs, coupled with education, can reduce risk behavior and probably the spread of HIV. Such programs often provide the only point of contact for health care workers with this population. For a comprehensive and reasonably compact review of the subject of injecting drug use and HIV/AIDS, the reader is referred to Des Jarlais et al. (1992). It is becoming apparent, however, in Canada that needle exchange programs slow the escalation of infection rates rather than stop them. This has recently been demonstrated in Vancouver, where the prevalence in street IV drug users has risen to upwards of 20 per cent from single digits in less than a year, and it is still rising. A similar trend is starting in other major Canadian cities.

RISK OF INFECTION FOR HEALTH CARE WORKERS

HIV is not easy to catch except by one of the high-risk behaviors noted above. Health care workers of all types may be exposed to body fluids from clients, but generally speaking the only fluid of concern is blood. It is very unlikely that HIV-infected blood on intact skin can transmit infection. However, blood on fresh cuts or on mucous membranes — such as the eye — may be capable of causing transmission, and, of course, blood on penetrating instruments such as needles can cause infection. The risk of infection from normal physical contact is therefore zero. Friends and family members will often want to know their risk in the course of day-to-day contact. Such activities as kissing, sharing utensils, etc., are not potential methods of transmission. However, it should be remembered that many HIV-infected individuals also have hepatitis B, which is much more infectious. Relatives whose anxiety persists should be referred to the local public health department for further advice.

Health care workers who encounter spills of blood or other body fluids should wear rubber gloves as a precaution when cleaning up. The virus is rapidly killed by diluted household bleach, which should be used to clear up blood spills. Remember, the basic principle of universal precautions is to assume that everyone is infected and to take appropriate precautions with *all* blood and body fluids. IV drug users are highly likely to be infected with hepatitis B (to which health care workers should have been immunized) and to hepatitis C (for which there is no vaccine). Both these viruses are much more likely than HIV to be transmitted through needle-stick accidents.

Health care workers who have significant exposure to HIV-positive blood — such as through a needle-stick accident — should be offered at least two anti-HIV drug prophylaxis within a few hours. This should be available with appropriate counselling at the nearest large hospital.

It is also worth noting that HIV-infected individuals may be carrying other, more easily transmissible diseases; the most worrying of these now is tuberculosis. The rise in tuberculosis seen over the last five years in the United States — a rise that is now appearing in Canada — is mostly occurring in HIV-positive individuals, particularly injection drug users. Most worrying of all is that some tuberculosis is resistant to most drugs. All individuals working with clients who may be HIV-infected should have a Tb skin test. If the results are negative, the test should be repeated annually. Every worker, regardless of skin-test results, should have an annual chest X-ray.

HIV COUNSELLING FOR SUBSTANCE USERS

HIV and AIDS raise many urgent issues for substance users and addictions counsellors. What is HIV/AIDS? How is it contracted? How is the substance user at increased risk of HIV infection? What does a client do about his or her HIV status (either positive or negative)? When does a client need counselling? How do I provide counselling for someone who is concerned about HIV? How are appropriate medical care and support services accessed? What are the mental health complications of HIV infection combined with addiction? These questions are addressed in this section.

Risks and Concerns for Substance Users

Substance users are at increased risk for HIV infection because, as a group, they share key risk factors: needle sharing, compromised immune status, decreased inhibitions leading to unsafe sex and drug use practices, low self-esteem, and poor access to HIV education and treatment programs. Any one of these factors can lead to HIV infection and related problems. In combination, the risk dramatically increases. The substance user may not be aware of the risk of transmission, or may not bring up the issue during substance abuse counselling. Because of these circumstances, all clients with a history of substance abuse require counselling about HIV/AIDS, its transmission, its prevention, and its impact on the substance user and his or her family.

Additionally, providing a variety of other HIV prevention programs can prevent an epidemic of HIV in a specific community, as well as stabilize prevalence of infection. These might include needle exchange programs, distribution of condoms and latex squares, peer education and HIV testing.

Women and Social Vulnerability

There is a clear link between physical and sexual abuse, and substance use in women. Women who abuse alcohol and other drugs are more likely to report both physical and emotional abuse during childhood and as adults. Some studies show that women who report recent rape are more likely to smoke crack cocaine, to be homeless, to be HIV- and STD-infected, and to engage in HIV risk behaviors.

As well, HIV-infected women with a history of injection drug use have a significantly higher risk for domestic violence. Their risk increases with disclosure of an HIV-positive test to their sex and needle-sharing partners (North, 1994).

Several recommendations stem from this information. Firstly, HIV-positive women should be assessed for the risk of domestic violence and offered appropriate interventions. Targeted HIV intervention strategies should be developed for women who abuse drugs, for survivors of domestic assault and rape, and for assailants. In addition, if domestic violence is in the picture, extreme caution should be used when considering partner notification.

Approaches in Counselling

Counselling substance users about HIV/AIDS requires a multi-issue approach. People bring to HIV counselling all of their issues, and other issues do not fall away in the face of a concern about HIV infection. They may recede for a time, but will inevitably return. People who live with HIV don't necessarily change the way they live their lives. Although the issue of HIV infection may appear paramount, it may obscure, exacerbate or transform other issues, such as physical and mental health problems, substance abuse, housing, finances, family relationships and other relationships (Drucker, 1991). Counselling must be open to the usual issues relevant to the client, as well as to specific issues of substance use and HIV.

When providing assistance with concrete concerns such as housing and finances, the counsellor must be sensitive to the additional difficulties often faced by the HIV-infected person. In the event of anticipated deteriorating health, considerations include, for example, the need for long-term housing that is accessible, affordable and close to physicians' offices and shopping. HIV-positive people are often subjected to discrimination by other tenants and landlords. Counsellors may need to help clients make decisions about disclosure, and advocate on their behalf.

Improved therapies are transforming AIDS from a life-threatening disease to a chronic illness with many of the same emotional, social and financial issues as other chronic conditions. Although this is good news, HIV-infected people must be able to manage long-term use of expensive medications, an emotional shift from thinking about and planning for imminent death to retrieving a lost social and work life as their health improves, and changing their relationship and family roles. Many people, having adjusted to a shortened lifespan, do not cope well with these changes. Counsellors must not assume that the transition will be a completely easy one for their clients.

The goals of HIV counselling should include HIV education, life skills, awareness of and changes in attitudes and ultimately changes in behavior. Motivation, incentives and barriers to change should be explored and used in the counselling process, to enhance support systems and to minimize the avoidance of other major issues such as substance use.

HIV Testing: Pre-Test and Post-Test Counselling

Pre-test and post-test counselling are important parts of caring for an individual who is concerned about HIV. The primary rationale for this is clear: HIV testing requires informed consent. This may seem obvious, but the risks and effects of undergoing testing are complex, as are the effects of receiving either positive or negative results. The actual act of being tested can produce anxiety and depression, suicide risk, uninsurability, and discrimination in the workplace and/or by friends and family. A positive test heightens these problems, and a negative test can lead to increased risk-taking behaviors and uncertainty. Counsellors must understand this complexity, and be knowledgeable about disease transmission. Lastly, counsellors should feel comfortable talking explicitly about sex.

The primary role of the HIV counsellor is to help define the complex areas that concern clients (Marks and Goldblum, 1990). The substance abuse counsellor must also understand the issues and the areas addressed during HIV testing. The purpose of this is two-fold. Firstly, the substance abuse counsellor can evaluate the services provided to their clients, ensuring they receive appropriate and complete counselling. Secondly, HIV counselling is rarely accomplished in one or two sessions. Additional assistance enhances information retention and behavior change.

The pre-test session involves:
- assessment of the client's knowledge level
- clarifying information about the mechanics and meaning of the test and transmission risks
- discussing relevant risk factors, the need for future testing and risk reduction strategies
- exploring the psychological effects of testing, including an assessment of individual coping mechanisms, support systems and suicide risk.

The post-test discussion, if the test is negative, should include:
- identification of the client (to prevent mix-up of results)
- interpretation of the result (no infection or the need for retest)
- reinforcement of risk reduction strategies.

Dealing with a Positive Test

A positive test result requires more involved counselling. This should include:
- identification of the client
- interpretation of the result (infected with the virus, not diagnostic of AIDS, and reassurance that a confirmatory test was performed to rule out a "false positive")
- discussion of issues important to the client
- discussion of coping and support systems
- assessment of mental status
- resource counselling (mental health agencies, support groups etc.).

Other issues to explore during this or a following session are:
- partner notification
- expanding on transmission reduction strategies to include avoiding donations of blood, organs, tissue and sperm, avoiding breastfeeding and pregnancy, and protecting others from blood and body fluids (semen, vaginal fluid)
- medical follow-up
- discussion of health enhancement.

All clients, with or without problems of addiction, might be overwhelmed by a diagnosis of HIV infection. Newly diagnosed individuals are prone to increased risk behaviors — such as needle sharing and unsafe sex — due to mental health complications, increased substance use and anxiety. Since denial is the psychic armor that allows for continued substance use, a challenge to that armor can result in suicide, depression or decreased acceptance of the diagnosis. Uncertainty about their health, life expectancy and the impact of HIV on everyday functioning can lead clients to try to assert maximum control over their lives. This can take the form of either seeking or avoiding knowledge about their illness, and either increased or decreased substance use (Weitz, 1989). Clients may be overwhelmed by illness, grief and a sense of loss. This powerful focus can result in overlooking or avoiding either the substance use or the HIV infection, again leading to high-risk activities, anxiety, depression and suicide. The counsellor must be alert to these possibilities.

Counsellors in any setting sometimes fall into a "parallel process" with clients: sharing the avoidance and control behaviors they use to manage anxiety. The HIV or substance abuse counsellor, for example, may unwittingly enable the client's high-risk activities, especially increased substance use. Initially, counsellors should consider *not* insisting that their clients totally abstain from what may be their only coping strategies. Insisting on abstinence often leads to an increased feeling of anxiety and loss of self-control. Prior to entering a formal substance abuse program, a goal of moderating a client's substance use may increase that client's motivation, and help the counsellor with this more complicated engagement process. Counselling strategies that provide information — the equipment for behavior change — while enhancing self-esteem have also been shown to increase the likelihood of behavior change.

Family Issues

Families may also be overwhelmed by HIV infection. They may experience feelings of helplessness and hopelessness, undermining the substance abuse treatment. This can take many forms: a withdrawal of personal and financial support for substance abuse treatment, a shift of focus to medical and emotional treatment for the HIV infection, and a shift in focus away from the client, toward personal concerns regarding infection transmission and the ability to cope with yet another crisis. Rejection of the substance abuser and relationship breakdown can result from role changes, anger, prejudice, ignorance, and fear of infection and discrimination (Miller, 1987). Any or all of these issues can also compromise medical treatment.

Practical Approaches

A counselling session at a clinic or doctor's office before an HIV test might be the first contact an individual has had with the health care system. Although this provides a good opportunity for the client to begin to access medical care, it should not be the first opportunity to hear about HIV. Counsellors in treatment programs should introduce this issue into their programming. In particular, counsellors should ask about needle use, needle sharing and whether the client has a sexual partner who uses needles. Many clients may not be aware of the issues and the risks of transmission. Others may either think their concerns are irrelevant or may experience embarrassment. The personal inquiry and weight given by the counsellor to HIV issues may raise the level of a client's awareness, which may have been compromised by denial or dulled by substance use. Intake sessions can include assessment of the client's risk factors for HIV, his or her concerns and desire to be tested. Other important areas to assess are the client's suicide risk, support systems, levels of anxiety and depression, and motivations and barriers to behavioral change. This information will allow the counsellor to provide services and referrals that are relevant and accessible to the client. The client may need referrals to medical facilities and community agencies specializing in HIV/AIDS, finances or housing. Clients and families living with, or at risk for, HIV can then have independent access to health-status monitoring and other services. Certainly, many clients will be aware of their HIV status and other related issues. These clients require a different level of support and information. They may be dealing with issues of living with HIV, death and dying, family issues and so on. Their sex and needle-sharing partners may also have similar issues, especially if an HIV-positive partner continues with high-risk behaviors.

Flexibility in substance abuse treatment plans and programming — to include, for example, self-esteem issues and HIV/AIDS-related topics for all participants — can increase behavior change for both clients and staff. Provision of HIV-related services and referrals, and a commitment to co-ordinated, co-operative care with other health care providers and agencies, can enhance all clients' level of well-being. Providing access to HIV-related support groups can help clients learn positive coping strategies and new information, and expand support systems to other agencies as well as affected and infected individuals.

Care must be taken, however, when referring clients to community HIV/AIDS support groups. These groups are often perceived as "gay" or too radical, or may not be sensitive to substance use issues. Clients often will not attend such groups. (See Chapter 16 for a discussion of homophobia.) Client education about, and actual contact with, such groups and their umbrella agencies often reduces their objections.

Some communities can support separate groups for substance users. Lastly, referrals and linkage with community agencies, family doctors and hospital-based clinics can decrease uncertainty and increase the client's and family's ability to cope (Hilton, 1992). Again, care must be taken to refer clients to services that are receptive to substance users. Improved support networks can be a major breakthrough toward improved health and self-care for substance users who are marginalized and disenfranchised. This may be especially important for specific client groups, such as HIV-positive clients who continue to use drugs or alcohol, or who are women and/or members of cultural and ethnic minorities. Individuals in these groups may be at increased risk for health care problems due to the substance use itself, minimal access to information, culturally insensitive programming, financial issues that affect purchasing medication, transportation and child care, lack of medical and social research, and lack of emphasis on non-gay subjects. For example, society often considers women at low risk for HIV infection. This can lead to continued risk behavior, decreased access to HIV testing and health care, and insensitive HIV counselling. Society also reinforces women's lack of power in relationship with their male partners and in women's traditional roles. The result may be women placing their own well-being at the bottom of their list of priorities, and therefore not having the financial and emotional resources to look after themselves.

HIV Concerns and the Counsellor

So, what is a counsellor to do? First and foremost, we must increase awareness of our personal attitudes regarding HIV/AIDS, such as homophobia, pity and denial. We must take responsibility to increase our knowledge base and begin to change our own behavior patterns. Personal awareness and professional knowledge about HIV can complement our counselling skills and knowledge of substance use and addictions.

Many feelings are generated when staff face HIV issues. These feelings can either help or hinder the provision of improved services and treatment. An agency that institutionally faces issues such as homophobia, AIDS phobia, and fears of transmission and death sets an example to all its staff, clients and the community. This can be a painful and difficult process, but the payoff is enormous. Crises can be prevented or minimized, staff and clients can more freely voice their own fears and concerns, and adequate information and referral sources are more likely to be in place before they are needed. Staff tension and anxiety can be addressed more openly, and staff can work more efficiently.

Staff in residential treatment settings are often concerned about confidentiality, infection control, hygiene and condom distribution. These issues are best addressed, and policies about these issues should be written and activated, prior to the admission of a known HIV-positive client. Unfortunately, most programs will not have to wait long until that day comes, so the development of such policies should not be postponed. Addressing these issues is best done in consultation with other treatment centres, local health units, doctors and social workers in HIV clinics and agencies, and ethicists. Nonjudgmental processing groups and information sessions ensure that all staff have an opportunity to voice their concerns and fears, and to receive accurate information. It helps to involve staff when developing policies, procedures and operational systems.

Needle Exchange Programs

Contact with a needle exchange program not only helps reduce the risk of HIV infection, it may be a client's first or only interaction with a skilled adviser. Needle exchange workers also provide information regarding HIV testing and education, referrals to treatment programs and health care agencies and access to latex products. The impact of such programs has been enormous, despite public outcry that they encourage and increase drug use. Drug use and high-risk behavior have decreased in areas with these programs, resulting in reduced rates of HIV infection and, overall, improved health status.

Prison Issues

Within correctional services, efforts to slow the spread of HIV infection lag far behind those in the non-incarcerated community. HIV infection not only affects other inmates, but increases the level of risk in the wider community. In Canadian federal institutions, condoms are now available. However, inmates do not have access to clean needles, and adequate education programs and specialized HIV health care may be hard to deliver. Since at least 70 per cent of all inmates with Correctional Services Canada are identified as substance users, all services discussed in this chapter should be available to the prison population. Peer education and support groups, already in place in some federal institutions in Ontario, provide a valuable resource for inmates whose traditional distrust of institutional initiatives makes them avoid normal channels of counselling. These peer groups should become a model and provide the impetus for improvements in HIV health care throughout all federal institutions, so that AIDS can be regarded as a health issue rather than a security problem.

CONCLUSION

It is worthwhile to include some of the recommendations from the report of the Advisory Committee on Drug Treatment to the Minister Responsible for the Ontario Provincial Anti-drug Strategy, entitled *Treating Alcohol and Drug Problems in Ontario: A Vision for the 90s.*

1. Treatment programs should develop a comprehensive HIV/AIDS program within their service, which considers the following key elements (depending on the population being served):

    (a) information

    (b) counselling regarding safer sex and safer drug use

    (c) condom distribution

    (d) sterile water and bleach kit distribution

    (e) needle and syringe exchange.

2. Programs should review their admission criteria and make any necessary revisions to ensure that individuals who are HIV-positive have equitable access to treatment.

3. Programs should emphasize behavior change that reduces the risk of HIV infection, even when it is not accompanied by desirable reductions in drug use.

REFERENCES

Des Jarlais, D.C., Friedman, S.R., Choopanya, K., Vanichseni, S., and Ward, T.P. (1992). International epidemiology of HIV and AIDS among injecting drug users. *AIDS* 6 (10): 1053–1068.

Drucker, E. (1991). Drug users with AIDS in the City of New York: A study of dependent children, housing and drug addiction treatment. In *The AIDS Reader: Social, Political and Ethical issues*, ed. McKenzie, N. New York: Meridian.

Ford, P.M., and Ford, S.E. (1995). AIDS and women. *Journal of the Society of Obstetrics and Gynecology* 17: 1229–1235.

Hilton, A. (1992). Perceptions of uncertainty: Its relevance to life-threatening and chronic illness. *Critical Care Nurse* 12: 7–73.

Marks, R., and Goldblum, P. (1990). The decision to test: A personal choice. In *Face to Face: A Guide to AIDS Counselling*. Berkeley AIDS Health Project. San Francisco: University of California.

Martin, G.W., et al. (1990). *Treating Alcohol and Drug Problems in Ontario: A Vision for the 90's*. A Report of the Advisory Committee on Drug Treatment. Toronto: Provincial Anti-drug Secretariat.

Meridith, L. (1996). *Establishing Links: Violence Against Women and Substance Abuse*. London, ON: Centre for Research on Violence Against Women and Children.

Miller, D. (1987). The ABC of AIDS. In *Counselling*, ed. Adler, M. London: British Medical Journal.

North, R.L., and Rothenberg, K.H. (1994). Partner notification and the threat of domestic violence against women with HIV infection. *New England Journal of Medicine* 329: 1194–1196.

Weitz, R. (1989). Uncertainty in the face of AIDS. *Journal of Health and Social Behaviour* 30: 270–281.

GENERAL REFERENCES

Adler, M. (ed.). (1987). *The ABCs of AIDS*. London: British Medical Journal.

Dilley, J., Pies, C., and Helquest, M. (1990). *Face to Face: A Guide to AIDS Counselling*. San Francisco: University of California, Berkeley AIDS Health Project.

King, A., Beazle, R.P., Warren, W.K., Hankins, C.A., Robertson, A.S., and Radford, J.L. (1987). *Canada Youth and AIDS Study*. Kingston, ON: Queen's University.

McKenzie, N.F. (ed.). (1991). *The AIDS Reader: Social, Political and Ethical Issues*. New York: Meridian.

Miller, R., and Bor, R. (1991). *AIDS: A Guide to Clinical Counselling,* with contributions by ed. Lee, C.A., and contributions by Dilly, J.W. Philadelphia and London: Science Press Ltd.

Ostrow, D. (ed.). (1990). *Behavioral Aspects of AIDS*. New York: Plenum Medical Company.

Chapter 28

Working with Probation and Parole Clients

CATE SUTHERLAND AND LYNN O. LIGHTFOOT

This chapter addresses the assessment and treatment issues that clients from the criminal justice system present to addictions agencies. Similarities and differences in clinical approaches are described. Practical suggestions are provided on how to establish an effective liaison with correctional agencies and a constructive counselling relationship with the client.

Addiction services are seeing increasing numbers of mandatory clients referred by probation and parole offices and the courts. This is not surprising, given that it has been consistently demonstrated in the literature that substance use is highly related to the commission of crime, particularly violent crime.

Conduct Disorder in children and Personality Disorder, particularly Antisocial Personality Disorder, predispose persons to the development of substance abuse problems. Surveys indicate that the majority of incarcerated offenders (80 per cent) had used alcohol or other drugs on the day that they committed the offence for which they were serving time (Lightfoot and Hodgins, 1988; Hodgins and Lightfoot, 1989). Using DSM-III-R criteria, a national survey of a large sample of Canadian offenders found that lifetime prevalence rates for alcohol abuse/dependence was 70 per cent, and 53 per cent for psychoactive substance dependence (CSC, 1991). More than one-third of the sample were dual diagnosis offenders — that is, they met the criteria for Antisocial Personality Disorder *and* had an alcohol or drug problem.

It is important to note that substance abuse problems among offenders are diverse, just as they are in non-offender populations (Hodgins and Lightfoot, 1988). Weekes et al. (1993) found that 32 per cent of incarcerated offenders had a low level of substance abuse, 16 per cent a moderate level, 14 per cent a substantial problem, and six per cent a severe problem. Those with moderate to severe problems were more likely to have used a psychoactive substance on the day of the offence. They were also more likely to have used substances during most of their previous crimes. Offences involving assaults or injuries were most common for moderately dependent alcohol abusers (Millson, Robinson, Porporino and Weekes, 1993).

Although fewer women are involved in the criminal justice system, when they are, they have a high likelihood of having some level of drug-related problems. A survey of federally incarcerated women (Lightfoot and Lambert, 1991) found that 65 per cent had some level of drug-related problem; 11.1 per cent had a low level of problem; 18.7 per cent, moderate; 21.3 per cent, substantial; and 13.6 per cent, severe. Women were, however, less likely than men to report symptoms of alcohol dependence.

This increase in mandatory correctional clients causes understandable concern for some workers in the addiction field. There is a commonly held belief that correctional clients are, in general, unmotivated, and that management of such clients is more difficult. In reality, this is not necessarily so.

The purpose of this chapter is to provide information that will increase your understanding of the correctional client and correctional systems; dispel the myth that it is difficult to deal with correctional clients; show that the management of these clients is only slightly different from that of non-correctional clients, and outline techniques that you may find helpful in dealing with probationers or parolees and their referring agents.

The terms "probationer," "parolee" and "correctional client" are used interchangeably, as there are no significant differences in the approaches to assessment and treatment among them.

In recent years, there has been increased emphasis in the courts on alternative sentencing options that include rehabilitative conditions. As part of the sentence following a criminal conviction, a judge may order that the person accept help for a particular problem. The type of mandated help the person must accept is specified by a condition in a probation supervision order, to which the person has agreed to abide. The problem areas might include, for example, emotional health concerns or financial difficulties. The most common area of concern, however, is a person's alcohol and/or drug use. Much of a court's docket on any given day is comprised of alcohol/drug-specific offences or other offences that were committed while a person was under the influence of a substance. It is not unusual for such offenders to receive a probation order containing a condition specifying that they must attend addictions treatment. The expectation is that such treatment will be provided by a community agency.

Offenders who are convicted of an offence and incarcerated in a provincial or federal correctional facility are usually required to participate in both institutional programs during incarceration and community substance abuse treatment programs following their release. Substance abuse is seen as a key factor in the commission of crimes for many offenders, and correctional treatment plans and parole conditions will frequently require that the offender participate in substance abuse treatment and aftercare programs throughout the duration of their warrant.

Traditionally, addiction agencies have only worked with clients who voluntarily seek assistance, and this influx of involuntary clients is disconcerting to some agencies. One of the problems may lie with an inherent belief in the addictions field — the belief that you cannot help a person who does not want to be helped. The dreaded unmotivated client is often perceived as unco-operative and unlikely to benefit from compulsory intervention. This can be true in some cases — a few clients may choose to be unco-operative or close-minded and gain nothing from their involvement with your agency. But, remember this important fact: motivation is not a static attribute of an individual; rather, it is a process. It is possible for a person to begin that process at your agency.

Further, we need to examine our definitions of voluntary and involuntary. *Webster's Dictionary* states that "voluntary" implies "freedom and spontaneity of choice or action without external compulsion." By this definition, how many of our clients are truly voluntary? By far, most clients who present at an addictions agency are propelled by external pressure — they have lost their jobs or families, suffered serious health problems, or are in legal or financial trouble. The external compulsion of court-ordered clients is just more obvious than for other clients, and they may display some initial resistance. Still, with the right attitude and a little innovation, an addiction worker can create an environment in which a probationer is more likely to benefit from involvement with the agency. As a bonus, the addiction worker may find that working with mandatory clients can be challenging and satisfying.

It is also important to note that the available research indicates that involuntary clients do as well as voluntary clients, and secondly, offenders who are treated have lower recidivism rates than do untreated offenders (Fagen and Fagen, 1982; New York State Governor's Task Force on Alcoholism Treatment in Criminal Justice, 1986; Weekes, Millson and Lightfoot, 1995).

First and foremost, a co-operative relationship must be established between your agency and the local correctional agency. While the courts order people to attend, referrals are generally handled by the probation office or, more specifically, by a probation officer (P.O.). It is crucial that you meet with probation office staff to clarify respective roles and expectations. This will make your job much easier in the long run and help prevent misunderstandings.

In Ontario, the Ministry of Correctional Services divides the province into different regions, and those regions into different areas, each headed by an area manager. The federal correctional system is organized in a similar manner. Your first contact should be with that person. In some cases, the area manager will designate a P.O. to work out the details of the working relationship, but usually you will work directly with the area manager. Be very specific in your discussions, and put your agreements and the results of your discussions in writing. Following are suggested topics that should be covered. In most cases, some advice is also offered.

• Who will make the actual referral, the P.O. or the client? We recommend that you arrange for the P.O. to make the referral and schedule the initial appointment. This arrangement helps reinforce for the client that it is the P.O. — by way of the probation order or stipulations of parole — who requires the client's attendance. This helps the addiction worker maintain a neutral position. Another point is that these matters sometimes end up back in court, or the client may have his or her parole suspended and be returned to custody, if he or she unwisely chooses to not attend and is charged with failing to comply with a probation order or parole conditions. The evidence is clearer when the appointment times are given to the client in person by the P.O.

• Inform probation/parole staff of the type of information that your agency needs upon referral. It would be helpful to provide copies of your intake/referral form.

• Specify the types of services that your agency will provide.

• What type and how much information will be relayed back to the P.O.? Keep in mind that appropriate consent forms must be signed, and that the client may allow only certain information to be released. There is a rather grey area regarding the exchange of information when your agency is under contract to the Ministry of Correctional Services. In such an instance, your agency staff could also be technically considered employees of the Ministry of Correctional Services and, as such, can exchange information with other employees of the Ministry without the written consent of the client. Still, this is open to interpretation and you are best advised to discuss the matter with your agency's legal counsel and the legal branch of the Ministry of Correctional Services.

• Will the information be conveyed verbally or in written form? A hint — if you insist that most information be given verbally, you will save yourself and the agency a lot of work. Accurate note-taking of each conversation on the part of both the worker and the P.O. is, of course, crucial. Written reports may then only be necessary when the information is to be presented to the court. If the probation office insists that all communication be written, then compromise with form letters. For example, a form letter from an assessment/referral centre might read:
    "Mr. _____ was seen on this date for a structured addiction assessment.
    The assessment indicates the presence of....
    The following treatment plan was negotiated...."

• Who reschedules missed appointments? Again, you can save yourself some work by maintaining that it is the P.O.'s responsibility to ensure that clients are aware of and attend appointments. If an appointment is missed, simply advise the P.O. by telephone — it is up to the P.O. to contact the client and make the necessary arrangements to reschedule the appointment. It is helpful to keep in mind that it is the P.O.'s job, not yours, to enforce any existing treatment conditions of the probation order. This will also help preserve your counselling relationship with the client.

• Insist that the P.O. take full responsibility for explaining to the client the reason for and the purpose of the referral to the addiction agency. Also, ask that the P.O. briefly tell the client what to expect when he or she arrives at your office. Hopefully, this will prevent people from showing up at your office for appointments without knowing fully why they are there or what is going to happen.

• Request detailed information from the P.O. regarding the other terms and conditions of parole and, if possible, the criminal history as outlined in an FPS (an RCMP Finger Printing Sheet). Most federal parolees will have a condition to abstain from the use of alcohol and drugs. This condition will often be monitored via random urinalysis, and breaches of this condition can result in a suspension of the client's parole. For many federal parolees, a return to custody can result in revocation of their parole and lengthy periods of incarceration. Develop a clear understanding of your responsibility vis-à-vis reporting breaches of these conditions with the referring probation and parole offices. If a client discloses substance use to you, are you prepared to report this information to the parole officer?

Clients with a history of violent offences, sexual or driving offences committed under the influence of alcohol or other drugs may represent a significant risk to the community if they relapse. Parole officers will, therefore, be eager to be apprised of lapses so that they can accurately assess risk. This is an example of another situation where your agency should seek legal guidance and develop a clear policy, which can be shared with correctional officials. This policy should also address how you will handle situations where the client expresses homicidal thoughts or describes plans to commit illegal activities, which have a high likelihood of putting others at risk. Obviously, the Tarasoff decision (described in Chapter 5) needs to be carefully considered in the development of this policy. "A health care professional who learns of a client's plan to commit a serious crime may be held accountable for failing to warn or otherwise protect the intended victim" (Solomon and Usprich, 1993). Addiction workers should also be aware that, because of a number of sensational incidents involving parolees, a heavy emphasis on ongoing risk assessment has been instituted within provincial and federal correctional jurisdictions. Information that you collect as part of your ongoing assessment and treatment efforts will be important if correctional risk assessments are to be accurate.

This foregoing list contained a number of suggested topics, but it may not include everything your agency wishes to discuss. The subject of correctional clients is a good agenda item for an agency staff meeting. In all likelihood, your agency has already had some experience with probation referrals — look at what worked, what did not, what needs to be changed, and how you would like to see things handled. Input from all staff — treatment and support — will be useful.

Once you have met with the area manager (or designate) and have ironed out all the details of the working relationship, request that you be allowed to attend a staff meeting at the probation or parole office. Ensure that everyone understands the guidelines set at the previous meeting and explain the philosophy, policies, procedures and services of your agency. Ideally, one P.O. can be designated, through whom all referrals would flow, to act as a liaison between your office and the probation office. It is not unusual for probation offices to break caseloads down by primary area of concern anyway. For example, one P.O. may deal with community sentencing orders, one with emotional health, and one with substance use. The purpose of using a liaison person is to provide clear communication routes and to reduce the likelihood of inappropriate referrals. The probation staff meeting is also a good time to make arrangements for probation officers to visit your facility to further familiarize themselves with it.

THE CLIENT INTERVIEW

Most agencies (or workers) have an accustomed format they follow in client interviews. Regardless of how you typically begin your interviews, there are several matters that we recommend you take care of first with correctional clients. First, make sure that the client understands why he is at your agency. Ask directly: "Can you tell me why your probation officer arranged this interview?" Hopefully, you will get a relatively accurate response and can go on to the second matter. If not, carefully explain your understanding of the purpose of the interview. This will leave you with two options, depending on the client's attitude: 1) if the client is resistant, refer him or her back to the P.O., whose job is to provide a proper explanation and enforce the treatment condition; or 2) if the client is compliant, proceed.

Second, determine how the client feels about having to attend. Again, be blunt: "How do you feel about being required to attend here?" Do not settle for vague answers, such as "It's O.K." Take some time to find out how the client really feels — positive or negative. If you receive a negative reaction regarding the required attendance, simply acknowledge it, and perhaps empathize a little. For example, politely say: "Thank you for being honest with me. I can understand how someone might feel that way," then move on to your next item. This is a subtle but important point. From the beginning, it establishes that honesty during the interview is expected and will not be judged nor have any negative repercussions.

Third, declare your neutrality. Ensure that the client understands that it is not your agency requiring his attendance, and that you are not an extension of the legal system. Explain that your agency has a co-operative relationship with the probation office, but that the focus of your responsibility is to provide appropriate addiction services.

The next matter only needs discussing should you encounter negativity or resistance on the part of the client regarding his or her mandatory attendance. To make the interview (and future sessions) productive, you must nullify the initial resistance. Appeal to the client's adult and logical sensibilities. Acknowledge that his or her attendance is probably not completely voluntary, but point out the advantages of complying and the disadvantages of not doing so. Consider the following example:

> COUNSELLOR: I know it probably doesn't seem that you had a choice about whether to come here. But, you could have chosen not to comply with the treatment condition and to deal with the resulting legal charges. I realize that doesn't seem like much of a choice, but it's still a choice. The fact that you chose to attend tells me that you are able to make logical decisions that are in your best interest. Now you have another choice to make — you can just get through this and waste your time, or you can try and make the best of it. You may not consider your alcohol/drug use as a problem, but it was an issue in court and resulted in your referral here. It might help to look at this as an opportunity to examine your drinking/drug using patterns and behaviors. The advantage to you is that this will help you figure out ways to prevent future problems.

It is also recommended that, before you begin the assessment process, you deal with the issue of consent. With your client, carefully review a written consent form that clearly addresses the limits of confidentiality. Answer all questions clearly and honestly and, if the client is not prepared to sign the form, we recommend that you do not proceed. Rather, refer the client to his or her P.O. to discuss the options. This is an important step to help avoid future misunderstanding with your client that could undermine the therapeutic relationship.

Now, proceed with the interview. It will be surprising to some workers that, from this point on, the interview should be conducted exactly the same as it would for a referral from any other source. There are no tricks or special techniques needed to interview correctional clients. Typically, they are no more or less truthful, forthright or co-operative than any other client. One caution in working with correctional clients, however, is that a substantial number will have features of antisocial personality disorder. These individuals often make an extremely positive first impression. They may be charming and convincing in their claims that their referral is a misunderstanding. They may minimize their use of substances and their criminal history. They may attempt to gain your sympathy and to vilify the correctional staff with whom they are working. This form of manipulative splitting can be counter-therapeutic and requires diligence on the part of the addictions worker to keep the channels of communication open with the supervising P.O. Individuals with this kind of personality disorder are impulsive, have difficulty learning from past experience and often have deficits in empathy, which can result in unstable social relationships. They may also have a history of behavior and learning problems in childhood, which limited their educational achievement. Some will have multiple problems in a variety of life areas, which will present challenges in treatment.

On the other hand, some addictions workers consider it easier to work with correctional clients because, in a sense, a treatment plan has already been set by the court. For example, a typical probation condition might read: "Attend for, and be amenable to, alcohol counselling/treatment as directed by a Provincial Probation Officer." It's already decided that the person will attend something — the only thing left to decide is what. Obviously, the most logical approach is for the probationer to be assessed to determine which treatment services would be most appropriate. If your area does not have an assessment/referral centre, the person will be referred directly to a treatment facility. Regardless, the addictions worker's job is simplified — you decide which services are most appropriate, ask if the client is willing to attend, and make arrangements for the provision of those services. Remember, it is not your job to enforce the treatment condition. It is not up to you to convince the person that a problem exists or that he or she should participate in treatment.

Yet, it cannot be stressed enough that the worker's attitude sets the tone for the interview. Ideally, your goal is to create an environment in which the client can openly examine his or her attitudes and behaviors, start the process of motivation, and make personal, informed decisions about his or her alcohol/drug use. Fortunately, immediate emotional insight is not always necessary for ultimate therapeutic success. Sometimes simply exposing the client to a nonjudgmental, positive treatment situation can precipitate constructive changes. A long-standing AA member once used a cryptic analogy when asked to give his views on the benefits of mandatory attendance in treatment. He said: "If you throw mud at the wall, some of it is bound to stick." Following this analogy, it would seem that the job of the addictions worker is to prepare the wall in such a fashion that it is more receptive to the mud.

Additional Assessment Considerations

Although we have asserted that service delivery with correctional clients requires only minor adjustment in practice for addictions workers, there are a number of considerations to keep in mind. As noted earlier, correctional clients are more likely to have features of antisocial personality. A small percentage may be psychopathic. Research has shown that these latter individuals can be dangerous, but most referrals will not be at high risk for violent behavior. Addiction workers should, however, be aware that correctional clients are more likely to present with these characteristics and should educate themselves accordingly. In order to increase the validity and reliability of assessment, it is recommended that this be achieved through a process of "convergent validity" (Sobell and Sobell, 1980). This process involves the consideration of a variety of indicators, including the interview, supplemented where possible with reliable and valid standardized tests, as well as information from official reports and collateral informants.

Many correctional clients were victims of neglect and abuse in childhood and have spent many years in institutional settings. As a result, they may have deficits and needs in many areas. It has been widely recognized that substance abuse assessment should encompass a variety of life areas thought to be affected by substance abuse. This is particularly true for correctional clients, where problems in social relationships, employment, mental health and the legal system will be prevalent.

Goal Selection: Moderation or Abstinence

One of the most controversial areas in the substance abuse field in recent years has been the topic of goal selection (Miller, 1986; Sanchez-Craig and Lei, 1987; Rosenberg, 1993), primarily in the treatment of *alcohol* abuse/dependence but also in the treatment of other drug dependence disorders (Martin and Wilkinson, 1989). Traditionally, abstinence has been identified as the only feasible goal for substance abusers considered to have disorders that are progressive. Research, however, has demonstrated that, particularly for young single males, moderation goals are more likely to be complied with than are abstinence goals (Sanchez-Craig et al., 1984; Sanchez-Craig and Lei, 1987). Reduced drinking goals are usually defined as including some limit on the amount and frequency of consumption and as drinking that does not result in signs of physical dependence or social, legal or health problems (Heather and Tebbut, 1989).

As noted earlier, the parole board, before releasing an offender back into the community, often includes a condition of abstinence if substance abuse was identified as being linked to the client's offence cycle. Urinalysis is usually required to monitor compliance. Because of the limitations of urinalysis, particularly for detecting alcohol use, many offenders will engage in substance use upon release. In our experience, treatment goal selection with correctional clients requires careful analysis of the choice to use. A "decisional matrix," including a detailed list of the risks (CONS) and benefits (PROS) of use, may help your clients carefully analyse their choices to make the best decisions for them. Reframing a parole condition of abstinence in positive terms — (i.e., providing an opportunity to learn and practise new coping skills) rather than framing it as an intrusive form of control — and encouragement to strive for abstinence, at least until warrant expiry, are effective strategies for some correctional clients.

Developing Collaborative Relationships

Many problems incurred by addiction agencies when dealing with correctional clients are due to the lack of communication between them and the referring agent. Preparatory work must be done. Roles and expectations must be clearly defined. Other problems may be more the result of the addiction workers' attitudes than the clients' attitudes. We tend to categorize and make assumptions about clients, based on the referral source. We assume that the manner in which a client comes to us will dictate the level of motivation and success. This is fundamentally wrong. Each client presents at an addiction agency with his or her own agenda, expectations and needs.

Addictions workers also have expectations when a client enters treatment. The situation involves attempting to determine whether the expectations are unrealistic or inaccurate, while attempting to meet the needs. Occasionally, you can only expect that the client will attend as requested, be honest, and participate, or at least not be disruptive.

Correctional clients sometimes present with the expectation that counselling or treatment will be boring and will not apply to them. But they still need to satisfy the treatment condition. In such cases, you may not be able to convince the client that his or her expectations could be more positive, but you can fulfil the immediate need by providing addiction services. It is quite possible to effect a secondary result, such as positive attitude change or increased awareness, from fulfilling the client's primary need to satisfy the probation condition. Ideally, correctional clients may come to the realization that the legal difficulty that they are experiencing is related, at least in part, to their use of substances. Often they will be of the view that they are not an alcoholic or drug addict and, therefore, don't require any kind of intervention from an addictions agency. But you could advise such clients that even occasional overuse or misuse of substances can increase the risk of making a poor choice that puts them or others at risk (e.g., drinking and driving). Their awareness of this fact may provide some motivation for behavioral change.

CONCLUSION

In summary, effective management of correctional clients entails three factors: shedding preconceptions about such clients; the development of a satisfactory relationship with the players in the correctional system; and a slight alteration to the orientation of the client. The numbers of correctional clients being referred to addiction agencies will undoubtedly increase with the ongoing trend of openness and awareness about alcohol and drug use.

It will be productive for workers in the addictions field to look at this situation as an opportunity, and a challenge, to provide services to a group of people who, in many cases, would not have taken the initiative to seek help. The old adage that you can't help a person who does not want help may still be true. But it is also true that, with some planning and innovation, you can create a situation that will make it easier for a person to realize that help may be needed.

REFERENCES

Correctional Service of Canada. (1991). *Task Force on the Reduction of Substance Abuse*. Ottawa: Author.

Fagan, R., and Fagan, N. (1982). The impact of legal coercion in the treatment of alcoholism. *Journal of Drug Issues* 12: 103–114.

Heather, N., and Tebbut, J. (1989). *The Effectiveness of Treatment of Alcohol and Drug Problems: An Overview*. Canberra: Australian Government Publishing Service.

Hodgins, D.C., and Lightfoot, L.O. (1988). Types of male alcohol and drug abusing incarcerated offenders. *British Journal of Addiction* 83: 1201–1213.

Hodgins, D.C., and Lightfoot, L.O. (1989). The use of the alcohol dependence scale with incarcerated male offenders. *International Journal of Offender Therapy and Comparative Criminology* 33: 59–67.

Lightfoot, L.O. (1995) Assessment and treatment of substance abuse in offenders: Practice guidelines for correctional psychologists. In *Forensic Psychology: Policy and Practices in Corrections,* eds. Leis, T., Motuuk, L., and Ogloff, J. September, 1995.

Lightfoot, L.O., and Lambert, L. (1991). *Substance Abuse Treatment Needs of Federally Sentenced Women. Technical Reports No. 1 and No. 2*. Kingston, ON: Correctional Service of Canada.

Martin, G.W., and Wilkinson, A.D. (1989). Methodological issues in the evaluation of treatment of drug dependence. *Addictive Behaviour Research Therapy* 11: 133–150.

Miller, W.R. (1986). Haunted by the Zeitgeist: Reflections on contrasting treatment goals in Europe and the United States. In *Alcohol and Culture: Comparative Perspectives from Europe and America,* ed. Babor, T.S. New York: Annals of the New York Academy of Sciences.

Millson, W.A., Robinson, D., Porporino, F.J., and Weekes, J.R. (1993). Substance abuse severity and criminal behaviour. Paper presented at the Annual Convention of Canadian Psychological Association. Montreal.

New York State Governor's Task Force on Alcoholism Treatment in Criminal Justice. (1986). *Alcoholism Treatment in Criminal Justice: Task Force Report to the Governor*. Albany: New York State.

Rosenberg, H. (1993). Prediction of controlled drinking by alcoholics and problem drinkers. *Psychology Bulletin* 113 (1): 109–139.

Sanchez-Craig, M., Annis, J.M., Bornet, A.R., and MacDonald, K.R. (1984). Random assignment to abstinence and controlled drinking: Evaluation of a cognitive-behavioural program for problem drinkers. *Journal of Consulting and Clinical Psychology* 52: 390–403.

Sanchez-Craig, M., and Lei, H. (1987). Disadvantages to imposing the goal of abstinence on problem drinkers: An empirical study. *British Journal of Addiction* 81: 505–512.

Solomon, R., and Usprich, S. (1993). An introduction to health care law for addiction professionals. In *Alcohol and Drug Problems: A Practical Guide for Counsellors,* eds. Howard, B.A., Harrison, S., Carver, V., and Lightfoot, L. Toronto: Addiction Research Foundation.

Sobell, L.C., and Sobell, M.B. (1980). Convergent validity: An approach to increasing confidence in treatment outcome conclusions. In *Evaluating Alcohol and Drug Treatment Effectiveness,* eds. Sobell, L.C., and Ward, E. New York: Pergamon.

Weekes, J.R., et al. (1993). Assessment of substance abuse in offenders: The computerized lifestyle assessment instrument. Paper presented at the Annual Convention of the Canadian Psychological Association. Montreal.

Weekes, J.R., Millson, W.A., and Lightfoot, L.O. (September 1995). Factors influencing the outcome of offender substance abuse treatment. *Forum* 7 (3).

Weekes, J.R., Millson, W.A., Porporino, F.J., and Robinson, D. (In press). Substance abuse treatment for offenders: The Pre-release Program. *Corrections Today.*

Chapter 29

Helping Cocaine and Heroin Users

WAYNE SKINNER AND JULIA DRAKE

INTRODUCTION

Among the myriad "street drugs" available, cocaine and heroin are perhaps the most notorious. Although these drugs have very different effects — cocaine stimulates the central nervous system, while heroin, an opiate, depresses it — they have some common features.

First, both can be highly addictive, although the likelihood of dependence is influenced by the mode of administration and many other factors. Furthermore, since both drugs are illegal in North America, their purity is difficult to control. As a result, both drugs have been associated with overdoses — even first-time users are at risk of serious and potentially fatal consequences.

The "forbidden fruit" aspect of these drugs may, however, be part of their allure. Clearly, both drugs have a mystique surrounding them. They are among the most sensationalized drugs cited in news media reports, partly because of their use by some high-profile entertainers. Songs celebrate these drugs and the rituals involved in taking them. Many popular movies and books also extol the benefits, as well as the risks, of taking cocaine or heroin.

In recent decades, the many celebrities attracted to these drugs have included rock diva Janis Joplin and punk rocker Sid Vicious, who both died in the 1970s from heroin overdoses. A lethal "speedball" injection, blending heroin and cocaine, killed comedian John Belushi. In 1993, the death of 23-year-old actor River Phoenix was linked with his use of heroin, cocaine, alcohol and a prescription tranquillizer. Despite the much-publicized risks of using cocaine or heroin, the pendulum of popularity for both drugs has swung back and forth over the past century.

While cocaine and especially heroin have reappeared in the media spotlight in recent years, the percentage of people who use these drugs is currently quite low. For example, a 1994 Canada-wide study found that 3.8 per cent of adults aged 15 or older reported *ever* using cocaine (CCSA and ARF, 1997). An even smaller percentage of people use heroin: the same study reported a combined figure for any lifetime use of heroin, LSD or speed (5.9 per cent). Worth noting, however, is that the use of prescription opiates is relatively high: 13.1 per cent of adults had used codeine or Demerol in the year before they were surveyed.

In a recent study of drug use in Ontario, 5.7 per cent of adults reported some lifetime use of cocaine, and 0.7 per cent reported some lifetime use of crack, a smokable form of cocaine (Adlaf, Ivis and Smart, 1994). While some studies show a recent increase in heroin use, 0.7 per cent of Ontarians reported, in 1994, that they had *ever* used the drug.

In Canada, illicit drug use tends to be highest among people who have low income levels, who are not working full time (this includes students), and who are living in larger urban centres (CCSA and ARF, 1995). Males are about twice as likely as females to report using cocaine (Erickson et al., 1994) and, generally, there are more men than women in treatment for cocaine or heroin problems.

Although the percentages of people who use cocaine or heroin are fairly low, the problems related to use are significant. A notable similarity between cocaine and heroin is that their impact — on users and on society — is enormous. These drugs can lead to serious problems with relationships, employment and, since cocaine and heroin are illicit drugs, with the law.

Cocaine and heroin can also have a major impact on the long-term health of users. For example, some studies show that opiate users are at particularly high risk for mortality — as high as 60 to 70 times greater than the general population (Ontario Substance Abuse Bureau, 1996).

In British Columbia, for example, illicit drug use had become the leading cause of death in 1993 for both men and women aged 30 to 44 (Task Force into Illicit Narcotic Overdose Deaths in British Columbia, 1994). For women, drug-related deaths exceeded deaths from breast cancer or motor vehicle crashes, and for men they exceeded deaths from acquired immune deficiency syndrome (AIDS) or suicide, the next highest causes of death reported in the study. Most drug-related deaths in the province involved heroin, used either alone or in combination with alcohol and/or other drugs. Cocaine was involved in about one-third of the drug deaths.

One deadly element that these drugs have in common is that they can be injected, a practice that is linked to the spread of bloodborne infections. Injection drug users who share needles, syringes or other equipment used for injection are at risk of acquiring viral hepatitis or the human immunodeficiency virus (HIV). According to recent statistics compiled by Canada's Laboratory Centre for Disease Control (1996), at least 20 per cent of injection drug users in Montreal and Vancouver are HIV-positive. The figures for Toronto, Ottawa and Quebec City range from eight to 10 per cent.

Workers in the field report that the transmission of HIV among intravenous needle users appears to be increasing, accounting for 20 to 40 per cent of new cases of infection in, for example, some Ontario cities. Also at increased risk of being infected with HIV and of developing AIDS are the sexual partners of, and the infants born to, injection drug users.

HIV and AIDS have underscored the fact that there are some things that can be more hazardous than drug use itself. In an age of HIV, while it is important to prevent and treat substance abuse problems, it is crucial to reduce the harmful consequences of drug use.

This chapter examines problems related to the use of cocaine and opiates, particularly heroin. It also describes some of the factors that counsellors should consider when working with clients who are dependent on these powerful drugs.

COCAINE

Cocaine, derived from the leaves of the coca plant, is a central nervous system stimulant. The drug is usually inhaled, smoked or injected.

Cocaine that comes in a white crystalline powder is usually inhaled, or "snorted," into the nostrils. The powder can also be rubbed onto the mucous lining of the mouth, rectum or vagina. In a process called "free-basing," the drug can be chemically altered into a pure form of cocaine that is smoked. "Crack," which is smoked, is a crude form of free-base cocaine.

People who inject or smoke cocaine get a faster, more intense "high" than they would by inhaling the drug. Injection may also quicken the development of physical dependence.

Cocaine has been used recreationally for its euphoric and energizing effects since the late 19th century, but it was introduced to the western world in the mid-19th century as a tonic in patent medicines and later as a local anesthetic in some surgery.

Legislation passed in 1908 and 1911 restricted cocaine's use in Canada, and the drug's popularity waned. But, beginning in the late 1960s, recreational use of cocaine seemed to increase in North America. In the 1970s and 1980s, cocaine was dubbed a "yuppie drug," because it was used by a fairly affluent group. Users have called cocaine the "caviar" and the "champagne" of drugs (Erickson et al., 1994), partly because of the drug's one-time exclusivity and partly because of its pleasurable effects. As its price fell, cocaine spread to other socioeconomic groups. By the 1980s, crack prices dropped far below earlier prices for powder cocaine, and concern about an "epidemic" of crack developed in the United States. Canada's crack problem (and the nation's cocaine problem) has not, however, mirrored that reported south of the border (Erickson et al., 1994).

In *The Steel Drug,* Erickson et al. (1994) reported that, in Canada, most people who try cocaine, including crack, do not end up needing treatment. "For many, the romance with cocaine is short lived and easily swept aside; for others, there is a more persistent involvement that is not easily discarded" (p. 215). This chapter focuses on people who find themselves in the second category.

A cocaine "high" is usually characterized by a sense of extreme pleasure, or euphoria, and typically lasts less than half an hour. In the short term, cocaine usually makes users feel more mentally alert and talkative. Many users report increased self-confidence, and sometimes aggression, although some find that the drug makes them anxious and contemplative. Because cocaine is a stimulant, other short-term effects include loss of appetite, sleeplessness, and increased heart rate and blood pressure. All cocaine users, even young, healthy people, risk heart attacks, seizures, strokes, brain hemorrhages and ruptured aneurysms.

Problems associated with heavy, long-term cocaine use include agitation, memory problems, insomnia, loss of sex drive, panic, anxiety, headaches, weight loss and malnutrition, although any of these could also be symptoms of psychiatric problems. People who sniff cocaine over an extended period risk damage to their nasal tissue, while crack smokers risk respiratory problems.

Among heavy cocaine users, intense psychological dependence, including severe cravings, can occur. Cocaine use has also been linked with a wide variety of psychiatric symptoms, including delusions, paranoia, hallucinations, delirium and severe anxiety. Cocaine use and withdrawal can induce severe depression, and heavy users are at risk of suicide. Indeed, suicide is a leading cause of death among illicit drug users.

As a result of excessive cocaine use, many people have reported problems with finances, work and family. In addition, many cocaine users have turned to other drugs, such as alcohol, sleeping pills, tranquillizers and even heroin, to help overcome the "crash" that follows heavy use (Washton, 1989).

Furthermore, people who inject cocaine — or other drugs — are at risk for HIV and AIDS, hepatitis B and C, tuberculosis and other diseases.

(See Chapter 10 for more information on the physical effects of cocaine use.)

OPIATES

Opiates are drugs made from the opium poppy. They include prescribed or over-the-counter painkillers, such as morphine and codeine, and illegal drugs, of which heroin is the most infamous. Opioids are opiate-related synthetic drugs, such as meperidine and methadone, whose effects are similar to those of opiates. Various opiates can be administered by snorting, swallowing or injecting the drug, or by inserting the drug in the rectum.

Heroin is usually a white or brownish powder, which is dissolved in water and then injected. Injection is popular with people who abuse opiates, because the method results in the fastest and most intense "high."

Opiates have been used both medically and non-medically for centuries. In the mid- to late 19th century, when morphine was freely available and unregulated, approximately four per cent of the adult population of the United States used morphine regularly. As societal attitudes towards drug use (including alcohol use) changed around the turn of the century, increasing levels of national and international restrictions were introduced in an effort to control, or decrease, opiate use.

Heroin was introduced in 1898 to replace morphine as a treatment for dependence and as a more potent analgesic, but it was soon apparent that the "replacement" drug was even more likely to lead to dependence.

Opioids such as Dilaudid (hydromorphone) and Demerol (meperidine) were first developed as analgesics to replace natural opiates and, it was hoped, to prevent drug dependence. But both the natural opiates and opioid synthetics are now known to produce dependence.

Many opioids and natural opiates are still used clinically in North America. For example, morphine is used to relieve pain among the terminally ill and in post-operative care, and codeine is found in many cough suppressants. Canada is unusual among western nations in permitting the availability of codeine preparations without prescriptions.

Heroin use has been chronicled over the years, and lately there has been somewhat of a resurgence of use in North America. Celebrity deaths and struggles with heroin addiction (e.g., Kurt Cobain of the band Nirvana) are well publicized. The recent preponderance of gaunt, dark-eyed young models on fashion runways and in magazines has even been dubbed "heroin chic" in the media.

In the Toronto area, a recent study by the Metropolitan Toronto Addiction Treatment Services Committee (1995) found that heroin use, especially among young people, is increasing. Another Metropolitan Toronto-based study found that 45 of the city's drug-related deaths in 1995 and 67 in 1994 had positive findings for heroin (Research Group on Drug Use, 1997). In 1986, heroin was detected in only 12 of Metropolitan Toronto's drug-related deaths.

All heroin users are at serious risk of overdose. The purity of heroin sold on the street is highly unreliable and in recent years the purity has increased. As a central nervous system depressant, heroin impairs breathing, and the drug's unpredictable strength has led to overdoses.

In addition, injecting heroin intravenously puts users at risk for HIV/AIDS, hepatitis B and C, tuberculosis and other diseases.

Heroin's short-term effects include a "rush" of euphoria and tranquillity, often accompanied, in the first-time user, by nausea and vomiting. Heroin's pleasurable high can make users oblivious to their surroundings.

Regular users develop tolerance to the effects of heroin, so that they require more of the drug to achieve the same effect. Users also develop physical and psychological dependence.

Long-term effects include severe weight loss. Long-term use is also linked with serious social and economic problems. There is a high risk of criminal activity associated with heroin: the drug is expensive, highly addictive and, as such, has been connected with criminal activities such as theft and fraud, which are committed to provide the user with cash to buy drugs (NIDA, 1995).

(See Chapter 10 for more information on the physical effects of opiate use.)

TREATING CLIENTS WHO USE COCAINE OR HEROIN

The impact of cocaine and heroin on individuals can be enormous. The impact on the addictions treatment system is also significant. In North America, cocaine is the number one illegal drug for which people seek treatment; the second-ranked illegal drug is heroin.

At Ontario's Addiction Research Foundation (ARF), for example, about 20 per cent of people presenting for treatment cite cocaine as the primary drug that is causing them problems. About 11 per cent of ARF's clients sought treatment for narcotics, primarily heroin, in 1995. A study in Metropolitan Toronto in 1996 found the following drug treatment figures: 24 per cent of clients cited cocaine as their major drug problem, and 14.2 per cent sought treatment for their problems with narcotics, primarily heroin (Research Group on Drug Use, 1997).

Some large American cities see greater percentages of clients whose main problems are heroin or crack cocaine abuse. For example, a 1995 survey identified heroin as the main problem drug for 65 per cent of clients in treatment in Newark, New Jersey, and 61 per cent for those in Los Angeles (CEWG statistics cited by the Research Group on Drug Use, 1996).

To help *any* client with a drug problem, counsellors need to understand how a drug works and the motivating factors that lead a person to use the substance despite personal problems that develop. The assessment and treatment process should examine the quantity and frequency of drug use, and the method of administering the drug. Counsellors must also investigate and understand their clients' patterns of drug use and how drugs have affected life functioning areas, including relationships with peers and family, and employment. In addition, counsellors need to appreciate the physical and psychological processes that their clients are likely to encounter as they withdraw from a substance on which they are dependent.

As noted above, withdrawal from long-term cocaine use has been associated with depression — something clients may call the "cocaine blues" — and with suicide. Clinicians describe a three-phase withdrawal process: the "crash"; a middle stage called withdrawal; and "extinction." During the first phase, the crash, the client may sleep for a day or two after a cocaine binge. This is followed by one or more weeks of intense cocaine cravings, as well as depression, irritability, insomnia and nightmares. In the "extinction" phase, clients experience periodic cravings for cocaine that gradually diminish over a period of months. Cravings, however, can be evoked — months or years after the last drug-taking episode — by the sight of a pipe or syringe, or other "cues" or situations associated with prior cocaine use.

For regular users of opiates such as heroin, withdrawal may occur as early as a few hours after the last administration. Withdrawal often includes diarrhea, abdominal cramps, restlessness, uneasiness, sweating, muscle aches, runny nose and eyes, chills, nausea, and strong cravings for the drug. Physical withdrawal peaks at two to three days after the last drug use, and resolves within five to seven days.

While every client presents with unique problems that therapists in the substance abuse field must understand and address, cocaine- or heroin-dependent clients often pose some of the strongest challenges. This is, in part, because cocaine and heroin are rarely the substances that people use first. Consequently, many heroin and cocaine users have long histories of drug use, and they are often polydrug users. Clients who have problems with these drugs bring a host of related issues to treatment.

These are the most potent and addictive illegal drugs available in our society. Individuals who have been unable to stop using cocaine or heroin have usually come to the point where their drug use has had a destructive impact on their psychosocial functioning and, perhaps, on their physical health.

It is crucial to remember that individuals with cocaine or heroin dependencies have very high rates of co-occurring mental health problems (Gawin and Ellinwood, 1988; Mirin et al., 1988; Rounsaville et al., 1983). Depression is a common complaint, along with other mood disorders. Eating disorders, anxiety and panic, as well as anger management concerns are often reported by these clients. An effective care plan needs to be able to identify and include these other dimensions.

Female opiate addicts are likely to have experienced physically abusive relationships in childhood or adulthood (Marsh and Skinner, 1997), so counsellors must be sensitive to this issue in treatment. Both male and female clients may have been involved in the sex trade, and many injection drug users may be infected with blood-borne viruses such as hepatitis C or HIV. Even when intravenous drug use is not an issue, cocaine or heroin use (or, in fact, any drug use) might impair judgment about safe sex and other matters of personal health and safety.

Counsellors also need to recognize that a lifestyle of illicit drug use likely means that many cocaine- or heroin-using clients have been caught up in an environment where dishonesty and manipulation may have been the norm.

But, as with counselling for any substance abuse problems, therapists working with cocaine- or heroin-using clients should avoid negative expectancies — i.e., the attitude that "junkies can't change." These particular client groups have likely already encountered negative attitudes from family, friends, the police, and other health care professionals. It's important that substance abuse counsellors encourage and support these clients, for whom self-esteem issues may be crucial.

When treating clients for cocaine or heroin use, counsellors must have realistic expectations. Change is a process, and it usually occurs gradually over an extended period of time.

Abstinence from cocaine or opiates may be the most appropriate long-term goal for users of these drugs, but many people will reject treatment that requires abstinence. As such, harm reduction — to reduce drug-related harm for the users, their families, employers, as well as for society — is helpful.

Harm reduction is defined as the attempt to reduce serious risks to health in clients through strategies such as health education, immunization and screening. With the advent of HIV infection, harm reduction strategies should be viewed as an essential component of any alcohol and drug treatment program. These strategies complement prevention and treatment efforts, and they emerge out of the expectation that we can't prevent or treat all problems. Specific strategies, such as methadone maintenance programs for opiate-dependent clients and needle exchange programs for injection drug users, are described later in this chapter, under the heading "Harm Reduction."

When a cocaine or heroin user first meets with a substance abuse counsellor, there are acute care needs that can require an intensive response. The client might need help with detoxification. Social support — even for basic things such as housing and funds for subsistence — might be lacking. It is important for the helper to be attuned to and able to identify the needs of the client in care. These needs will change as the client moves from the phases of initial withdrawal and detoxification, to preliminary drug-free status and active change, and to a stage of building new patterns of living that include alternatives to drug use. Beyond that, the client has the persisting challenge of maintaining change over the long run. This is often the hardest part — even after the client has gone through the difficult process of relinquishing drug use.

In planning care, it is important to support the client toward treatment options that are appropriate for his or her level of need. There is evidence that cocaine and heroin users can do well in the full range of addiction services — from outpatient through day treatment, to short- and long-term residential care. Intensive interventions such as residential programs may be a counsellor's first choice for clients who are severely dependent, who are unhealthy, who have few "healthy" social supports, and whose lifestyle leaves them no opportunity for a break from drug use. But the client's readiness to engage in a particular type or level of care is a crucial variable to know and work with.

While the *intensity* of care that the client receives during the active treatment phase is important, a key point for counsellors to keep in mind is that they need to ensure that ongoing, external care and support are available for the client. The *extensity* of the care plan — ensuring the client has access to support over an extended span of time — is at least as important to the client's long-term success as whatever front-end plans are made.

The use of heroin and other opiates is especially known to isolate users. Counsellors should work with opiate users to identify and promote social support among family members and friends who are concerned and willing to play a supportive role. Some research shows that the involvement of even one family member or peer can improve treatment outcome with opiate users (Wermuth and Scheidt, 1986; Weidman, 1985). Likewise, strong social supports must be established for heavy, long-term users of cocaine.

The key to success in arranging social support is to find someone the client sees as a positive force in his or her life. Mutual support groups such as Narcotics Anonymous or Cocaine Anonymous can also have a positive impact on some clients. Some cocaine and opiate users have found help in Alcoholics Anonymous groups, particularly if no specialized CA or NA group exists in their communities. Mutual help groups, however, tend to be abstinence-oriented, and some clients are unwilling to accept abstinence as an immediate requirement (see Chapter 9 for more information on mutual aid groups).

In treatment, clinicians should strive to establish a therapeutic relationship of trust, honesty, openness and respect, but one with clear, consistent boundaries. Jerome Frank (1976) states that, in all forms of psychotherapy, counsellors should strive to inspire the client's hope; provide opportunities for both cognitive and experiential learning; enhance the client's sense of mastery by providing or stimulating success experiences; and encourage working through and applying what the client has learned in therapy to day-to-day living.

A variety of theoretical frameworks for counselling can be employed to help cocaine- or heroin-dependent clients (Marsh and Skinner, 1997). A few of these are summarized below:

Motivational Interviewing
The needs of people with severe cocaine or heroin dependence will vary from client to client and within the same client over time. Counsellors are in the position to assess each client's readiness for change by helping the client evaluate the advantages and disadvantages of both continuing drug use as well as stopping. By matching interventions to the client's readiness to address a particular problem, counsellors can help the client make important changes. (See Chapter 2 for more information about the stages of change and motivational interviewing.)

Cognitive and Behavioral Therapy
Cognitive therapy has much in common with motivational interviewing techniques (see Chapter 2). Both rely on an empathic, collaborative therapeutic relationship in which the therapist and client work together to find solutions, but with cognitive therapy, the theoretical framework is elaborated. Cognitive therapy relies on structured sessions, homework assignments, self-monitoring, guided discovery, analysis of the advantages and disadvantages of drug use, and other techniques to explore the client's cognitive system. The client and therapist examine and clarify the client's basic beliefs, automatic thoughts and facilitating beliefs that lead to drug use. This therapy involves helping the client replace existing thoughts and beliefs with patterns that do not lead to drug use and, over time, he or she will acquire the cognitive tools to maintain a change in behavior.

Behavior therapy techniques can be extremely helpful in treating drug use problems. Therapy can include techniques such as contracting and goal-setting. A widely used approach for clients in methadone programs for heroin addiction is contingency management, which relies on variations in methadone doses as positive and negative reinforcement for providing drug-free urine samples. In some programs, the methadone dose is decreased after a urine sample is found to contain drugs; in others, methadone therapy ceases if a certain number of positive urine samples is detected. There is a lack of evidence, however, that decreasing dosage is effective in promoting decreased drug use. At the Addiction Research Foundation's Opiate Clinic, in Toronto, dose reduction is not used as a negative reinforcement for drug use.

Instead, "carry privileges" (allowing clients to take home some doses of methadone) are designed to motivate clients.

Psychodynamic Therapy

This approach has been used with cocaine- and heroin-using clients. But some clients, particularly in the early stages of treatment for opiate dependence, may lack the ego strength to benefit from this form of therapy, which involves a relatively silent therapist who encourages the client to engage in free association. On the other hand, brief, time-limited, structured psychodynamic psychotherapies have been well studied and found to be effective for drug clients with more severe mental health problems (Woody et al., 1995).

Group vs. Individual Therapy

The above-noted therapeutic approaches can be applied in either group or individual treatment settings. Group therapy has its benefits, including a cost savings for treatment programs, but there are some cautions to consider. It may be difficult for some clients to be open and honest in groups, when their former experiences with fellow drug users, dealers or the legal system has taught them to be secretive. There is a high rate of more serious mental health problems among injection drug users. Although certain individuals, because of their psychiatric condition, may be unable to participate in group therapy, group sessions can be of great value to many clients. In each case, clinicians must be sensitive to the client's needs.

Family Therapy

Some researchers have found family therapy valuable in treating clients who abuse opiates or cocaine. For individuals with a history of illicit drug use who are raising children, family therapy may help prevent the development of drug problems in another generation. In the case of clients in methadone programs, family members are often misinformed or ignorant about opiate dependence and methadone maintenance. Family therapy can help them be more supportive and understanding of the needs of their drug-involved partner or relative.

HARM REDUCTION: A VIABLE RESPONSE

What you cannot turn to good, you must make as little bad as you can.
— Sir Thomas More
(year unknown)

The words of the famous British statesman and writer, Thomas More, help set the stage for a review of harm reduction measures. More's statement, recorded in the 16th century, proves that the obligation to reduce harm is a belief that had support hundreds of years ago. It has, however, taken a while to apply his sentiments, on any widespread basis, in the field of addictions.

Skip ahead to the 21st century and the age of AIDS. To reiterate an important point, HIV and AIDS have reminded society that there are some things that can be more hazardous than drug use. The World Health Organization has stated that the spread of HIV is a greater public threat than injection drug use itself.

In 1987, Canada's National Drug Strategy proposed wide-scale adoption of a harm reduction philosophy to drug use. From a public health perspective, harm reduction is a well-proven strategy. The use of condoms, for example, has reduced the spread of sexually transmitted diseases, even though most members of society continue to have concerns about sexual promiscuity. Condoms do not stop the behavior, but they reduce the harmful consequences. Likewise, telling people not to drive if they drink does not reduce intoxication, but it targets one of the most worrisome risks of alcohol use.

In the area of injection drug use, a similar harm reduction approach is a necessary complement to prevention and treatment initiatives — and not just because of HIV, which has a low prevalence rate in Canada. The rate of hepatitis in major Canadian cities such as Toronto, Vancouver and Montreal exceeds 80 per cent among injection drug users seeking treatment for their drug problems.

When drug users don't know the quality or nature of the substances they use, when they don't know how to use drugs in the safest way possible, and when they use dirty equipment — all too often the case with intravenous drug users — they put themselves and their intimate contacts at risk.

Counsellors generally share a desire to make the world a safer place — they want to alleviate problems caused by substance use. One way of achieving this goal is to prevent problems in the first place; another is to treat the problems that do develop. A third way — one we've come to rather slowly in the addictions field — is harm reduction. A comprehensive approach to health and social policies and practices on addiction involves all three areas.

Wide-ranging measures can reduce substance use-related harm in a variety of ways. With regard to people who use cocaine or heroin, particularly by injecting these drugs, there are several specific methods of reducing harm:
- sharing information
- educating drug users
- providing equipment (e.g., needle exchanges, bleach kits, condom distribution)
- providing "less harmful" substitute drugs (e.g., methadone maintenance therapy for heroin users).

Intravenous drug use can harm the individual, in the form of physical and mental health risks, including the risk of AIDS. Families and intimate partners of drug users are also at risk of financial and legal difficulties, and health problems, not the least of which is the risk of viruses such as HIV, which is spread through intimate contact with drug users.

Illicit drug use also entails a cost to society and the economy. For example, costs for law enforcement and health care are incurred because of drug use. Harm reduction measures offer economic benefits for society by reducing illicit activities related to drug use and by cutting health care costs by reducing the spread of disease.

The city of Amsterdam has an approach to harm reduction that is a modern-day reflection of Thomas More's attitude about the topic. In Amsterdam, the guiding principle is: "If a drug user is not capable or willing to give up their use, they should be assisted in reducing the harm caused to themselves or others." Amsterdam's multi-faceted approach is controversial: many consider it progressive and a model of harm reduction; others call the approach too permissive.

Critics of harm reduction believe that measures such as needle exchange programs are anti-abstinence, but this is not necessarily the case. Others may complain that harm reduction "enables" drug users to continue unhealthy or illegal habits. It is significant in this regard to note that all of the national and international legislation and regulations, the criminalization of use, and the focus in treatment on abstinence have failed to reduce the level of opiate use in society.

While a drug-free lifestyle may be the best choice for people who have serious drug-related problems, the fact is, many people will not accept a treatment goal of abstinence. For those who reject treatment that requires abstinence, harm reduction measures are necessary.

In addition, it is important to note that harm reduction may, on an individual basis, also lead to eventual abstinence. Change is a process, rather than a single step or action, and harm reduction efforts include education and information that can help people change their behavior. Measures such as needle exchange programs, methadone maintenance therapy and condom distribution programs include efforts to help clients change their problematic behavior.

Described below are two key harm reduction measures involved in a comprehensive approach to treating intravenous drug users: needle exchange programs and methadone maintenance programs.

Needle Exchange Programs

The main purpose of needle exchanges is to ensure that intravenous drug users are using only sterile needles, which helps control the spread of HIV/AIDS, hepatitis and other diseases. Needle exchange programs also help reduce the "lifetime" of a needle. These programs take dirty or damaged needles out of circulation. They may also provide bleach kits that drug users can use to sterilize their injection equipment when they are unable to access new equipment. Some programs also distribute condoms to reduce the spread of sexually transmitted diseases.

Some needle exchange programs operate out of vans, bringing their services to the areas frequented by their clients. Some operate at fixed sites, often sharing space or operating as a program within community health centres, public health units or addictions agencies.

Needle exchange workers don't just provide equipment; they share information about HIV/AIDS and safer drug use practices. They may also provide referrals to treatment and health care agencies.

One of the concerns that the public has about needle exchanges is that they put more needles into circulation, which presents a danger to the community. Generally, however, needle exchanges report that more needles are returned than are handed out.

According to several studies, needle exchanges have been linked with reduced HIV infection rates. Currently, the prevalence of HIV infection among injection drug users in Toronto is about eight per cent, a low rate that has been credited, in part, to the city's needle exchanges.

(See Chapter 27 for more information about HIV/AIDS and about the value of needle exchange programs.)

Methadone Maintenance Programs

Methadone is a synthetic drug that was developed in the 1940s as a substitute for morphine. Since the 1960s, methadone has been used to treat withdrawal symptoms and as a "maintenance medication" in individuals who are dependent on heroin or other opiates. Methadone has become the lead treatment response for opiate dependence.

Clients in methadone maintenance programs usually drink a methadone solution daily in the presence of a nurse or pharmacist. A single dose for a stabilized client lasts at least 24 hours. Methadone relieves cravings and withdrawal symptoms, but it does not cause sedation or euphoria. As a result, methadone enables clients to perform mental and physical tasks without impairment — in other words, it helps clients lead "normal" lives. In addition, sufficient doses of methadone can block the euphoric effects of self-administered opiates, which reduces the likelihood that people will continue to use substances that can cause problems for them.

Counselling is an important part of methadone programs. McLellan et al. (1993), for example, found that counselling helps increase the effectiveness of methadone maintenance. The various interventions used in treating methadone clients are described under the heading "Treating Clients Who Use Cocaine or Heroin."

Researchers have found that adequate doses of methadone, combined with supportive therapy, reduce illicit opiate use. Methadone treatment has also been found to reduce criminal activity, improve social health, productivity and physical health, and reduce HIV transmission (NIDA, 1995). It also lowers the pregnancy risk for pregnant women who are addicted to opiates (ARF, 1996).

In addition to its benefits for drug users and the people close to them, methadone maintenance has economic benefits for society. For example, America's National Institute on Drug Abuse (NIDA, 1995) estimated the following annual costs to maintain an opiate addict in New York in 1991: $43,000 (U.S.) for someone untreated and living on the street; $34,000 for someone in prison; $11,000 for someone in a residential drug-free program; and $2,400 for someone in methadone maintenance treatment. Several American studies have estimated the benefit-to-cost ratio for methadone programs as high as about four to one (NIDA, 1995).

Not all heroin-dependent individuals are interested in or appropriate for methadone treatment, but many drug users have been helped by this form of treatment.

In Canada, the authority to prescribe methadone is issued by the Bureau of Drug Surveillance of Health Canada, in consultation with the provincial bodies that license and regulate physicians. Recently, the federal government devolved responsibilities for regulating methadone treatment to provincial ministries of health and to colleges of physicians and surgeons. These groups are now responsible for issuing guidelines regarding limits on dosage and take-home medicine, counselling requirements, and special rules for pregnant women.

In the province of British Columbia, there are more than 1,600 methadone patients and more than 150 doctors licensed to prescribe methadone. In Ontario, however, demand for admission to a program currently exceeds the number of available spaces, despite a doubling of the availability of treatment spaces from April 1996 to April 1997. For people seeking treatment in some provinces, waiting lists for methadone maintenance programs can be long.

Waiting lists aren't the only barriers to methadone treatment. Many existing treatment programs in Canada have "high thresholds" for admission and continuance in treatment. Individuals must have abstinence goals and be willing to attend compulsory counselling and to provide supervised urine samples. If clients don't comply with these expectations, they will be discharged from such programs. While these requirements help highly motivated clients with abstinence goals achieve successful outcomes, there are others who are discharged or who do not even enter treatment because of the requirements they have to meet.

Ontario's Addiction Research Foundation has introduced a low-threshold methadone maintenance program, which is a more flexible, client-centred treatment model than some of the high-threshold programs. It offers elective rather than mandatory coun-selling and case management services; increases the number of take-away doses a client may be eligible to receive; and reduces the frequency of urine tests. Low-threshold programs will, it is hoped, be able to reach and help more people who are dependent on opiates.

SUMMARY

Drug use is about making contact — about connecting with people to find and buy drugs. HIV and all infectious diseases are about contact, since they can only occur when people have intimate contact with one another. Counselling services are also about contact — they're about people in the substance abuse field reaching out to drug users to make their lives, and the lives of people who drug users connect with, safer.

Among illegal drugs, cocaine and heroin are the most powerful and addictive sub-stances available, and clients who inject these drugs face some of the greatest risks of drug use. Because users may expose others to the risk of HIV/AIDS and other dis-eases, their drug use also has a major impact on society.

In the addictions field, we often refer to the "treatment continuum." When people are on the low end of the continuum, the goal is to prevent problems from developing. On the other end, the goal is to treat problems that have emerged. Since it might be hard to find a place for harm reduction in this kind of model, it might be useful to think about a new model — a circular model that has three key points on it: preven-tion, treatment and harm reduction. Working, effectively, at any point of the circle — prevention, treatment, harm reduction — helps make the world a safer place.

In a perfect world, there would be no problems with cocaine, heroin or other drugs. Some would argue that, in a perfect world, we wouldn't need drugs. But, in our imperfect world, health care professionals are charged with the task of addressing problems related to drug use, problems that range from the personal (such as physical symptoms of addiction) to the societal (such as the drug-related spread of AIDS).

In dealing with the high-risk behaviors associated with cocaine or heroin injection, harm reduction complements treatment initiatives. Where people are willing to move to less risky behaviors or to stop the risky behavior altogether, access to treatment is essential. But, where there are users, there will be those who are not ready or able to stop. It is necessary to have initiatives that minimize the harmful consequences for users themselves, for their significant others, and for the community. As long as people have access to drugs as addictive and appealing as cocaine and heroin, the full range of responses will be required to ensure optimal effectiveness.

ACKNOWLEDGMENTS

The authors would like to thank David C. Marsh, of the Addiction Research Foundation, for his contributions to this chapter, particularly the section on therapeutic approaches. We would also like to thank Tony Toneatto, also of ARF, for reviewing this chapter.

REFERENCES

Addiction Research Foundation. (1993). *Harm Reduction: A New Approach to Alcohol and Drug Problems*. One of the Best Advice series. Toronto: Author.

Addiction Research Foundation. (1996). *Methadone Maintenance: Treatment for Opioid Dependence*. One of the Best Advice series. Toronto: Author.

Adlaf, E.M., Ivis, F.J., and Smart, R.G. (1994). *Alcohol and Other Drug Use among Ontario Adults in 1994 and Changes Since 1977*. Toronto: Addiction Research Foundation.

Boudreau, R. (1997). Addiction and the family. In *Alcohol and Drug Problems: A Practical Guide for Counsellors,* eds. Harrison, S., and Carver, V. Toronto: Addiction Research Foundation.

Canadian Centre on Substance Abuse and the Addiction Research Foundation. (1995). *Canadian Profile: Alcohol, Tobacco and Other Drugs 1995*. Toronto: Authors.

Canadian Centre on Substance Abuse and the Addiction Research Foundation. (1997, In Press). *Canadian Profile: Alcohol, Tobacco and Other Drugs 1997*. Toronto: Authors.

Des Jarlais, D.C., Friedman, S.R., Choopanya, K., Vanichseni, S., and Ward, T.P. (1992). International epidemiology of HIV and AIDS among injecting drug users. *AIDS* 6 (10): 1053–1068.

Erickson, P.G., Adlaf, E.M., Smart, R.G., and Murray, G.F. (1994). *The Steel Drug*. New York: Lexington Books.

Frank, J.D. (1961). *Persuasion and Healing*. Baltimore, MD: Johns Hopkins University Press.

Gawin, F.H., and Ellinwood Jr., E.H. (1988). Cocaine and other stimulants: Actions, abuse, and treatment. *The New England Journal of Medicine* 318 (18): 1173–1182.

Gawin, F.H., and Kleber, H.D. (1986). Abstinence symptomatology and psychiatric diagnosis in cocaine abusers. *Archives of General Psychiatry* 43: 107–113.

Gossop, M., Griffiths, P. Power, B., and Strang, J. (1994). Cocaine: Patterns of use, route of administration, and severity of dependence. *British Journal of Psychiatry* 164: 660–664.

Halikas, J.A., Crosby, R.D., Pearson, V.L., Nugent, S.M., and Carlson, G.A. (1994). Psychiatric comorbidity in treatment-seeking cocaine abusers. *The American Journal on Addictions* (Winter): 25–35.

James, D. (1990). Issues in the treatment of cocaine abuse. Internal document of the Alberta Alcohol and Drug Abuse Commission.

Laboratory Centre for Disease Control. (Dec. 1996). *Epi Updates*. Bureau of HIV, AIDS and STD Update Series. Ottawa: Laboratory Centre for Disease Control, Health Canada.

Lazarus, A.A. (1966). Behaviour rehearsal vs. non-directive therapy vs. advice in effecting behaviour change. *Behavioural Research & Therapy* 4: 209–212.

Marlatt, G.A. (1990). Cue exposure and relapse prevention in the treatment of addictive behaviors. *Addictive Behaviors* 15: 395–399.

Marsh, D.C., and Skinner, W. (1997, In Press). Counselling patients on methadone maintenance therapy. In *Methadone Maintenance: A Clinician's Manual,* ed. Brand, B. Toronto: Addiction Research Foundation.

McLellan, A.T., Arndt, I.O., Metzger, D.S., Woody, G.E., and O'Brien, C.P. (1993). The effects of psychosocial services in substance abuse treatment. *Journal of the American Medical Association* 269 (15): 1953–1959.

Metropolitan Toronto Addiction Treatment Services Committee. (1995). *Heroin Activity in Metropolitan Toronto.* Toronto: Southtown Consulting Inc.

Metro Toronto Research Group on Drug Use. (1997). *Fax on Drugs* 2 (2): 1–2.

Mirin, S.M., Weiss, R.D., Michael, J., and Griffin, M.L. (1988). Psychopathology in substance abusers: Diagnosis and treatment. *American Journal of Drug and Alcohol Abuse* 14 (2): 139–157.

National Institute on Drug Abuse. (1995). *Methadone Maintenance Treatment: Translating Research into Policy.* Manual prepared for the American Methadone Treatment Association Conferences, NIDA International Forum, Nov. 1, 1995. Bethesda, MD: Department of Health and Human Services, NIDA.

Ontario Substance Abuse Bureau. (1996). *Ontario Addiction Treatment Services Rationalization Project: Guidelines for Restructuring Services.* Toronto: Ontario Substance Abuse Bureau of the Ministry of Health.

Ralston, G.E., and Wilson, P. (1996). Methadone programmes: The costs and benefits to society and the individual. *PharmacoEconomics* 10 (4): 321–326.

Research Group on Drug Use. (1997). *Drug Use in Metropolitan Toronto, 1997.* Toronto: City of Toronto Department of Public Health.

Riley, D. (1993). *The Harm Reduction Model: Pragmatic Approaches to Drug Use from the Area between Intolerance and Neglect.* Ottawa: Canadian Centre on Substance Abuse.

Rounsaville, B.J., Glazer, W., Wilber, C.H., Weissman, M.M., and Kleber, H.D. (1983). Short-term interpersonal psychotherapy in methadone maintained opiate addicts. *Archives of General Psychiatry* 40: 629–636.

Task Force into Illicit Narcotic Overdose Deaths in British Columbia. (1994). *Report of the Task Force into Illicit Narcotic Overdose Deaths in British Columbia.* Burnaby, BC: Ministry of the Attorney General, Office of the Chief Coroner.

U.S. Department of Health and Human Services. (1994). *Assessment and Treatment of Cocaine-Abusing Methadone-Maintained Patients*. Centre for Substance Abuse Treatment's Treatment Improvement Protocol (TIP) Series, No. 10. Rockville, MD: Author.

Wallace, B.C. (1989). Psychological and environmental determinants of relapse in crack cocaine smokers. *Journal of Substance Abuse Treatment* 6: 95–106.

Washton, A.M. (1989). *Cocaine Addiction: Treatment, Recovery, and Relapse Prevention*. New York: W.W. Norton & Company, Inc.

Washton, A.M., and Gold, M.S. (eds.) (1987). *Cocaine, A Clinician's Handbook*. New York: The Guilford Press.

Weidman, A. (1985). Engaging the families of substance abusing adolescents in family therapy. *Journal of Substance Abuse Treatment* 43: 927–938.

Wermuth, L., and Scheidt, S. (1986). Enlisting family support in drug treatment. *Family Process* 25: 25–33.

Williams, B., Chang, K., Van Truong, M., and Saad, F. (1994). *International Profile 1994: Alcohol & Other Drugs*. Toronto: Addiction Research Foundation.

Woody, G.E., McLellan, A.T., Luborsky, L., and O'Brien, C.P. (1995). Psychotherapy in community methadone programs: A validation study. *American Journal of Psychiatry* 152: 1302–1308.

Chapter 30

Treating People
with Gambling Problems

BARRY ANDRES AND SUSAN D. HAWKEYE

THE SOCIAL-POLITICAL CONTEXT OF GAMBLING

In addition to being an enjoyable and harmless pastime for many people, gambling provides an increasingly important source of revenue to governments and charitable organizations. In Alberta, for example, gambling revenues totalled $2.2 billion ($207 million from video lottery terminals) in 1993–1994. Two years later, in 1995–96, gambling revenue exceeded $2.9 billion, of which $1.7 billion was from video lottery terminals (Alberta Lotteries, 1996).

In the face of reduced government funding and dwindling charitable donations, many social programs and services are sustained by the gambling revenues they receive. As a result, governments and charitable organizations alike face the challenge (and conundrum) of balancing the need for revenue with the social responsibility of promoting a behavior that is potentially addictive.

Growing revenues reflect increased opportunities to gamble. Gambling has become more accessible. Bingo halls and casinos have proliferated and are open extended hours. Advertising legitimizes gambling and offers a dream for all to chase. A greater variety of games have been legalized and new types of gambling, such as video lottery terminals (VLTs), have been introduced. Many communities are actively involved in vigorous controversy over gambling accessibility. Issues such as the introduction of VLTs and the legalization of gambling on Sundays are being debated in several provinces. While some community groups are garnering petitions to remove VLTs, others are demanding a greater share of the revenue. First Nations leaders are advocating for band-operated casinos on reserve lands, just as elected officials are calling for more casinos and touting the lure of tourism dollars in their cities.

Not surprisingly, in recent years, the number of clients appearing with problems associated with their gambling has increased. Calls to Alberta's 1-800 Gambling Help Line nearly doubled — from 1,473 in 1994 to 2,702 in 1995 (AADAC, 1996).

On a national level, gambling losses averaged $166 for every person in Canada in 1995 (Canadian Centre on Substance Abuse, 1996). It comes as no surprise that, not only are substance abuse counsellors seeing more gamblers, but this "hidden addiction" is also appearing more often in the offices of physicians, therapists, financial advisers, lawyers and members of the clergy, to name a few. As a result of these changes, as well as the growing awareness of problem gambling, increasing numbers of clients are asking for help.

Problem gambling has been called the "hidden addiction" due to the general lack of public awareness, the absence of physical impairment and the fact that no substance is involved. But awareness is growing. In many ways, the recognition of problem gambling has followed a similar path to that of substance abuse. For example, Alcoholics Anonymous was founded in the mid-1930s; Gamblers Anonymous in the 1950s. The psychiatric community recognized substance abuse as a disorder in the 1950s; pathological gambling was included in the DSM-IIIR, published in the 1980s. Today, problem gambling is on its way to becoming as well known clinically and as widely recognized as substance abuse — and equally as treatable. Therapists are becoming fluent in a variety of effective treatment techniques for problem gamblers.

THE CONTEXT OF PROBLEM GAMBLING

In the context of increased gambling opportunities, addiction counsellors are faced with a growing proportion of problem gamblers in their caseloads. Gamblers themselves, and the public, are quick to focus on the proliferation of gambling as the root of this problem. However, accessibility to gambling is only one part of the equation, and one that counsellors have little opportunity to influence.

To obtain a comprehensive perspective of the context of problem gambling, we have found Zinberg's (1984) model to be particularly useful. Zinberg argues that any addiction has three dimensions. These are described below from the perspective of problem gambling:

1. Set. The characteristics of the individual who is involved in gambling. The gambler brings a particular set of needs, desires and vulnerabilities, as well as risk and protective factors, that affect the likelihood that an addiction will develop. For example, degree of competitiveness, self-worth, values around money and negative thought patterns all have a bearing on gambling.

2. Setting. The environment in which the use (or in this case, the gambling) occurs. Gambling exists and is sustained by a consumer-driven, individualistic society in which it is actively promoted. If gambling becomes problematic, this same environment often makes it difficult for people to accept that they are unable to control or manage their behavior and ask for help.

3. Substance. Zinberg identifies the properties of the drug itself as factors that influence the risk for addiction. Similarly, forms of gambling or gambling venues have inherent risks for abuse and dependence. For example, some clients claim that they are able to handle playing bingo, but unable to enter a casino.

The various gambling products differ in their potential for harm based on their rate of play, the player's perception of skill, and other factors. Continuous games, such as bingo or VLTs, are more likely to result in problem gambling than games that have distinct beginning and end points. Similarly, forms of gambling that have immediate payoffs or a fast cycle of play, such as scratch tickets or VLTs, are more likely to become a problem than those that have more delayed payoffs. In addition, the potential for problems is greater if there is a perception that the player's level of skill can influence the outcome of the wager, such as in card games or sport betting.

The "substance" involved in gambling addiction is the subject of some controversy. A common belief is that the basis of problem gambling is the desire to win money. However, experience does not support this view. Rather, for problem gamblers, the objective is to experience the feeling of anticipation or excitement — a feeling termed "action" — which occurs between the bet and the outcome. This is why problem gamblers continue to gamble even when they lose repeatedly. In a sense, problem gamblers are "hooked on a feeling." One famous gambler is reputed to have said, "Gambling and winning is the best feeling I know. Gambling and losing comes second."

Defining the Problem

Gambling is generally described as the act of risking or betting something of value on an event in which the outcome is uncertain. Several terms exist to describe gambling at problematic levels.

Problem Gambling: A term used by many professionals and laypersons to describe a wide range of harmful consequences associated with gambling behaviors; includes compulsive and pathological gambling.

Compulsive Gambling: A common term used by laypersons and by Gamblers Anonymous. "Compulsive" implies a loss of control and that the individual is engaged in an activity that is not enjoyable. (In recognition that gambling can be a pleasurable activity, even for those who gamble compulsively, the term "pathological gambling" is considered more accurate.)

Pathological Gambling: Originally developed by the medical and psychiatric community, this term describes a chronic and progressive disorder characterized by continuous or periodic loss of control over gambling, preoccupation with gambling and with obtaining money with which to gamble, irrational thinking, and a continuation of the behavior despite adverse consequences. It refers to gambling behavior that compromises, disrupts, or damages personal, family or vocational pursuits (see DSM-IV criteria).

DSM-IV — Diagnostic Criteria for Pathological Gambling

A. Persistent and recurrent maladaptive gambling behavior as indicated by five (or more) of the following:
1. Preoccupied with gambling (e.g., preoccupied with reliving past gambling experiences, handicapping or planning the next venture, or thinking of ways to get money with which to gamble);
2. Needs to gamble with increasing amounts of money in order to achieve the desired excitement;
3. Has repeated unsuccessful efforts to control, cut back or stop gambling;
4. Is restless or irritable when attempting to cut down or stop gambling;
5. Gambles as a way of escaping from problems or of relieving a dysphoric mood (e.g., feelings of helplessness, guilt, anxiety, depression);
6. After losing money gambling, often returns another day to get even ("chasing" one's losses);
7. Lies to family members, therapist or others to conceal the extent of involvement with gambling;
8. Has committed illegal acts such as forgery, fraud, theft or embezzlement to finance gambling;
9. Has jeopardized or lost a significant relationship, job, or educational or career opportunity because of gambling;
10. Relies on others to provide money to relieve a desperate financial situation caused by gambling.

B. The gambling is not better accounted for by a Manic Episode.

Source: American Psychiatric Association. (1994). *Diagnostic and Statistical Manual of Mental Disorders* (4th ed.). Washington, DC, p. 618.

Signs of Problem Gambling

A useful way to conceptualize problem gambling is on a continuum. At one end of the scale is no gambling at all. At the other end is pathological (or compulsive) gambling — behavior that has become out of control and harmful to personal, family or vocational pursuits. In the middle, we find what could be called recreational gambling, at various levels of intensity.

THE GAMBLING CONTINUUM

No Involvement	Casual Social Gambling	Serious Social Gambling	Harmful Involvement	Pathological Gambling

A common estimate of the incidence of problem gambling is about five per cent of those who gamble. And, the reality is, most adults gamble. A 1994 Alberta survey (Wynne et al., 1994) found that 90 per cent of the subjects had gambled in the previous year — 40 per cent gambled at least once a week. Of those surveyed,
- seven per cent didn't gamble at all
- 84.4 per cent reported that their gambling had no adverse effects
- 3.2 per cent had experienced problems in the past, but not now
- four per cent said that their gambling sometimes created problems
- 1.4 per cent admitted that their gambling was causing serious emotional and financial problems.

Translated into actual numbers, it is estimated that between 74,000 and 125,000 Albertans currently experience some level of problems related to gambling. Alberta's overall prevalence rate for problem gambling is slightly higher than other Canadian jurisdictions, while its severe problem rate is comparable to other jurisdictions (AADAC, 1996). Ladouceur (1996), in a review of six provinces, notes that the liberalization of gambling in Canada has put us in a position similar to the United States in terms of problem gambling. Again, it is not surprising that so many clients are appearing at our doors. What is surprising (and a concern), is that there are not more.

For many new clients, the problems resulting from their gambling are severe and devastating. Clinical observations suggest that problem gamblers seek help for a limited number of reasons and often in a time of crisis. The primary reasons typically involve the following areas:
- **Financial:** gambled and lost money allocated for basic needs or committed to other essentials (e.g., gambled away the rent, grocery money, car loan payment).
- **Emotional:** experiencing severe distress, depression and suicide risk.

- **Legal:** criminal charges arising from theft or fraud to support the gambling.
- **Family:** experiencing severe family conflict; separation from partner or child neglect due to gambling.

Regardless of the reason for the specific crisis, upon reflection gamblers are usually able to identify earlier indicators of a gambling problem. Reviewing the following signs with the client is often helpful:

Signs of Problem Gambling

Spends large amounts of time gambling.
Gambling takes time away from family and friends, and reduces involvement in community activities, volunteer work, hobbies and so forth.

Spends excessive amounts of money gambling.
The problem gambler spends more than was planned and can be afforded on gambling, and places larger, more frequent bets. Larger bets (with corresponding larger risk) are necessary to get the same level of excitement.

"Chases" losses.
Returns to gambling soon after a loss to try to recover the loss.

Has growing debts.
A person with a gambling problem is secretive or defensive about money, and may borrow money from family members or friends.

Pins hopes on the "big win."
The problem gambler believes the big win, rather than changing the gambling behavior, will solve financial or other problems.

Promises to cut back on gambling.
A problem gambler may think about cutting back on gambling, or may have tried to reduce or stop gambling, but was unable to do so.

Refuses to explain behavior, or lies about it.
A person with a gambling problem may be away from home or work for long periods of time, or may make an unusually high number of personal telephone calls.

Feels frequent highs and lows.
If unable to gamble, the problem gambler misses the thrill of the action and may be bad-tempered, withdrawn, depressed or restless. During a winning streak, the gambler is exhilarated and "on a high."

Boasts about winning.
The person with a gambling problem loves to relive a win but will make light of losses when others express their concern. Wins and losses may also be kept a secret.

Prefers gambling to special family occasions.
The problem gambler may arrive late or miss family events such as birthdays, school activities and other family gatherings.

Seeks new places to gamble close to home and away.
The problem gambler may insist that evenings out or even family vacations be at places where gambling is available.

"Spaces out" while gambling.
Achieving a dissociate state during gambling is characteristic of problem gamblers.

Progression of Problem Gambling

Many experts believe that problem gambling is progressive. In other words, as problem gambling continues, it becomes more extreme and its consequences more severe. Recent research suggests that certain types of gambling — particularly bingo, horse racing, VLTs, and casino games such as roulette — are more likely to progress this way than others (Bergh and Kuhlhorn, 1994). Our experience supports this finding. Clients who are VLT gamblers, for example, frequently report an interval of a year or less between starting to play to experiencing gambling-related problems.

Robert Custer, a psychiatrist and well-known expert in the treatment of problem gambling, has identified three stages in the development of problem gambling (Custer and Milt, 1985):

- In the first stage, the **winning phase,** the financial rewards or the internal escape that gambling provides are sufficient to cause the behavior to continue.

- As gambling progresses, losses begin to accumulate and gambling behavior becomes more out of control. This second phase, known as the **losing phase,** may last for years. In spite of the incredible betting, borrowing, juggling and repaying, the gambler somehow manages to stay afloat.

- At the final stage, the **desperation phase,** there is extreme emotional and often physical distress as well as severe family and financial problems. Criminal acts and legal problems are common. The problem gambler feels overwhelmed and may ultimately give up all attempts to maintain control or manage life responsibilities.

Lesieur and Rosenthal (1991) have identified a fourth phase, the **giving-up phase,** in which any attempts to maintain control or manage life responsibilities are abandoned.

CUSTER'S V-CHART

A CHART OF COMPULSIVE GAMBLING AND RECOVERY

WINNING PHASE

- Frequent Winning
- More Frequent Gambling
- Fantasies about Winning / Big Shot
- Unreasonable Optimism
- Occasional Gambling
- Excitement Prior to and with Gambling
- Increased Amount Bet
- Big Win

LOSING PHASE

- Bragging About Wins
- Prolonged Losing Episodes
- Covering Up, Lying
- Losing Time from Work
- Personality Changes Irritable, Restless, Withdrawn
- Heavy Borrowing / Legal & Illegal
- Bailouts
- Gambling Alone
- Thinking Only About Gambling
- Can't Stop Gambling / Borrowing Legally
- Careless About Spouse and Family
- Delays Paying Debts
- Homelife Unhappy
- Unable to Pay Debts

DESPERATION PHASE

- Marked Increase in Amount & Time Spent Gambling
- Remorse
- Panic
- Reputation Affected
- Alienation from Family and Friends
- Blaming Others
- Illegal Acts

(Center circle)
- Hopelessness
- Arrests, Divorce
- Emotional Breakdown
- Suicide Thoughts & Attempts
- Withdrawal Symptoms
- Alcohol

CRITICAL PHASE

- Return to Work
- Decision Making
- Responsible Thinking
- Hopeful
- Spiritual Needs Examined
- Problem Solving
- Thinking Clearer
- Personal Stock
- Realistic, Stops Gambling
- Honest Desire for Help

REBUILDING PHASE

- More Relaxed
- Less Irritating Behavior
- More Family Time
- Family & Friends Begin to Trust
- Self-Respect Returning
- Accept Self-Weakness and Strengths
- Restitution Plans
- More Family Time
- Less Impatience
- Resolve Legal Problems
- Develop Goals
- New Interests
- Improved Spouse & Family Relationships
- Paying Bills, Budget

GROWTH PHASE

- Sacrificing for Others
- Giving Affection to Others
- Insight into Self
- Understanding Self & Others
- Facing Problems Promptly
- Preoccupation with Gambling Decreases

Although it is widely recognized, Custer's phases of winning, losing and desperation have limited use based on our experience with problem gamblers. The clients we see have typically experienced intermittent winning and losing phases. What progresses is the frequency and length of gambling sessions, the amount spent on gambling, and the severity of negative consequences and obsessive thoughts about gambling. Although gamblers commonly identify a winning period followed by a losing period, this perception tends to result from cognitive fallacies that support the gambling, rather than actual experience. Nevertheless, Custer's V-chart can be used as a helpful tool when working with problem gamblers by helping them identify explicit consequences they have experienced as their gambling progressed.

The effects of problem gambling on the partner, like the effects of problem gambling on the gambler, also have a predictable progression. Describing these phases can be helpful for family members and clinical practice. Many families experience the following pattern as the gambling progresses:

DENIAL PHASE

In this first phase, there is moderate impact on the family. The gambler is frequently not home or involved with the family. Early on, the partner realizes the problem. Adjusting his or her expectations of the relationship causes additional tension, so accommodating the gambling is easier than changing.

A "discovery cycle" has been identified in this stage, in which there is discovery of the gambling behavior, request for forgiveness, forgiveness, reduction or abstinence, relapse and concealment, and then further discovery.

STRESS PHASE

As the gambling continues, the partner increases the effort to intervene and control the behavior and its consequences. The partner can no longer deny the problem but continues to operate with the belief that he or she can change it. The partner blames himself or herself for the inability to stop the gambling. Verbal abuse and periods of anxiety, confusion, resentment and depression are experienced.

EXHAUSTION PHASE

The partner recognizes his or her inability to control the gambling. Panic and rage may be experienced as a result of not being able to protect the family from the negative consequences of the gambling. Divorce, drug and alcohol abuse, and suicide attempts may be experienced by the partner as he or she feels a greater sense of helplessness and loss of control.

Types of Problem Gamblers

Various typologies have been suggested to describe the nature of problem gamblers. Based on his experience with psychiatric patients in a Veterans Administration Hospital in the 1960s, Custer (1985) identified the following six types of gamblers:

Professional Gamblers make their living by gambling and exercise control in the time and amount of money spent gambling. They have a well-researched strategy and stick to it. They do not experience negative effects in relationships as a result of gambling, nor does their self-esteem depend on the outcome of the wager. Incidentally, we have yet to see any professional gamblers clinically as they don't appear to experience problems requiring help. We have seen problem gamblers who aspire to be professional gamblers, but the nature of their behavior precludes this vocation.

Antisocial or Criminal Gamblers use gambling as a tool to con others. They are not driven to gamble as a means in itself.

Casual Social Gamblers participate for the fun and excitement. There is little ego investment in winning and no negative consequences.

Serious Social Gamblers gamble more often and with greater bets. They may experience conflict in the amount of time and money expended, however, they retain control of the gambling. Serious social gamblers may be likened to devoted sporting enthusiasts.

The two categories described below comprise problem gamblers:

Relief-and-Escape Gamblers have a binge aspect to their gambling. They use gambling as a way of dealing with negative emotions such as anxiety depression, loneliness or anger. Their gambling serves to anesthetize their emotional distress. In times of stability, the gambling need diminishes. For example, a female professional in her forties described a pattern of destructive gambling regularly following confrontations with her supervisor in which her self-worth was challenged.

Compulsive Gamblers exhibit four essential characteristics:

a. Progression. The gambler spends increasing time and money gambling, and needs to take increasing risks in order to achieve the desired excitement or escape. This characteristic is evidenced by a recovering gambler who commented that, as long as he had less than $100 in his pocket, there was no risk for him to gamble.

b. Preoccupation. Thoughts about gambling become more frequent and strong. Anticipating the excitement, planning for funds to gamble, and worrying about debts consume the gambler's thoughts. Even in the absence of gambling, obsessive thoughts can keep underlying issues at bay. For example, a client who had not gambled for three months, reported that she found herself imagining "spinning" (playing the VLTs) whenever she felt angry.

c. Intolerance for losing. For compulsive gamblers, losing is not only a blow to their finances but also to their self-image. It therefore becomes vital to attempt to win back the money lost. Chasing becomes the norm as they spend more to win back the money that they perceive belongs to them.

d. Disregard for consequences. Moral and ethical prohibitions are broken as the gambler obtains funds by questionable means in order to keep gambling long enough to achieve the "big win" that will make everything right. These acts always occur with full intention to repay the "borrowed" funds. It is no surprise that clients say that it wasn't like them to steal.

Exploring the above characteristics with clients can be extremely helpful. Problem gamblers readily identify with these characteristics. This acknowledgment builds acceptance, provides a way to understand their behavior other than as being "bad," and builds belief in the potential of problem gambling being treatable. Comments of "Yeah, that's just like me" are typical during this discussion.

Another typology has been suggested by McGurrin (1992) who identified two sub-types of problem gamblers:

Sub-Type A, **Recurring Depressed Gamblers,** often have a long history of depression, which precedes their gambling, as well as significant life trauma. They are typically self-blaming to an excessive degree. This type of gambler feels better when gambling, as the high stimulus gambling environment leads to escape from unpleasant emotions and realities. When the reality of the gambling losses is experienced, a need to return to gambling is intensified in degree to control the depressive feelings by an optimistic escape into action.

For example, Tom, an executive in a mid-sized company and a VLT gambler, typified this subtype in that his depression, loneliness and search for self-worth through career status sustained his need to gamble. Also, these gamblers tend to prefer venues where they can gamble without interacting with others. As such, bingo and VLT gambling are popular among these types of gamblers.

Sub-Type B, **Chronically Understimulated Gamblers,** have a strong need for almost constant excitement. These problem gamblers typically have a poorly defined value system. They are gregarious and quite narcissistic. They have poor impulse control, poor even when compared to other gamblers, and often demonstrate poor control in many areas of their life.

Hyperactivity, low frustration tolerance, and a constant search for arousal are key elements. Gambling, because of its high arousal level and variety of options, leaves other activities looking boring in comparison. Popular venues for this type of gambler include casinos, the race track, card games or VLTs in a social context.

General addiction theory (Jacobs, 1986) can be applied to problem gambling as well as to other forms of addictive behavior patterns in order to identify common denominators of these behaviors. The theory proposes that there are two sets of psychological factors that predispose people to addiction:
• a unipolar physiological resting state that is either chronically depressed or excited (hypo- or hyper-aroused); and
• childhood or adolescent experiences that have produced a deep sense of personal inadequacy and rejection.

We have found Jacobs' theory to be particularly useful in identifying two basic types of problem gamblers:

Relief/Escape — These problem gamblers have a basic state of over-stimulation or hyper-arousal. They are often anxious, worried or ill at ease. Seeking relief from their feelings, they gamble to escape.

Action — These gamblers have a basic state of under-stimulation or hypo-arousal. They are often bored or disinterested in things around them. Uncomfortable with these feelings, they gamble to find excitement.

Both relief/escape and action gamblers live in an uncomfortable stressful state that is relieved by gambling. When gambling ends, the stress returns.

Jacobs also identifies the presence of a dissociative-like state while engaging in the addictive behavior as a feature that differentiated addicted from non-addicted people. Our clinical experience with VLT players, in particular, illustrates the dissociative nature of the addiction. Clients report losing track of time and failing to look after basic physical needs while in a dissociative state. As a result, stress and exhaustion may be so acute that a form of "detox" is required to stabilize the clients' physical condition prior to treatment.

TREATMENT CONSIDERATIONS

Screening and Assessment

Screening and assessment are often considered separately from treatment. However, it is our experience that screening and assessment, in and of itself, is an important component of treatment. We have found that clients often change their behavior, or at least gain significant insights into their gambling, on the basis of screening and assessment alone.

The following instruments provide quick indication of whether a gambling problem may exist and more assessment is required:

AADAC Gambling Screen — Gambling problems are relatively common among the alcohol and/or drug-dependent population. Therefore, all clients seeking help for a substance use problem are asked the following questions at intake:

1. In the past 12 months, have you: played bingo; bet on sporting events; purchased lottery tickets; played games of skill for money (e.g., cards); played slot machines, video lottery machines (poker machines); gambled in a casino; gambled at the track (include off-track betting as well); participated in any other form of gambling?
2. In the past 12 months, have you spent more money than you intended on any of these activities? Yes/No
3. In the past 12 months, has your involvement in the above activities created financial difficulties for you or your family? Yes/No
4. In the past 12 months, has anyone expressed concern about your involvement in these activities? Yes/No
5. In the past 12 months, have you been concerned about your involvement in these activities? Yes/No

An affirmative answer to one (or more) of questions 2 to 5 indicates a need for further investigation.

South Oaks Gambling Screen (SOGS) — This 16-item questionnaire can be quickly and easily administered. Developed in the 1980s, it is based on the criteria for pathological gambling from the DSM-III-R. As such, it provides a scientifically validated and useful means of identifying problem gamblers (Lesieur and Blume, 1987, 1993).

We have found that SOGS scores must be interpreted with caution, because they may give "false positive" results. The SOGS measures only lifetime prevalence. However, to reduce this problem, a two-column format was developed and we ask for incidence of problems during the previous 12-month period as well as for problems prior to the past 12 months. These scores are useful, not only for identifying that problem gambling exists, but they also provide indications of onset and time of development, severity at various phases, and rate of progression.

20 Questions — The 20 Questions of Gamblers Anonymous can be a helpful tool for enhancing motivation in clients. A cut-off score of seven or more affirmative responses is used to differentiate between problem and non-problem gambling. Note that the 20 Questions tool is not a validated instrument. It is effective as a tool to build awareness of the gambling severity.

DSM-IV Criteria — These criteria are research-based and provide a valid screen for problem gambling (American Psychiatric Association, 1994). They are not as likely as other screening measures to result in false positive or negative results. The DSM-IV criteria should be considered when the client's situation involves legal or medical concerns, i.e., when the validity and reliability of an instrument may be called into question.

In addition to these gambling-specific instruments, factors pertaining to the precipitating crisis also require screening and often possible intervention. We therefore also screen for the following:

Financial crisis — Financial crisis is the most common reason why problem gamblers seek help. A quick screen for the presence and severity of financial pressures is the four-item CAPE. Clients are asked the following questions, with further questions to gain a complete understanding of their current financial status:

1. Are you Concerned about your financial situation?
2. Are you more than two months in Arrears in any of your payments?
3. Are any creditors Pressuring you for payment?
4. Are there more bills than money at the End of the month?

Suicide risk — Clients in crisis also have an increased risk of suicide. We use the Suicide Screening Tool to observe whether verbal or behavioral clues are present that indicate suicidal ideation and to ascertain risk factors for suicide (e.g., previous attempts, family history, recent losses).

Substance abuse — Research has shown a substantial overlap between pathological gambling and other addictions (Lesieur and Blume, 1991). The percentage of pathological gamblers who have substance abuse problems is estimated to be as high as 39 per cent to 52 per cent (Rosenthal and Lesieur, 1992). Similarly, it has been estimated that seven per cent to 28 per cent of clients with substance abuse problems also have gambling problems (Lesieur and Rosenthal, 1991). Practicality necessitates screening for substance abuse for all gamblers and vice versa.

A quick screen for potential problem drinking is the four-item CAGE (Ewing, 1984). The Alcohol Dependence Scale (Skinner and Horn, 1984) and/or the Drug Abuse Screening Test (Skinner, 1982) are also helpful for detecting substance abuse problems. In treatment, substance abuse problems are typically addressed first, followed by problem gambling.

To understand the complexity of problem gambling as it relates to a client, various factors must be considered. A comprehensive assessment involves the following areas:
• Gambling behavior — pattern, type, frequency, duration, feelings, triggers
• Major life areas — medical, financial, employment/support, alcohol/drug use, legal status, family/social, psychological, leisure
• Contributing factors — family history, personality characteristics, emotional state, high stress, grief issues
• Other addictive behavior (i.e., substance abuse).

In addition, it is helpful to obtain a sense of the client's level of readiness for change. We do this by asking clients which of the following statements best describes their situation:

1. I am not worried about my use of alcohol or drugs or my gambling, and I am here only because someone else requested I come. (Precontemplation)
2. I am not sure if I have a problem with alcohol, drugs or gambling. (Contemplation)
3. I know I have a problem with alcohol, drugs or gambling, but I am not sure how to change it. (Preparing for Action)
4. I am ready to make changes, and I am here to get help to make those changes. (Action)
5. I have already made the changes I need to make and I want help to maintain those changes. (Maintenance)

(Adapted from Miller and Rollnick, 1991)

As information from the screening and assessment interview(s) is gathered, it may be recorded on the Screening/Assessment Results Worksheet (next page). This infomation can be shared with the client. Problem gamblers are often quite interested in the background of the tests and may wish to discuss their purpose and how they are used.

While the magnitude of the screening and assessment process described above may appear daunting, it is well worthwhile. As the screening and assessment process progresses, clients tend to self-identify as problem gamblers and become increasingly open to change. Moreover, treatment planning is a critical component of working with problem gamblers, and screening and assessment provide the information needed to develop a sound treatment plan.

Treatment Strategies

An individualized treatment plan, which includes negotiated and clear goals based on assessment findings and takes into account the degree of readiness for change, enhances the client's chances of success. Because change takes time, treatment planning involves setting both short-term and long-term goals.

Flexibility is required to make these goals work for the individual client. Short-term goals may be one week for some clients, but one or two months for others. With some clients, a long-term goal may be three months away, but, for others, it may mean a year or five years. Ask the client directly what timeframe is realistic.

We have found it helpful to conceptualize treatment in three phases: stabilization; rebuilding; and maintenance.

WORKSHEET – SCREENING/ASSESSMENT RESULTS

GA 20 Questions 1 ···20

DSM-IV Criteria 1 ···10

SOGS 1 ···20

Client Perception 1 ···10

Gambling Pattern _____

Type (VLT, Bingo, etc.) _____

Frequency (How often) _____

Duration (How long does it last) _____

Previous attempts to control their gambling _____

Feelings Before, During (Relief, Action) _____

Triggers _____

ASSESSMENT OF MAJOR LIFE AREAS:

MINIMUM IMPACT   SEVERE IMPACT

Medical 1 ···10

Financial 1 ···10

Employment/Support 1 ···10

Alcohol/Drug Use 1 ···10

Legal Status 1 ···10

Family/Social 1 ···10

Psychological 1 ···10

Leisure 1 ···10

Motivation for Change _____

Contributing Factors _____

Other Addictive Behavior _____

Stabilization

The first few meetings typically focus on stabilizing the crisis, addressing the guilt and self-blame through gaining understanding of the addiction, and building confidence and hope in the ability to change. Education and behavioral contracting are the primary approaches used.

In this phase, it is important to keep the focus on short-term goals and to ensure these goals are realistic and attainable. Many problem gamblers have had a history of failure and need to feel successful in order to maintain the change momentum. Initial goals are typically set in three areas:

1. Addressing the crisis

Negotiating strategies to deal with the financial, physical or emotional crisis is a priority. It is important to avoid "bailing out" the client, but the counsellor should provide resources and help the client obtain adequate stability from anxiety in order to work on recovery issues. Referrals to a financial adviser, physician and Gamblers Anonymous are typical in this phase.

Too often, clients try to set unattainable goals at this stage, particularly with regard to debt repayment. It is important to guide the client's choice of goals to ensure they are realistic. For example, a goal of $100 per week debt repayment may not be realistic and, in fact, may result in additional stress on the client. Rather, a goal of $100 per month may be advisable.

2. Abstaining from gambling

Significant controversy exists regarding the issues of controlled gambling and total abstinence. Although this debate is acknowledged, we believe that the most practical goal is ultimately abstinence from gambling. However, intermediate goals involving controlled gambling may provide a means to this end.

Clients occasionally insist that they want to continue to gamble, but in a "controlled" manner (e.g., limits on amount spent, games played, etc.). Typical is Joan, who insisted initially on playing bingo while embracing a goal of abstinence from the VLTs. Through contracting to stay away from VLTs and to chart how much time and money she spent on bingo for two weeks, she was eventually able to see how bingo reinforced her desire to play the VLTs.

When discussing the abstinence issue with clients, the following questions may be helpful:

- Have you attempted abstinence from gambling for any length of time?
- What is to be gained by continuing to gamble in a modified way?
- What needs are being met by gambling?
- What is the biggest fear/concern if you quit?
- What will replace the gambling?

3. REDUCING RISK FACTORS

Specific treatment components with regard to reducing risk factors are discussed by Legg-England and Gotestam (1991), who identified the following key components:

- Removal of conditioned stimuli for gambling: Reducing the stimuli associated with gambling is a critical initial step. Changing such behaviors as driving past gambling venues, reading sporting results, and handling money are important. Managing the risk associated with money can be addressed through having pay cheques directly deposited to the bank and giving up automatic teller cards.

- Establish alternative means of financial control: Treatment must address the perception that gambling is the best way of managing financial situations. Unrealistic expectations about winning and beliefs about the necessity of chasing losses can be addressed through cognitive restructuring techniques. Keeping a diary of expenditures can help clients test the reality of their beliefs about their success at gambling. A debt repayment scheme must also be arranged.

- Reduce financial need: Counselling should explore the client's financial needs. Is excessive alcohol or other drug use contributing to a higher level of financial need? Unrealistic perceptions about the standard of living required for happiness may need to be challenged. Budgeting skills may also be required.

- Establish alternative means of controlling internal states: Treatment is prone to failure if it removes the primary means of gaining excitement, pleasure or distraction, while offering no replacement. Exploring the perceived internal rewards of gambling and building alternatives is vital. Physical exercise, recreational activities with family, social activities with friends, and participation in Gamblers Anonymous are but a few strategies used.

- Reduce negative internal states: Treatment should address maladaptive coping styles that contribute to negative emotional states, which the client then attempts to modify by gambling. Dysfunctional communication patterns, fear of intimacy and unresolved neglect or abuse issues, as well as chronic anxiety and depression, may provide reasons for the gambling behavior. These conditions may become pronounced when the gambling stops. In addition, unrealistic expectations of quick improvement may reinforce feelings of failure and inadequacy if lapses occur. Counselling should help the client develop realistic expectations for change.

Rebuilding

As the initial crisis subsides and the client begins to achieve a modicum of stability, the rebuilding phase begins. In this phase, treatment may occur in several formats, including one-on-one counselling, participation in a support group such as Gamblers Anonymous and/or a therapy group, attendance at a day-treatment program, or residential treatment. Treatment in the rebuilding phase typically addresses the following areas:

What is problem gambling?

An initial part of treatment often involves helping clients put their own experience into context in order to develop a more comprehensive picture of their gambling behavior and how it has affected their lives. This process takes time. It begins as clients explore the nature of problem gambling and relate it to their own experience. As clients progress in treatment, they see their gambling and its effects more realistically and accurately.

Gambling as a lifestyle

Clients need to consider factors that may have contributed to their current situation and take an introspective look at themselves and their gambling behavior. In treatment, aspects of lifestyle are examined as well as the cognitive processes involved in impulsive decision making. Predisposing factors, such as family history, childhood experiences and personality characteristics, also need to be addressed.

Problem gamblers frequently approach their life (or many areas of their life) from a gambling perspective. Many have high-risk lifestyles and they often tend to look for a "quick fix" when solving problems. Problem gamblers frequently think and behave in an abbreviated "leap frog" fashion. In treatment, problem gamblers need to consider factors that may have contributed to their current situation and take an introspective look at themselves and their gambling behavior. They need to examine aspects of their lifestyle as well as the cognitive processes involved in impulsive decision making.

Self-Awareness Wheel — An effective tool for addressing impulsive decision making is the Self-Awareness Wheel. This model can be applied in various areas of the client's life in order to illustrate how problems may have arisen in the past and how they may be potentially resolved in the future. According to the Self-Awareness Wheel model, problem gambling results from the failure or inability to go through all of the stages prior to acting in a certain way.

1. Our senses — sight, hearing, smell, touch, taste — provide input or sensory stimuli.
2. What we see and hear gives birth to our thoughts.
3. Thoughts generate feelings.
4. Feelings, in turn, result in wants and needs.
5. These are followed by the decision-making process, in which we explore options and make choices.
6. Once we decide on an option, we take action.

A "healthy" person solves problems by progressing around the wheel, in sequence, completing all the steps. The problem gambler, however, tends to follow a 1-2-6 cycle.

The abbreviated cycle of the problem gambler reflects contributing characteristics such as impulsivity, inability to delay gratification, and not being able to tolerate discomfort, as well as poor coping strategies. When the model is considered in terms of the treatment of problem gamblers, the following guidelines emerge:

• Emphasize that problem gamblers need to identify and verbalize their feelings as an important step in the process (most have difficulty in doing so).
• Note that, in step 4 (i.e., wants and needs), problem gamblers always say they want/need money, but what they really want/need is excitement or relief.
• Emphasize the need to break the impulse cycle of 1-2-6.

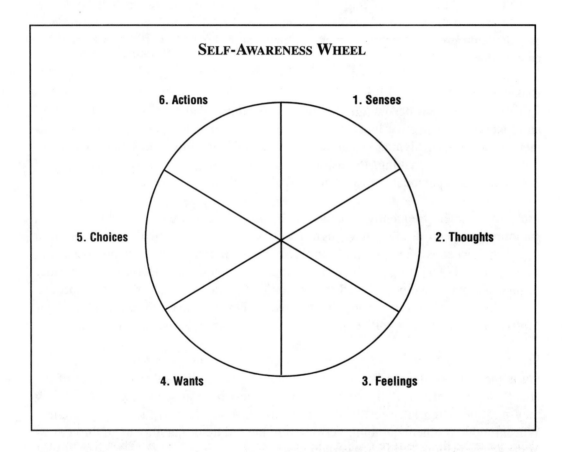

SELF-AWARENESS WHEEL

6. Actions   1. Senses
5. Choices   2. Thoughts
4. Wants   3. Feelings

Establishing Support — A supportive environment is a fundamental aspect of problem gambling treatment. Social support plays a key role in helping problem gamblers change their behavior and adjust to a new lifestyle. One aspect of treatment involves participation in a support group and, if possible, attendance at Gamblers Anonymous meetings. These sources of support can play an important role in recovery from problem gambling. Support groups can enhance personal well-being, improve social functioning, and help clients cope with the consequences of problem gambling. They also address the isolation and self-blame that is common.

Financial Management — Financial distress is a common feature of problem gambling. Dealing with indebtedness, budgeting, and financial planning are important areas to address in treatment. The assessment needs to include all outstanding debts and, if the client is married or in a serious relationship, is best reviewed with the partner present. As well, all sources of income need to be accounted for. Unaccounted income (e.g., tax refunds, money from extra work) presents an extra high-risk situation to the gambler and a plan to manage this money needs to be in place. Appointing or retaining a financial manager and receiving a weekly allowance in order to avoid handling or having access to money is critical, especially in the early stages of treatment.

Negative and Irrational Thinking — Many contemporary views on treatment for problem gambling advocate the use of cognitive therapy (see, for example, Blaszczynski and Silove, 1995; Waltman, 1995). Such techniques focus on negative thinking patterns as well as irrational or false beliefs that help to perpetuate the problem gambling behavior. By modifying the client's negative thinking patterns, self-esteem is enhanced, mood improves, and the need to escape from feelings through gambling is reduced. Moreover, problem gamblers often hold false or irrational beliefs about gambling and the likelihood of winning. It has been suggested that an important aspect of recovery involves helping clients recognize the irrationality of these beliefs and replacing them with realistic and accurate views (see Taber, 1987; Taber and Chaplin, 1988).

Stress Management and Relaxation — Inability to relax is often a contributing factor to problem gambling. The hyper- or hypo-arousal condition, which is often a contributing factor to problem gambling, results in a chronically stressful state. Gambling serves as a way of relieving this stress. Moreover, the consequences of problem gambling create even greater stress. The result is a deepening spiral of gambling to relieve stress, causing more stress as a result. Stress management strategies and relaxation techniques are often useful for helping clients learn to manage uncomfortable feelings. Imaginal desensitization strategies are helpful here. Negative emotional states often become more acute when the gambling stops. Therefore, alternative ways of dealing with these feelings must be identified early in treatment.

Leisure Planning — Problem gamblers commonly experience a void in their leisure activities when they stop gambling. They may require leisure counselling to help them increase their leisure options and enlarge their range of recreational activities. Treatment for action gamblers, in particular, often requires investigating other ways in which excitement can be found. New leisure activities also contribute to the development of a positive support network and help establish a lifestyle without gambling. Additionally, physical exercise is helpful for dealing with stress and alleviating depression — conditions that are prevalent in problem gamblers.

Dealing with Loss — Many problem gamblers experience a sense of loss and feelings of grief when they quit gambling. These feelings need to be addressed in treatment.

Moreover, losses and the grief associated with these losses may also be a factor contributing to problem gambling. Losses include events such as retirement, children leaving home, the death of loved ones, and so forth. Similarly, unresolved past neglect or abuse may also play a role in problem gambling. Grief issues may help to explain why depression is common among problem gamblers.

Skill Development — Many problem gamblers have difficulty expressing their needs and feelings, and communicating honestly and clearly with others. Therefore, building effective communication skills and learning to deal with and express emotions is often an important part of rebuilding. Also, many problem gamblers, particularly relief and escape gamblers, have problems being assertive. Part of the treatment required by these clients may involve skill development in this area.

Family Considerations — Although problem gambling can have significant effects on the gambler, sometimes it has even more profound effects on the family, particularly the life partner. For example, the wife of a problem gambler described it this way: "At least he has his gambling to take his mind off all the problems. I have nothing. The stress never lets up."

Severe conflict and distress as well as stress-related illnesses are common in partners of problem gamblers. Dysfunctional coping strategies have also been noted, such as excessive drinking, heavy smoking, under- or over-eating, and shopping sprees.

Family conflict and loss of trust are common problems that many problem gamblers experience. Especially when the partner takes over all financial management, issues such as anger and resentment toward each other require addressing. An important part of treatment is helping problem gamblers address these difficulties and learn how to develop healthy relationships.

Relapse Prevention — It is not uncommon for clients to return to gambling, in some form or at some level, during or after treatment. Therefore, addressing the issue of relapse is both prudent and worthwhile. Although treatment's primary focus is to provide clients with the skills and knowledge they need to avoid gambling behavior, it is also important that clients understand the dynamics of relapse, and recognize and be able to interrupt the process in its early stages. Accepting a slip or isolated gambling incident as normal, while not condoning it, is an important part of most treatment. Significant learning can be gained by examining the factors leading up to a relapse.

MAINTENANCE

Ultimately, the client begins to feel comfortable with the new lifestyle. Skills for dealing with difficulties without resorting to gambling are developed. Issues of self-esteem, values about money, and relationships continue to be addressed. Treatment moves from contracting around the gambling behavior to insight-oriented therapy, which seeks resolution of underlying issues and fosters personal growth.

CONCLUSION

Gambling clients bring intensity and creativity to counselling sessions. They are eager and often able to address underlying issues that are formative to the gambling early in treatment. As a result, working with gamblers is not only challenging but also highly rewarding. To enhance the effectiveness of counselling with problem gamblers, the following guidelines have proven to be particularly helpful in clinical practice:

• Think of each session as the last. Look for effective ways of engaging clients immediately. Frequently, clients present at a time of crisis and discontinue treatment after the precipitating crisis has subsided. Effective use of brief interventions fosters awareness of the broader issues and builds motivation for additional change.

• Deal with financial issues directly, as issues around money are central to treatment and recovery. Simply handling money is a risk for gamblers, and worrying about debts and the effect of losses on personal or family finances provides real risk to return to gambling. These issues must be addressed and concrete plans developed to deal with finances as well as attitudes and values about money.

• Keep family members involved in treatment. From the initial point of assessing the extent of the problem and level of debt, to working through anger about the various types of losses incurred as a result of gambling, the partner needs to be involved. This builds additional honesty, keeps expectations realistic, and helps ensure all issues are addressed or at least acknowledged.

• Expect clients to present with intense guilt and shame. Gamblers often have great difficulty accepting that they were unable to control their gambling, when they have been very successful in managing other areas of their life. Acknowledging dishonest actions and learning how to accept these as part of problem gambling is also a challenge. Helping clients to understand the nature of problem gambling, fostering connections to a support groups, and providing opportunities to define themselves in ways other than as a gambler are important.

• Keep sessions focused and goal-oriented, especially early sessions. While requiring empathy, clients also need to develop concrete plans that address the stress and build hope that change is possible. Behavioral contracting is vital in the early stages of treatment.

• Be prepared for setbacks. Relapse is common and reinforces the hopelessness that clients feel. Addressing warning signs and high-risk situations is an important part of treatment.

• Assist the client to establish goals with realistic expectations. The gambler's expectation of immediate results typically transfers into treatment as well. Keeping goals short-term and attainable is critical to giving clients a sense of progress.

• Encourage attendance in a support group. Involvement in Gamblers Anonymous and/or a gambling support group is effective for normalizing the addiction, addressing guilt and shame, and building hope that recovery is attainable.

573

REFERENCES

Alberta Alcohol and Drug Abuse Commission. (1996). *Summary Report, April 2, 1995 to March 31, 1996*. Edmonton, AB: AADAC.

Alberta Lotteries. (1996). *Annual Report, 1995/96*. Edmonton, AB: Alberta Lotteries.

American Psychiatric Association. (1994). *Diagnostic and Statistical Manual of Mental Disorders*, 4th ed. Washington, DC: Author.

Bergh, C., and Kuhlhorn, E. (1994). The development of pathological gambling in Sweden. *Journal of Gambling Studies* 10 (3): 261–274.

Blaszczynski, A., and Silove, D. (1995). Cognitive and behavioral therapies for pathological gambling. *Journal of Gambling Studies* 11 (2): 195–220.

Canadian Centre on Substance Abuse. (1996). *Action News* 7 (2).

Custer, R., and Milt, H. (1985) *When Luck Runs Out: Help for Compulsive Gamblers and Their Families*. New York: Facts on File Publications.

Ewing, J.A. (1984). Detecting alcoholism: The CAGE questionnaire. *Journal of the American Medical Association* 252 (14): 1905–1907.

Jacobs, D.G. (1986). A general theory of addictions: A new theoretical model. *Journal of Gambling Behavior* 2: 15–31.

Legg-England, S., and Gotestam, K.G. (1991). The nature and treatment of excessive gambling. *Acta Psychiatrica Scandinavica* 84: 113–120.

Lesieur, H., and Blume, S. (1987). The South Oaks Gambling Screen (SOGS): A new instrument for the identification of pathological gamblers. *American Journal of Psychiatry* 144 (9): 1184–1188.

Lesieur, H., and Blume, S. (1993). Revising the South Oaks Gambling Screen in different settings. *Journal of Gambling Studies* 9 (3): 213–223.

Lesieur, H.R., and Rosenthal, R.J. (1991). Pathological gambling: A review of the literature (prepared for the American Psychiatric Association Task Force on DSM-IV Committee on disorders of impulse control not elsewhere classified). *Journal of Gambling Studies* 7 (1): 5–39.

Ladouceur, R. (1996). The prevalence of problem gambling in Canada. *Journal of Gambling Studies* 12 (2): 129–142.

McGurrin, M.C. (1992). *Pathological Gambling: Conceptual, Diagnostic, and Treatment Issues*. Sarasota, FL: Professional Resource Press.

Miller, W., and Rollnick, S. (1991). *Motivational Interviewing: Preparing People to Change Addictive Behaviors*. New York: Guilford.

Rosenthal, R.J., and Lesieur, H.R. (1992). Self-reported withdrawal symptoms and pathological gambling. *The American Journal of Addictions* 1 (2): 150–154.

Skinner, H.A. (1982). *Drug Abuse Screening Test: Guidelines for Administration and Scoring.* Toronto: Addiction Research Foundation.

Skinner, H.A., and Horne J.L. (1984). *Alcohol Dependence Scale: User's Guide.* Toronto: Addiction Research Foundation.

Taber, J.I. (1987). Compulsive gambling: An examination of relevant models. *Journal of Gambling Behavior* 3 (4): 219–223.

Taber, J.I., and Chaplin, M. (1988). Group psychotherapy with pathological gamblers. *Journal of Gambling Behavior* 4 (3): 183–196.

Waltman, D. (1995). Key ingredients to effective addictions treatment. *Journal of Substance Abuse Treatment* 12 (6): 429–439.

Wynne, H., et al. (1994). *Gambling and Problem Gambling in Alberta: Final Report.* Edmonton, AB: Alberta Lotteries and Gaming.

Zinberg, N.E. (1984). *Drug, Set, and Setting: The Basis for Controlled Intoxicant Use.* New Haven, CT: Yale University Press.

About the Authors

BARRY ANDRES, B.A., B.Ed., is a counselling supervisor with the Alberta Alcohol and Drug Abuse Commission (AADAC) in Edmonton. He currently supervises at an outpatient counselling centre that provides individual, family and group counselling services to adults concerned about alcohol, drug abuse and/or gambling. During his 10 years in the addictions field, he has provided training to allied professionals in the areas of group and individual counselling, treatment of cocaine addiction and gambling. He has been trained by the Minnesota Council on Compulsive Gambling. Most recently he has been involved in developing treatment services for gamblers in Alberta, treatment resources for counsellors working with gamblers, and providing training on treating problem gambling.

HELEN ANNIS, Ph.D., is a professor in the Department of Behavioural Science at the University of Toronto and is the retired chief of the Behaviour Change and Relapse Prevention Clinic at the Addiction Research Foundation. She has published extensively over the past 20 years on the treatment of addictive behaviors, and has given workshops across Canada, the United States and Europe on relapse prevention counselling strategies for alcohol and other substance abusers.

JANE BARON, R.N., M.Sc., is the program co-ordinator for Lifestyle Enrichment for Senior Adults Program (LESA), Ottawa, a treatment program for people over age 55 who are experiencing social and/or health problems related to their use of alcohol or other psychoactive drugs. Jane has been advocating, through LESA, for a holistic approach toward seniors' drug treatment since the program's inception in 1981. Along with her program responsibilities, she develops materials and provides training on how to identify and intervene with an older person with substance use problems.

CHRISTINE BOIS holds an M.A.Sc. (University of Waterloo) in psychopharmacology and clinical psychology. Her experience in addictions includes treatment, research and education. She is currently a program director for the Addiction Research Foundation in eastern Ontario. Previously, she was a manager of an assessment referral agency operated by the Addiction Research Foundation. Christine's areas of interest include substance use and older adults, and alcohol and violence.

FRED J. BOLAND, Ph.D., is a faculty member and former chair of clinical training in the Psychology Department, Queen's University, Kingston. His major research interests include theoretical, treatment and relapse prevention aspects of substance abuse and eating disorders.

RICHARD J. BOUDREAU received his undergraduate degree from Boston College. While completing graduate work in Washington, D.C., he did specialized studies in clinical behavioral sciences at Georgetown University and the National Institute of Health. He also completed a diploma program with the Department of Psychiatry at McMaster University, Hamilton, with specialization in family therapy, as well as an M.Ed. at the University of Toronto. He is currently a senior education consultant with the Addiction Research Foundation.

DOUG BULLOCK received his Bachelor of Arts (psychology and mathematics) and Bachelor of Education degrees from Queen's University, Kingston, and a Master of Social Work degree from Carleton University, Ottawa. He has been involved in a variety of activities in the substance abuse field, including program evaluation, treatment delivery, systems planning, public education and professional training. He helped the Ottawa-Carleton Independent Living Centre develop a peer support training manual. As a member of the Addiction Research Foundation's Disability Issues Advisory Committee, he was active in advocating for the development of accessible addiction services in Ontario. He is employed with ARF's Ottawa office and works with a variety of community organizations developing training and prevention programs.

VIRGINIA CARVER, Ph.D., is a senior program consultant with the Ottawa office of the Addiction Research Foundation, working mainly on issues related to the development of substance abuse treatment services. She has a special interest in older persons and has been involved in policy, research, program development, and in the development of information and training materials related to older persons and their use of alcohol and medications.

BLAIR E. COLLINS, B.A., B.TH., is currently in private counselling practice, and facilitates retreat and workshop presentations. He has worked for a number of years with people living with AIDS and HIV, and has a special interest in dealing with various lesbian/gay-related issues, including personal acceptance, psycho-sexual integration and homophobia.

JULIANNE CONRY, Ph.D. (educational psychology) is in the Department of Educational Psychology and Special Education at the University of British Columbia. Since 1984, she has been active in research and the clinical assessment of children with fetal alcohol syndrome (FAS). She has appeared as an expert witness on FAS in the Provincial and Supreme Courts of British Columbia. She is co-investigator on a recently completed study of the prevalence of adolescents with FAS in the justice system and is co-editor of *Legal Manual: FAS and the Justice System.* She was the principal writer and researcher for the B.C. Ministry of Education (1996) document *Teaching Students with Fetal Alcohol Syndrome/Effects: A Resource Guide for Teachers.*

GERRY COOPER, M.Ed., has worked in the addictions field throughout Ontario since 1976. In 1984, he joined the Addiction Research Foundation where he continues to work as a program director in Sudbury. His special interests include the areas of substance abuse/psychiatric co-morbidity, rural applications of various treatments (such as detoxification) and the promotion of unobtrusive clinical interventions (such as telephone assessments and self-help manuals) to non-addiction-specific professionals/care-givers. As such, much of his time is spent in the planning, delivery and evaluation of high-quality training programs. Over the years, Gerry has also been affiliated with several post-secondary institutions where he has taught a variety of courses related to the treatment of substance use disorders. Currently, he is pursuing his doctorate, specializing in adult education, from the Ontario Institute for Studies in Education, University of Toronto.

JULIA DRAKE worked in communications at the Addiction Research Foundation. She is currently a freelance writer, editor and communications consultant whose clients include organizations specializing in health care and health promotion. She studied print journalism at Ryerson Polytechnic University, Toronto, and completed a B.A. (English) at Queen's University, Kingston.

PETER M. FORD, M.B., F.R.C.P.(C), is a faculty member in the department of medicine, Queen's University, Kingston. He is director of the regional AIDS clinic that operates out of Kingston General Hospital and serves a wide area of both urban and rural eastern Ontario, as well as providing services for the local penitentiaries. He has a research interest in the epidemiology of HIV infection within the penitentiary system and is currently organizing a prevalence study of HIV infection in a male medium-security prison.

KATHRYN GRAHAM, Ph.D. (psychology), is a senior scientist with the Addiction Research Foundation. Her areas of research include alcohol and aggressive behavior, addictions treatment and prevention among older people, use of tranquillizers and sleeping pills, case management, relapse prevention, evaluation and measurement.

SUSAN HARRISON, B.A. (Hon.), B.Ed., M.S.W., was a teacher for several years before pursuing a degree in social work, graduating in 1979. Her career since then has included experience in the fields of child welfare and school social work but has been primarily in addictions. Prior to her current position as east regional manager, Addiction Research Foundation, Susan was the director of a women's addiction treatment centre. She has given many workshops and presentations on addiction-related topics, her special interest and expertise being women and addictions.

SUSAN HAWKEYE, Ph.D., is a consultant who specializes in the design of educational systems and the development of resources that support learning and change. Over the past 10 years, she has worked extensively with the Alberta Alcohol and Drug Abuse Commission (AADAC). Projects include production of curriculum materials on substance abuse prevention for elementary and junior high schools, and development of the package Well Informed, a resource for preventing substance abuse and misuse in seniors. She has been extensively involved in the development of the Problem Gambling Program of Studies, a training package for allied professionals, and most recently, in the design and development of a modularized Intensive Day Treatment Program for Problem Gamblers.

MARILYN A. HERIE, M.S.W., is a project leader, trainer and therapist in the Clinical Research and Treatment Institute at the Addiction Research Foundation. Her experience in addictions includes treatment, research and education. Marilyn co-ordinates the dissemination and adaptation of Structured Relapse Prevention (SRP) treatment to practitioners across Ontario via ARF-sponsored projects. She is co-author (with Helen Annis and Lyn Watkin-Merek) of the recently published book, *Structured Relapse Prevention: An Outpatient Counselling Approach.* Marilyn is also a Ph.D. candidate at the University of Toronto in the Faculty of Social Work.

AUDREY HILL, M.A., Mohawk of the Six Nations Reserve, is supervisor of the Native Services Branch (Children's Aid Society of Brant County). She is particularly interested in the development of culturally appropriate services for native people.

BETTY-ANNE M. HOWARD, M.S.W., has worked in the addictions field for 15 years. She is currently a counsellor at Queen's University Student Counselling Centre, teaching addictions and related courses at St. Lawrence College, also in Kingston. She provides clinical supervision to employee assistance counsellors with Off-Site Resources in eastern Ontario and across Canada, conducts critical incident responses, and is a project manager for a number of employee assistance programs in eastern Ontario. She provides training and education in addictions throughout Ontario and recently developed a course at St. Lawrence College, entitled Introduction to Entrepreneurship, to help social service graduates develop skills to become self-employed. She also has a particular interest in addressing issues of violence in our society, racism, classism, homophobia and ageism.

DEBORAH HUDSON, M.S.W., Registered Trager Practitioner, is a psychotherapist and consultant in private practice in Kingston. For the last 10 years she has specialized in work with survivors of assault. Her major interest is the body/mind connection and how this is affected by trauma.

EVA INGBER, M.S.W., C.S.W., has worked at the Addiction Research Foundation since 1989 as a clinician. She has worked as a co-ordinator of both men's and women's day treatment programs at ARF. She is active on various community committees that focus on program development, particularly in the area of women and addictions. In her role in developing the women's program at ARF, she collaborates with various agencies in order to help clients make links to outside support. She has also facilitated a variety of workshops on addictions and related gender issues.

MELDON KAHAN, M.D., C.C.F.P, F.R.C.P.C., is a staff physician at the Addiction Research Foundation and assistant professor in the Department of Family and Community Medicine at the University of Toronto. He has a particular interest in the education of family physicians.

HANNAH KAUFMAN, M.S.S., is a professional social worker at the Clinical Immunology Outpatient Clinic (HIV/AIDS) at Kingston General Hospital. Her particular focus is providing psychotherapy for individuals, couples and families during periods of high stress, such as a new HIV diagnosis, deterioration in health, hospitalization and family conflicts. She also provides case management and professional and corporate consultations and workshops.

CARL KENT, M.S.W., C.S.W., worked for a number of years in Ontario hospital and general hospital psychiatry and then switched to the field of substance abuse by joining the Addiction Research Foundation. At ARF he has worked in a variety of clinical settings. He is currently a clinical program consultant with the ARF's Community Programs and Services Department within the Metro Toronto Region. He is interested in developing and promoting effective ways of treating elderly substance abusers and people with concurrent disorders.

LYNN LIGHTFOOT received her Master of Applied Science degree and her Ph.D. in psychology at the University of Waterloo. She was the research director of the Treatment Program Research Development Project, Queen's University, Kingston, for three years and then joined the Addiction Research Foundation for 10 years. She is currently in private practice, and is an adjunct assistant professor of psychology at Queen's University and at the Ontario Institute of Studies in Education. She is the author of over 50 scientific articles, book chapters, conference proceedings and government reports in the field of substance abuse, and has specialized in the development and evaluation of substance abuse treatment programs for forensic populations since 1985. She has written and co-authored two treatment manuals and a staff training manual for Correctional Services Canada, and has conducted many training workshops and seminars.

DENNIS LONG, M.S.W., is executive director of Breakaway Youth and Family Services. Previously, he was the Metro Toronto treatment services consultant for the Addiction Research Foundation, and has been a trainer for the ARF's School for Addiction Studies, a psychiatric social worker at Humber Memorial Hospital, and a child care worker. In addition, he is currently president of the board of the Ontario Federation of Community Mental Health and Addictions Programs, executive member of the Metro Toronto Addictions Treatment Services Committee and a member of the Ontario Substance Abuse Bureau's Health Recovery Committee. He has spoken on the subject of harm reduction at the International Conference on the Reduction of Drug Related Harm in Florence, Italy, and at Symposia in North York and Toronto. He has also provided training in youth treatment throughout Ontario.

ROBERT MURRAY, M.S.W., I.C.A.D.C., is a professional social worker and a senior program consultant for the Addiction Research Foundation. He has been active in the addictions field for many years, including eight years as co-ordinator of an assessment/referral service. Robert has an extensive background in counselling clients with substance use problems and has a particular interest in the area of violence/abuse and substance use. He has 12 years of experience in providing group treatment to men who have been abusive to their partners/children, and has taken national leadership in developing and disseminating educational materials on violence and substance use and a variety of other addiction-related topics.

ALAN C. OGBORNE, Ph.D., is a senior scientist with the Addiction Research Foundation. He holds a bachelor's degree in psychology from the University of Exeter, England, and a Ph.D. in social psychology from the London School of Economics. His main professional interest has been in the evaluation of addiction treatment services and systems.

MARTHA SANCHEZ-CRAIG earned a Ph.D. in counselling psychology at the University of Toronto in 1972. In 1973, she joined the Addiction Research Foundation, and was a senior scientist when she recently retired. In a 20-year program of research with numerous colleagues, she developed a cognitive-behavioral approach for early intervention with alcohol and other drug use problems, which has been tested in parts of Canada, South America and Europe. The methods are described in numerous publications, including a therapist's manual for secondary prevention of alcohol problems and a self-help book, both published by the Addiction Research Foundation.

WAYNE SKINNER, M.S.W., has over two decades of experience in working with people with problems related to substance use. His interests include assessment, brief treatments, family and couple counselling, and community-based services for people with severe substance use problems. In addition to being a therapist and clinical supervisor, he has led projects in treatment program and treatment system development. He has been a co-investigator in a number of treatment research initiatives. He is an experienced educator and trainer. Recently, he headed ARF's HIV and Opiate Programs. Currently, he is team leader of the ARF's Concurrent Disorders Program, Addictions and Mental Health.

TERRY E. SODEN, M.S.W., C.C.P., I.C.A.D.C., C.C.S., has over 25 years of experience in clinical practice. He currently teaches at and is president of School for Addiction Studies Ltd. and is president of Soden, Murray, Moore & Associates. Terry